Jo

ΔΤΔ — 7
150 E. Maiden St.
Wash. Penna.
1/29/58

*Introduction to*

# GEOMETRICAL AND
# PHYSICAL OPTICS

(a)                                    (b)

Fabry-Perot patterns with green light 5461 A from (a) natural mercury and from (b) artificial mercury 198.   (*By courtesy of Dr. William F. Meggers, National Bureau of Standards.*)

*Introduction to*

# GEOMETRICAL AND
# PHYSICAL OPTICS

JOSEPH MORGAN, Ph.D.

*Professor of Physics*
*Texas Christian University*

New York   Toronto   London

McGRAW-HILL BOOK COMPANY, INC.

1953

THE MAPLE PRESS COMPANY, YORK, PA.

*To*

MY WIFE

# PREFACE

With our present undergraduate physics curriculum being called upon to accommodate such fields of study as electronics, microwaves, atomic and nuclear physics, and quantum mechanics, in addition to the usual necessary subjects, the author has felt a need for a text that could be used to cover the principles of geometrical and physical optics in one long semester or two quarter sessions. Accordingly, this book represents the content of a four-semester-hour course (three lecture hours and one three-hour laboratory per week) which the author has been giving for the past ten years. Those departments which prefer to cover the material in the equivalent of two long semesters may easily do so by going at a somewhat slower rate (perhaps two lecture hours per week) and augmenting certain of the topics which have been included for completeness but which have, of necessity, been taken up rather briefly.

The book is intended to serve as a basis for an intermediate course for undergraduate students. It therefore presupposes a knowledge of general college physics, and although all concepts are developed from fundamental principles, it is more desirable for the student to have been introduced to the optical phenomena that are usually covered in such a course. The formal prerequisite in mathematics is a course in analytical geometry. Also, it has been the author's experience that some of the material in a course in optics can more profitably be developed with the use of the calculus. On the other hand, it is felt that the lack of the calculus on the part of some of the students should not necessarily bar them from enrollment. The author has attempted to meet this situation by presenting, where feasible, the noncalculus development on the left side of certain double-column pages and giving the parallel calculus development on the corresponding right side of the page. In this way, the student with as yet no knowledge of the calculus may still study the material with no break in continuity. The calculus student of course has the benefit of both developments.

The material covered is based upon the lecture notes used by the author in courses in geometrical and physical optics. It is aimed to fulfill the needs of the physics major as well as of the student who seeks a general comprehensive treatment of the field. No attempt at complete coverage of all the different phases of study is made, but rather the aim throughout is to develop the basic principles, to illustrate with typical applications, and to introduce methods of analysis and exactness of thought.

The first nine chapters are devoted to the development and study of geometrical optics. Chapter 1 considers the principle of rectilinear propagation and the laws of reflection and refraction; and on the basis of these, the generalized refraction equation for spherically refracting surfaces is taken up in Chap. 2. Spherical mirrors are covered in Chap. 3, considering reflection as a special case of refraction. The properties of thin lenses are covered in Chap. 4, and thick-lens systems are taken up in Chap. 5. This is followed by a study of stops and apertures in Chap. 6 and aberrations in Chap. 7. Chapter 8 goes into optical instruments, and Chap. 9 takes up the principles of photometry. The sign convention adopted is strictly in accord with that of coordinate geometry. Notwithstanding the fact that such a convention does not necessarily result in the greatest number of positive signs in the reflection and refraction equations, it is felt that the universality of this mathematical convention justifies such a choice.

Chapters 10 to 16 are devoted to the development of physical optics. Chapter 10 discusses the corpuscular and wave theories of light, the principles of wave motion, and the measurement of the finite velocity of light. The theories of light are taken up in relation to the classical and modern developments which lead to the dual particle and wave theory of light. The subjects of interference and diffraction are then taken up in Chaps. 11 to 13. This is followed by unified treatments of resolving power in Chap. 14 and of absorption, scattering, and dispersion in Chap. 15. Chapter 16 goes into the phenomenon of polarization, including double refraction, and optical activity.

The last two chapters take up some of those subjects which are more rightfully representative of the category called quantum optics. As much of quantum theory as is necessary to describe the origin of spectra is developed in Chap. 17 on Spectra. Chapter 18 deals with the wave-particle aspects of light and matter and discusses some of the aspects of the modern quantum mechanics.

Where necessary, some of the earlier chapters are concluded with a summary, and each chapter ends with a set of carefully selected problems. The ability to work these problems, in the author's opinion, is essential to a proper understanding of the principles covered in the text. Some of the exercises are intended to augment the textual discussion and to demonstrate some of the practical applications of the principles developed. The student is given hints to some of the more difficult and involved problems and is thereby guided to a solution. Answers to the odd-numbered problems are given at the back of the text.

The symbols employed conform, for the most part, to those recommended by the Committee on Letter Symbols, as listed in the *American Journal of Physics*, volume 16, pages 164 to 179, 1948.

The author is indebted to Prof. Louis W. Ramsey of the Mathematics Department of Texas Christian University for his invaluable aid in preparing many of the photographs appearing in the chapters on Interference and Diffraction and to his wife, Edith L. Morgan, for helpful suggestions throughout the entire writing of the manuscript, for typing and preparing the manuscript, and for aid in proofreading and checking.

JOSEPH MORGAN

FORT WORTH, TEXAS
*January,* 1953

# CONTENTS

# CHAPTER 1

## FUNDAMENTALS OF REFLECTION AND REFRACTION

From the earliest dates in history, man has been curious about the surrounding world, and many of his impressions were a direct consequence of his ability to see. He began to conjecture, early, about the nature of light and about the formation of images. At the beginning, his conceptions of the phenomena of reflection and refraction were hazy, and he thought that light traveled from his eye to the viewed object in order that he might see it. Today we know that objects which are self-luminous are visible by the physiological action of the light that proceeds from the object to the eye. When an object, such as a table, is in a perfectly darkened room, it can be made visible by bringing a self-luminous body, such as a lamp, into the vicinity. When this is done, we are able to see the table by the same physiological sensations as above but produced now by the light which has been reflected from the table. In either of these situations, the object is seen exactly where it is in space, undisplaced and undistorted. On the other hand, if the table and the lamp are held submerged in water, then the positions of each appear to be displaced with respect to their actual locations. This apparent shift of an object is due to the phenomenon of *refraction*, or change in direction of a light beam as it passes from one medium into another of different optical densities.

These three facts, the phenomenon of reflection, the phenomenon of refraction, and the observation that light apparently travels in straight lines, may be used to build up the entire science of geometrical optics. One needs only to look about him to see the wide practical applications of the results of this field. For instance, think how indispensable optical instruments are in the fields of medicine, astronomy, biology, photography, television, navigation, surveying, ordnance, and scores of others. In all these, the principles involved are primarily those of reflection and refraction. With the property that light travels in straight lines is associated such phenomena as the casting of "sharp" optical shadows, the production of eclipses, the operation of pinhole cameras, and the effectiveness of ordinary gunsights. But on further study and closer examination, we discover that *rectilinear propagation* is followed only approximately; we note that the edge of a shadow is never really sharp and also that light does bend around objects and corners with the result,

1

for instance, that a bright spot of light can be observed at the center of the shadow of a small circular obstacle.   To be sure, the amount that light bends, or *diffracts*, is so small that its effect around the corner of a room cannot be observed with the naked eye; but with sharp edges and optical instruments, the amount of bending can be measured.

The fascinating subject of diffraction will be studied in detail in a later chapter; for the present, it is important to indicate that rectilinear propagation is followed by light to such a high degree of approximation that for all practical purposes the deviation from it may be ignored.   We shall therefore deal with the *ray* of light, a concept that implies a straight line along which light is traveling between two points.   As will become evident, this concept is very useful in the development of the laws of reflection, the laws of refraction, the formation of images, and the study of optical instruments.

**1.1. Reflection.**   When light strikes a reflecting medium, some of the light is thrown back into the original medium.   This is done according to the laws:

1. The angle of incidence equals the angle of reflection.

2. The incident ray, the reflected ray, and the normal to the reflecting surface lie in the same plane.

The angles of incidence and reflection are the angles that the incident and reflected rays, respectively, make with the normal to the surface.

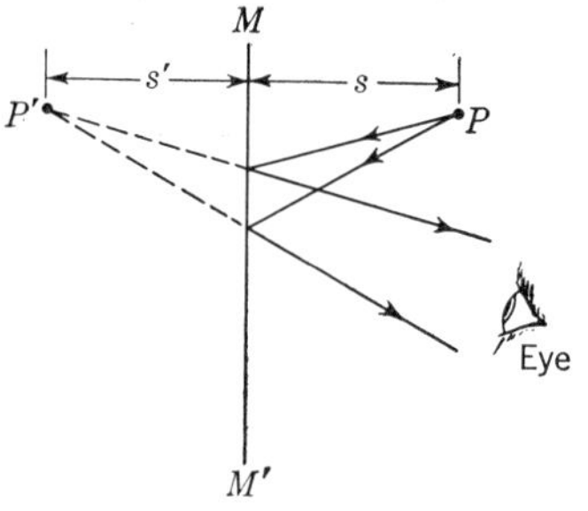

Fig. 1.1. Image formation of a point object by a plane mirror.

Figure 1.1 shows the ray construction of the formation of a point image $P'$ of a luminous point object $P$ in a plane mirror in accordance with the reflection laws. Any two rays from $P$ are drawn to the reflecting surface $MM'$ and are made to reflect in accordance with these laws.   The reflected divergent rays entering the eye are projected to meet at one point to form the image of the point object $P$.   From the geometry of the figure, it is easily seen that $s' = s$.   For an extended object, this construction holds for each point of the object, thus producing many point images which combine to form the entire image.

Plane mirrors have extremely useful properties.   The rotation of a plane mirror through an angle causes the reflected ray to rotate through twice the angle.   This property has many practical applications, including its use in the optical lever, the sextant, and the wall galvanometer. Two mirrors may be used to form multiple images; the image produced by one mirror may be considered as the object of the other mirror. When two mirrors form an angle with each other, the number of images formed of an object placed between them is a simple function of this angle. The development of this function is given as a problem at the end of the chapter.

Prismatic reflectors made of three mutually perpendicular mirrors have the property of reflecting any ray of light parallel to the incident direction. Such reflectors are used as taillights on bicycles and trailers and as guide markers on the highway. When the light from the headlights of an approaching vehicle strikes these mirrors, it is reflected in the direction from which it came.

**1.2. Refraction.** Figure 1.2 shows a light ray passing from medium $a$ into an optically denser medium $b$. In this case the light ray bends away from its undeviated direction toward the downward normal. The angle of incidence and the angle of refraction are related by Snell's law

$$\frac{\sin \phi}{\sin \phi'} = {_a}n_b \qquad (1.1)$$

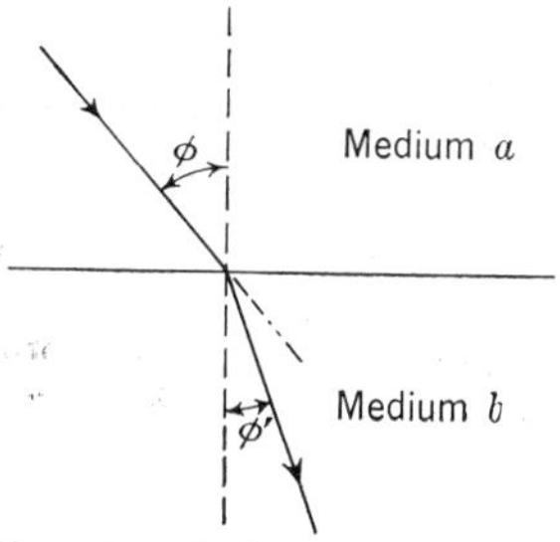

Medium $a$

Medium $b$

Fig. 1.2. Refraction of light.

The subscripts on the index of refraction $n$ refer to the media. Thus ${_a}n_b$ means the relative index of refraction of medium $b$ with respect to medium $a$. The arrows on the rays may be reversed so that if $\phi'$ is the angle of incidence then the ray will refract into medium $b$ at the angle $\phi$. In that case, Snell's law would take the form

$$\frac{\sin \phi'}{\sin \phi} = {_b}n_a \qquad (1.2)$$

where ${_b}n_a$ denotes the index of medium $a$ with respect to medium $b$. Thus by comparing Eq. (1.1) with Eq. (1.2),

$$_a n_b = \frac{1}{_b n_a} \qquad (1.3)$$

With one of the media vacuum, say medium $a$, the index is designated ${_0}n_b$ or simply $n_b$ and is called the absolute index of refraction. The absolute index of refraction of air is given by ${_0}n_{air} = n_{air} = 1.0003$ so that the refractive index with respect to air is, for most practical purposes, taken as the absolute index of refraction. Table 1.1 gives values for the refractive indices of several substances.

As will be shown in Sec. 1.7, the index of refraction has the physical significance of being the ratio of the velocities of light in the two media;[1] thus

$$_a n_b = \frac{v_a}{v_b} \qquad (1.4)$$

[1] This result is also easily obtained by using the wave theory of light. See Sec. 10.7.

where $v_a$ and $v_b$ are the velocities of light in media $a$ and $b$, respectively. Since $\phi > \phi'$, $v_b < v_a$ and the velocity in the denser medium is less than the velocity in the less dense medium.

Consider now a light ray which originates in air (or vacuum), refracts through medium $a$, then refracts through medium $b$, and finally emerges again into air (or vacuum). Using Eq. (1.4), we have

$$_0n_a \, _an_b \, _bn_0 = \frac{v_0}{v_a} \frac{v_a}{v_b} \frac{v_b}{v_0} = 1$$

$$_an_b = \frac{1}{_0n_a \, _bn_0} = \frac{_0n_b}{_0n_a} \qquad (1.5)$$

Equation (1.5) shows that the relative index of refraction is a ratio between the absolute indices of refraction of the substances.

TABLE 1.1.   INDICES OF REFRACTION*

| Solids | | Liquids | | Gases† | |
|---|---|---|---|---|---|
| Amber | 1.546 | Bromine | 1.661 | 15°C | Air | 1.00029 |
| Canada balsam | 1.530 | Carbon bisulfide | 1.629 | 15°C | Carbon | |
| Calcite: | | Carbon dioxide | 1.195 | 15°C | dioxide | 1.00045 |
| O ray | 1.658 | Chlorine | 1.385 | 20°C | Chlorine | 1.00077 |
| E ray | 1.486 | Ethel alcohol | 1.360 | 20°C | Helium | 1.000036 |
| Diamond | 2.417 | Oxygen | 1.221 | −181°C | Hydrogen | 1.00013 |
| Glass: | | Sulfur | 1.929 | 110°C | Hydrogen | |
| Zinc crown | 1.517 | Water | 1.333 | 20°C | sulfide | 1.00063 |
| Light flint | 1.575 | | | | Sulfur dioxide | 1.00069 |
| Ice | 1.310 | | | | | |
| Sodium | 4.22 | | | | | |
| Sodium chloride | 1.544 | | | | | |
| Quartz: | | | | | | |
| O ray | 1.544 | | | | | |
| E ray | 1.553 | | | | | |

* All values are for the sodium $D$ line, wavelength 5893 A.

† At normal temperature and pressure.

**1.3. Total Internal Reflection.** By considering the ray of light as originating in the denser medium and refracting into the less dense medium, we arrive at a situation as shown in Fig. 1.3. The symbols $P_1$, $P_2$, $P_c$ represent the successive positions of the light source which define the increasing angles of incidence $\phi_1$, $\phi_2$, $\phi_c$ (all the rays incident at $O$). Corresponding to the ray making an angle of incidence $\phi_1$, the refracted ray makes the angle $\phi_1'$; for the ray with the angle $\phi_2$, there is the refracted ray of angle $\phi_2'$, etc. As the angle of incidence $\phi$ increases, the angle of refraction $\phi'$ must increase according to Snell's law; but since $\phi_i < \phi_i'$, there is some angle $\phi_c$ for which the refracted angle $\phi_c' = 90°$. *The angle $\phi_c$, known as the "critical angle," is that angle of incidence in the denser medium for which the refracted angle in the less dense* *medium is* 90°.   We know, from Fig. 1.3, that

$$\frac{\sin \phi'}{\sin \phi} = {}_a n_b$$

and for $\phi = \phi_c$, $\phi' = \phi'_c = 90°$; then

$$\sin \phi_c = \frac{1}{{}_a n_b} = \frac{n_a}{n_b} = {}_b n_a \tag{1.6}$$

From a knowledge of the relative index of refraction and by the use of Eq. (1.6), the critical angle may always be determined.

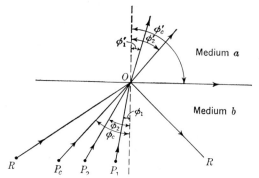

Fig. 1.3. Total internal reflection.   $n_b > n_a$.

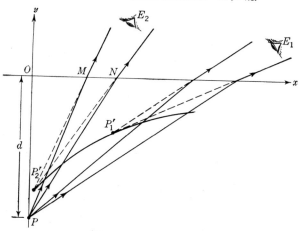

Fig. 1.4. The diacaustic.

All the light from the light rays making angles greater than the critical angle reflects back into the denser medium so that there is no transmitted beam into the less dense medium as illustrated by the ray *ROR*.

**1.4. Formation of a Point Image by Refraction at a Plane Surface; the Diacaustic.**   In Fig. 1.4, *P* is a light source situated in a medium of refractive index $n$ with respect to the medium above the surface indicated by the $x$ axis. Here $n$ is greater than 1. When the eye is at position $E_1$, it sees the image of $P$ at position $P'_1$ formed by a pair of refracted rays. At position $E_2$, the image appears to be at some other point $P'_2$. In general, the apparent position of the image $P'$ is a function of the angle that the incident (or refracted) rays make with the surface $Ox$. Every refracted ray cuts the one next to it, and their points of intersection $P'$ form a curve which is known as a *diacaustic*. The caustic curve is shown in Fig. 1.4. The equation of this curve[1] is given by

$$n^{2/3}y^{2/3} + (n^2 - 1)^{1/3}x^{2/3} = d^{2/3} \tag{1.7}$$

where $n$ is the refractive index, $d$ is the distance of $P$ below $O$, and $(x,y)$ are the Cartesian coordinates of any point on the diacaustic. When $x = 0$, the curve touches the $y$ axis at points

$$y = \pm \frac{d}{n} \tag{1.8}$$

and when $y = 0$, the curve touches the $x$ axis at points

$$x = \pm \frac{d}{\sqrt{n^2 - 1}} \tag{1.9}$$

The properties of the function (1.7) are such that the curve comes in tangent to the $x$ and $y$ axes forming cusps at each of these positions. In Eq. (1.8), we are interested in the minus sign only. The cusp above the $x$ axis, although mathematically valid, does not correspond to the physical situation. In the same way we take the plus sign in Eq. (1.9) as the physical case.

Equation (1.8) shows that when the eye looks down normally so that the incident angles that the light rays make with the normal to the surface are sufficiently small, the apparent shift in the image is practically vertically upward above the object point $P$. The amount of this shift may be shown again by the fact that if $M$ and $N$ are close to $O$, then the angles are small and the sines of the angles may be approximated by the tangents. Thus, considering $P'_2$ vertically above $P$,

$$n = \frac{\sin \angle NP'_2O}{\sin \angle NPO} = \frac{\tan \angle NP'_2O}{\tan \angle NPO} = \frac{NO/OP'_2}{NO/OP} = \frac{OP}{OP'_2}$$

$$OP'_2 = \frac{OP}{n}$$

and in the notation of Eq. (1.8), $OP'_2 = y$ and $OP = -d.$

[1] For the derivation of this equation, see Appendix IA.

When the eye is in the optically more dense medium and the source is in the less dense medium, the image appears to be farther away from the refracting surface than the object.

**1.5. Optical Path Length of a Ray.** If a ray of light traverses a distance $l_b$ in medium $b$ with a velocity $v_b$, it covers this distance in time $l_b/v_b$. In this same time the distance the ray would traverse in medium $a$ with velocity $v_a$ is

$$\frac{l_b}{v_b} v_a = {}_an_bl_b \tag{1.10}$$

The expression (1.10) indicates the optical length of the ray in medium $b$ with respect to medium $a$. The product, the index of refraction times

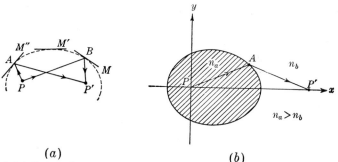

*(a)* *(b)*

FIG. 1.5 *(a)* Aplanatic surface for reflection. *(b)* Aplanatic surface for refraction.

the distance traversed, is known, in general, as the *optical path length* and is a concept that will be employed throughout the text in various developments. If the path goes through different media of indices $n_1$, $n_2$, $n_3$, . . . , $n_k$ and the corresponding lengths traversed in these media are $l_1$, $l_2$, $l_3$, . . . , $l_k$, then the optical path length is $n_1l_1 + n_2l_2 + n_3l_3 + \cdots + n_kl_k$.

**1.6. The Aplanatic Surface.** As we shall observe in later chapters, curved mirrors and lenses, in general, form images that are relatively imperfect; for example, they may be distorted, indistinct, or not sharp. However, there are theoretical surfaces that do give perfect images, and these are called *aplanatic* surfaces.

Figure 1.5a illustrates the aplanatic surface for reflection. In order that $P'$ be the image point of $P$ for all possible positions of the mirror $M$, such as $M'$, $M''$, etc., the reflection point of contact $B$ must describe a locus such that the lines $PB$ and $P'B$ make equal angles with $M$ and with the normal to $M$. It is left as an exercise for the student to show that in general this locus is an ellipsoid of revolution so that the aplanatic reflecting surface is more conveniently stated in terms of the optical-path-length equation

$$PA + AP' = \text{constant} \tag{1.11}$$

The important special cases of Eq. (1.11) are taken up in problems.

Figure 1.5*b* shows the aplanatic surface that gives rise to a perfect point image $P'$ in a medium of refractive index $n_b$ by a point object $P$ in a medium of refractive index $n_a$.   In this case the surface is given by the optical-path-length equation

$$PA + {}_an_bAP' = k = \text{constant} \tag{1.12}$$

which is the equation of a Cartesian oval,[1]

$$[(x^2 + y^2)(1 - {}_an_b^2) + 2_an_b^2cx + k^2 - {}_an_b^2c^2]^2 = 4k^2(x^2 + y^2)$$

where $c$ is the distance $PP'$.

That Eq. (1.11) is a special case of Eq. (1.12) is evident.   These equations for aplanatic surfaces have numerous practical applications, and some of these will be considered in the sections of this book having to do with optical instruments.

**1.7. Fermat's Principle of Least Time.**   The three fundamental maxims of light—rectilinear propagation, the laws of reflection, and the laws of refraction—may be summed up in a very general law known as Fermat's principle of least time.   This law may be stated as follows: *When a ray of light passes from one point to another by any number of reflections or refractions, the path taken by the light ray is the one for which the corresponding time of traversal is the least or a minimum.*   The proof of this principle is beyond the scope of this text; however, here we shall use this principle to show how rectilinear propagation and the laws of reflection and refraction follow from it.

The distance $x$ traveled by a ray of light with velocity $v$ in time $t$ is $x = vt$.   For an isotropic medium, the speed in all directions is the same, so that the path of least time between any two points is the path for which $x$ is least, *i.e.*, a straight line.   Thus rectilinear propagation for an isotropic medium follows at once from Fermat's principle.

The application of the principle to the case of reflection is now given. A fundamental geometrical proof is presented in the left column of the page.   For those students who are familiar with some of the methods of the calculus there is, in addition, a corresponding proof in the right column of the page.

---

[1] In order that $P'$ be the point image of $P$, $PA$ and $AP'$ must, with the normal to the surface, make angles that are related by Snell's law.   This and other properties of the Cartesian ovals are developed in Appendix IB.

Light from $A$ (Fig. 1.6) is considered to be reflected from the mirror $MM'$ and to reach point $B$ by

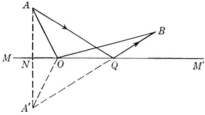

FIG. 1.6. Law of reflection by Fermat's principle (geometric proof).

any path $AOB$. The line $AN$ is constructed perpendicular to $MM'$ and extended to $A'$ so that

$$AN = A'N$$

Thus $AO = A'O$ for all positions of $O$, and the optical path length $AO + OB$ is equivalent to $A'O + OB$. However, the minimum or least value of the path is that one, $AQ + QB$, whose equivalent is $A'Q + QB$, a straight line. Hence $AQB$ is the true optical path. A normal may now be constructed at $Q$, and from the similar triangles $NAQ$ and $NQA'$ it is easily

Light from $A$ (Fig. 1.7) is reflected by mirror $MM'$ to $B$, forming the angle of incidence $i$ and the angle of reflection $r$. The time for the ray of light to traverse the optical path $AO + OB$ is given by

$$t = \frac{AO + OB}{v}$$

where $v$ is the velocity of light. Thus

$$t = \frac{\sqrt{b^2 + x^2} + \sqrt{a^2 + (c - x)^2}}{v}$$

The condition that this time be an extreme is

$$\frac{dt}{dx} = \frac{\dfrac{x}{\sqrt{b^2 + x^2}} - \dfrac{c - x}{\sqrt{a^2 + (c - x)^2}}}{v}$$

$$= 0$$

$$\frac{x}{\sqrt{b^2 + x^2}} = \frac{c - x}{\sqrt{a^2 + (c - x)^2}}$$

$$\sin i = \sin r$$

so that $i = r$, or the angle of incidence is equal to the angle of reflection.

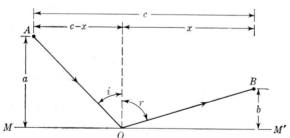

FIG. 1.7. Law of reflection by Fermat's principle (calculus proof).

seen that for the path $AQB$ the angle of incidence equals the angle of reflection.

Fermat's principle also demands

The second derivative is easily shown to be positive so that the function is a minimum or the time is least.

that the incident ray, the reflected ray, and the normal all be in the same plane. The student should have no difficulty in showing this by taking the two points $A$ and $B$ in a vertical plane and assuming the point $O$ in a horizontal plane so that $AO$ and $OB$ are in different planes. The observation may then be made that the minimum value of $AO$ and $OB$ occurs when $O$ is also in the same plane as $A$ and $B$.

The following gives a similar treatment proving the law of refraction.

In Fig. 1.8, $POP'$ is the true ray that is proceeding from medium $a$ to medium $b$ where $n_b > n_a$.

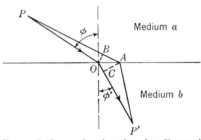

FIG. 1.8. Law of refraction by Fermat's principle (geometric proof).

The path $PAP'$ is a neighboring one. The lines $OB$ and $AC$ are drawn perpendicular to $OP$ and $OP'$, respectively. Now consider that $A$ gets infinitely close to $O$; then $PB$ approaches the value $PO$, and $P'A$ approaches the value $P'C$. In the limit, then, since the time for the ray to traverse the path $POP'$ is a minimum, it follows that the time it takes the light to travel the distance $BA$ is equal to the time it takes the ray to travel the distance $OC$. If the velocity

In Fig. 1.9, $POP'$ is the actual path of a ray of light starting in medium $a$ at $P$ and arriving in

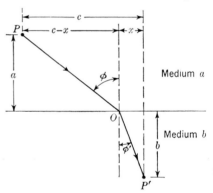

FIG. 1.9. Law of refraction by Fermat's principle (calculus proof).

medium $b$ at $P'$ where $n_b > n_a$. All other neighboring paths start at $P$ and end at $P'$, so that the distance between these points is a constant and taken as $c$ in the figure. The time it takes the ray to traverse this distance $POP'$ is

$$t = \frac{PO}{v_a} + \frac{OP'}{v_b}$$

where $v_a$ is the ray velocity in

of light in medium $a$ is $v_a$ and that in medium $b$ is $v_b$, then

$$\frac{BA}{v_a} = \frac{OC}{v_b}$$

$$\frac{BA/OA}{OC/OA} = \frac{v_a}{v_b}$$

$$\frac{\sin \phi}{\sin \phi'} = \frac{v_a}{v_b} = \text{constant}$$

$$= {}_a n_b$$

which proves Snell's law and evaluates the index of refraction as the ratio of the velocities of light in the two media.

medium $a$ and $v_b$ is the ray velocity in medium $b$, or

$$t = \frac{\sqrt{a^2 + (c - x)^2}}{v_a} + \frac{\sqrt{b^2 + x^2}}{v_b}$$

By Fermat's principle, the derivative of $t$ with respect to the variable $x$ is zero; thus

$$\frac{dt}{dx} = -\frac{(c - x)}{v_a \sqrt{a^2 + (c - x)^2}}$$

$$+ \frac{x}{v_b \sqrt{b^2 + x^2}}$$

$$= 0$$

and from the figure this is seen to be

$$\frac{\sin \phi'}{v_b} - \frac{\sin \phi}{v_a} = 0$$

or

$$\frac{\sin \phi}{\sin \phi'} = \frac{v_a}{v_b} = \text{constant}$$

$$= {}_a n_b$$

which is Snell's law with the index of refraction equal to the ratio of the velocities of light in the two media.

**1.8. The Refracting Prism.** In Fig. 1.10 is traced the path of a ray incident on a prism at an angle of incidence $\phi_1$. The prism is in air and

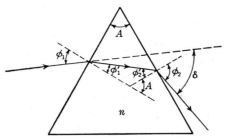

FIG. 1.10. Refraction by a prism.

has an apex angle $A$ and a refractive index $n$. The angle $\delta$ between the incident and emergent rays is known as the angle of deviation. We shall find an expression for this angle in terms of $n$, $\phi_1$, and $A$. From the figure,

$$\delta = \phi_1 - \phi_1' + \phi_2 - \phi_2'$$
$$\delta = \phi_1 + \phi_2 - (\phi_1' + \phi_2')$$
$$\delta = \phi_1 + \phi_2 - A \qquad (1.13)$$

From Snell's law,

$$\sin \phi_1 = n \sin \phi_1'$$
$$\sin \phi_2 = n \sin \phi_2' \qquad (1.14)$$

so that Eq. (1.13) is easily thrown into the form

$$\delta = \phi_1 + \sin^{-1}[n \sin (A - \phi_1')] - A$$

or

$$\delta = \phi_1 + \sin^{-1}[(n^2 - \sin^2 \phi_1)^{1/2} \sin A - \sin \phi_1 \cos A] - A \qquad (1.15)$$

Although Eq. (1.15) will determine $\delta$ for any value of $\phi_1$, for a given prism, it is rather tedious to employ. It is of value to investigate the characteristics of the form of Eq. (1.15). This we do below in two ways; in the left column is given the graphical plot of Eq. (1.15) assuming $A = 60°$ and $n = 1.5$. In the right column is given an analysis, using the calculus, which has the advantage of being general for all values of $n$ and $A$.

Values of $\delta$ corresponding to given values of $\phi_1$ have been calculated from Eq. (1.15) and presented in Table 1.2.

TABLE 1.2

| $\phi_1$, deg | $\delta$, deg |
|---|---|
| 30 | 47.2 |
| 40 | 38.3 |
| 50 | 37.2 |
| 60 | 38.9 |
| 70 | 42.8 |
| 80 | 49.1 |

$\delta_m = 37°11' = 37.2°$

The above values are plotted in Fig. 1.11, where it is seen that the angle of deviation is a minimum for some corresponding angle of incidence. This minimum angle of deviation, $\delta_m$ occurs when the ray refracts through the prism symmetrically and so forms an isosceles section with the upper part of the prism. Under these conditions, the incident and emergent

We may equate to zero the first derivative with respect to $\phi_1$ of Eq. (1.15) to find that angle of $\phi_1$ for which $\delta$ is a minimum $\delta_m$. However, it is perhaps simpler to proceed from Eq. (1.13). Thus for a minimum,

$$\frac{d\delta}{d\phi_1} = 1 + \frac{d\phi_2}{d\phi_1} = 0$$
$$\frac{d\phi_2}{d\phi_1} = -1$$

Now differentiating Eq. (1.14),

$$\cos \phi_1 \, d\phi_1 = n \cos \phi_1' \, d\phi_1'$$
$$\cos \phi_2 \, d\phi_2 = n \cos \phi_2' \, d\phi_2'$$

Dividing one by the other of these last two equations and using the relationships $d\phi_2 = -d\phi_1$ and $d\phi_2' = -d\phi_1'$, the last one obtained from $A = \phi_1' + \phi_2'$, there results

$$\frac{\cos \phi_1}{\cos \phi_2} = \frac{\cos \phi_1'}{\cos \phi_2'}$$

angles are equal, and the two refracting angles are equal. Thus for $\delta = \delta_m$,

$$\phi_1 = \phi_2$$

and

$$\phi_1' = \phi_2'$$

That $\phi_1$ must equal $\phi_2$ at minimum deviation follows from the fact

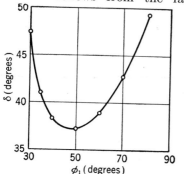

FIG. 1.11. Angle of deviation as a function of the angle of incidence.

that if the incident light were along the emergent direction so that the situation were reversed, then the ray would have to retrace its path and still refract through the prism at the same angle of minimum deviation. This obviously could not happen for two different angles of incidence.

which is readily put into the form,

$$\frac{\sqrt{1 - \sin^2 \phi_1}}{\sqrt{1 - \sin^2 \phi_2}} = \frac{\sqrt{n^2 - \sin^2 \phi_1}}{\sqrt{n^2 - \sin^2 \phi_2}}$$

Simplifying this expression gives the result that

$$\phi_1 = \phi_2$$

and

$$\phi_1' = \phi_2'$$

so that the ray refracts through the prism symmetrically. The second derivative test on the function shows that these conditions correspond to a minimum.

for all values of $n$ and $A$.

When the above conditions are satisfied,

$$\phi_1 = \frac{\delta_m + A}{2} \quad \text{and} \quad \phi_1' = \frac{A}{2}$$

Therefore, Snell's law for the condition of minimum deviation is

$$\sin \frac{\delta_m + A}{2} = n \sin \frac{A}{2}$$

or

$$n = \frac{\sin \left[ (\delta_m + A)/2 \right]}{\sin (A/2)} \tag{1.16}$$

Equation (1.16) affords a convenient and very precise method of determining the refractive index of a transparent material. By shaping the sample in the form of a prism and measuring the prism angle $A$ and the minimum deviation angle $\delta_m$, $n$ may be determined. The prism is placed on a spectrometer table equipped with a collimator to define the incident light, and a telescope is situated on the emergent side (see the chapter on Optical Instruments). The angles are measured with the aid of circular scales and verniers attached to the fixed and moving parts of the instrument. The angle of minimum deviation is easily located as that position where the image, as seen through the telescope, reverses its direction when the table on which the prism is mounted is turned in one sense (either clockwise or counterclockwise).

For a prism whose apex angle $A$ is small, we may replace the sines of the angles in Eq. (1.16) by the angles and obtain

$$n = \frac{\delta_m + A}{A}$$

or

$$\delta_m = (n - 1)A \tag{1.17}$$

an approximate form that is very convenient to employ.

**1.9. Dispersion.** The reader has certainly witnessed the presence of color when observing the sunlight through a piece of prismatic glass. It was Sir Isaac Newton who proved the following by a series of brilliant researches with sunlight or white light:

1. White light consists of a group of independent pure colors, red, orange, yellow, green, blue, indigo, and violet, called the spectrum.

2. Every different color is characterized by its own different and invariable index of refraction in a given refracting substance.

3. When different-colored light is sent through a refracting material such as a prism, blue color is deviated more than red color.

4. The spectrum colors may be put together, or synthesized, to form white light.

It is clear that in our discussions thus far on the topic of refraction we have assumed light of one color, or as it is more usually expressed, *monochromatic.* Light of more than one color is called *polychromatic,* and in Fig. 1.12 we show such a beam (white light) incident on a prism.

After refraction, each color is deviated by a different amount, and a spectrum is produced on the emergent side of the prism. Only the rays for the extreme colors have been drawn. The violet, being deviated more than the red, has the greater refractive index and hence travels through the prism with the slower velocity. The constituent colors have been dispersed in passing through the prism, and this variation of refractive index with color is known as dispersion. The *angular dispersion* for any two colors represents the difference between the deviations for those two colors. Thus for two colors in the red and blue regions with deviations, respectively, $\delta_1$ and $\delta_2$, the angular dispersion is $\delta_2 - \delta_1$. As can be seen from Eq. (1.15), the angular dispersion is a function not only of the refracting material but also of the angle of incidence and of the apex angle of the prism. However, for a prism, of small apex angle, set for minimum deviation for each different color, the angular dispersion for

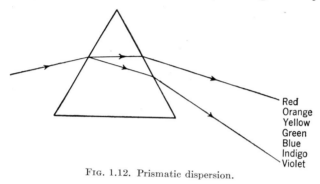

FIG. 1.12. Prismatic dispersion.

any two rays is $(n_2 - n_1)A$. If this expression is divided by the minimum deviation angle $(n - 1)A$ of the mean ray for the whole spectrum, where $n$ is the refractive index for the mean ray, a quantity $(n_2 - n_1)/(n - 1)$, which is characteristic of the refracting material alone, is obtained. Accordingly, the *dispersive power* $\omega$ for a material is defined as

$$\omega = \frac{n_F - n_C}{n_D - 1} \tag{1.18}$$

where the two extreme colors are designated as $F$ and $C$ and that corresponding to the mean ray is $D$. Although the color designations $F$, $C$, and $D$ are taken up in greater detail in Chap. 17, we shall here introduce a few preliminary explanatory remarks.

When the light from a gas-discharge tube is rendered parallel, sent through a fine slit, and then analyzed with a prism spectrometer (see Chap. 8), the resulting spectrum consists of many narrow colored lines, each line being an image of the slit which is illuminated by all the colors of the light emitted from the discharge tube. This is known as a bright-line spectrum, and each line or color has its own index in the refracting material. When the light from the sun is analyzed in this way, the spectrum obtained consists of a colored region or band which gradually proceeds from the red at one end to the violet at the other end as in Fig. 1.12. Such a spectrum is termed *continuous,* but in the case of sunlight the spectrum is crossed by a number of narrow dark lines each of which corresponds to a particular color that is missing. These are known as the *Fraunhofer lines* and are due to the fact that those colors are absorbed by the sun's atmosphere.   The Fraunhofer lines carry the designations $A$, $B$, $C$, . . . and represent definite constituent colors of sunlight.[1] The $C$, $F$, and $D$ lines are, respectively, in the red, blue-green, and yellow portions of the spectrum.   Thus $n_F$, $n_C$, and $n_D$ in Eq. (1.18) represent the indices of refraction of these solar lines in the dispersing material. The $D$ line is the one that is taken to represent the mean refractive index of the material as a whole.   The hundreds of Fraunhofer lines have been identified with certain of the emission lines of the elements; for instance, the $C$ and $F$ lines correspond, respectively, to a red and a blue-green line in the hydrogen-line spectrum, and the $D$ line is identified with the yellow line in the sodium bright-line spectrum.

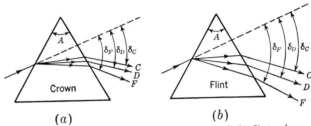

FIG. 1.13. Dispersive powers of (a) crown and (b) flint prisms.

The meaning of $\omega$ is perhaps better understood by considering Fig. 1.13, illustrating the dispersion and dispersive powers for crown and flint glass.   Using the indices of refraction for these materials listed in Table 1.3, we have, for ordinary crown glass,

$$\text{Angular dispersion} = \delta_F - \delta_C = (n_F - n_C) A = 0.008 A$$

$$\omega_{\text{crown}} = \frac{n_F - n_C}{n_D - 1} = \frac{0.008}{0.517} = 0.015$$

and for heavy flint glass,

$$\text{Angular dispersion} = (n_F - n_C) A = 0.020 A$$

$$\omega_{\text{flint}} = \frac{0.020}{0.65} = 0.031$$

The angular dispersion, as well as the dispersive power, is greater for the flint glass.

[1] As we shall see in the chapter on Spectra (see also Secs. 15.7 and 15.8), each spectral line or color is specified by a corresponding wavelength number. This is necessary for a quantitative study of spectra.   Wavelengths are designated in centimeters but are more commonly expressed in angstrom units.   1 A is equal to $10^{-8}$ cm. Thus the $C$ color is designated by $6563 \times 10^{-8}$ cm $= 6563$ A.   The $F$ and $D$ lines are, respectively, 4861 A and 5893 A.

TABLE 1.3. INDICES OF REFRACTION OF OPTICAL GLASS

| | $n_C$ | $n_D$ | $n_F$ |
|---|---|---|---|
| Silicate crown................... | 1.504 | 1.508 | 1.513 |
| Silicate flint..................... | 1.613 | 1.620 | 1.632 |
| Ordinary crown................. | 1.515 | 1.517 | 1.523 |
| Dense barium flint............. | 1.616 | 1.621 | 1.633 |
| Heavy flint..................... | 1.644 | 1.650 | 1.664 |
| High dispersion crown.......... | 1.517 | 1.520 | 1.527 |

$\left[ n_F - n_C = \omega \right]$

**1.10. Prism Combinations.** We see that a prism will in general produce dispersion as well as deviation. Suppose we should like to send a beam of white light through a prism so that the dispersion is destroyed but some average amount of deviation is still present. A prism combination designed to give deviation without dispersion is called *achromatic*. On the other hand, we might like to have the situation where the emergent light has no average deviation but does possess dispersion. Such a combination of prisms is known as a *direct-vision prism*. It is possible to accomplish either one of these situations since it is a fact that, although large dispersions are accompanied by large mean deviations, dispersion is not proportional to mean deviation. Thus if a flint-glass prism, for example, produces, say, three times the dispersion of a crown-glass prism, the mean deviation of the flint prism is not three times that of the crown-glass prism. Therefore, if the mean deviation produced by two prisms made of different substances is the same, the angular dispersion of the two ends of the spectrum will in general be different. Also, if the angular dispersions produced by two prisms made of different substances is the same, then the mean deviations will be different. Thus by utilizing two prisms of different dispersive powers, the achromatic and direct-vision combinations may be accomplished. Crown and flint glass are usually employed to effect these combinations.

First consider the achromatic case. We shall adopt the use of a superscript $C$ or $F$ to denote crown or flint and a subscript $C$ or $F$ to denote the Fraunhofer lines or colors. The angular dispersion produced by the crown prism of small apex angle $A$ is

$$\delta_F^C - \delta_C^C = (n_F^C - n_C^C)A \tag{1.19}$$

and that produced by the flint prism of small apex angle $A'$ is

$$\delta_F^F - \delta_C^F = (n_F^F - n_C^F)A' \tag{1.20}$$

For achromatism, we wish to have no dispersion, or

$$(n_F^C - n_C^C)A + (n_F^F - n_C^F)A' = 0 \tag{1.21}$$

Thus Eq. (1.21) permits the determination of the apex angle $A'$ for the flint prism that will nullify the dispersion of crown prism of apex angle $A$. The value of $A'$ is negative, indicating that the flint prism must be placed so that the deviation of the light is opposite in sense to that produced by the crown prism.   Figure 1.14a illustrates the achromatic combination. On the emergent side, the constituent colors are parallel and so combine to form white light again.   Strictly, the combination achromatizes only for the two extreme colors, the $F$ and $C$ lines, and only approximately for

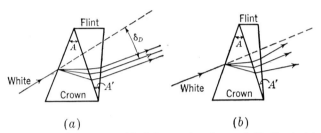

(a)                                    (b)

Fig. 1.14. Prism combinations.   (a) Achromatic prism and (b) direct-vision prism.

the intermediate colors.   That the emergent beam has some residual mean deviation $\delta_D$ is shown as follows:

$$\delta_D = \delta_D^C + \delta_D^F = (n_D^C - 1)A + (n_D^F - 1)A' \tag{1.22}$$

Substituting for $A'$ from Eq. (1.21) and simplifying, we have

$$\delta_D = A(n_D^C - 1)\left(1 - \frac{\omega^C}{\omega^F}\right) \tag{1.23}$$

Thus, since the dispersive power of crown $\omega^C$ and that of flint $\omega^F$ are not equal, the mean deviation is not destroyed.

For the direct-vision combination, we wish to specify no deviation, or

$$(n_D^C - 1)A + (n_D^F - 1)A' = 0 \tag{1.24}$$

and this equation determines the angle $A'$ of the flint prism so that its mean deviation will nullify that of the crown prism.   Figure 1.14b shows the direct-vision combination.   On the emergent side, a spectrum is produced, but the mean deviation is zero.   To show that with such a combination there is residual dispersion, consider the total dispersion for the $F$ and $C$ lines,

$$\begin{aligned} \text{Total dispersion} &= (\delta_F^C - \delta_C^C) + (\delta_F^F - \delta_C^F) \\ &= (n_F^C - n_C^C)A + (n_F^F - n_C^F)A' \end{aligned} \tag{1.25}$$

Now substitute the value for $A'$ from Eq. (1.24),

$$\text{Total dispersion} = A(n_D^C - 1)(\omega^C - \omega^F) \tag{1.26}$$

which is not zero since $\omega^C \neq \omega^F$. Direct-vision prisms are used in direct-vision spectroscopes which are convenient for rapid and rough examination of spectra.

We shall see that the principles used in this section have their greatest application to lenses (Chap. 7).

**1.11. Reflecting Prisms.** We have seen how a prism may be used to measure the index of refraction. Since the critical angle of most glass out of which prisms are made is about 42°, the totally reflecting property of the prism may be used to deviate a ray through a large angle, to displace a ray without causing deviation, or to invert or revert an image. A totally reflecting prism that deviates a ray by internal specular reflection is advantageous over such other reflectors as metallic reflectors, first-surface plane mirrors, or second-surface plane mirrors in that the reflecting surface is not subject to tarnishing, the light is totally reflected, and there is no intensity loss. Of course, there is some loss of light on reflection at the faces where it enters and leaves the prism. Nevertheless, in a reflecting prism, chromatic effects are absent if the rays enter and leave the prism perpendicular to its faces.

Figure 1.15 shows some types of reflecting prisms. The two arrows in mutually perpendicular planes on the incident and emergent rays reveal the effect of the prism on the image. The following is a brief description of each prism:

(*a*) This is a 45°-45°-90° prism and is used to deviate a ray through 90°. Note that the prism causes *reversion*, *i.e.*, it interchanges the top and bottom of the image but does not affect the left and right sides of the image. The altered and unaltered dimensions of the image are interchanged if the prism is rotated through 90°.

(*b*) This is a *Porro* prism, or two right-angle prisms fused together. This prism reverts the image in the reflecting plane. The deviation is 180° and so makes these prisms very convenient to use for the purpose of erecting the image in binoculars. The prism is the same as in (*a*) but is used in the fashion shown.

(*c*) When two Porro prisms are combined in this way, both dimensions of the image are reversed and this is known as *inversion*.

(*d*) The *rhomboidal* prism is used to displace the axis of a beam of light without introducing any other change.

(*e*) This is a *rotating*, or *Dove*, prism which reverts the image without deviating the beam or displacing the axis. It possesses the property that if it is rotated about its longitudinal axis through an angle, the image rotates through twice this angle. These prisms are used in camera view finders.

(*f*) The *Penta* prism deviates a beam through exactly 90° and has the unusual property of doing this even if the beam does not strike the end

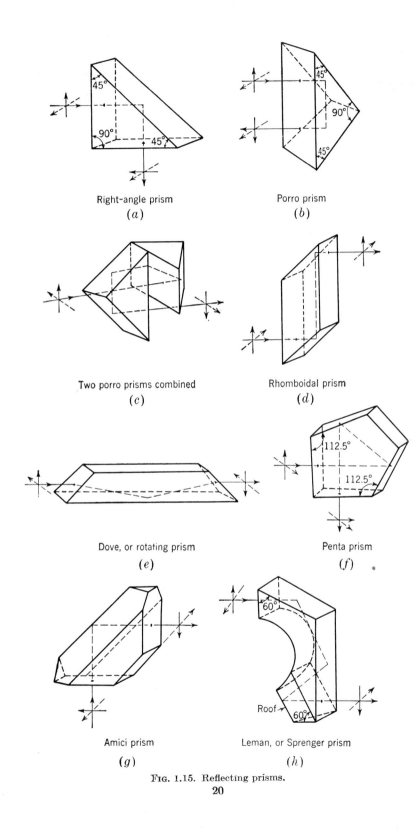

Right-angle prism

(a)

Porro prism

(b)

Two porro prisms combined

(c)

Rhomboidal prism

(d)

Dove, or rotating prism

(e)

Penta prism

(f)

Amici prism

(g)

Leman, or Sprenger prism

(h)

FIG. 1.15. Reflecting prisms.

faces exactly at right angles. The rays, however, must be parallel to the plane of the figure. At the reflecting faces the rays are incident at an angle which is less than the critical angle, and so these faces are silvered. These prisms are used in the range finder where the deviation must be 90°.

(*g*) The *Amici* prism inverts the image and deviates the beam through 90°. The reflection takes place inside the prism at two surfaces that intersect at 90° to form a roof so that rays that strike one side of the roof reflect over to the other side and then emerge. When a double image is produced by an improperly constructed Amici prism, this indicates that the two reflecting surfaces do not intersect at 90°.

(*h*) The *Leman*, or *Sprenger*, prism inverts the image and displaces the beam laterally. The angle of the roof that is used to invert the image is 90°. These prisms are used in gunsights.

## PROBLEMS

**1.1.** An object is placed between two mirrors whose reflecting surfaces make an angle of 90° with one another. Draw a ray diagram locating all the images formed by reflection from the mirrors, showing the pencil of light rays by which each image is seen.

**1.2.** Show that the images in Prob. 1.1 all lie on a circle.

**1.3.** A man, 5 ft 8½ in. tall, wishes to mount a vertical plane mirror in order that he might see his full length. What is the smallest mirror that will serve his purpose? (Do not assume that the man's eyes are on the top of his head!)

**1.4.** Two vertical mirrors are hinged so that the angle between them may be varied when an object is placed on and off the angle bisector between the mirrors. The following observations are made for the corresponding number of images seen as a function of the angle between the mirrors. The original object is included as an observed image.

| Angle, deg.................. | 180 | 90 | 72 | 60 | 45 | 40 | 36 | 30 |
|---|---|---|---|---|---|---|---|---|
| No. of images seen: | | | | | | | | |
| Object on bisector........ | 2 | 4 | 5 | 6 | 8 | 9 | 10 | 12 |
| Object off bisector........ | 2 | 4 | 6 | 6 | 8 | 10 | 10 | 12 |

Deduce the law of multiple images from these data.

**1.5.** (*a*) Prove that the reflected ray from a plane mirror turns through an angle 2θ when the mirror is rotated through an angle θ.

(*b*) Discuss the applications of this principle in wall galvanometers, optical levers, and sextants.

**1.6.** The figure shows what is known as a constant-deviation-type prism. It is made of one piece but may be considered as made up of two 30°-60°-90° prisms and one 45°-45°-90° prism. The incident and emergent directions are fixed, and as the

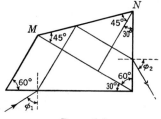

PROB. 1.6.

prism rotates, every color in a spectrum is incident in succession at 45° on the face $MN$. In this way each ray undergoes minimum deviation and is turned through 90°. The prism acts on each ray as a 60° prism at minimum deviation. Show that $\phi_1 = \phi_2$ and that the incident and emergent rays are perpendicular.

**1.7.** Two rays pass through the same medium, and in the path of one of the rays is placed a transparent sheet of unknown thickness. If the optical-path difference between the two rays is measured to be 0.00351 mm and the relative index of refraction of the sheet with respect to the medium is 1.54, find the thickness of the sheet.

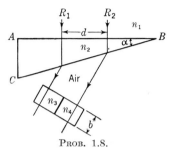

PROB. 1.8.

**1.8.** Two parallel rays $R_1$ and $R_2$ distance $d$ apart and traveling in medium $n_1$ strike a refracting prism $ABC$ of index $n_2$ ($R_1$ and $R_2$ are perpendicular to $AB$). The rays then travel through an air region and finally emerge through different media $n_3$ and $n_4$ as shown. Prove that the difference in optical-path lengths between the emergent rays is given by $b(n_3 - n_4)$.

**1.9.** (a) Find the index of refraction of carbon bisulfide with respect to diamond.

(b) What is the critical angle for the bisulfide-diamond interface? Draw a figure illustrating this.

**1.10.** A slab of glass 12.0 cm in thickness has a refractive index 1.50.

(a) It is held with its lower surface on a table scratch. How deep does the scratch appear to an observer looking down normally at the glass surface?

(b) Where does the scratch appear to be to an eye looking along an angle of 15° with the surface? HINT: The $x$ coordinate of the image is given by $x = d(n^2 - 1) \tan^3 \phi$ where $\phi$ is the angle of incidence in the glass [see Eq. (A.3)]. The $y$ coordinate is then obtainable by substitution in Eq. (1.7).

**1.11.** If the slab of glass in Prob. 1.10 is held 5.00 cm above the scratch, where does the scratch appear to the observer looking down normally at the surface?

**1.12.** An air cell may be used to measure the absolute index of refraction of a liquid (with respect to air). The cell is composed of two parallel-sided glass plates that are cemented together so that they enclose a film of air. The cell is immersed in a clear liquid, light is made to be incident on one of the glass surfaces, and the transmitted light on the opposite glass plate is observed. Draw a diagram of the arrangement, and show that when the angle on the incident surface is varied to the value $\phi$ so that total reflection occurs at the glass-air interface then $n = 1/\sin \phi$, where $n$ is the index of the liquid with respect to air.

**1.13.** Fermat's principle is often stated in a form known as the law of the extreme path. This means that the actual optical path of a ray from one point to another is a maximum or a minimum, or that for all paths which are infinitely close to the actual one the time taken for the ray over the neighboring path differs from the actual time by terms of second or higher order. In the figure $POP'$ is the actual path, and $PAP'$ is an infinitely close neighboring path. Show that the time of travel for path $PAP'$ differs from the true time of travel $POP'$ by terms of higher order in the infinitesimal lengths $OB$ and $AC$. (HINT: Since $OA$ is an infinitesimal of the first order, the line $OB$ drawn perpendicular

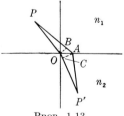

PROB. 1.13.

to $PO$ may be considered to cut off an isosceles triangle $OPB$; likewise for $AC$ drawn perpendicular to $OP'$.)

F — **1.14.** (*a*) A prism whose apex angle is 60° has a refractive index of 1.60 for a given color. When this prism is in air, what is the smallest angle of incidence for which an emergent ray is possible?

(*b*) Find the angle of minimum deviation for this color in the prism.

F — **1.15.** Using $n = 1.50$, calculate $\delta_m$ corresponding to the apex angles 2°, 5°, 10°, 15°, work only 20°, 25°, 30°, 35°, 40° using Eqs. (1.16) and (1.17). Compare the values obtained from one part both equations. What conclusions can you reach?

**1.16.** The figure represents the following construction: Two circles of radii $r_1$ and $r_2$ are drawn such that $r_2/r_1 = {_1}n_2$, $r_2 > r_1$. A ray $AO$ making an angle of incidence $\phi$ is extended to point $B$ on the circumference of the smaller circle. Line $DB$ is constructed perpendicular to the refracting surface and extended to point $C$ on the circumference of the larger circle. Prove that when the line $OC$ is drawn, then $\phi$ and $\phi'$ satisfy Snell's law. (This illustrates Snell's own construction for his law.) By considering the reflected ray show that reflection may be regarded as a special case of refraction in which ${_1}n_2 = -1$.

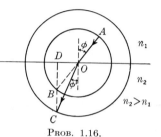

PROB. 1.16.

**1.17.** For many transparent isotropic substances the Lorenz-Lorentz law

$$\left(\frac{n^2 - 1}{n^2 + 2}\right)\left(\frac{1}{\rho}\right) = \text{constant}$$

is closely followed where $n$ is the index of refraction of the substance and $\rho$ is the density. Using the following measured data for water, plot $(n^2 - 1)/(n^2 + 2)$ as a function of $\rho$, and find the value of the constant, known as the specific refraction. What conclusions can you draw from your graph?

| $t$, °C | $n$ (for $D$ light) | $\rho$, gm/cm³ |
|---|---|---|
| 0 | 1.3340 | 0.99987 |
| 10 | 1.3337 | 0.99973 |
| 20 | 1.3330 | 0.99823 |
| 30 | 1.3320 | 0.99567 |
| 40 | 1.3306 | 0.99224 |
| 50 | 1.3290 | 0.98807 |
| 60 | 1.3272 | 0.98324 |
| 70 | 1.3252 | 0.97781 |

F — **1.18.** The figure represents a construction based on a refracting sphere of radius $r$ and of refractive index $n$, an imaginary inner spherical surface of radius $r_i = r/n$, and an imaginary outer spherical surface of radius $r_o = nr$. A ray of light $OM$ from the object at $O$ refracts in direction $MN$, which is determined by the point $I$ formed by $CO$ extended to meet the outer surface. Prove that this construction makes $I$ the image point of $O$ for all positions of $M$, that is, that the refraction is aplanatic.    (HINT: Prove that $\sin \beta / \sin \alpha = n$.)    This is the principle of the high-power oil-immersion lens in microscopes.

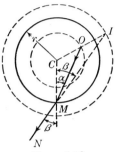

PROB. 1.18.

**1.19.** Plot Eq. (1.7) for $n = 1.50$ and $d = 8.00$ cm.

**1.20.** Show that if $P'$ is the image point of $P$ in Fig. 1.5a for any position of $A$, then $PA + AP' = $ constant and the reflecting surface is an ellipsoid of revolution.

**1.21.** Discuss the limiting cases of the aplanatic equation (1.12), corresponding to the ellipse, the circle, the hyperbola, and the parabola.

**1.22.** Find the prism angle for a silicate-crown-glass prism required to form a direct-vision prism in combination with a silicate-flint-glass prism whose apex angle is $10°$.

**1.23.** (a) Using the same data as in Prob. 1.22, solve the problem for the formation of an achromatic prism combination.

(b) What is the net mean deviation for the achromatic prism?

**1.24.** Which of the prisms shown in Fig. 1.15 are achromatic?    Why?

## CHAPTER 2

# THE SPHERICALLY REFRACTING SURFACE

We are now in a position to build up the theory of geometrical image formation behind all optical systems employing mirrors and lenses. Although spherical surfaces do not form perfect point images of point objects (see Chap. 7), the development of image formation by spherical surfaces has at least three advantages: (1) Since a spherical surface has a constant radius of curvature, it is the least complicated with which to deal and, as a consequence, the mathematical developments are comparatively simple. (2) From an economical point of view, spherical mirrors and lenses are much less expensive than the more exacting parabolic and other aplanatic forms. (3) The first two reasons would hardly be justifiable if it were not for the fact that, from a practical point of view, a spherical surface, under the proper limitations of use, produces an image whose purity is relatively free from the effect of sphericity. We therefore shall develop the principles of image formation by a spherically refracting surface in this chapter; then we shall take up the formation of images by spherically reflecting surfaces in Chap. 3 and by lenses in Chaps. 4 and 5. Although reflections from spherical surfaces are simpler in treatment than spherically refracting surfaces, we treat the spherical mirrors in the next chapter since reflection may be dealt with as a special case of refraction with the refractive index considered as $-1$ (see Prob. 1.16). The developments in this chapter, then, are fundamental to all reflecting and refracting systems, and the student is urged to grasp the facts as thoroughly as possible.

**2.1. General Considerations. The Sign Convention.** The essential terms that are used in dealing with a refracting surface are illustrated in Fig. 2.1. The refracting surface $MON$ is considered convex as viewed from the side of refractive index $n$ and concave as viewed from the region of refractive index $n'$.

Fig. 2.1.

The horizontal line drawn through the center of curvature $C$ of the surface is called the *axis* of the system, and the point of intersection $O$ with the surface is known as the *vertex*.

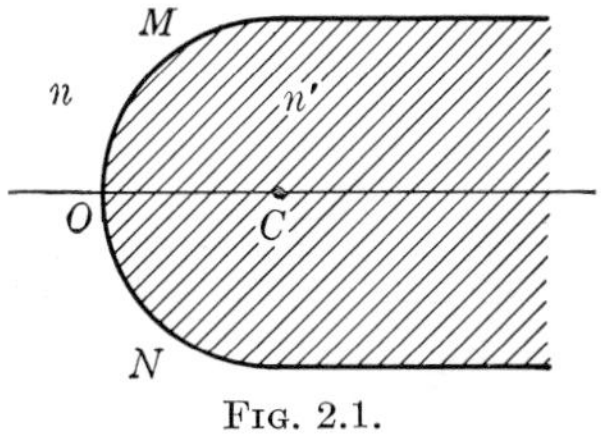

As in all measuring systems, it is necessary to set up a coordinate system and sign convention for the measurement of distances. In general, for

25

geometrical optics, some of the more frequent distances involved are

$s$ = object distance
$s'$ = image distance
$R$ = radius of curvature of refracting surface
$y$ = height of object
$y'$ = height of image

Other symbols will be introduced as they are needed.   In this book we adopt the convention that is strictly in accord with the conventions of analytical geometry, with the vertex $O$ as the coordinate origin.   Accordingly we specify:

1. All figures are drawn with the light incident on the refracting (or reflecting ) surface from the left.

2. All distances measured to the left of $O$ are considered negative, and all distances measured to the right of $O$ are taken as positive.

3. For distances measured upward and normal to the axis the sign is positive, and for downward measurement the sign is negative.

4. The *slope angle* that a ray makes with the axis is positive when the axis must be rotated counterclockwise through this acute angle to bring it into coincidence with the ray.   The slope angle is negative if the axis must be rotated clockwise to make it coincide with the ray.

5. The angle of incidence (or refraction) that a ray makes with the normal to the surface is positive if the normal (the radius of curvature) must be rotated counterclockwise through this angle to bring it into coincidence with the ray.

As a consequence of these conventions, the following consistencies result:

1. The radius of curvature of a convex refracting surface is positive.

2. The radius of curvature of a concave refracting surface is negative.

3. In Fig. 2.2, angles $u$, $\phi$, $\phi'$ are positive.   Angle $u'$ is negative.

It is worth mentioning here that much time will be saved and confusion avoided if these conventions are *studied* and *learned* at this point.

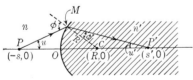

Fig. 2.2. Refraction at a convex surface forming a real image.

**2.2.   Refraction at a Spherical Surface.**   In Fig. 2.2, a convex refracting surface is used to form an image of a point object $P$ whose coordinates are $(-s,0)$.   One oblique ray at an angle $u$ with the axis is incident at an angle $\phi$ with the normal to the surface and bends downward with an angle of refraction $\phi'$.   This ray intersects the ray $PO$, which proceeds, without bending, to form the image $P'$ with coordinates $(s',0)$, forming the angle $u'$ in the image space. We now wish to obtain the relationships that exist between the quantities

$s$, $s'$, $\phi$, $\phi'$, $u$, $u'$, and $R$. These are obtained by considering the triangles $PMC$ and $MCP'$. In triangle $PMC$, the law of sines yields

$$\frac{\sin u}{R} = \frac{\sin (180 - \phi)}{|s| + R} = \frac{\sin \phi}{|s| + R} \tag{2.1}$$

*[handwritten annotations: "+ in I, II Quadrants", "sine is + in I Quadrant", "this is in I Quadrant"]*

Triangle $MCP'$ gives

$$\frac{\sin \phi'}{s' - R} = \frac{\sin |u'|}{R} \tag{2.2}$$

and by combining Eqs. (2.1) and (2.2) with the law of refraction

$$n \sin \phi = n' \sin \phi'$$

there follows

$$\frac{|s| + R}{s' - R} = \frac{n' \sin |u'|}{n \sin u} \tag{2.3}$$

Since $|u'| = \phi - \phi' - u$, then

$$\frac{|s| + R}{s' - R} = \frac{n' \sin (\phi - \phi' - u)}{n \sin u} \tag{2.4}$$

Equation (2.4) shows that, in general, the image distance $s'$ is different for different slope angles $u$ of the incident ray, since $\sin (\phi - \phi' - u)/\sin u$ for a spherical surface is not constant. This variation gives rise to what is known as spherical aberration and is a defect of all spherical surfaces. Equation (2.4) is most useful in its application to ray tracing where selected rays are traced through an optical system in order to ascertain the performance of the system. In this way the quality of the image formed may be determined and the constants of the system altered to meet some chosen specifications.

However, if the incident rays are restricted to the vicinity of the axis, so that $u$ is small, there may be obtained a much simpler expression which shows that all rays near the axis and emerging from a point object unite to form a point image. Rays that satisfy these restrictions are known as *paraxial* rays. For paraxial conditions,

$$\left| \frac{\sin |u'|}{\sin u} = \frac{|u'|}{u} = \frac{|s|}{s'} \right|$$

so that Eq. (2.3) becomes

$$\frac{|s| + R}{s' - R} = \frac{n'|s|}{ns'}$$

In accordance with the sign convention the object distance, being to the left of the refracting surface, is to be taken as negative. Hence, using $|s| = -s$,

$$\frac{-s + R}{s' - R} = \frac{-n's}{ns'} \tag{2.5}$$

or

$$\frac{n'}{s'} - \frac{n}{s} = \frac{n' - n}{R} \qquad (2.6)$$

Although we derived Eq. (2.6) for a convex refracting surface forming a real image of a real object, the equation holds for all other possible cases. We leave it as an exercise for the student to derive Eq. (2.6) for the remaining two cases, *viz.*, the case of a convex refracting surface forming

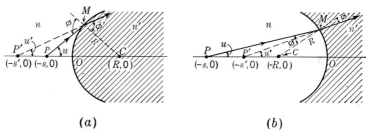

(a)                                  (b)

Fig. 2.3. A virtual image formed by refraction (a) at a convex surface and (b) at a concave surface.

a *virtual* image of a real object, illustrated in Fig. 2.3a, and the formation of a virtual image by a concave surface, illustrated in Fig. 2.3b. When the rays, after refraction (or reflection), actually pass through the image, the image so formed is *real* and may physically be thrown onto a screen, whereas when the rays after refraction (or reflection) only appear to pass through the image, the image so formed is termed *virtual* and cannot be cast onto a screen.

**2.3. Further Discussion of Refraction Equation (2.6).** We can see under what conditions Fig. 2.3a is obtained. By letting $s = -s_1$, where $s_1$ is some object distance, Eq. (2.6) then gives

$$\frac{n'}{s'} = \frac{s_1(n' - n) - nR}{Rs_1} \qquad (2.7)$$

which shows that the image position $s'$ is positive, indicating a real image when

$$s_1 > \frac{n}{n' - n} R$$

This corresponds to Fig. 2.2, and it is negative and indicates a virtual image when

$$s_1 < \frac{n}{n' - n} R$$

This corresponds to Fig. 2.3a. When the object is placed at the intermediate position corresponding to

$$s = -s_1 = \frac{-n}{n' - n} R \qquad (2.8)$$

Eq. (2.7) shows that $s' = \infty$ so that the refracted rays are parallel to the axis. This value of $s$ given by Eq. (2.8) locates what is known as the first principal focus of the convex surface, and lies to the left of the pole at a distance called the first principal focal length.

On the other hand, when $s = -\infty$, Eq. (2.6) shows that

$$s' = \frac{n'}{n' - n} R$$

which locates what is known as the second principal focus of the surface and lies to the right of the pole at a distance called the second principal focal length.

For the concave surface, Eq. (2.6) shows that since here $R$ is negative, $s'$ will always be negative, thus forming only a virtual image of a real object. This is the case illustrated in Fig. 2.3b. As before, it follows that the principal focal position on the left of the concave refracting surface, corresponding to the second principal focal length, is given by

$$s' = -\frac{n'}{n' - n} R_1$$

and the principal focal position on the right, corresponding to the first principal focal length, is given by

$$s = \frac{n}{n' - n} R_1$$

where the radius of curvature has been taken as $R = -R_1$.

Equation (2.6) is the most fundamental equation in all geometrical optics. Although valid for paraxial conditions, it is true that these restrictions are the ones generally realized in practice. As we shall see in Chaps. 3 and 4, Eq. (2.6) leads to the general mirror and lens equations which are fundamental to all optical systems.

When a series of refracting surfaces are employed, the method of computing the ultimate image is to apply Eq. (2.6) successively to each refracting surface, considering the image formed by one surface as the object for the following surface. An example illustrating this procedure is given below. Here it is significant to point out that if the vertex of a second refracting surface is situated to the right of the image formed by a first refracting surface (*i.e.*, to the right of $P'$ in Figs. 2.2 and 2.3a, b) then the point $P'$ acts in every way like a real object and the corresponding position $s'$ is negative. This holds whether the first surface forms a real or virtual image. On the other hand, if the second surface is situated so that it intercepts a converging pencil of rays, for instance, as would happen if the second surface were placed between $O$ and $P'$ in Fig. 2.2, then the position $P'$, where the image would have been formed in the absence of the second surface, serves as the object for the second surface. In such a case $P'$ is called a virtual object as shown in Fig. 2.4, and its

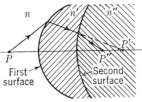

distance from the second surface is to be taken as positive. The solution for the final image $P''$ is then obtained with reference to the vertex of the second surface.

**2.4. Linear Lateral Magnification.** Consider an object of height $y$, the light from which is incident on the refracting surface as in Fig. 2.5. If $PQ$ is perpendicular to the axis and if $y$ is not too large, the image of $Q$ will fall at $Q'$ in a plane through $P'$ and be perpendicular to the axis. (Actually if $PQ$ is an arc with $C$ as center, then $P'Q'$ is the corresponding arc about the same center.)   For sufficiently small arcs, the linear lateral magnification is given by

FIG. 2.4. Illustrating a virtual object.

$$m = \frac{y'}{y} \tag{2.9}$$

and is called simply the magnification.   From the similar triangles $PQC$ and $P'Q'C$, we have

$$\frac{-y'}{y} = \frac{s' - R}{|s| + R} = \frac{s' - R}{-s + R} \tag{2.10}$$

and using Eq. (2.5),

$$m = \frac{y'}{y} = \frac{ns'}{n's} \tag{2.11}$$

When $m$ is positive, $s$ and $s'$ have the same sign, $y$ and $y'$ have the same sign, and hence the image is erect.   If $m$ is negative, then the image is inverted with respect to the object.

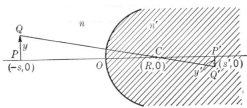

FIG. 2.5. Illustrating linear lateral magnification.

It must be remembered that Eq. (2.11), which determines the image height $y'$, is true for paraxial conditions.   For several surfaces giving successive magnifications $m_1, m_2, \ldots,$ the final magnification is the product $m = m_1 m_2 \cdots$.

**2.5. Abbe's Sine Condition and Lagrange's Law.**   By combining Eq. (2.10) with Eq. (2.3), we obtain

$$m = \frac{y'}{y} = -\frac{n \sin u}{n' \sin |u'|}$$

and introducing $|u'| = -u'$ in accordance with the sign convention,

$$m = \frac{y'}{y} = \frac{n \sin u}{n' \sin u'} \tag{2.12}$$

Thus, unless $\sin u / \sin u'$ is constant for all points of the refracting surface, the magnification will not be constant. The condition

$$\frac{\sin u}{\sin u'} = \text{constant}$$

is known as *Abbe's sine condition*, and unless it is satisfied, an optical system suffers from an aberration known as coma. This aberration is discussed in Chap. 7.

To the approximation of paraxial conditions we have seen that

$$\frac{\sin u}{\sin u'} = \frac{u}{u'}$$

and Eq. (2.12) yields

$$\frac{y'}{y} = \frac{nu}{n'u'}$$

or

$$nyu = n'y'u' \tag{2.13}$$

This equation, known as *Lagrange's law*, may be applied to any number of refracting surfaces for which small angles and paraxial conditions may be assumed to exist. Note that when $y$ and $y'$ are of opposite sign so that the image is inverted, then $u$ and $u'$ are of opposite sign.

**2.6. Summary of Signs for Use in the Refraction Equation.** In applying the equations developed in this chapter, it is advisable to think over and keep in mind the following generalizations:

1. When a known value is substituted for a quantity, it is put in with its associated sign; *e.g.*, for $R$ the value is inserted with a plus or minus sign according as the surface is convex or concave, respectively. On the other hand, for an unknown quantity, the sign in its algebraic solution will indicate something of its character; *e.g.*, in the solution for $R$, the surface is convex or concave according as $R$ comes out plus or minus, respectively.

2. For real objects $s$ is $(-)$; for virtual objects $s$ is $(+)$.

3. For real images $s'$ is $(+)$; for virtual images $s'$ is $(-)$.

4. For erect images, $m$ is $(+)$; for inverted images $m$ is $(-)$.

**Examples.** A glass dumbbell of index 1.60 has ends of 2.00 cm radius of curvature.

(*a*) With the dumbbell in air and its end 5.00 cm from a point object situated in line with the long axis, find the position and character of the image formed by one dumbbell end (see Fig. 2.6).

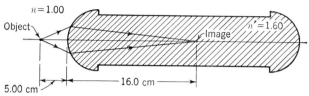

FIG. 2.6. Not to scale.

Applying the refraction equation,

$$\frac{n'}{s'} - \frac{n}{s} = \frac{n' - n}{R} \qquad n' = 1.60, \; n = 1.00, \; R = 2.00 \text{ cm}, \; s = -5.00 \text{ cm}$$

$$\frac{1.6}{s'} + \frac{1}{5} = \frac{1.6 - 1}{2}$$

$$\frac{1.6}{s'} = \frac{1}{10}$$

$$s' = 16.0 \text{ cm}$$

Since $s'$ is positive, the image is real and formed 16.0 cm to the right of the vertex.

(*b*) If the object is 1.00 cm from the dumbbell end, what are the character and position of the image?   Here we have

$$\frac{1.6}{s'} + \frac{1}{1} = \frac{1.6 - 1}{2}$$

$$\frac{1.6}{s'} = -0.7$$

$$s' = -2.29 \text{ cm}$$

The image is virtual and 2.29 cm to the left of the vertex.

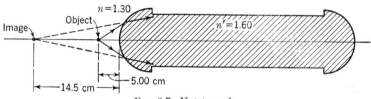

FIG. 2.7. Not to scale.

(*c*) With the dumbbell immersed in a liquid of index 1.30 and the object placed as in (*a*) above, solve for the image (see Fig. 2.7).   Here we have

$$\frac{1.6}{s'} + \frac{1.3}{5} = \frac{1.6 - 1.3}{2}$$

$$s' = -14.5 \text{ cm}$$

Hence the image is virtual, and the rays appear to diverge from it at 14.5 cm to the left of the vertex.

(d) In (a) above, if the distance between the two vertices is 20.0 cm, find the position and character of the image formed by the right refracting surface.

The image formed in (a) acts as a real object for the refracting surface. Hence

$$\frac{1}{s'} + \frac{1.6}{4} = \frac{1 - 1.6}{-2} \qquad n = 1.60, \; n' = 1.00, \; R = -2.00 \text{ cm}$$

$$\frac{1}{s'} = -0.1$$

$$s' = -10.0 \text{ cm}$$

The final image is virtual and formed midway between the vertices.

### PROBLEMS

**2.1.** A small bubble is inside a spherical glass ball at a distance of 0.500 cm from the center. The diameter of the ball is 5.00 cm, and its index is 1.50. Find the position and nature of the image formed by paraxial rays directed along a diameter. Solve for both cases.

**2.2.** Find the solution corresponding to Example (d) if the distance between the vertices of the dumbbell is 10.0 cm.

**2.3.** Find the solutions corresponding to Examples (a) and (b) if the dumbbell and light source are in water of index 1.33.

**2.4.** Obtain the expressions of the two principal focal positions for the concave refracting surface given in the text.

**2.5.** A glass stopper of refractive index 1.60 has a spherical knob of 2.00 in. diameter. A 0.500-mm illuminated object is situated in air 4.00 in. from the vertex of the curved surface and along the longitudinal axis of the stopper. Find the nature, position, and size of the image for paraxial rays.

**2.6.** Develop Eq. (2.6) corresponding to Fig. 2.3a.

**2.7.** Develop Eq. (2.6) corresponding to Fig. 2.3b.

**2.8.** Given $k - 1$ coaxial refracting surfaces separating $k$ media of indices $n_1$, $n_2, \ldots, n_k$, show that successive applications of Lagrange's law gives $n_1 y_1 u_1 = n_k y_k u_k$.

**2.9.** A small filament is at the center of a hollow glass sphere of inner radius 4.00 cm and outer radius 4.50 cm. Where will paraxial rays from the filament be brought to a focus if the index of refraction of the glass is 1.50?

**2.10.** A glass rod of refractive index $N$ and with ends of radii of curvature $R$ and $R/2$ as shown in the figure is used to image a point object $O$ at a distance $2R$ from the

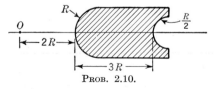

PROB. 2.10.

convex end. If the distance between the apexes of the ends is $3R$, show that the paraxial image is formed at a distance from the right-hand vertex given by $R(9 - 4N)/$

$(N - 2)(10N - 9)$.  What are the limiting values for $N$ that determine whether the final image is real or virtual?

**2.11.** A glass spherical fish bowl has an inner radius of 8.00 in. and an outer radius of 8.50 in.  The refractive index of the glass is 1.50, and that of the water in the bowl is 1.33.  When a small fish is 2.00 in. from the center of the bowl, where is the image formed by the refraction of paraxial rays traveling in the direction of the displacement of the fish from the center?  Is the image real or virtual, magnified or diminished, erect or inverted?

**2.12.** A glass paperweight (index 1.50) has five faces that are plane and the other spherically convex outward of radius 15.0 cm.  The block is held with the convex surface upward and with the bottom face 5.00 cm above a point object in air.  If the thickness of the block through the spherical apex is 3.00 cm, where is the image formed as viewed vertically from above through the block?

**2.13.** A liquid (index 1.80) stands in a glass capillary tube with a concave meniscus of radius of curvature 5.00 mm.  Where is the paraxial image of a point object situated in air along the capillary axis 8.00 mm from the vertex of the meniscus?  Is the image real or virtual?

**2.14.** Two concave refracting surfaces of equal radii of curvature and refractive index 1.5 face each other in air as shown in the figure.  A point object $P$ is placed

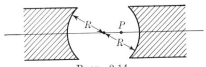

PROB. 2.14.

midway between the center and one of the vertices.  What is the separation between the images of $P$ formed by each refracting surface?

**2.15.** What must be the refractive index of the left-hand refracting surface in Prob. 2.14 so that the image of $P$ formed by it coincides in position with that formed by the right-hand refracting surface?

**2.16.** An object with a depth $\epsilon$ in the axial direction is in medium $n$ in front of a convex refracting surface.  The image in medium $n'$ has a corresponding depth $\epsilon'$ in the axial direction.  Using the refraction equation, show that for small values of $\epsilon$ and $\epsilon'$, $\epsilon'/\epsilon = -(n/n')m^2$, where $m$ is the linear lateral magnification.  This ratio of axial image depth to axial object depth is called the *longitudinal magnification*.  (HINT: $s + \epsilon$ and $s' - \epsilon'$ are also a set of object and corresponding image positions.  Use these in the refraction equation, and combine with the equation for $s$ and $s'$.)

## CHAPTER 3

## SPHERICAL MIRRORS

In this chapter we apply the refraction equation to curved reflecting mirrors. All optical systems have as their fundamental components either mirrors or lenses or combinations of these. Since the relationships between object positions, image positions, and the constants of the system are derived from Eq. (2.6), they are strictly true for paraxial conditions. However, the resulting equations have the advantage of being relatively simple in form, and as already noted, they are sufficient for most practical purposes for the location of optical images. The development, of course, is in accordance with the sign convention outlined in Chap. 2.

**3.1. The Spherical-mirror Equation.** When a polished surface has a constant radius of curvature, it is termed a *spherical mirror*. Obviously, these may be of the convex type or the concave type. The relationship between the object distance $s$, the image distance $s'$, and the radius of curvature $R$ for a spherical mirror may be derived by reflecting a ray from the surface and using the laws of reflection. However, it is more elegant to consider reflection as a particular case of refraction and obtain the relationship by a simple substitution. Thus, referring to Fig. 2.3$b$ and considering the left-hand surface of $OM$ as a mirror, the reflected ray would come back into the medium of index $n$ in accordance with the laws of reflection. By our convention of signs, $\phi' = -\phi$, so that from $n \sin \phi = n' \sin \phi'$, $n' = -n$. With these substitutions, the refraction equation (2.6) becomes

$$\frac{-n}{s'} - \frac{n}{s} = \frac{-n - n}{R}$$

or

$$\frac{1}{s'} + \frac{1}{s} = \frac{2}{R} \tag{3.1}$$

which is the equation connecting $s$, $s'$, and $R$ for any spherical mirror. For a real object there are three possible image formations by spherical mirrors, one for a convex mirror and two for a concave mirror. These are indicated in Fig. 3.1. It should be noted that a real image must lie to the left of the mirror in order that the reflected rays may pass through it. Hence $s'$ is negative for real images and positive for virtual images. When the mirror is convex, $s$ is negative and so Eq. (3.1) yields a positive value for $s'$ since $R$ is positive. This holds for all positions of the real object $P$ so that a convex mirror always forms a virtual image of a real object (Fig. 3.1$a$). On the other hand, for a concave mirror, $R$ is negative so that $s'$ will be negative (real image) if $|s| > |R|/2$ and positive (virtual image) if $|s| < |R|/2$. These cases are illustrated in Fig. 3.1$b$, $c$. For $s = -\infty$, so that the rays are coming in parallel to the mirror axis from a very distant object, the mirror equation yields $s' = R/2$, and the image

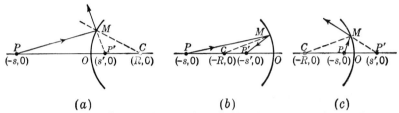

(a)                      (b)                      (c)

Fig. 3.1. (a) Formation of a virtual image of a real object by a convex mirror.  (b) Formation of a real image of a real object by a concave mirror.  (c) Formation of a virtual image of a real object by a concave mirror.

$P'$ is formed at $F$ midway between the pole of the mirror and the center of curvature. This construction is shown in Fig. 3.2 with $P'$ falling midway between $O$ and $C$ within the limits of paraxial conditions. As $P$ moves to the right from infinity, $P'$ moves to the left so that for all positions of $P$ from $-\infty$ to $C$, the corresponding image is between $F$ and $C$. When $P$ is at $C$, the image $P'$ also falls at $C$ since all rays outward from $C$ are perpendicular to the mirror and therefore reflect undeviated. As $P$ moves from $C$ to $F$, $P'$ moves from $C$ to $-\infty$, so that object and image positions have interchanged. This illustrates the general rule of reversibility of rays that, in any optical system, the object and image may be interchanged with the result that if the object is positioned at the place formerly occupied by the image, its image will be at the place originally occupied by the object. Such pairs of corresponding object and image points are called *conjugate points*.

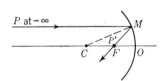

Fig. 3.2. Illustrating the principal focus of a mirror.

Thus far, for all positions of $P$ from $-\infty$ to $F$, the image $P'$ is real; this is illustrated in Fig. 3.1$b$. Now as $P$ assumes a position between $F$ and the pole of the mirror, the reflected ray will slope upward at $M$ (in accordance with the law of reflection) and will appear to come from a point behind the mirror, thus forming a virtual image (Fig. 3.1$c$). This point $F$, where parallel rays are imaged, is called the *principal focus* of the mirror. The corresponding distance from $O$ to $F$ is called the *focal length* of the mirror and is designated by the symbol $f$. Thus,

$$f = \frac{R}{2} \tag{3.2}$$

and the focal length of a concave mirror is negative; that of a convex mirror is positive.

Equation (3.1) may now alternatively be written as

$$\frac{1}{s'} + \frac{1}{s} = \frac{1}{f} \tag{3.3}$$

Hence, if $P$ lies at a distance greater than the focal length of a concave mirror, a real image is formed, whereas if this distance is less than $f$, a virtual image is formed. For the convex mirror, all positions of the real object $P$ have corresponding image positions between the mirror and its focal distance. In Fig. 3.3 is shown how rays, converging to the focal point of a convex mirror, are reflected parallel to the axis forming the image at $-\infty$.

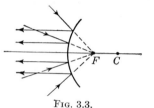

Fɪɢ. 3.3.

The properties of the mirrors outlined above may be obtained again by the following analysis: Suppose we wish to find where the image is formed in a concave mirror corresponding to the real object situated anywhere from $-\infty$ to the center of curvature. We let $R = -r$, $s = -a$, and Eq. (3.1) gives

$$s' = \frac{ra}{r - 2a}$$

Since $s$ is to vary from $C$ to $-\infty$, let $a = r + \epsilon$, where $\epsilon$ takes on any value from 0 to $+\infty$. Hence

$$s' = \frac{r^2 + r\epsilon}{-r - 2\epsilon} = \frac{(r^2/\epsilon) + r}{(-r/\epsilon) - 2}$$

For $\epsilon = 0$,

$$s' = -r$$

and for $\epsilon = \infty$,

$$s' = \frac{-r}{2} = -f$$

The image will then lie between $C$ and $F$ as already observed. All regions may be mapped in a similar fashion.

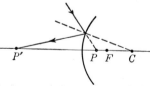

Fɪɢ. 3.4. A convex mirror forming a real image of a virtual object.

The formation of a real image in a convex mirror by a virtual object is illustrated in Fig. 3.4. This and other cases such as the formation of a virtual image in a convex mirror by a virtual object and the formation of a real image in a concave mirror by a virtual object are taken up in problems.

**3.2. Image Formation of Objects of Finite Size.** So far we have considered the formation of a point image by a spherical mirror of a point object.  If the object is small and perpendicular to and near the axis of a spherical mirror, then the image will also be perpendicular to the axis as shown in Fig. 3.5.  There, point $P'$ is the paraxial image of point $P$, and

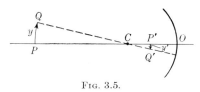

FIG. 3.5.

if the axis is rotated about the center of curvature $C$, then $Q'$ is the paraxial image of point $Q$.  Thus $PQ$ is imaged at $P'Q'$, and if the size of the object is small, a vertical object in a vertical plane through $P$ may be considered imaged as a vertical object in a vertical plane through $P'$.  The height of the object $y$ is then related to the height of the image $y'$ by the magnification equation (2.11) with $n' = -n$, so that

$$m = \frac{y'}{y} = \frac{-s'}{s} \tag{3.4}$$

When $m$ is positive, $s$ and $s'$ are of opposite signs, $y$ and $y'$ have the same sign, and the image is erect.  If $m$ is negative, $s$ and $s'$ have the same sign, $y$ and $y'$ have opposite signs, and the image is inverted.  Equation (3.1) or Eq. (3.3) and Eq. (3.4) are sufficient to locate the position and character of an image formed by a spherically reflecting mirror.  If there is more than one mirror in an optical system, the position and character of the final image are obtained by successively applying these equations to each mirror, using the image of one mirror as the object (real or virtual as the case may be) for the next mirror.  The total magnification is the product of the magnifications of the individual mirrors.

**3.3. Graphical Method for Mirrors.**  The image of an object formed by a spherical mirror may be located by a graphical method that depends

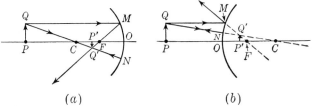

(a)                              (b)

FIG. 3.6. Graphical construction of the image of a real object formed by (a) a spherical concave mirror, (b) a spherical convex mirror.

on the fact that every point image of a point object is formed by the intersection of any two rays which have proceeded from the point object and undergone reflection at the reflecting surface.  To the approximation that a straight object forms a straight image, the construction locating the extremities of the image corresponding to the extremities of the object will locate the image. For the real object $PQ$, Fig. 3.6$a$ illustrates the construction that locates the real image formed by a concave mirror, and Fig. 3.6$b$ illustrates the formation of the virtual image formed by a convex mirror. From point $Q$, rays of light are given off in all directions, and although we may use the law of reflection to trace the course of any of the rays striking the reflecting surface, there are three rays whose courses we readily know. One of these is a parallel ray $QM$, which either passes through the focal point $F$ after reflection [as in $(a)$] or appears to come from $F$ after reflection [as in $(b)$]. The second ray usually chosen is the one that is directed through the center of curvature $C$ of the mirror $QN$. This ray reflects back on itself. The third ray that may be employed is a ray that is directed toward the focal point $F$, and this one proceeds parallel to the axis after reflection.

However, this third ray is not necessary, and the rays $QM$ and $QN$ are the ones usually employed. The rays either intersect after reflection, forming the point $Q'$ [as in $(a)$], or they will appear to diverge from an intersection point $Q'$ [as in $(b)$]. In any case, $Q'$ is the image point of $Q$.

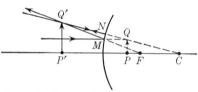

FIG. 3.7. Graphical construction for the image of a virtual object in a convex mirror.

Since the ray $PO$ passes through both points $C$ and $F$ and then reflects back on itself, and since, in accordance with our previous considerations, a straight image is formed by a straight object, $P'$ is the point image of $P$. In this way the image $P'Q'$ is located. The method not only locates the position of the image but also gives its character, whether it is erect or inverted, whether it is magnified or diminished, and whether it is real or virtual. Quite accurate solutions may be obtained by graphical means, but, of course, the results are limited to the amount of accuracy that is possible with any graphical method.

When the optical arrangement is such that a spherical mirror is in the path of a pencil of rays which is converging toward an image so that this image is a virtual object of the mirror, the graphical construction is carried through in a similar manner. Figure 3.7 illustrates the formation of a real image of a virtual object by a convex mirror. The ray construction follows the same scheme except that the incident rays are drawn *toward* the virtual object from the other side of the mirror and then these rays are permitted to be modified in the usual manner by reflection. Thus in Fig. 3.7 the parallel ray is drawn toward $Q$ where $PQ$ is the virtual object. This ray reflects at $M$ as if it were proceeding from $F$. The ray in the direction of $C$ is drawn toward $Q$ and reflects on itself at point $N$. These two rays intersect to give the image point $Q'$ of the point $Q$.

**3.4. Relative Aperture of a Mirror.** The relative aperture of a spherical mirror (Fig. 3.8) is the ratio of its diameter $D$ to its focal length $f$,

$$\text{Relative aperture} = \frac{D}{f} \tag{3.5}$$

where the diameter is determined by the extremities of the part of the mirror that is actually in use. This ratio is a measure of the amount of surface that is available for the formation of an image. The formulas obtained for spherical mirrors are restricted to paraxial conditions, and that implies that the mirrors are of small aperture. Only for mirrors of small aperture is it true that the rays lie close to the mirror axis. The effect of a mirror of large aperture is considered in the following section.

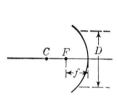

FIG. 3.8. Relative aperture.

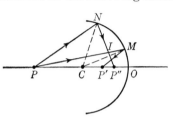

FIG. 3.9. Spherical aberration.

**3.5. Large-aperture Mirrors.** In Fig. 3.9 is shown the effect of a mirror of large aperture on the rays striking it from a point source on the axis. A paraxial ray $PM$ is imaged at $P'$, while a ray such as $PN$ is imaged at $P''$, so that the rays from $P$ do not come to a point focus. Rays reflected from points in the immediate vicinity of the pole $O$ are imaged very nearly at the same point, but as the point at which reflection occurs becomes more remote from the pole, the reflected ray is imaged at a point nearer the mirror. In this same way, if a spherical mirror of large aperture is used to bring to a focus rays coming from infinity, the rays that are reflected from portions of the mirror such as $N$ cut the axis at points to the far right of the principal focus, while those rays reflected near $O$ pass closer to the principal focus. This phenomenon, characterized by a departure from sharp focusing, is called *spherical aberration* and is a defect that is inherent in all spherical reflectors.

It should be noticed in Fig. 3.9 that any two rays reflected from two points, such as $M$ and $N$, intersect each other at $I$ before arriving at the axis. A curve drawn through such intersection points formed by a parallel bundle of rays incident on a spherical mirror of large aperture is drawn in Fig. 3.10. This curve is called the caustic by reflection of parallel rays incident on a circle. All reflected rays touch this curve. The equation of this caustic is given by[1]

[1] For the derivation of this equation see Appendix IC.

$$[4(x^2 + y^2) - R^2]^3 = 27R^4y^2 \qquad (3.6)$$

where $(x,y)$ are the coordinates of any point on the curve with respect to the origin $O$ and $R$ is the radius of curvature of the mirror with center at $O$. This curve is the envelope to the family of reflected rays and is the well-known two-cusped epicycloid. When $y = 0$, $x = R/2$, showing that the cusp occurs at the focal point of the mirror. The other cusp is situated at the diametrically opposite focal point corresponding to parallel rays incident on the other half of the spherical mirror.

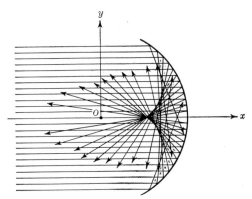

Fig. 3.10. Caustic by reflection.

By utilizing surfaces of the right shape the effect of spherical aberration may be eliminated. We have met such an aplanatic surface in Sec. 1.6; it is the ellipsoid of revolution which is free from spherical aberration with respect to its two conjugate foci. Also, a mirror shaped in the form of a paraboloid of revolution will focus to a single point all parallel rays falling on it. The mirror used in an astronomical telescope is ground down to paraboloidal shape since it is used to image objects that are effectively an infinite distance from the instrument.

### 3.6. Summary of Signs for Use of Mirror Equation

1. It should again be emphasized that a known value for a quantity is substituted in the mirror equation with its appropriate sign, while the unknown quantity is solved for from the equation and then its sign indicates some character of the quantity. For instance, if the focal length is unknown and its value is determined as negative, the mirror is concave.

2. For real objects, $s$ is $(-)$; for virtual objects, $s$ is $(+)$.

3. For real images, $s'$ is $(-)$; for virtual images, $s'$ is $(+)$.

4. For erect images, $m$ is $(+)$; for inverted images, $m$ is $(-)$.

**Examples.** (a) An object ¼ in. high is located 1.50 ft in front of a concave mirror of radius 2.40 ft. Find the position and character of the image.

Applying the mirror equation,

$$\frac{1}{s'} + \frac{1}{s} = \frac{2}{R} \qquad s = -1.50 \text{ ft}, \; R = -2.40 \text{ ft}$$

$$\frac{1}{s'} - \frac{1}{1.5} = \frac{-2}{2.4}$$

$$s' = -6.00 \text{ ft}$$

Since $s'$ is negative, the image is real and lies 6.00 ft to the left of the concave mirror.

$$m = -\frac{s'}{s} = -\frac{-6}{-1.5} = -4$$

so that the magnification is 4 and since it is negative the image is inverted. The size of the image is

$$y' = (\tfrac{1}{4})(-4) = -1.00 \text{ in.}$$

so that the size of the magnified image is 1.00 in. and the minus sign indicates that it points downward with respect to an upright object.

(b) What are the radius and type of mirror that must be employed to produce an erect 5.00-cm image of a 1.00-cm object placed 3.00 cm from it?

Since the image is to be magnified five times and is to be erect,

$$m = 5 = -\frac{s'}{s}$$

$$s' = (-5)(-3) = 15.0 \text{ cm}$$

The mirror equation now becomes

$$\frac{1}{15} - \frac{1}{3} = \frac{2}{R}$$

$$R = -7.50 \text{ cm}$$

The mirror must therefore be concave and have a radius of curvature of 7.50 cm.

## PROBLEMS

**3.1.** (a) A point object is placed 60.0 cm in front of a concave mirror of 40.0 cm radius of curvature. Find the location of the image. Is the image real or virtual? (b) Solve for the case of a convex mirror.

**3.2.** An object is placed 15.0 cm in front of a spherical mirror. The mirror forms a virtual image at a distance of 60.0 cm from it. Find the focal length and type of mirror.

**3.3.** An object is placed 60.0 cm in front of a spherical mirror. The mirror forms a virtual image at a distance of 15.0 cm from it. Find the radius of curvature and type of mirror. What is the magnification?

**3.4.** An object 4.00 cm long is situated on and perpendicular to the axis of a concave mirror of 40.0 cm radius. If the object is located 60.0 cm in front of the mirror, find the location of the image and its size and character.

**3.5.** Solve Prob. 3.4 for the case of a convex mirror.

**3.6.** A 4.00-cm object is placed 15.0 cm in front of a concave mirror of 40.0 cm radius. Solve for the position, size, and nature of the image.

**3.7.** A concave mirror, 40.0 cm radius, forms a 16.0-cm virtual erect image at a distance of 60.0 cm from the mirror. How large is the object, and how far in front of the mirror is it located?

**3.8.** A concave mirror of 30.0 cm radius and a convex mirror of 120 cm radius are 30.0 cm apart, and their reflecting surfaces are facing each other, their principal axes coinciding. An object 2.00 cm long is placed between them and 20.0 cm from the concave mirror. Give a complete description (position, size, and nature) of the images formed by three reflections, considering the first reflection to occur at the concave mirror.

**3.9.** Solve Prob. 3.8 by the graphical method.

**3.10.** Derive Eq. (3.1) by the ray method for a point object on the axis of a convex mirror.

**3.11.** A hollow spherical ball with a reflecting coating and of radius $r$ floats half submerged in a liquid (index 1.5) that is contained in a hemispherical glass bowl of radius $R$ so that the liquid fills the top of the bowl; $R > r$. The bowl rests on a table, and a luminous point object is situated a horizontal distance $R$ from the vertex of the glass bowl. Find an expression for the position of the image, with respect to the circumference of the hollow ball, formed by refraction and reflection, when the ball is in the center of the liquid surface. Neglect the effect of the glass. Consider paraxial rays directed radially inward toward bowl and ball.

**3.12.** (a) Plot the mirror equation (3.3), using $s'$ as ordinate and $s$ as abscissa. Interpret the resulting plot in the light of the developments in the chapter. (b) Transform Eq. (3.3) to a new form so that it is a function of $x$, $x'$, and $f$ by the relations $s = x + f$, $s' = x' + f$. Discuss in relation to the plot in (a). The transformed equation is known as the Newtonian form.

**3.13.** Using the mirror equation, show analytically that when the object moves toward the mirror, the conjugate image always moves away from the mirror.

**3.14.** Using Fig. 3.2, prove geometrically that $f = R/2$ for paraxial conditions.

**3.15.** (a) Show by analytical means that for a virtual object situated between a convex mirror and its focal point, the image is always real, erect, magnified, and situated at a distance from the mirror that is greater than the object distance.

(b) Using a straight virtual object located between the pole and the focal point of a convex mirror, locate the image by graphical means. Compare with the results obtained in part (a) of this problem.

**3.16.** Solve as in Prob. 3.15 but using the virtual object situated outside the focus of a convex mirror. The image here is virtual, inverted, and outside the focus.

**3.17.** Solve as in Prob. 3.15 but using the virtual object in any position with respect to a concave mirror. The image here is real, erect, diminished, and closer to the mirror than the object.

**3.18.** Plot Eq. (3.6).

**3.19.** A parallel ray makes an angle of incidence $\phi$ at a point $A$ on a concave mirror of radius $R$, and the reflected ray intersects the mirror axis at a point $B$. Show that the distance of $B$ from the pole of the mirror is given by $R[1 - (\sec \phi)/2]$. (HINT: Draw a figure, and apply the law of sines to triangle $ABC$, where $C$ is the center of curvature.)

# CHAPTER 4

## THIN SPHERICAL LENSES

Although thin-lens optics is really a special case of the more generalized thick-lens development, we take up the more simplified theory of the thin lens first and then pass on to the thick-lens and the thick-lens systems. This we do for at least two reasons. First, the conditions under which thin-lens formulas are obtained are usually valid in practice, and one can go rather far, from an elementary point of view, in the formation of images by means of thin-lens theory. Second, in practice, from the point of view of the student, it has turned out to be a more fruitful approach to develop first the thin-lens theory, which is based on the refraction equations already learned with the addition of no new concepts, and then to pass on to the more general thick-lens theory, as we do in Chap. 5, with the developments of the concepts of the cardinal points of a lens system.

**4.1. Lens Types.** Any portion of a refracting medium bounded by given surfaces is termed a lens. When the refracting medium is bounded

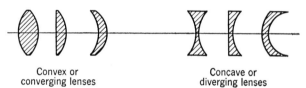

Convex or
converging lenses

Concave or
diverging lenses

Fig. 4.1. Lens types.

either by two spherical surfaces or by one spherical and one plane surface, the lens is termed a spherically refracting lens. It is the spherical lens that is most generally employed in optical systems and the one to which the refraction equations are directly applicable.

Lenses are divided into two classes corresponding, on the one hand, to those which cause a bundle of rays falling on them to become more convergent (less divergent) and, on the other hand, to those which cause a bundle of rays to become more divergent (less convergent) after refraction. The former are known as convex or convergent lenses; the latter as concave or divergent lenses. These are shown in Fig. 4.1 for lenses whose refractive indices are greater than the surrounding medium. In the convergent group, reading from left to right, the lenses are named biconvex, planoconvex, and concavoconvex or convex meniscus; and in the diverging group they are named biconcave, planoconcave, and convexo-concave or concave meniscus. A straight line connecting the two centers of curvature, or drawn through one radius of curvature and perpendicular to the plane surface, is called the lens axis. Figure 4.2 shows the refraction effect of each type of lens on a parallel bundle of rays. The convergent or divergent property of the lens is obtained by bending the ray at each surface in accordance with the law of refraction. The figures illustrate the fact that when the refractive index of the lens is greater

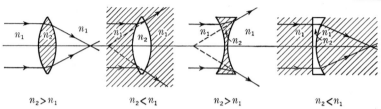

$n_2 > n_1$ $n_2 < n_1$ $n_2 > n_1$ $n_2 < n_1$

FIG. 4.2. Convergent and divergent properties of lenses.

than that of the surrounding medium, convergent lenses are thicker at their mid-sections than at their edges and divergent lenses are thinner at their centers than at their edges. The reverse holds for lenses whose refractive indices are less than that of the surrounding medium.

When the axial thickness of the lens is small compared with its radii of curvature and object and image distances, it is called a *thin lens* and its thickness is taken to be zero. It must be understood that such a consideration always leads to an approximation and the validity of the

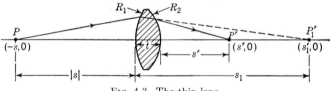

FIG. 4.3. The thin lens.

resulting expressions is limited to this restriction associated with a thin lens.

**4.2. The Thin-lens Equation.** In Fig. 4.3 is shown a thin lens whose index of refraction with respect to the surrounding medium is $n$, where $n > 1$, and the radii of curvature of its faces are $R_1$ and $R_2$ as shown. This is the situation most often employed in practice, that of a glass lens in air. The more general case of having a different medium on each side of the lens is so seldom employed that we shall not explicitly make the corresponding development although the procedure may easily be followed and each step accordingly altered if required. We shall, however, occasionally call attention to the form that a derived expression would have taken if the media on either side of the lens were of different refractive indices. This we shall do to emphasize certain of the optical properties. The paraxial rays from the object point $P$ are refracted at the left surface of the lens and the position $s_1'$, of the corresponding image point $P_1'$, is given by applying the refraction equation (2.6), which yields

$$\frac{n}{s_1'} - \frac{1}{s} = \frac{n-1}{R_1} \tag{4.1}$$

The image point $P_1'$ now acts as a virtual object for the right-hand refracting surface, forming the final image $P'$ at the position $s'$. Applying the refraction equation to this surface gives

$$\frac{1}{s'} - \frac{n}{s_1' - t} = \frac{1-n}{R_2} \tag{4.2}$$

Adding Eqs. (4.1) and (4.2),

$$\frac{1}{s'} - \frac{1}{s} - n\frac{t}{s_1'(s_1' - t)} = (n-1)\left(\frac{1}{R_1} - \frac{1}{R_2}\right) \tag{4.3}$$

For a thin lens, $t$ is set equal to zero, and

$$\frac{1}{s'} - \frac{1}{s} = (n-1)\left(\frac{1}{R_1} - \frac{1}{R_2}\right) \tag{4.4}$$

which is the well-known thin-lens equation relating the object distance $s$, the image distance $s'$, the radii of curvature $R_1$, $R_2$, and the relative index of refraction $n$. In accordance with our sign convention $R_2$ is negative for the biconvex lens used in Fig. 4.3. In view of the thin-lens approximation, the distances $s'$ and $s$ in Eq. (4.4) may be measured from either vertex or from the lens center.

**4.3. The Principal Foci and Focal Lengths.** As in the case with mirrors, a paraxial parallel bundle of rays incident on a lens is imaged at a point known as the *principal focus*. In the case of a lens, however, it may

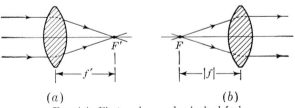

(a)                                    (b)

Fɪɢ. 4.4. First and second principal foci.

be turned through 180° so that the image and object spaces are interchanged. A lens then has two principal foci, one on each side of it. If parallel rays are incident on a lens as in Fig. 4.4a, they are brought to a focus at a point $F'$ known as the *second principal focus* and the distance of $F'$ from the center of the lens is known as the *second focal length f'*. If an object is placed at a point $F$ so that the rays after refraction are parallel (Fig. 4.4b), then $F$ is known as the *first principal focus* and its distance from the lens is the *first focal length f*. The planes perpendicular to the axis and passing through $F$ and $F'$ are called the *focal planes*. From Eq. (4.4) the value of $s$, corresponding to $s' = \infty$, is

$$\frac{1}{f} = -(n-1)\left(\frac{1}{R_1} - \frac{1}{R_2}\right)$$

and for $s = -\infty$, the value of $s'$ is

$$\frac{1}{f'} = (n-1)\left(\frac{1}{R_1} - \frac{1}{R_2}\right)$$

so that the focal lengths on either side of the lens are equal in magnitude but opposite in sign. It can be shown that they are equal in magnitude because the media on both sides of the lens are the same.[1] This is left as a problem at the end of the chapter. When the medium is the same on both sides of a lens, it is more usual and convenient to speak of the *focal length* of a lens and this is taken to mean the second principal focal length $f'$ since it is more frequently employed. This choice is in harmony with the definition that the "focal length" of a thin lens is the distance from the lens at which all incident rays parallel to the axis meet after refraction. Thus, we have the two fundamental equations

$$\frac{1}{f'} = (n-1)\left(\frac{1}{R_1} - \frac{1}{R_2}\right)$$

lens makers equation (4.5)

and

$$\frac{1}{s'} - \frac{1}{s} = \frac{1}{f'}$$

(4.6)

Because lenses are ordinarily used in air, it is common practice to designate a lens as positive or negative in accordance with $n > 1$. Thus from Eq. (4.5), $f'$ is positive for a convex lens, which is therefore called a positive lens, and is negative for a concave lens, which is therefore called a negative lens.

We see that the focal length of a lens is a function only of $n$, $R_1$, and $R_2$ so that it is characteristic of the lens alone. In fact, the magnitude of $f'$ is indicative of the degree to which a lens bends the rays after refraction, and a measure of this degree is termed the power of the lens. The power $D$ of a lens is expressed by the reciprocal of its focal length, thus:

power: $$D = \frac{1}{f'}$$

(4.7)

[1] If the medium in the object space is of index $n_1$ and that in the image space is of index $n_1'$, then it is easy to see that $f'/f = -n_1'/n_1$.

Opticians express the power of spectacle lenses in terms of a unit called the *diopter.* The power of a lens in diopters is the reciprocal of its focal length expressed in meters. Convex lenses have positive dioptric values, and concave lenses have negative dioptric values. Spectacle lenses of a given refractive index are usually ground to have those radii of curvature which will produce the required dioptric value, and Eq. (4.5) is known as the lens-maker's equation.

**4.4. Linear Lateral Magnification Produced by a Thin Lens.** Consider the object at $P$ in Fig. 4.3 of finite size, of linear height $y$, and perpendicular to the axis of the lens. Since the position of the final image was obtained by an application of the paraxial refraction equation, the image formed at $P'$ and of size $y'$ is also linear and perpendicular to the axis of the lens. The total magnification $m$ is the product of the individual magnifications $m_1$ and $m_2$ produced by the first and second refracting surfaces, respectively. Using Eq. (2.11), the magnification produced by the first surface is $m_1 = s_1/ns$, and that produced by the second surface is $m_2 = ns'/s_1$, so that

$$m = m_1 m_2 = \frac{s_1}{ns}\frac{ns'}{s_1}$$

$$m = \frac{y'}{y} = \frac{s'}{s} \tag{4.8}$$

Equation (4.8) holds when the object and image space have the same refractive index.[1] When $m$ is negative, $s$ and $s'$ are of opposite sign, $y$ and $y'$ are of opposite sign, and the image is inverted. This case is the one illustrated in Fig. 4.3. When $m$ is positive, $s$ and $s'$ are of the same sign, $y$ and $y'$ are of the same sign, and the image is erect.

Equations (4.6) and (4.8) are the most fundamental ones for thin lenses and are sufficient to determine the position of an image and its character, *i.e.*, whether it is erect or inverted, enlarged or diminished, real or virtual. As in the mirror equations, if there is more than one thin lens placed coaxially, the position and character of the final image are obtained by applying these equations successively to each lens, using the image of one lens as the object for the next lens. The total magnification is a product of the individual magnifications, where of course the word magnification means either enlargement or diminution as the case may be.

**4.5. Graphical Method for Thin Lenses.** The image of an object formed by a thin lens may be located by a graphical method that is similar to the one outlined for spherical mirrors. Again two rays whose paths are known are chosen from a point in the object, and these are followed through in the image space until they intersect at the corresponding

[1] If the medium in the object space is of index $n_1$ and that in the image space is of index $n_1'$, then $m = y'/y = n_1 s'/n_1' s$.

image point. Figure 4.5 illustrates the method for a convex lens forming
a real image in (*a*) and for a concave lens forming a virtual image in (*b*).
In both cases, *QM* is a parallel ray from the object point *Q*, and this ray
is brought up to the mid-point *M* of the curved surfaces. This ray is
considered to refract at *M* so that it either passes through the second
focal point *F″*, as in (*a*), or appears to proceed from it, as in (*b*). A ray
*QO* directed through the center of the lens passes through practically

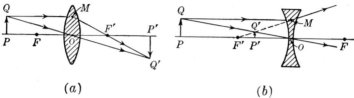

(a) (b)

Fɪɢ. 4.5. Graphical construction of images formed by thin lenses.

undeviated, since for a thin lens the curved surfaces are very nearly coincident with the tangent planes at the vertices, so that effectively the ray
passes through a parallel-sided slab of refracting material. The image
point *Q′* of the object point *Q* is where these rays intersect. The image
point *P′* of the object point *P* must be on the lens axis so that this completes the formation of the entire image. The third ray that may
optionally be employed is the one that is directed from *Q* toward the first
principal focal point *F*. It will then be directed parallel to the lens axis
after refraction and will intersect the other rays at *Q′*.

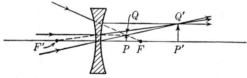

Fɪɢ. 4.6. Graphical construction of image of a virtual object in a thin lens.

If the object is a virtual one, being the image of a previous refraction
or reflection, then the construction is followed through in a similar manner
except that the incident rays are drawn *toward* the virtual object from the
other side of the lens as explained in Sec. 3.3 for mirrors. Such a construction is shown in Fig. 4.6 for the formation of a real image of a virtual
object by a concave lens. A parallel ray, a ray through the center of the
lens, and one through *F* are shown drawn toward the object point *Q*.
These intersect in *Q′*, forming the real image *P′Q′* of the virtual object
*PQ*.

It is to be noted that the graphical methods reveal the position and
character of the image. In Fig. 4.5*a* the image is real, magnified,
inverted, and farther from the lens than the object. In fact, for all

positions of $PQ$ from $-\infty$ to $F$, the image is real and inverted and has a magnification greater than unity if $s' > |s|$ and a magnification less than unity if $s' < |s|$. This property may be obtained from Eq. (4.6), from which $s' = f's/(s + f')$; and setting $s = -(f' + \epsilon)$, then

$$s' = \frac{f'(f' + \epsilon)}{\epsilon}$$

Now, when $\epsilon = 0$, then

$$s' = \infty$$

and when $\epsilon = \infty$, then

$$s' = f'$$

so that the image is real and inverted with the magnification changing from a region in which the values are greater than unity to a region in which the values are less than unity. The division point is at $\epsilon = f'$, for which $s' = 2f'$, so that the magnification is unity here. When the object is between the focal length and the lens, the image is virtual, erect, and always magnified. For the diverging lens in Fig. 4.5b, the image of a real object is always virtual, erect, and diminished, as can be shown from the lens equation. This and other cases are left as exercises in the chapter's problems.

In accordance with our sign convention, observe that, for lenses, the positive values of $s'$ correspond to real images and negative values of $s'$ correspond to virtual images.

**4.6. Thin Lenses in Contact.** By applying the lens equation successively to two thin lenses of focal lengths $f_1'$ and $f_2'$ in contact, it can be shown that the combination is equivalent to a single thin lens of focal length $f'$ given by

$$\frac{1}{f'} = \frac{1}{f_1'} + \frac{1}{f_2'} \tag{4.9}$$

and this result can be extended to three or more thin lenses in contact. The proof of Eq. (4.9) is taken up in a problem, and it shows that the power of a system of thin lenses in contact is the sum of the powers of the individual lenses.

**4.7. The Newtonian Form of the Thin-lens Equation.** Equation (4.4) may be put in the form

$$\frac{\dfrac{1}{(n-1)\left(\dfrac{1}{R_1} - \dfrac{1}{R_2}\right)}}{s'} - \frac{\dfrac{1}{(n-1)\left(\dfrac{1}{R_1} - \dfrac{1}{R_2}\right)}}{s} = 1$$

and using the expressions for the first and second principal focal lengths, we have

$$\frac{f'}{s'} + \frac{f}{s} = 1 \qquad (4.10)$$

which, of course, reduces to Eq. (4.6) by substituting for $f$ the value $-f'$. Equation (4.10), relating the principal foci with the object and image positions, is a perfectly general relationship, and we shall use it in subsequent developments. We shall now transform Eq. (4.10) by using the translation equations

$$s' = f' + x'$$
$$s = f + x \qquad (4.11)$$

Equation (4.10) now becomes

$$\frac{f'}{f' + x'} + \frac{f}{f + x} = 1$$

and simplifying,

$$xx' = ff' \qquad (4.12)$$

which is the Newtonian form of the lens equation relating the conjugate quantities $x$ and $x'$ with the conjugate quantities $f$ and $f'$. We can see

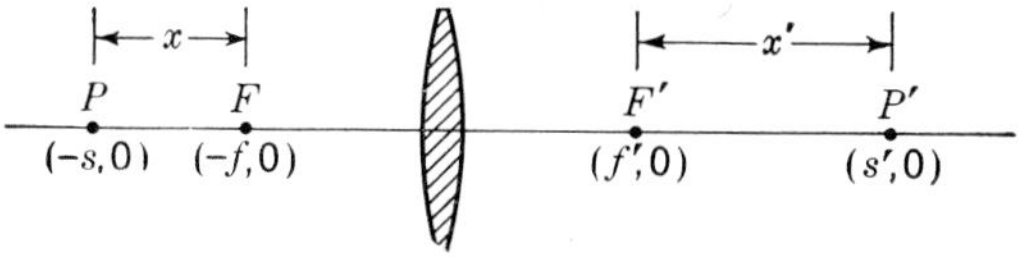

Fig. 4.7.

the significance of $x$ and $x'$ from Fig. 4.7. The object $P$ is indicated by its position $x$ from the first principal focal point $F$, and the image $P'$ is indicated by its position $x'$ from the principal focal point $F'$. By our sign convention, $x$ is considered negative when $P$ is to the left of $F$ and positive when it is to the right of $F$. Likewise, $x'$ is negative when it is at the left of $F'$ and positive when at the right of $F'$.

For the thin lens in air, or with the same medium on both sides of the lens, $f = -f'$, Eq. (4.12) becomes

$$xx' = -(f')^2 \qquad (4.13)$$

which shows that the conjugate distances $x$ and $x'$ must have opposite signs. Thus if an object lies outside the first focal point, the image will be outside the second focal point, and conversely.

The magnification equation (4.8) may be expressed in terms of $x$ and $x'$, thus:

$$m = \frac{s'}{s} = \frac{f' + x'}{f + x} = \frac{(xx'/f) + x'}{f + x} = \frac{xx' + x'f}{f(f + x)}$$
$$= \frac{x'}{f} = \frac{f'}{x} = \frac{-x'}{f'} = \frac{-f}{x} \qquad (4.14)$$

**4.8. Summary of Signs for Use in the Thin-lens Equation**

1. When a value is substituted for any of the quantities $s, s', f, f', x, x'$, it must be inserted with its appropriate sign. An unknown quantity is carried in the equation as it appears, and then its sign, when solved for, will indicate the character of the quantity.

2. For real objects, $s$ is $(-)$; for virtual objects, $s$ is $(+)$.

3. For real images, $s'$ is $(+)$; for virtual images, $s'$ is $(-)$.

4. For erect images, $m$ is $(+)$; for inverted images, $m$ is $(-)$.

**Examples.** (a) A thin converging lens of 20.0 cm focal length is 30.0 cm behind an object, in air, that is 3.00 cm high. Find the position, size, and character of the image. Apply

$$\frac{1}{s'} - \frac{1}{s} = \frac{1}{f'} \qquad s = -30.0 \text{ cm}, f' = 20.0 \text{ cm}$$

$$\frac{1}{s'} + \frac{1}{30} = \frac{1}{20}$$

$$s' = 60.0 \text{ cm}$$

Hence the image is real and 60.0 cm to the right of the lens.

$$m = \frac{s'}{s} = \frac{60}{-30} = -2$$

Hence the image is inverted, and its size is

$$y' = ym = (3)(-2) = -6.00 \text{ cm}$$

the negative sign indicating that it is inverted.

(b) If the lens in (a) above is planoconvex and has an index of refraction of 1.50, find the radius of curvature of its surface.

$$\frac{1}{f'} = (n-1)\left(\frac{1}{R_1} - \frac{1}{R_2}\right) \qquad n = 1.50, R_1 = \infty, f' = 20.0 \text{ cm}$$

$$\frac{1}{20} = (1.5 - 1)\frac{-1}{R_2}$$

$$R_2 = -20.0 \text{ cm}$$

assuming that the plane face is toward the object.

(c) A lens forms a virtual erect image of an object placed 4.00 cm from it in air. If the image is one-fifth the size of the object, what are the nature and focal length of the lens? Since the image is erect,

$$m = \frac{1}{5} \qquad s = -4.00 \text{ cm}$$

$$\frac{s'}{s} = \frac{1}{5}$$

$$s' = -\frac{4}{5} \text{ cm}$$

$$\frac{1}{-\frac{4}{5}} - \frac{1}{-4} = \frac{1}{f}$$

$$f = -1.00 \text{ cm}$$

and the lens is concave and of 1.00 cm focal length.

(*d*) A small object in air is 30.0 m from a thin converging lens of 30.0 cm focal length, and 25.0 cm beyond is a thin diverging lens of 5.00 cm focal length. Find the position, character, and magnification of the final image.

Applying the thin-lens equation to the converging lens, and using the subscript 1 for this lens, we have

$$\frac{1}{s_1'} - \frac{1}{s_1} = \frac{1}{f_1'} \qquad s_1 = -3{,}000 \text{ cm}, \; f_1' = 30.0 \text{ cm}$$

$$\frac{1}{s_1'} + \frac{1}{3{,}000} = \frac{1}{30}$$

$$s_1' = 30.3 \text{ cm}$$

This image may be considered as a virtual object for the diverging lens. Using the subscript 2 for this lens,

$$\frac{1}{s_2'} - \frac{1}{s_2} = \frac{1}{f_2'} \qquad s_2 = 30.3 - 25 = 5.30 \text{ cm}, \; f_2' = -5.00 \text{ cm}$$

$$\frac{1}{s_2'} - \frac{1}{5.3} = \frac{-1}{5}$$

$$s_2' = -88.3 \text{ cm}$$

The final image is virtual and 88.3 cm to the left of the diverging lens The total magnification is a product of the individual magnifications,

$$m = m_1 m_2$$
$$= \frac{s_1'}{s_1} \frac{s_2'}{s_2}$$
$$= \left(\frac{30.3}{-3{,}000}\right)\left(\frac{-88.3}{5.3}\right) = 0.168$$

so that the final image is diminished and erect. The student should draw a figure showing the disposition of the two lenses and the positions used in the above solution. The optical system illustrated here represents that employed in the opera glass or Galilean telescope.

**4.9. Remarks.** The conditions imposed on a thin lens require an axial thickness $t = 0$, which of course is never true. This entails measuring distances from any point of the lens, an ambiguous specification. However, in practice it is not nearly as bad as it sounds, for experimental results, which are the final test of every development, justify the procedure. To illustrate by a representative case, the actual positions of object and image as determined experimentally with a lens whose thickness is about 15 per cent of its focal length do satisfy the lens equation to the order of about 0.1 per cent, so that thin-lens theory is very useful.

Nevertheless, for thick lenses or systems of lenses, it becomes necessary to select specific convenient points connected with the lens or system from which the pertinent quantities are measured. We shall devote the next chapter to a development of thick lenses, but before proceeding we list in Table 4.1 a résumé of the signs of those quantities which are indicative of the character of an object and an image for refracting surfaces, mirrors, and lenses.

TABLE 4.1. RÉSUMÉ OF SIGNS FOR USE WITH REFRACTING SURFACES, MIRRORS, AND LENSES

| Image | Quantity | Sign of quantity | | |
|---|---|---|---|---|
| | | Refracting surfaces $\dfrac{n'}{s'} - \dfrac{n}{s} = \dfrac{n'-n}{R}$ | Mirrors $\dfrac{1}{s'} + \dfrac{1}{s} = \dfrac{2}{R} = \dfrac{1}{f}$ | Lenses $\dfrac{1}{s'} - \dfrac{1}{s} = \dfrac{1}{f'}$ |
| Real.................. | $s'$ | + | − | + |
| Virtual............... | $s'$ | − | + | − |
| Erect................ | $m$ | + | + | + |
| Inverted............. | $m$ | − | − | − |

For real objects $s$ is $(-)$.
For virtual objects $s$ is $(+)$.

## PROBLEMS

**4.1.** Calculate the focal length of a double convex lens made of glass of refractive index 1.50 and radii of curvature 30.0 and 15.0 cm (*a*) when in air, (*b*) when in water of refractive index 1.33.

**4.2.** If one of the surfaces in Prob. 4.1*a* is plane, find the new focal length for both possible cases.

**4.3.** Calculate the focal length of a double concave lens made of glass of refractive index 1.50 and radii 30.0 and 15.0 cm.

**4.4.** Calculate the focal length of a meniscus lens that is thicker in the middle than at the periphery if it is made of glass of index 1.50 and radii 30.0 and 15.0 cm.

**4.5.** A diverging lens of 60.0 cm focal length is made of glass of index 1.50. One radius of curvature is 30.0 cm. Calculate the other radius of curvature.

**4.6.** An object 4.00 cm long is situated on and perpendicular to the axis of a converging lens of 20.0 cm focal length. If the object is located 60.0 cm in air in front of the lens, find the position, size, and character of the image. Solve analytically in two ways, (*a*) using the lens equation, (*b*) using the Newtonian form of the lens equation. Solve graphically also.

**4.7.** An object 4.00 cm high is placed in air at a distance of 60.0 cm in front of a diverging lens of 20.0 cm focal length. Find the position, size, and character of the image. Solve analytically in two ways as specified in Prob. 4.6. Solve graphically also.

**4.8.** An object 4.00 cm high is placed 15.0 cm in air in front of a converging lens of 20.0 cm focal length. Find the position, size, and character of the image. Solve analytically and graphically as specified in Prob. 4.6.

**4.9.** A converging lens of 20.0 cm focal length produces a virtual image 16.0 cm high at a distance of 60.0 cm from the lens. Find the position, size, and character of the object. Solve analytically and graphically as specified in Prob. 4.6.

**4.10.** (*a*) A lens in air produces a real image 5.00 cm high of an object 5.00 cm high placed 40.0 cm in front of it. Find the focal length of the lens. Is it converging or diverging?

(*b*) Assuming that its faces have equal curvature, find the radii of curvature of the faces. The refractive index is 1.60.

**4.11.** A converging lens is used to form an image of an object. If the distance between object and screen is constant, show that there are two positions of the object for producing an image on the screen and that the distance between object and screen is greater than $4f'$. Also show that if the images are of heights $y_1'$ and $y_2'$, the object is of height $\sqrt{y_1' y_2'}$.

**4.12.** An object 1.00 cm long is placed in air 25.0 cm in front of a converging lens of 20.0 cm focal length, and a diverging lens of 10.0 cm focal length is placed 85.0 cm behind the converging lens. Find the position, size, and character of the final image.

**4.13.** An object 4.000 cm long is located 100.0 cm in front of a converging lens of 20.00 cm focal length. A second converging lens of 10.00 cm focal length is situated 45.00 cm behind the first lens, and a third converging lens of 2.000 cm focal length is situated 21.95 cm behind the second. Find the position, size, and character of the final image.

**4.14.** What kind of lens would be required in contact with a diverging lens of 20.0 cm focal length to make a diverging-lens combination with 30.0 cm focal length? Also express the result in terms of diopters.

**4.15.** A thin lens of refractive index $n$ separates the object space of refractive index $n_1$ from the image space of refractive index $n_1'$. Show that the first and second principal focal lengths are related by $f'/f = -n_1'/n_1$. From this show that Eq. (4.10) still holds.

**4.16.** Prove by analytical means, using the thin-lens equation, that when a real object is situated between the positions corresponding to $f'$ and $2f'$ of a converging lens, the image is situated at a distance greater than $2f'$ and is real, magnified, and inverted.

**4.17.** Using the lens equation, show analytically that when the object moves toward (or away from) the lens, the conjugate image moves correspondingly away from (or toward) the lens.

**4.18.** Find by the graphical method the position and nature of the image formed by a converging thin lens of a virtual object in any position.

**4.19.** Find by the graphical method the position and nature of the image formed by a diverging thin lens of a virtual object situated at a distance (*a*) less than, (*b*) greater than the lens's focal length.

**4.20.** The focal length of a thin lens is 30.0 cm. It is desired to determine the focal length experimentally to within 1 per cent by using a distant object and observing the distance of the image from the lens. How far away must the object be?

**4.21.** Using the thin-lens equation, obtain Eq. (4.9) for two thin lenses in contact.

**4.22.** Plot Eq. (4.6) for a lens of focal length $f'$, and compare with the plot of Eq. (4.13). What advantage does the Newtonian form have in the measurement of focal length?

**4.23.** A converging thin lens of focal length 4.00 cm and a concave mirror of 10.0 cm radius of curvature are placed coaxially and separated by 20.0 cm. An object is situated between the two at a distance of 7.50 cm from the mirror. Find the position and nature of the image after a single reflection and successive refraction.

**4.24.** Solve Prob. 4.23 with the lens and mirror separated by 10.0 cm.

**4.25.** A thin convex and a thin concave lens each of 50.0 cm focal length are coaxially situated and separated by 10.0 cm. Find the position and nature of the final image formed of an object placed 20.0 cm from the convex lens (30.0 cm from the concave lens).

**4.26.** Solve Prob. 4.25 but with the object placed 20.0 cm from the concave lens (30.0 cm from the convex lens).

**4.27.** A thin converging lens whose focal length is 20.0 cm is used to form, on a screen, an image that is four times as large as the object. What is the distance of the screen from the object?

**4.28.** A projection lantern is required to produce a picture 4.00 by 4.00 ft of lantern slides 3.00 by 3.00 in. What is the focal length of a thin lens that will do this if the slide is 50.0 ft from the screen? If the lens is equiconvex and made of glass of refractive index 1.60, what is the radius of curvature?

**4.29.** When a point source is on the axis of a converging thin lens, a real image is formed 20.0 cm from the lens. If a second thin lens is placed in contact with the first, the real image is formed 30.0 cm from both lenses. Find the focal length of the second lens.

**4.30.** A thin equiconvex lens of refractive index 1.60 has a focal length of 10.0 cm. The lens is mounted so that one of its surfaces is in air and the other is in water of refractive index 1.33. A point object in air is on the axis of the lens at a distance of 15.0 cm from it. Find the position of the image.

**4.31.** A thin convex lens of focal length $f'$ produces a real image of magnification $m$. Show that the distance of the object from the lens is $[(m + 1)/m]f'$.

**4.32.** An object is 12.0 in. from a convergent lens of focal length 10.0 in. When a divergent lens is placed 36.0 in. beyond the first lens, the final image falls at the position of the object. What is the focal length of the concave lens?

**4.33.** An object is 8.00 in. from a convergent lens of focal length 6.00 in. A divergent lens of focal length 12.0 in. is 14.0 in. beyond the first lens, and 10.0 in. beyond the divergent lens is a convex mirror of 10.0 in. radius of curvature. Find the position and nature of the final image after two refractions and one reflection.

## CHAPTER 5

# THICK SPHERICAL LENSES

In this chapter we follow the scheme outlined in Chap. 4 and show that the working equations for the thick lens have the same simplified forms as those of the thin lens if the distances of the object, image, etc., are measured from certain specialized locations. This consequently leads to the development of the cardinal points and their properties.

**5.1. The Thick Lens.** We shall now investigate the refraction of paraxial rays by a lens of nonnegligible thickness and with the same refractive index in the object and image spaces. Such a lens, made of a single piece of glass, or a system of two or more coaxial lenses or refracting surfaces is called a *thick lens*.

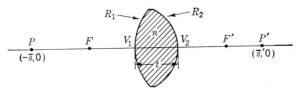

FIG. 5.1. The thick lens.

Figure 5.1 shows a lens of axial thickness $t$, with object point $P$ and image point $P'$ as in Fig. 4.3, with the first principal focus at $F$ and the second principal focus at $F'$. We have replaced the symbols $s$ and $s'$ by $\bar{s}$ and $\bar{s}'$, respectively, in order that the final derived expressions may be put in terms of the conventional symbols $s$ and $s'$. The refraction equation applied successively to both spherical surfaces yields Eqs. (4.1) and (4.2), which are here repeated as

$$\frac{n}{s'_1} - \frac{1}{\bar{s}} = \frac{n-1}{R_1}$$

$$\frac{1}{\bar{s}'} - \frac{n}{s'_1 - t} = \frac{1-n}{R_2}$$

where, as shown in connection with Fig. 4.3, $s'_1$ is the position, with respect to the vertex $V_1$, of the image formed by the convex refracting surface. As discussed on page 29, $(n-1)/R_1 = 1/-f_1$, where $f_1$ is the first principal focal length of the first refracting surface, and $(1-n)/R_2 = 1/f_2$, where $f_2$ is the first principal focal length of the second refracting surface. The above equations rewritten are

$$\frac{n}{s_1'} - \frac{1}{\bar{s}} = -\frac{1}{f_1}$$

$$\frac{1}{\bar{s}'} - \frac{n}{s_1' - t} = \frac{1}{f_2}$$

Eliminating $s_1'$ between these two equations yields

$$t = \frac{n}{(1/\bar{s}) - (1/f_1)} + \frac{n}{(1/f_2) - (1/\bar{s}')}$$

which may be put into the form

$$\bar{s}\bar{s}' + \frac{f_2(nf_1 + t)}{n(f_2 - f_1) - t}\,\bar{s} + \frac{f_1(t - nf_2)}{n(f_2 - f_1) - t}\,\bar{s}' - \frac{tf_1f_2}{n(f_2 - f_1) - t} = 0 \quad (5.1)$$

In this equation, $\bar{s}$ is measured with respect to $V_1$, $\bar{s}'$ is measured with respect to $V_2$, and the other quantities are constants of the surfaces and of the medium. Obviously Eq. (5.1) is much too cumbersome for use in image locations. It may be simplified by choosing other points from which $P$ and $P'$ are to be measured. Let us transform Eq. (5.1) to the form

$$\frac{1}{\bar{s}' - h'} - \frac{1}{\bar{s} - h} = \frac{1}{f'} \quad (5.2)$$

where $f'$ is the second principal focal length of the lens and $h$ and $h'$, whose physical significance will be brought out later, are to be determined. Clearing Eq. (5.2) of fractions and collecting terms, we have,

$$\bar{s}\bar{s}' - (f' + h')\bar{s} + (f' - h)\bar{s}' + f'(h - h') + hh' = 0 \quad (5.3)$$

Equations (5.1) and (5.3) will be identical if the coefficients of their corresponding terms are equal. Thus,

$$f' + h' = -\frac{f_2(nf_1 + t)}{n(f_2 - f_1) - t} \quad (5.4)$$

$$f' - h = \frac{f_1(t - nf_2)}{n(f_2 - f_1) - t} \quad (5.5)$$

$$f'(h - h') + hh' = -\frac{tf_1f_2}{n(f_2 - f_1) - t} \quad (5.6)$$

The three equations, (5.4), (5.5), and (5.6), may be solved for the three unknowns $h$, $h'$, and $f'$. From Eqs. (5.4) and (5.5) the expressions for the difference $h - h'$ and the product $hh'$ are

$$h - h' = 2f' + \frac{f_2(nf_1 + t) - f_1(t - nf_2)}{n(f_2 - f_1) - t}$$

$$hh' = -\left[f' + \frac{f_2(nf_1 + t)}{n(f_2 - f_1) - t}\right]\left[f' - \frac{f_1(t - nf_2)}{n(f_2 - f_1) - t}\right]$$

and substituting these in Eq. (5.6), there obtains

$$(f')^2 = -\frac{f_1 f_2 (nf_1 + t)(t - nf_2)}{[n(f_2 - f_1) - t]^2} - \frac{t f_1 f_2}{n(f_2 - f_1) - t}$$

which reduces to

$$(f')^2 = \frac{n^2 f_1^2 f_2^2}{[n(f_2 - f_1) - t]^2}$$

$$f' = \pm \frac{n}{n \left( \dfrac{1}{f_1} - \dfrac{1}{f_2} \right) - \dfrac{t}{f_1 f_2}}$$

$$f' = \pm \frac{1}{-(n-1)\left[ \dfrac{1}{R_1} - \dfrac{1}{R_2} + \dfrac{t(n-1)}{nR_1 R_2} \right]} \qquad (5.7)$$

In Eq. (5.7), $t$ is essentially a positive quantity, and the equation must be true for all values of $t$. Hence, for $t = 0$, the expression should reduce to the value obtained previously for the thin lens [Eq. (4.5)]. We must therefore use the minus sign when taking the square root for $f'$. This gives

$$f' = -\frac{nf_1 f_2}{n(f_2 - f_1) - t} = \frac{1}{(n-1)\left[ \dfrac{1}{R_1} - \dfrac{1}{R_2} + \dfrac{t(n-1)}{nR_1 R_2} \right]} \qquad (5.8)$$

The values for $h$ and $h'$ now follow:

$$h = \frac{-f_1 t}{n(f_2 - f_1) - t} \qquad (5.9a)$$

$$= \frac{-R_1 t}{n(R_2 - R_1) + (n-1)t} \qquad (5.9b)$$

$$= \frac{-t f'(n-1)}{R_2 n} \qquad (5.9c)$$

$$h' = \frac{-f_2 t}{n(f_2 - f_1) - t} \qquad (5.10a)$$

$$= \frac{-R_2 t}{n(R_2 - R_1) + (n-1)t} \qquad (5.10b)$$

$$= \frac{-t f'(n-1)}{R_1 n} \qquad (5.10c)$$

Thus we see that the object-position image-position Eq. (5.1) is expressible in the more convenient form of Eq. (5.2) with the values of $h$, $h'$, and $f'$ depending on the constants of the system and given by Eqs. (5.8), (5.9), and (5.10). If we now let

$$s = \bar{s} - h$$
$$s' = \bar{s}' - h' \qquad (5.11)$$

then the thick-lens equation is

$$\frac{1}{s'} - \frac{1}{s} = \frac{1}{f'} \qquad (5.12)$$

a form that is identical with the one employed for a thin lens with this one difference: in Eq. (5.12) the position $s$ for the object point $P$ is measured not from the vertex $V_1$ but from a point $H$ on the axis distant $h$ from $V_1$, and the position $s'$ for the image point $P'$ is measured from a point $H'$ distant $h'$ from $V_2$, as shown in Fig. 5.2. These points $H$ and $H'$ are known as the *principal points* of the lens (sometimes called *Gauss* points), and the planes through them perpendicular to the axis are called the

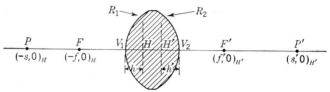

Fɪɢ. 5.2. The thick lens showing principal planes.

principal planes. When Eq. (5.12) is applied to a thick lens, the first principal point $H$ is used as the origin for the measurement of distances in the object space, such as the object point $P$ and the first principal focal point $F$. The second principal point $H'$ is used as the origin for distances in the image space, such as the image $P'$ and the second focal point $F'$. Since in utilizing the principal points there are two coordinate origins, we have indicated the origin for a coordinate set by the appropriate subscript such as $(-s,0)_H$, which is to mean that the indicated coordinates are with respect to the origin $H$. It should be realized, however, that, since the image position $s'$, for $s = -\infty$, is at the second principal focal point $F'$, the value for $f'$ given by Eq. (5.8) is the position relative to the principal point $H'$. This, of course, is indicated by $(f',0)_{H'}$.

In Eq. (5.12), $s$, $s'$, and $f'$ follow our established convention of signs with respect to their corresponding principal points as origins. The quantity $h$ is positive, and therefore $H$ lies to the right of the first vertex $V_1$, when $f'/R_2$ is negative; and $h$ is negative, and therefore $H$ lies to the left of $V_1$, when $f'/R_2$ is positive. Likewise, $h'$ is positive or negative, according as $f'/R_1$ is negative or positive, and correspondingly $H'$ lies to the right or left of the vertex $V_2$. This follows from Eqs. (5.9c) and (5.10c), so that $h$ and $h'$ fall in with our convention of signs.

In locating the image position for a thick lens, it must be remembered that the location of the vertices of the lens is known at the start. Then $f'$ is obtained from Eq. (5.8), and $h$ and $h'$ are calculated from Eqs. (5.9) and (5.10). From the first of Eqs. (5.11), $s$ is obtained, and the lens equation (5.12) may be applied to obtain $s'$. An example of this procedure is given at the end of the chapter.

**5.2. Principal Points and Planes.** From Eqs. (5.9) and (5.10) it follows that

$$\frac{h}{h'} = \frac{f_1}{f_2} = \frac{R_1}{R_2} \tag{5.13}$$

an important relationship that we shall have occasion to use in subsequent developments. For an equiconvex or equiconcave lens, Eq. (5.13) shows that the principal points are situated symmetrically in the lens. This is

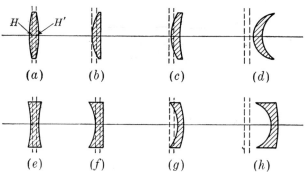

FIG. 5.3. Principal planes of thick lenses. For all cases, $H'$ is to the right of $H$ as in (a).

illustrated in Fig. 5.3a, e. However, in general, the principal planes are not symmetrically situated. When the lens is plano-convex or plano-concave as in (b) and (f), one of the principal points is always at the vertex of the curved surface. As the lens is bent more, the points keep shifting in position as shown in (c) and (g). When the lens is sufficiently bent, the principal planes are outside of the lens as in (d) and (h).

It is of interest to find the ratio of $h$ to $t$, thus,

$$\frac{h}{t} = \frac{R_1}{n(R_1 - R_2) - (n-1)t} \tag{5.14}$$

which for an equiconvex lens becomes

$$\frac{h}{t} = \frac{R_1}{2nR_1 - (n-1)t}$$

and using $n = 1.5$ for the order of magnitude of lens glass,

$$\frac{h}{t} = \frac{1}{3 - (0.5t/R_1)} = \frac{1}{3} + \frac{0.5t}{9R_1} + \frac{0.25t^2}{27R_1^2} + \frac{0.125t^3}{81R_1^3} + \cdots$$

Thus, for the usual thick lens, $0.5t/3R_1 < 1$, so that the principal points are located symmetrically in the lens approximately one-third of the distance in from the lens vertices. This would also hold true for $H$ and $H'$ in (*e*) and for $H'$ in (*b*) and (*f*) of Fig. 5.3.

The separation of the two principal points is given by

$$HH' = t - (h - h')$$

$$= t - \frac{tf'(n-1)}{n}\left(\frac{1}{R_1} - \frac{1}{R_2}\right)$$

$$= t - \frac{t(R_1 - R_2)}{n(R_1 - R_2) - (n-1)t} \tag{5.15}$$

From Eq. (5.15), $HH'$ is positive when $R_1 - R_2 > t$; it is negative when $R_1 - R_2 < t$ and is zero when $R_1 - R_2 = t$. The normal situation is when $HH'$ is positive and then $H$ lies to the left of $H'$. When $HH'$ is negative, the principal points are reversed: $H'$ lies to the left of $H$, and the principal points are said to be *crossed*.

In general, the focal length and position of the principal points of a lens are a function of the axial thickness $t$ of the lens as shown by Eqs. (5.8), (5.9), (5.10), and (5.15). A great deal of useful information can be obtained by analyzing these for some special cases. For instance, for the case of a biconvex lens with $R_1 = r_1$ and $R_2 = -r_2$,

$$\frac{1}{f'} = (n-1)\left[\frac{1}{r_1} + \frac{1}{r_2} - \frac{t(n-1)}{nr_1r_2}\right]$$

so that $f'$ is positive or negative according as $t < [n/(n-1)](r_1 + r_2)$ or $t > [n/(n-1)](r_1 + r_2)$. When $t = [n/(n-1)](r_1 + r_2)$, $f'$ is infinite and a beam of parallel rays after refracting at the first surface will converge to a point inside the lens, diverge from there to refract at the second surface, and emerge as a parallel beam. For this value of $t$, $h = +\infty$ and $h' = -\infty$ so that the principal points have crossed, and for lens thicknesses greater than this the lens acts as a divergent lens even though it is thicker in the middle than at the edges. Other cases of interest are taken up in the problems.

**5.3. Magnification of a Thick Lens.** The linear lateral magnification of the lens in Fig. 5.1 may be obtained by taking the product of the magnifications produced by the two refracting surfaces. Thus, for the left-hand surface

$$m_1 = \frac{s_1'}{n\bar{s}}$$

and for the right-hand surface,

$$m_2 = \frac{n\bar{s}'}{s_1' - t}$$

so that

$$m = \frac{s_1'\bar{s}'}{\bar{s}(s_1' - t)}$$

From the two top equations on page 58,

$$\frac{s_1'}{s_1' - t} = \frac{\bar{s}' - f_2}{\bar{s} - f_1}\frac{\bar{s}f_1}{\bar{s}'f_2}$$

so that

$$m = \frac{(\bar{s}' - f_2)f_1}{(\bar{s} - f_1)f_2} \tag{5.16}$$

which is the expression for the magnification in terms of the positions $\bar{s}$ and $\bar{s}'$ referred to the respective vertices of the lens. In terms of the quantities $s$ and $s'$ referred to the principal points, we have, using (5.11),

$$m = \frac{(s' + h' - f_2)f_1}{(s + h - f_1)f_2} \tag{5.17}$$

Substituting in Eq. (5.17) the values

$$h' = -\frac{tf'(n - 1)}{nR_1} = \frac{tf'}{nf_1}$$

$$h = \frac{h'f_1}{f_2}$$

$$s = \frac{s'f'}{f' - s'}$$

and simplifying,

$$m = \frac{f' - s'}{f'} = 1 - \frac{s'}{f'} \tag{5.18}$$

$$= \frac{s'}{s} \quad \text{from Eq. (5.12)}$$

so that the magnification is given by the same expression as Eq. (4.8) for the thin lens but with $s$ and $s'$ measured from the principal planes. This means that the principal planes of a thick lens are planes of unit magnification and we show this in Sec. 5.5. From Eq. (5.12) we may have the alternative form

$$m = \frac{f}{f - s} \tag{5.19}$$

where $f(= -f')$ is the first principal focal length. In Eqs. (5.17) to (5.19), our convention of signs still holds so that an erect image corresponds to a positive value of $m$.

**5.4. Newtonian Form of the Thick-lens Equation.** If we now let $x$ represent the position of the object point $P$ from the first principal focal point $F$ and $x'$ the position of the image point $P'$ from the second principal focal point $F'$, we may proceed as in Sec. 4.7 and obtain the same

[1] If the medium in the object space is of refractive index $n_1$ and that in the image space is the index $n_1'$, then $m = n_1s'/n_1's$ (see Prob. 5.16).

relationships as for the thin lens.   These relationships that now also hold for the thick lens are

*Thin lens equations that hold for thick lenses*

$$\frac{f'}{s'} + \frac{f}{s} = 1$$

$$s' = f' + x'$$

$$s = f + x \qquad (5.20)$$

$$xx' = ff'$$

$$m = \frac{x'}{f} = \frac{f'}{x} = -\frac{x'}{f'} = -\frac{f}{x}$$

where $s$, $s'$, $f$, $f'$ are measured from the principal planes.

**5.5. Properties of Principal Planes.**   There are several very important properties of the principal points and principal planes.   The first property

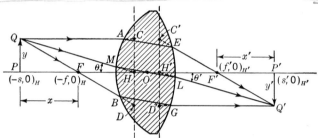

FIG. 5.4.   Properties of principal planes.

is that the principal points are conjugate points and the principal planes are conjugate planes.   The truth of this is evident from Eq. (5.12) which shows that when $s = 0$, thus locating the object at the first principal point or plane, $s' = 0$, which is the location of the second principal point or plane.   This is in general true even when the lens separates media of different refractive indices.

The second property has already been mentioned, that the principal planes are planes of unit magnification.   This may be obtained from Eq. (5.17), which for $s = s' = 0$ becomes

$$m = \frac{(h' - f_2)f_1}{(h - f_1)f_2}$$

and now, using $h' = hf_2/f_1$,

$$m = \frac{[(hf_2/f_1) - f_2]f_1}{(h - f_1)f_2} = 1$$

This result is true even when the image space has a different refractive index from that of the object space (see Prob. 5.16).

Two more useful properties may be obtained with the aid of Fig. 5.4. An object $PQ$ of height $y$ is imaged at $P'Q'$ by the thick lens, and the rays are constructed as follows: A parallel ray $QA$, after refraction, passes through the second principal focal point $F'$ in the direction $EF'Q'$. Point $C$ is the intersection of the ray $QA$ with the first principal plane, and $C'$ is the intersection of the refracted ray, $EQ'$ extended back, with the second principal plane. A second ray $QB$ passing through the first principal focal point $F$ after refraction takes the parallel direction $GQ'$. Rays $EQ'$ and $GQ'$ intersect to form the image point $Q'$. Point $D$ is the intersection of $QB$ with the first principal plane, and $D'$ is the intersection of $GQ'$ with the second principal plane. For this construction we have utilized the property of principal focal points and the law of refraction. The triangles $C'H'F'$ and $F'P'Q'$ are similar so that

$$\frac{-y'}{H'C'} = \frac{x'}{f'}$$

Using the relationships given by Eqs. (5.12) and (5.20),

$$H'C' = \frac{-y'f'}{x'} = \frac{-y(f' + x')f'}{(f + x)x'}$$
$$= \frac{-yf'}{f}$$

and when the indices of refraction on each side of the lens are equal, $f = -f'$ and

$$H'C' = y = HC$$

In the same way $HD = H'D'$. Thus a parallel ray incident on a thick lens refracts in such a way that the emergent ray, when extended backward, intersects the second principal plane in a point on the same side and as far from the axis as the point in which the incident ray intersects the first principal plane. In other words, $QA$ and $EQ'$ intersect in a point $C'$ on the second principal plane. A similar analysis follows for the point $D$ on the first principal plane.

A fourth useful property is obtained by considering the ray $QM$, drawn so that it is directed toward the first principal point $H$. After refraction it too will intersect the image point $Q'$. From the magnification equation, $y'/s' = y/s$, but $y/s = \tan \theta$ and $y'/s' = \tan \theta'$, so that $\theta' = \theta$. Since $s'$ is measured from the principal plane, we deduce the property that a ray incident onto a thick lens, so that it is directed toward one of the principal points, refracts in such a way that when it emerges it appears to be coming from the other principal point and is parallel to the incident ray.

The last two properties make it possible to construct images graphically just as was outlined for a thin lens, which, as the reader has already concluded, is a special case of the thick lens with its two principal planes coinciding at the center. For the thick lens, then, any two of the three rays illustrated in Fig. 5.4 may be employed to locate the image point $Q'$ of the object point $Q$. Usually a parallel ray is brought up to the first principal plane, and the emergent ray is drawn through the focal point in such a direction as to intersect the incident ray in the second principal plane. Then a ray is drawn toward the first principal point, and the emergent ray is drawn parallel to the incident ray as if it were coming from the second principal point. It must, however, be remembered that the actual paths of the rays through the lens are along $AE$, $ML$, and $BG$ as shown and that these properties of principal planes are utilized to obtain a more simplified construction.

**5.6. Combinations of Lenses.** So far we have considered and worked out the optical properties of a single thick lens. In general, optical systems are made up of several lenses mounted on a common axis and

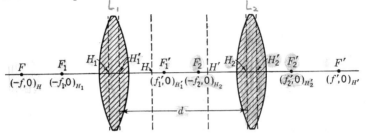

Fig. 5.5. A system of two thick lenses.

arranged so that the image formed is as free from defects or aberrations as is possible. We shall make a study of these aberrations in a later chapter and see what we must do in general to correct for them. It is the purpose, here, to see how the thick-lens theory may be used to determine the optical characteristics of any compound lens system.

In Fig. 5.5 are shown two simple thick lenses, each with its own set of focal points, principal points, and principal planes. The refractive index is the same for both lenses, which are in air. The subscripts 1 and 2 refer to the corresponding lenses. Such a system may be looked upon as a thick lens in the general sense and as such has associated with it its first and second focal points $F$ and $F'$ and its principal points $H$ and $H'$. Let $d$ be the distance from the second principal point of the first element to the first principal point of the second element. The principal planes $H$ and $H'$ for a compound system are obtained as they are for a simple element. Thus, a ray parallel to the axis is considered to be incident on the first element and then traced through the system. The intersection of the entering ray and the emergent ray gives the location of the second principal plane. The first principal plane may similarly be located.

Let the object and image positions with respect to the principal points of element (1) be $s_1$ and $s_1'$, respectively, those with respect to the principal planes of element (2) be $s_2$ and $s_2'$, respectively, and those for the compound system with respect to the planes $H$ and $H'$ be $s$ and $s'$, respectively. The magnification of the system is given by the product of the magnification of each element, thus:

$$m = \frac{s_1'}{s_1} \frac{s_2'}{s_2} = \frac{s'}{s} \tag{5.21}$$

By considering an object at infinity we can obtain an expression for the focal length of the system. Hence, with $s = s_1$, $s_1' = f_1'$, $s_2 = -(d - f_1')$, $s_2' = s_2 f_2'/(s_2 + f_2')$, $s' = f'$,

$$f' = f_1' \left( \frac{s_2 f_2'}{s_2 + f_2'} \right) \frac{1}{s_2}$$
$$= \frac{f_1' f_2'}{f_1' + f_2' - d}$$

or

$$\frac{1}{f'} = \frac{1}{f_1'} + \frac{1}{f_2'} - \frac{d}{f_1' f_2'} \tag{5.22}$$

which is the expression for the combined or equivalent focal length of the system. It must be remembered that $f'$ is measured with respect to $H'$. In the special case where the lenses may be assumed to be thin, $f_1'$ and $f_2'$ may be measured from the centers of the elements and if, further, these thin lenses are in contact, so that $d = 0$, then the result is $\frac{1}{f'} = \frac{1}{f_1'} + \frac{1}{f_2'}$ already described in the thin-lens theory.

One may now go on to obtain expressions for the distances $H'H_2'$ and $HH_1$,

$$HH_1 = \frac{f'd}{f_2'} \tag{5.23}$$

$$H'H_2' = \frac{-f'd}{f_1'} \tag{5.24}$$

The details of obtaining Eqs. (5.23) and (5.24) are left to be worked out in the problems. These equations locate the positions of the principal planes $H$ and $H'$.

If the lens system consists of more than two elements, the principal points and focal points of the first two may be determined from Eqs. (5.22) to (5.24). Then this combination is considered as a thick lens and combined with the third element, and so on for all the elements. Once the focal points and principal points of a system are determined, the equations developed for a thick lens for finding the image and magnification may be applied.

**5.7. Angular Magnification and Nodal Points.**   In Fig. 5.4 consider a ray incident on the lens from $P$ upward at a slope angle $u$ in the object space.   It will refract through the lens and come down to its conjugate point $P'$ at a slope angle $u'$ in the image space.   The ratio

$$\gamma = \frac{\tan u'}{\tan u} \tag{5.25}$$

or, for the paraxial region,

$$\gamma = \frac{u'}{u} \tag{5.26}$$

is known as the *angular magnification* or *convergence ratio* in the planes at $P$ and $P'$.

In the general case, when the index of refraction in the object space is different from that in the image space, the fourth property obtained in Sec. 5.5 is not valid since then $y'/y = ns'/n's$ so that it is no longer true that $\theta = \theta'$.   However, in this case there are two other points called

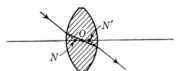

FIG. 5.6. The nodal points.

*nodal points* which are points on the axis that have the property that a ray traversing the first medium and directed toward the first nodal point $N$ emerges in the second medium in a parallel direction as if it had come from the second nodal point $N'$.   This is illustrated in Fig. 5.6, where the intersection point $O$ is called the *optical center* of the lens. The nodal points (and the planes, passing through them and perpendicular to the axis, known as *nodal planes*) also have the property of being conjugate points, and the angular magnification referred to them is unity and positive.   In the general case where the lens is bounded by two different media, the nodal points and principal points are not coincident, but for the special important case where the media are the same, $N$ coincides with $H$ and $N'$ coincides with $H'$ so that for the principal planes under these conditions there is also unit angular magnification.

The principal points, the focal points, and the nodal points are known as *cardinal points* and, as we have seen, are of great value in the solution of thick-lens systems.   Of these cardinal points, the principal points and focal points are the most important.   However, nodal points are more easily obtained in the laboratory, and the principal points are difficult to obtain empirically.   Since for a lens in air, which exemplifies the commonest use, the principal points and nodal points coincide, one experimentally locates the nodal points and then uses these as the principal points.   To illustrate how the property of nodal points is employed to obtain the principal points of a thick lens in air, consider rotating the lens in Fig. 5.6 about the nodal point $N'$. Since the incoming-ray direction has not changed, the emergent ray must also proceed in the same direction and be parallel to the incident direction. Hence, if the incoming rays are from an infinitely distant object, the image will not shift in spite of the rotation about the nodal point $N'$. The lens is mounted on a slide, known as a *nodal slide*, which can be rotated about a vertical axis. Then the image of an infinite object is examined when the lens is rotated. If an image shift is observed, the lens is not being rotated about its nodal point. In that case the lens is moved back and forth along the slide until a place is found where no image shift occurs upon rotation of the slide. This locates the point $N'$. The lens is then reversed and the procedure repeated to locate the other nodal point $N$.

This property of nodal points is utilized in the *panoramic camera*, in which the lens is pivoted at its second nodal point so that rotation about it gives a continuous picture covering a very wide angle.

**5.8. Summary.** It is clear that the refraction equation (2.6) and the magnification equation (2.11) are all that are necessary to determine the position and size of an image that is formed by paraxial rays that pass through any system of spherically refracting surfaces. However, for thick lenses and for systems of lenses, the successive applications of the refraction equation become involved and tedious so that it is generally advisable to determine the positions of the cardinal points of the system and then employ the more simplified formulas developed in this chapter.

We have seen that these more simplified expressions have the same form as the expressions developed in Chap. 4 for the thin lens, so that only one set of generalized equations need be remembered for all cases. In view of this, the tabular form given at the end of Chap. 4 applies here also, since the sign convention has been carried through into the thick-lens development.

In general, the principal points of a lens system are located by first finding the focal points. This may be done either by applying the equations developed for an infinite object or by actually tracing rays parallel to the system's axis. Then the focal lengths may be calculated by using the appropriate expressions. The principal points are located by measuring off distances equal to the focal lengths from the focal points. The position and character of the image may then be determined by applying the generalized lens equation and magnification equation.

**Examples.** (a) A thick lens has the following constants: $R_1 = 4.00$ cm, $R_2 = -6.00$ cm, $t = 2.00$ cm, and $n = 1.50$. An object is situated in air in front of the face of positive radius of curvature and 8.00 cm from it. Find the position of the image. *Find* $f'$, $h$, $s$, $s'$

The focal length of the lens is obtained from Eq. (5.8),

$$\frac{1}{f'} = (n - 1)\left[\frac{1}{R_1} - \frac{1}{R_2} + \frac{t(n - 1)}{nR_1R_2}\right]$$

$$= (1.5 - 1)\left[\frac{1}{4} + \frac{1}{6} + \frac{(2)(1.5 - 1)}{(1.5)(4)(-6)}\right] = \frac{7}{36}$$

$$f' = 5.14 \text{ cm}$$

The principal planes are located by applying Eqs. (5.9c) and (5.10c). Thus

$$h = -\frac{tf'(n - 1)}{R_2n} = -\frac{(2)(5.14)(1.5 - 1)}{(-6)(1.5)} = 0.571 \text{ cm}$$

$$h' = -\frac{tf'(n - 1)}{R_1n} = -\frac{(2)(5.14)(1.5 - 1)}{(4)(1.5)} = -0.857 \text{ cm}$$

The object position with respect to the first principal plane is

$$s = \bar{s} - h = -8 - 0.57 = -8.57 \text{ cm}$$

Now applying the lens equation (5.12),

$$\frac{1}{s'} - \frac{1}{-8.57} = \frac{1}{5.14}$$

$$s' = 12.8 \text{ cm}$$

The position of the image with respect to the second vertex is obtained from the second of Eqs. (5.11),

$$\bar{s}' = s' + h' = 12.8 - 0.86 = 11.9 \text{ cm}$$

The principal planes and image and object positions found are depicted in Fig. 5.7.

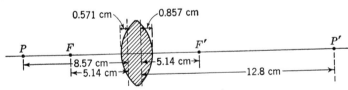

FIG. 5.7. Not to scale.

(b) Two thin converging lenses of 20.0 and 30.0 cm focal lengths are placed coaxially 10.0 cm apart in air. An object is located 60.0 cm in front of the lens of smaller focal length. Find the position of the image.
Consider the system as a thick lens of focal length

$$f' = \frac{f_1'f_2'}{f_1' + f_2' - d} = \frac{(20)(30)}{20 + 30 - 10} = 15.0 \text{ cm}$$

Since the lenses are thin, the distance from the center of the first lens to the first principal plane is

$$HH_1 = \frac{f'd}{f_2'} = \frac{(10)(15)}{30} = 5.00 \text{ cm}$$

and the distance from the center of the second lens to the second principal plane is

$$H'H_2 = \frac{-f'd}{f_1'} = - \frac{(10)(15)}{20} = -7.50 \text{ cm}$$

Therefore,

$$s = -60 - 5 = -65.0 \text{ cm}$$

and

$$\frac{1}{s'} + \frac{1}{65} = \frac{1}{15}$$

or

$$s' = 19.5 \text{ cm}$$

This is the position of the image with respect to the second principal point. Its position with respect to the second lens is

$$19.5 - 7.5 = 12.0 \text{ cm}$$

The quantities found are shown in Fig. 5.8. Note that the principal planes here are crossed.

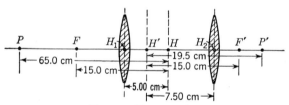

Fig. 5.8. Not to scale.

## PROBLEMS

**5.1.** Find the principal focal length and the positions of the principal planes of the following lenses. Sketch each case. For each, $R_1 = 4.00$ cm, and $n = 1.50$.

| $R_2$, cm | $-\infty$ | $-6.00$ | $-4.00$ | $-3.00$ | $-2.00$ | 3.00 | 6.00 | $-\infty$ | $-6.00$ | $-3.00$ | 3.00 | 6.00 |
|---|---|---|---|---|---|---|---|---|---|---|---|---|
| $t$, cm | | | | 1.00 | | | | | | | 5.00 | |

**5.2.** A thick equiconvex lens has faces of 25.00 cm radius. The axial thickness is 1.000 cm, and the refractive index is 1.500. An object is positioned in air 60.00 cm in front of one face. (*a*) Find the position of the image by calculation. (*b*) Find the position of the image by the graphical method, drawing a figure to scale.   (*c*) Taking the lens as thin, solve for the image position, and compare with the result obtained in (*a*).

**5.3.** A thick lens with radii of curvature $R_1 = 10.0$ cm and $R_2 = -15.0$ cm has an axial thickness of 2.00 cm and an index of refraction of 1.50.   An object 3.00 cm high is placed in air 3.00 cm in front of the face of smaller radius.   Find the position, size, and character of the image by computation and by graphical means.

**5.4.** What is the significance of the value $t = [n/(n - 1)]R_1$?   Substitute this value into Eq. (5.8), and interpret the result, illustrating with a diagram.

**5.5.** A biconvex lens with radii of curvature 2.00 and 3.00 cm has an axial thickness of 18.0 cm and a refractive index of 1.50.   Draw a plane section of this lens to scale, and trace two parallel rays (one on each side of the principal axis) through the lens. What is the focal length of the lens?   Where are the positions of its principal planes? Is the lens converging or diverging?

**5.6.** Where are the principal points of a thin lens?   Justify your result mathematically.

**5.7.** Obtain the expressions given in the text for the distances $HH_1$ and $H'H'_2$.

**5.8.** Two thin lenses each of focal length 3.00 in. in air are coaxially placed and separated by 0.750 in.   Locate the positions of the principal planes (*a*) by computation, (*b*) by graphical means.

**5.9.** Solve Prob. 5.8 if the first lens has a focal length of 3.00 in. and the second a focal length of $-2.00$ in.

**5.10.** Develop the equations and relationships given in Sec. 5.4.

**5.11.** A glass sphere of refracting index 1.50 and radius $r$ is used as a thick lens to form an image of a point object distant $r$ from its surface.   Find the position of the image.

**5.12.** A thick lens has a focal length of 5.00 cm in air.   If the distance between its focal points is 12.0 cm and an object 5.00 mm high is placed 10.0 mm to the left of the first focal point, find the position, size, and nature of the image by (*a*) use of the thick-lens equations, (*b*) use of the Newtonian forms of the lens equations.

**5.13.** Solve Prob. 5.12 for the case where the object is virtual and situated 10.0 mm to the left of the second focal point.

**5.14.** Solve Prob. 5.13 if the principal points are crossed and the distance between the focal points is 8.00 cm.   Consider all other data the same.

**5.15.** Solve Prob. 4.13 by the methods of this chapter.

**5.16.** Consider that the medium to the left of the lens in Fig. 5.1 has a refractive index $n_1$ and that of the image space is $n'_1$.   Derive the indicated relationships.

(*a*) Show that

$$\frac{n}{s'_1} - \frac{1}{\check{s}/n_1} = \frac{-1}{f_1^*/n_1}$$

$$\frac{1}{\check{s}'/n'_1} - \frac{n}{s'_1 - t} = \frac{1}{f_2^*/n'_1}$$

where       $f_1^* = -n_1R_1/(n - n_1)$       and       $f_2^* = n'_1R_2/(n'_1 - n)$.

(*b*) Note that these equations are identical in form with the corresponding ones in Sec. 5.1 with $\check{s}$ replaced by $\check{s}/n_1$, $\check{s}'$ replaced by $\check{s}'/n'_1$, $f_1$ replaced by $f_1^*/n_1$, and $f_2$ replaced by $f_2^*/n'_1$.   Show that

$$\frac{n'_1}{s'} - \frac{n_1}{s} = \frac{1}{f'}$$

where $s = \bar{s} - h^*$ and $s' = \bar{s}' - h^{*'}$, with the distances of the principal planes $h^*$ and $h^{*'}$ from the vertices $V_1$ and $V_2$, respectively, given by $h^* = n_1 h$ and $h^{*'} = n'_1 h'$. Show also that

$$\frac{f^{*'}}{f^*} = -\frac{n'_1}{n_1}$$

where $f^{*'}$ is the second principal focal length and $f^*$ is the first principal focal length, given by

$$f^{*'} = n'_1 fn = \frac{-n'_1 nf^*_1 f^*_2}{n(n_1 f^*_2 - n'_1 f^*_1) - n_1 n'_1 t}$$

$$f^* = -n_1 f' = \frac{n_1 nf^*_1 f^*_2}{n(n_1 f^*_2 - n'_1 f^*_1) - n_1 n'_1 t}$$

(c) Show that the magnification is given by

$$m = \frac{n_1 s'}{n'_1 s}$$

and that, for the principal planes,

$$m = \frac{(h^* - f^*_2) f^*_1}{(h^* - f^*_1) f^*_2} = 1$$

# CHAPTER 6

## THEORY OF STOPS

When a lens is used to form an image of an object, only those rays which pass through the lens combine to form the image. The rim, or edge, of the lens thus acts as an aperture that determines which rays emanating from the object eventually get to the image. In the same way, every optical system has an aperture that effectively limits the rays traversing the system; such an aperture may be a lens periphery, a diaphragm, or some physical obstacle and is referred to as the *aperture stop*.

The aperture stop of an optical instrument controls the quantity of light transmitted. In addition, such an instrument contains a lens rim or a stop that limits the size of the object which is being imaged and so restricts the *field of view;* a stop that controls the field of view is designated the *field stop*. Stops are also employed to reduce aberration effects by eliminating objectionable rays.

A study of stops and their functions is therefore most essential to a proper understanding of optical systems, and we shall develop here the theory and nature of the various stops. Their usefulness in optical instruments is taken up in Chap. 8.

**6.1. The Aperture Stop; Entrance and Exit Pupils.** In Fig. 6.1 is shown an optical system composed of two thin lenses $L_1$ and $L_2$, with a diaphragm $G$ between them. The system images the object point $P$ at $P'$. We are interested in ascertaining which one of the three stops is functioning as the aperture stop of the system with respect to $P$. The stops that must be considered are the rim of the lens $L_1$, the rim of the lens $L_2$, and the diaphragm $G$ since each of these is capable of limiting pencils of rays that traverse the system. The criterion that we must use here may be stated as follows: *Of all possible stops, that one which limits the divergence of the rays from P, or which permits the least number of rays to traverse the system, is the aperture stop.*

First consider the diaphragm $G$ and its optical image $E$ formed by the lens $L_1$. The ray $PM$, shown passing through the system and just touching the edge of the diaphragm $G$, is directed so that its extension just touches the edge of the image $E$ in accordance with optical-image construction. This means that any ray drawn from $P$ that will just touch the edge of $E$, if it is not refracted, will just touch the edge of $G$ after refraction. Thus $E$ may be considered to limit effectively the size of the

74

cone of light coming from $P$ corresponding to its actual limitation by $G$. The effectiveness of the diaphragm $G$ is then measured by the angle $u$ that defines half the image-forming pencil in the object space. In the same way, the angle subtended at $P$ by the image of the rim of lens $L_2$, considered formed by $L_1$, is a measure of the effectiveness of $L_2$ as a stop. A little thought (observe the position and size of the image of $L_2$ as formed by $L_1$; in the diagram, $L_2$ lies closer to $L_1$ than the focal length of $L_1$) will reveal the fact that this angle is larger than the angle $u$ shown in Fig. 6.1. Likewise the periphery of lens $L_1$ subtends at $P$ an angle that is

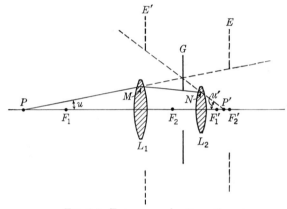

FIG. 6.1. Entrance and exit pupils.

greater than angle $u$. Since $G$ satisfies the condition that it permits the fewest number of rays to pass through the system, it is the aperture stop with respect to the object point $P$. The image $E$ of the aperture stop $G$, formed by the optical system between $G$ and $P$, is known as the *entrance pupil*.[1] An observer looking through the optical system with his eye near $P$ would see the image of $G$ at $E$.

It is clear that the image $E'$ of the aperture stop formed by lens $L_2$ limits the size of the emergent beam which comes to a focus at $P'$ forming the half angle $u'$ in the image space. The image $E'$ of the aperture stop $G$, formed by the optical system between $G$ and the image space, is known as the *exit pupil*. An observer looking through the optical system with his eye near $P'$ would see the image of $G$ at $E'$. It is to be noted that an incident ray which grazes the edge of the entrance pupil will, after refraction, when produced, graze the edge of the exit pupil.

The aperture stop and entrance and exit pupils of any system may be determined in a similar fashion. The procedure, as discussed above, is to

---

[1] The term entrance pupil has been chosen because the image of the aperture stop of the eye (the iris), formed by the lens system of the eye in its image space, is the so-called "pupil" of the eye.

find, for each potential stop, the position and size of its image formed by the optical elements that are to its left. These are found in the usual manner by applying the equations already developed for locating the position of an image and its magnification. Then compare the angles subtended at the object point by these various images; the image subtending the smallest angle is the entrance pupil, and its corresponding stop is the aperture stop of the system with respect to the object point. The image of the aperture stop formed by the optical elements to its right is then the exit pupil. The comparison of the subtended angles may be accomplished graphically by positioning the various images and

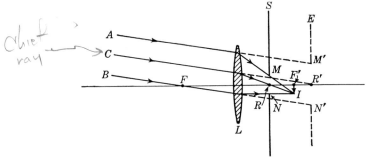

Fig. 6.2. The chief ray.

drawing in the angles at the object point. A better procedure is to tabulate the positions and sizes of the images and to calculate the tangents of the subtended angles.

It must be realized that the aperture stop with respect to some position of $P$ in the object space is not necessarily the aperture stop with respect to another location of $P$. For instance, in Fig. 6.1, if we consider shifting $P$ to the left, a point is reached with respect to which $G$ and $L_1$ are equally effective in limiting the rays; to the left of this point, $L_1$ would be more effective than $G$. In good optical systems, however, the aperture stop will function properly over the entire range of object positions for which the system is intended.

**6.2. The Principal Ray, or Chief Ray.** Consider a lens $L$, its aperture stop $S$, and the entrance pupil $E$ shown in Fig. 6.2. The bundle of rays, incident on the lens, is from an infinitely distant object point which is located off the principal axis of the optical system. The bundle is bounded by the extreme rays $AM'$ and $BN'$ which have been directed to the entrance pupil edges $M'$ and $N'$, respectively. Since the entrance pupil $E$ is the optical image of $S$, then $M'$ is the image of $M$, $N'$ is the image of $N$, and $R'$ is the image of $R$. Therefore, by optical-image formation, the rays $A$ and $B$, after refraction through the lens, will pass through the aperture stop edges $M$ and $N$, respectively, forming the

image *I*. This construction is the same as that outlined in the preceding
section, and we have here included the complete bundle of rays that can
pass through the aperture stop. In considering such a bundle it is helpful to represent it by a single ray. That ray which is taken to be representative of the bundle is the one that passes through the center of the
aperture stop after refraction. It must therefore have the direction *CR'*
so that it passes through the point *R*. That ray which is directed toward
the center of the entrance pupil, or which passes through the center of
the aperture stop, is called the *principal ray*, or *chief ray*. In Fig. 6.2,
*CRI* is the chief ray. The chief ray acts as an axis of symmetry for the
bundle of rays it represents and so defines the direction of a pencil as it
traverses an optical system. We shall make use of the chief ray in the
analysis of the performance of optical systems. The fact that it may be
employed as the representative "central" ray of a pencil is very useful.

**6.3. Object and Image Positions Referred to Entrance and Exit Pupils.**
Let us make a partial transformation of Eq. (4.13) and the two middle

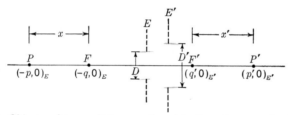

FIG. 6.3. Object and image distances referred to the entrance and exit pupils.

forms of Eq. (4.14) [which are also represented by Eqs. (5.20)], so that
the distances in the object space are designated with reference to the
center of the entrance pupil as origin and those in the image space are
designated with reference to the center of the exit pupil as origin. It is
desirable to effect such a transformation because the resulting expressions
make it possible to determine the position and magnification of an image
when, for an optical system, the following are known: the locations and
sizes of the entrance and exit pupils, the distance of the object from the
entrance pupil, and the focal length of the system.

In Fig. 6.3, *E* and *E'* are the entrance and exit pupils of diameters *D*
and *D'*, respectively. The coordinates of the focal point *F* are shown as
$(-q,0)$, and those of the object point *P* are $(-p,0)$, both of which are
reckoned with respect to the entrance pupil *E*. The coordinates of the
focal point *F'* are $(q',0)$, and those of the image point *P'* are $(p',0)$, both
of which are taken with respect to the exit pupil *E'*. From the figure,
we have

$$p = q + x \quad \text{and} \quad p' = q' + x' \tag{6.1}$$

which transform Eq. (4.13) into the form

$$(p - q)(p' - q') = -(f')^2 \tag{6.2}$$

From Eq. (4.14), $m = -x'/f'$, which becomes

$$m = \frac{-(p' - q')}{f'} \tag{6.3}$$

A little reflection will show that $E$ and $E'$ are conjugate to one another, so that the magnification of $E'$ with respect to $E$ is given by

$$m_{EE'} = \frac{D'}{D} \tag{6.4}$$

Also applying the expressions $m = -x'/f'$ and $m = f'/x$ from Eq. (4.14) to $E$ and $E'$ yields the alternative forms

$$m_{EE'} = \frac{q'}{f'} \tag{6.4a}$$

and

$$m_{EE'} = -\frac{f'}{q} \tag{6.4b}$$

From Eqs. (6.4), (6.4a), and (6.4b), $q = -f'/m_{EE'}$, and $q' = f'm_{EE'}$, and substituting these into Eq. (6.2), there results

$$\frac{m_{EE'}}{p'} - \frac{1}{m_{EE'}p} = \frac{1}{f'} \tag{6.5a}$$

or

$$\frac{D'^2}{p'} - \frac{D^2}{p} = \frac{DD'}{f'} \tag{6.5b}$$

which is the desired equation giving $p'$ in terms of $p$, $D$, $D'$, and $f'$. Now substituting for $q'$ and $f'$ in Eq. (6.3), there obtains

$$m = \frac{1}{m_{EE'}} \frac{p'}{p} \tag{6.6a}$$

or

$$m = \frac{D}{D'} \frac{p'}{p} \tag{6.6b}$$

which gives the magnification of the image in terms of the object and image distances, as measured from the entrance and exit pupils, respectively, and the diameters of the entrance and exit pupils. In accordance with our sign convention $p$ is negative when $P$ is situated to the left of $E$, and $p'$ is positive when $P'$ is situated to the right of $E'$.

**6.4. The Field Stop; Entrance and Exit Windows.** In addition to the aperture stop whose image, by the optical elements to the left of it, forms

the entrance pupil and whose image, by the optical elements to the right
of it, forms the exit pupil, other stops or diaphragms that are present
put a limit on the size of the object whose image can be formed.    To
illustrate this, we show in Fig. 6.4 the images, in the object space, of the
elements considered in Fig. 6.2.    Lens $L$ has no optical element to the
left of it, so that its stop is shown in the original position of $L$.    The
image of the aperture stop is at $E$, which is the entrance pupil with
respect to the object at $P$.    We are interested in the extra-axial point $Q$
of the extended half object $PQ$.    First consider the figure in the absence

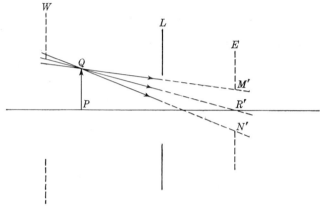

Fɪɢ. 6.4. The field stop.

of the stop $W$.    As with an axial object point the size of the pencil of
light that comes from $Q$ and passes through the system is limited by the
entrance pupil $E$.    This pencil, with the extreme rays $QM'$ and $QN'$, will
get through the aperture stop, traverse the optical system, and form the
image point conjugate to $Q$.    Now consider the stop image $W$ which
represents the image in the object space of a corresponding lens or stop
situated at the appropriate position to the right of lens $L$ in Fig. 6.2.
The size of the pencil through $Q$ will now be additionally limited, and
the extent of this limitation by $W$ depends on how far $Q$ is above $P$.
Thus in the case shown in Fig. 6.4, the chief ray through $Q$ just touches
the edge of the stop image $W$, so that roughly one-half the pencil gets
through the system.    If $Q$ were displaced vertically upward, more of the
pencil would fail to get through the system, while if displaced downward,
more of the pencil would get through.    The image stop $W$, then, effectively limits the extent of the field that can be imaged by the system.
When the chief ray $QR'$ just grazes the edge of $W$, as shown in Fig. 6.4,
then the field is said to be limited in extent by this ray.    In the illustration, $2PQ$ defines the extent of the field as limited by the image stop $W$.
It should be clear that, of all the images formed by the optical elements

to the left of each stop, that one, *W*, whose edge subtends the smallest angle at the center of the entrance pupil limits the field to the greatest extent and is called the *entrance window*. The physical stop of which the entrance window is the image is called the *field stop*. Any ray that cannot get through the entrance window will be unable to reach the image for the reason that it will not be able to get through the field stop. Similar considerations show that the image of the field stop, formed by the optical components to its right, is known as the *exit window*, which controls the emerging rays. Thus the exit window is that stop image which subtends the smallest angle at the exit pupil. The angle that the diameter of the entrance window subtends at the center of the entrance pupil is known as the *angular field of view* in the object space. The angle subtended at the

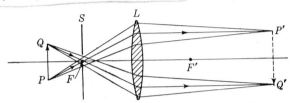

FIG. 6.5. A system telecentric on the image side.

center of the exit pupil by the diameter of the exit window is known as the *angular field of view* in the image space.

In the case shown in Fig. 6.4, the plane of *W* does not coincide with the plane of the object, and this situation is, in general, characterized by the fact that the field of view lacks sharp boundaries. On the other hand, if *W* is made to fall in the plane of the object, every point of the object can completely fill the entrance pupil with rays and so produce a sharp field of view.

We shall see in the chapter on Optical Instruments that to make full use of the field of view in a visual instrument it is best to have the entrance pupil of the eye coincide with the exit pupil of the instrument. If the entrance pupil of the eye is placed some distance from the instrument's exit pupil, the entrance pupil acts as an additional stop that may diminish the field of view. In accordance with this, the exit pupil of a visual optical instrument is called the *eye ring*.

**6.5. Telecentric Systems.** When the aperture stop is placed at the first principal focal point *F* of a system, the exit pupil is at infinity, so that the chief rays in the image space are parallel to the axis. Such a system, called *telecentric on the image side*, is shown in Fig. 6.5. The object is *PQ*, the aperture stop is *S*, *L* is the lens, and *P'Q'* is the image. This kind of system is advantageous when the size of the object *PQ* is to be ascertained by measuring the size of the image *P'Q'*. For this purpose, a measuring scale (such as that in the eyepiece of a microscope) is focused on the plane of the image $P'Q'$ for measurement. Even if the scale is not quite in the same plane as $P'Q'$, a true reading will be obtained since all the chief rays are parallel to the axis. If the aperture stop is not at the focal point, the chief rays will not traverse the system parallel to the axis and the size of the image will apparently change if the scale is displaced slightly in front of or behind the image. Only when the aperture stop is at the focal point is the size of the object independent of a precise focusing upon the image.

A system that is *telecentric on the object side* has the aperture stop at the second focal point of the system, so that the entrance pupil is at infinity. In this case the size of the image is independent of an exact focusing upon the object. The student should draw a figure illustrating this type of system. Its advantages are taken up in the problems at the end of the chapter.

**6.6. Relative Aperture and $f$ Number.** The angle $u$, in Fig. 6.1, governs the amount of light that traverses the system and that reaches the image. A measure of this is the ratio of the diameter of the entrance pupil to the focal length and is known as the *relative aperture*. (The definition for the relative aperture of a mirror, given in Sec. 3.4, is in accord with this one.) In photographic terminology, the reciprocal of the relative aperture is known as the $f$ number and is written, for instance, as $f/3.5$, which indicates that the focal length is 3.5 times the diameter of the entrance pupil. Obviously, a smaller $f$ number permits a greater amount of light to reach the photographic plate so that it is "speedier." The time of a photographic exposure for a very distant object is directly proportional to the square of the $f$ number [see Eq. (9.19) and Prob. 9.14], so that an $f/3.5$ lens is 1.65 times as fast as an $f/4.5$ lens.

**Example.** An optical system consists of two thin lenses, the first of 6 cm focal length and 4 cm diameter, and the second of 2 cm focal length and 3 cm diameter. They are separated by 4 cm, and a diaphragm with a 1-cm opening is between them at a distance of 3 cm from the lens of larger focal length. An object is axially located 9 cm in front of the first lens. (*a*) Find the aperture stop and the location and size of the entrance and exit pupils. (*b*) Find the field stop and the location and size of the entrance and exit windows.

(*a*) To determine the aperture stop, we must find the stop whose image in the object space subtends the smallest angle at the object. Figure 6.6 shows the object $P$, the lenses $L_1$ and $L_2$ with their focal points, and the diaphragm $G$.

For lens $L_1$, which is already in the object space,

$$u = \tan^{-1} \tfrac{2}{9} = 12.5° \quad \text{2=radius of Lens 1, } 9 = \text{object dist.}$$

For the diaphragm $G$, its image in the object space may be obtained by applying either Eq. (4.6) or Eq. (4.13).  Using the latter, $xx' = -(f')^2$, in the conventional manner with $G$ considered to the left of $L_1$, we may set $x = 3$ cm, then $x' = -12$ cm, so that the image of $G$, as formed by $L_1$, falls at the position $F'_1$.  Its magnification, from Eq. (4.14), is

$$\frac{x'}{f} = \frac{-12}{-6} = 2$$

so that the radius of the opening of the image of $G$ is 1 cm.  Therefore for this stop

$$u = \tan^{-1} \tfrac{1}{15} = 3.8°$$

For lens $L_2$, the image is at a point 6 cm to the right of $F'_2$, the radius of its opening is 4.5 cm, and

$$u = \tan^{-1} \frac{4.5}{21} = 11.9°$$

Therefore $G$ is the aperture stop.  The entrance pupil, which is the image of $G$ formed by the lens $L_1$, is at the position $F'_1$ and has a diameter

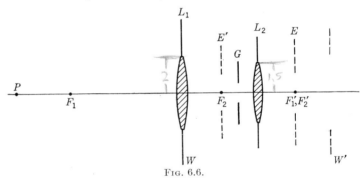

Fig. 6.6.

2 cm.  This is indicated by $E$ in the figure.  The exit pupil, which is the image of the aperture stop formed by $L_2$, is similarly found to be at the point $F_2$, and the diameter of its opening is 2 cm.  It is represented by $E'$.

(b) Of all the stop images in the object space, that one whose radius subtends the smallest angle at the center of the entrance pupil is the image of the field stop.

Since there are no optical elements to the left of lens $L_1$, it coincides with its image in the object space.  Therefore the angle $\alpha$, that its radius subtends at the entrance pupil, is

$$\alpha = \tan^{-1} \tfrac{1}{3} = 18.4°$$

The image of the aperture stop $G$ in the object space is the entrance pupil, so that for the aperture stop

$$\alpha = 90°$$

The image of lens $L_2$, formed by $L_1$, was found to be 6 cm to the right of $F'_2$ with a radius of its opening 4.5 cm. Thus for this image,

$$\alpha = \tan^{-1} \frac{4.5}{6} = 36.9°$$

Therefore $L_1$ is the field stop, and since it coincides with its own image in the object space, it is also the entrance window $W$.

The exit window is the image of $L_1$ in the image space and is located 2 cm to the right of $F'_1$ with a 4-cm-diameter opening. This is shown as $W'$ in the figure.

## PROBLEMS

**6.1.** A thin lens of 2.00 cm focal length has a diameter of 2.00 cm. A stop with a circular opening of 1.00 cm diameter is placed 0.500 cm to the left of the lens, and a point object is placed on the axis 2.50 cm to the left of the stop. (*a*) Find the aperture stop and the location and size of the entrance and exit pupils. (*b*) What is the *f* number? (*c*) For what point on the axis are the lens and diaphragm equally effective in limiting the rays? (*d*) Make a scale diagram, and by means of rays locate the image. Check this by calculation.

**6.2.** Do Prob. 6.1 for the case where the diaphragm and object are on opposite sides of the lens. Keep the numerical specifications the same.

**6.3.** An optical system is made up of two thin converging lenses, separated by 10.0 cm, each of 5.00 cm focal length and 3.00 cm diameter. An axial point object is 6.00 cm in front of one of the lenses, and a diaphragm of 2.00 cm diameter is 2.00 cm behind the lens and between both lenses. (*a*) Find the aperture stop. (*b*) Find the location and size of the entrance and exit pupils.

**6.4.** In Prob. 6.3 find the field stop, the angular field of view in the object space, and the linear field in the plane of the object.

**6.5.** An optical instrument has two thin lenses, one with a focal length of 20.0 cm and diameter 3.00 cm, and the other, situated 22.0 cm to the right of it, with a focal length of 2.00 cm and diameter 1.00 cm. Find the sizes and positions of the entrance and exit pupils with respect to an object a very large distance away, and find the angular field of view in the object space. Where should the eye be placed to realize the maximum field of view?

**6.6.** Do Prob. 6.5, but consider the 2.00-cm-focal-length lens as diverging and separated 18.0 cm from the positive lens.

**6.7.** Do Prob. 6.5, but replace the lens of smaller focal length by a combination of two thin lenses, each of diameter 1.00 cm, each of focal length 2.00 cm, and separated from each other by $\frac{1}{3}$ cm. The combination is placed so that the distance from the lens of larger focal length to the nearest of the two smaller focal length lenses is 20.5 cm.

**6.8.** An optical system is characterized by a focal length of 10.0 cm, an entrance pupil of 3.00 cm diameter, and an exit pupil of 2.00 cm diameter. An object 0.200 cm high is placed axially 25.0 cm in front of the entrance pupil. Find the position and size of the image.

**6.9.** (*a*) Show that the entrance and exit pupils are conjugate to one another. (*b*) Show that the entrance and exit windows are conjugate to each other. (*c*) Show that Eqs. (6.5) and (6.6) are true for any pair of conjugate planes.

**6.10.** A symmetrical system is made up of two similar thin lenses, and midway between them is a diaphragm which is the aperture stop. If the lenses are separated by a distance less than the focal length of either lens, prove that the entrance and exit pupils have equal diameters. Show also that the entrance pupil lies in the first principal plane and the exit pupil lies in the second principal plane.

**6.11.** Draw a diagram illustrating the properties of a system that is telecentric on the object side. Discuss its advantages, and show how it may be used to make measurements with no parallax present.

**6.12.** A thin lens of 3.00 cm diameter and 6.00 cm focal length is 30.0 cm from a point object located axially. One centimeter beyond the lens is a diaphragm, and 4.00 cm beyond that is another thin lens of 2.00 cm diameter and $-10.0$ cm focal length. If the diaphragm is to be the aperture stop, what is its maximum size and what are the corresponding sizes and locations of the entrance and exit pupils?

**6.13.** A lens system is designed as follows: Lens $L_1$ has a focal length of 30.0 cm and diameter 4.00 cm. To the right of it, at a distance of 2.00 cm, is a diaphragm $G_1$ of diameter 3.00 cm. To the right, at a distance of 4.00 cm from $G_1$, is lens $L_2$ of focal length $-36.0$ cm and diameter 3.00 cm. This is followed by another stop $G_2$ of diameter 2.40 cm and distant 3.00 cm from $L_2$. Following $G_2$, at a distance of 3.00 cm, is lens $L_3$, of focal length 30.0 cm and diameter 3.20 cm. A point object is axially situated 10.0 cm in front of lens $L_1$. (*a*) Find the aperture stop. (*b*) Find the sizes and locations of the entrance and exit pupils. (*c*) Find the field stop. (*d*) Find the locations and sizes of the entrance and exit windows. All lenses are thin, and the surrounding medium is air.

# CHAPTER 7

## MIRROR AND LENS ABERRATIONS

Thus far in our developments of the formation of images by mirrors and lenses, we have made the restrictions that the object and image points be very close to the principal axis and that the cone, or pencil, of rays coming from the object point, or forming the image point, is of so small an angular opening that the sine of the slope angle $u$ may be replaced by the angle $u$. The use of these paraxial conditions in Sec. 2.2 led to relatively simple relations between the object and image distances and constants of the system. Accordingly a point image is formed of a point object. In view of the fact that the expansion of the sine of the slope angle into a power series in the angle is

$$\sin u = u - \frac{u^3}{3!} + \frac{u^5}{5!} - \cdots \tag{7.1}$$

the theory based on these restrictions is often termed the first-order theory.

Now, in general, the rays that are incident on an image-forming surface come from points that are removed from the axis, and since the apertures of the optical system are not infinitesimal, the ray pencils are of finite angular dimensions. The result is that the image formed is not sharp and the consequent departures from the first-order theory, known as *aberrations*, may be ascertained by including the higher orders of $u$ in the series expansion. For practical purposes the inclusion of the third-order term in $u$ plus the consideration of the effects of oblique rays is sufficient and gives rise to what is called the third-order theory, which was first developed by Ludwig von Seidel in 1855. This development leads to five expressions each of which, when applied to the first-order theory, acts as a correction term for one of the corresponding five aberrations. For rays that behave in accordance with first-order theory, each of the five expressions is zero; otherwise one or more of the five expressions is not zero and there is present some form of aberration. The five aberrations corresponding to the five Seidel conditions are *spherical aberration, coma, astigmatism, curvature,* and *distortion.* These are known as the *monochromatic aberrations* since they may occur with light of one color or wavelength. In addition to these is the type of aberration in lenses known as *chromatic aberration,* which occurs also in the first-order theory and is due to the different refrangibilities of light of different colors or wavelengths, causing the image to be affected with residual color effect.

We shall now undertake a study of these aberrations, keeping in mind that only for a plane mirror are the conditions of a point-to-point correspondence between the object region and the image region ever accurately satisfied. Since reflection is a special case of refraction, we shall concern ourselves primarily with the developments for the thin lens, pointing out the applications to the mirror as we proceed.

**7.1. Spherical Aberration.** In Fig. 7.1 is illustrated the effect of spherical aberration on rays refracted at a convex spherical surface. The

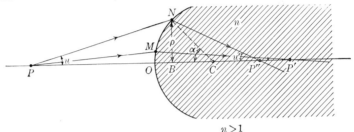

$$n > 1$$

FIG. 7.1. Spherical aberration by a convex refracting surface.

ray $PN$, forming a slope angle $u$ in the object space, refracts in general in the direction $NP''$, forming the slope angle $u'$ in the image space which has a refractive index $n$ with respect to the object space. The center of curvature of the refracting surface is $C$. Point $B$ is the projection of $N$ on the axis so that $NB = \rho$ is the radius of the zone, on the refracting surface, corresponding to the point $N$. The zone is a ring, on the surface, all points of which are the same distance from the axis. Equation (2.3) applies here

$$\frac{|s| + R}{s' - R} = \frac{n \sin |u'|}{\sin u}$$

or

$$\frac{|s| + R}{s' - R} = n \frac{PN}{NP''} \tag{7.2}$$

The distance $PN$ is given by

$$\overline{PN}^2 = R^2 + (|s| + R)^2 - 2R(|s| + R) \cos \alpha$$

and in accordance with the third-order approximation

$$\cos \alpha = 1 - \frac{\alpha^2}{2} \quad \text{where} \quad \alpha = \frac{\rho}{R}$$

so that

$$\overline{PN}^2 = R^2 + (|s| + R)^2 - 2R(|s| + R) \left( 1 - \frac{\rho^2}{2R^2} \right)$$

or

$$\overline{PN}^2 = |s|^2 + (|s| + R) \frac{\rho^2}{R}$$

Since $\rho$ is small, we may retain the first two terms when extracting the square root of the right-hand member, obtaining

$$PN = -s \left[ 1 + \left( \frac{1}{s} - \frac{1}{R} \right) \frac{\rho^2}{2s} \right] \tag{7.3}$$

In the same way, the length of the oblique refracted ray is given by

$$NP'' = s' \left[ 1 + \left( \frac{1}{s'} - \frac{1}{R} \right) \frac{\rho^2}{2s'} \right] \tag{7.4}$$

Substituting the values given by Eqs. (7.3) and (7.4) into Eq. (7.2) yields

$$\frac{n}{s'} - \frac{1}{s} = \frac{n-1}{R} + \left( \frac{1}{s'} - \frac{1}{R} \right) \left( \frac{1}{s} - \frac{1}{R} \right) \left( \frac{1}{s'} - \frac{n}{s} \right) \frac{\rho^2}{2}$$

Into the right-hand member of this equation it is permissible to substitute for $s'$ the first-order approximation $\dfrac{1}{s'} = \dfrac{n-1}{nR} + \dfrac{1}{sn}$ so that

$$\frac{n}{s'} - \frac{1}{s} = \frac{n-1}{R} + \frac{n-1}{n^2} \left( \frac{1}{s} - \frac{1}{R} \right)^2 \left( \frac{1}{R} - \frac{n+1}{s} \right) \frac{\rho^2}{2} \tag{7.5}$$

Now consider the object at infinity—for a marginal ray, one far removed from the axis and incident at $N$,

$$\frac{1}{s'} \text{ (parallel marginal ray)} = \frac{n-1}{nR} + \frac{(n-1)\rho^2}{2n^3R^3} \tag{7.6}$$

and for a paraxial ray, incident at a point $M$ very close to the axis,

$$\frac{1}{s'} \text{ (paraxial ray)} = \frac{n-1}{nR} \tag{7.7}$$

Since Eqs. (7.6) and (7.7) differ by a positive quantity, the marginal rays focus at a point on the axis nearer to $O$ than the paraxial rays. Accordingly in Fig. 7.1, the image of $P$ is shown at $P'$ for the paraxial rays and at $P''$ for the marginal rays. For those rays incident on the surface between $O$ and $N$, the corresponding images fall between $P'$ and $P''$, thus causing the image to have poor definition. This phenomenon is known as *spherical aberration*. It is clear that the second term of the right-hand member of Eq. (7.5) measures the spherical aberration of the refracting surface.

We have met the spherical aberration of a mirror in Sec. 3.5 (see Fig.

3.9), where we have seen that for mirrors of large aperture the marginal rays focus on the axis closer to the pole of the mirror than the paraxial rays. This is shown by placing $n = -1$ in Eq. (7.5) so that

$$\frac{1}{s'} + \frac{1}{s} = \frac{2}{R} + \left(\frac{1}{s} - \frac{1}{R}\right)^2 \frac{\rho^2}{R} \tag{7.8}$$

which gives the corresponding spherical-aberration expression for a mirror.

Figure 7.2 shows the effect of spherical aberration of a lens for an axial point $P$. The paraxial rays are brought to a focus at $P'$, whose location is given by the first-order theory. For the marginal ray the image is formed at $P''$, closer to the lens. In general, the rays which come

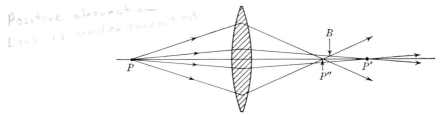

*Positive aberration*
*Lens is under correction*

Fig. 7.2. Spherical aberration of a lens.

together to form the different image points between $P'$ and $P''$ come from different zones of the lens. The distance between the point of intersection of the paraxial rays, $P'$, and that of rays from any given zone of the lens, $P''$, is taken as a measure of the *axial* or *longitudinal* value of the spherical aberration of that zone. The aberration illustrated in Fig. 7.2 is called *positive*, and a lens acting in this manner is said to be *undercorrected*. When a lens or lens system acts in such a way that $P'$, due to the paraxial rays, is closer to the lens than $P''$, due to marginal rays, the aberration is called *negative* and the lens is said to be *overcorrected*. A screen at $P'$ would show a sharp paraxial image at the center surrounded by a circular halo due to the cones of rays falling on the screen from the marginal points $P''$. The best image is obtained at the position $B$ where the diameter of the circular cross section of the rays is least, and this image is called the *circle of least confusion*. The radius of this circle may be taken as the measure of the *lateral spherical aberration*.

**7.2. Longitudinal Spherical Aberration of a Thin Lens.** An expression for the longitudinal spherical aberration of a thin lens of index $n$ in air is now readily obtainable by applying Eq. (7.5) to both sides of the lens. For refraction at the first surface of radius $R_1$,

$$\frac{n}{s_1'} - \frac{1}{s} = \frac{n-1}{R_1} + \frac{n-1}{n^2} \left(\frac{1}{s} - \frac{1}{R_1}\right)^2 \left(\frac{1}{R_1} - \frac{n+1}{s}\right) \frac{\rho^2}{2}$$

where $s_1'$ represents the location of the point where the marginal ray cuts the axis after refraction at the first surface. The expression for refraction at the second surface of radius $R_2$ is obtained by considering the direction of the ray reversed. Then,

$$\frac{n}{s_1'} - \frac{1}{s'} = \frac{n-1}{R_2} + \frac{n-1}{n^2}\left(\frac{1}{s'} - \frac{1}{R_2}\right)^2\left(\frac{1}{R_2} - \frac{n+1}{s'}\right)\frac{\rho^2}{2}$$

where $s'$ represents the position of the final image point. Combining these equations yields

$$\frac{1}{s'} - \frac{1}{s} = (n-1)\left(\frac{1}{R_1} - \frac{1}{R_2}\right) + \frac{n-1}{n^2}\left[\left(\frac{1}{s} - \frac{1}{R_1}\right)^2\left(\frac{1}{R_1} - \frac{n+1}{s}\right)\right.$$
$$\left. - \left(\frac{1}{s'} - \frac{1}{R_2}\right)^2\left(\frac{1}{R_2} - \frac{n+1}{s'}\right)\right]\frac{\rho^2}{2} \quad (7.9)$$

Into the right-hand member of this equation it is permissible to substitute for $s'$ its first-order approximation $\dfrac{1}{s'} = \dfrac{1}{s} + (n-1)\left(\dfrac{1}{R_1} - \dfrac{1}{R_2}\right)$. Thus

$$\frac{1}{s'} - \frac{1}{s} = (n-1)\left(\frac{1}{R_1} - \frac{1}{R_2}\right) + \frac{n-1}{n^2}\left[\left(\frac{1}{s} - \frac{1}{R_1}\right)^2\left(\frac{1}{R_1} - \frac{n+1}{s}\right)\right.$$
$$\left. - \left(\frac{1}{s} + \frac{n-1}{R_1} - \frac{n}{R_2}\right)^2\left(\frac{1-n^2}{R_1} + \frac{n^2}{R_2} - \frac{n+1}{s}\right)\right]\frac{\rho^2}{2} \quad (7.10)$$

Comparing the reciprocal of the image distance for a marginal ray with that for a paraxial ray shows that the second term of the right-hand member of Eq. (7.9) or Eq. (7.10) is the spherical aberration of the lens.

The longitudinal spherical aberration is equal to the difference between the value of $s'$ for the marginal ray, as given by Eq. (7.10), and the value of $s'$ for the paraxial ray (*i.e.*, for $\rho = 0$). Thus, calling the longitudinal spherical aberration L.S.A.,

$$\text{L.S.A.} = -\left[\frac{1}{s'(\text{marginal})} - \frac{1}{s'(\text{paraxial})}\right]s'(\text{marginal})s'(\text{paraxial})$$

$$\text{L.S.A.} = -\frac{(n-1)}{n^2}\left[\left(\frac{1}{s} - \frac{1}{R_1}\right)^2\left(\frac{1}{R_1} - \frac{n+1}{s}\right)\right.$$
$$\left. - \left(\frac{1}{s} + \frac{n-1}{R_1} - \frac{n}{R_2}\right)^2\left(\frac{1-n^2}{R_1} + \frac{n^2}{R_2} - \frac{n+1}{s}\right)\right]\frac{\rho^2}{2}$$
$$\left[\frac{1}{\dfrac{1}{s} + (n-1)\left(\dfrac{1}{R_1} - \dfrac{1}{R_2}\right)}\right]^2 \quad (7.11)$$

where we have again approximated by

$$s'(\text{marginal})s'(\text{paraxial}) = [s'(\text{paraxial})]^2$$

It is seen, therefore, that the longitudinal spherical aberration depends on the refractive index, the radii of curvature, the object distance, and the zone radius. For a given lens and object position, the longitudinal spherical aberration varies as the square of the zone radius.

The expressions that we have obtained, especially Eq. (7.11), are not very convenient for analytical applications. Coddington has shown how they may be expressed in a form that is simpler and much better adapted, for instance, for finding the form of a lens that will give a certain amount of spherical aberration. We shall therefore show how this may be done in the next section before discussing the ways in which spherical aberration may be eliminated or minimized.

**7.3. Coddington's Shape and Position Factors.** The method is that of expressing the difference in the reciprocal values of the object and image distances in terms of a shape factor and a position factor here designated as $\sigma$ and $\pi$, respectively. These are defined as

$$\sigma = \frac{R_2 + R_1}{R_2 - R_1} \tag{7.12}$$

and

$$\pi = \frac{s' + s}{s' - s} \tag{7.13}$$

Using $\dfrac{1}{s'} - \dfrac{1}{s} = \dfrac{1}{f'} = (n - 1)\left(\dfrac{1}{R_1} - \dfrac{1}{R_2}\right)$, the following values for reciprocals are easily obtained:

$$\frac{1}{s} = -\frac{\pi + 1}{2f'} \tag{7.14}$$

$$\frac{1}{s'} = \frac{1 - \pi}{2f'} \tag{7.15}$$

$$\frac{1}{R_2} = \frac{\sigma - 1}{2(n - 1)f'} \tag{7.16}$$

$$\frac{1}{R_1} = \frac{\sigma + 1}{2(n - 1)f'} \tag{7.17}$$

It is significant to note that $\sigma$ is a dimensionless quantity which governs the shape of the lens. In the first-order-theory equations, the position of the image remains the same if $R_1$ and $R_2$ are varied in such a way as to keep $f'$ constant. On the other hand, in the third-order theory, the image depends on how much the marginal ray bends at the first surface and the extent to which it bends at the second surface, *i.e.*, on the way in which the total refraction is divided between the first and second surfaces. Thus even if different sets of radii produce the same focal length, they correspond to lenses of different shapes. With the above notation, a lens is completely determined by $\sigma$, $n$, and $f'$. The value of $\sigma$ varies from $-\infty$, when $R_1$ and $R_2$ are both negative and equal, to $+\infty$, when $R_1$ and

$R_2$ are both positive and equal. For example, for $\sigma = 0$ the lens is either equiconvex or equiconcave. When $\sigma = 1$, $R_2 = \infty$ so that the second surface is plane and the lens is either convex or concave. When $\sigma = -1$, $R_1 = \infty$, the first surface is plane and either convex or concave. When $\sigma < -1$ or when $\sigma > +1$, the lens is of the meniscus type. Observe that if the signs of the curvatures of the lens faces are changed, $\sigma$ retains the same value, and if the lens is turned so that the incident and emergent faces are interchanged, $\sigma$ retains the same absolute value but its sign changes.

The quantity $\pi$ is also dimensionless, ranging from $-\infty$ to $+\infty$, and is characteristic of the degree to which the rays are convergent or divergent. Thus if $\pi = -1$, the incident rays are parallel; if $\pi = 0$, $s = -s'$ and the conjugate object and image positions are equal; and if $\pi = +1$, the emergent rays are parallel. For real objects, $s$ is negative, and $\pi$ lies between $-1$ and $+\infty$ for positive lenses and between $-1$ and $-\infty$ for negative lenses.

To obtain the spherical-aberration correction in terms of the shape and position factors, substitute the values from Eqs. (7.14) to (7.17) into the right-hand member of Eq. (7.9). There obtains

$$\frac{1}{s'} - \frac{1}{s} = (n-1)\left(\frac{1}{R_1} - \frac{1}{R_2}\right) + \frac{\rho^2}{16n^2(n-1)^2(f')^3}$$
$$\{[\pi(1-n) - n - \sigma]^2[\pi(n^2-1) + n^2 + \sigma]$$
$$- [\pi(1-n) + n - \sigma]^2[\pi(n^2-1) - n^2 + \sigma]\}$$

which simplifies to

$$\frac{1}{s'} - \frac{1}{s} = (n-1)\left(\frac{1}{R_1} - \frac{1}{R_2}\right) + \frac{\rho^2}{(f')^3}\left[\frac{n+2}{8n(n-1)^2}\sigma^2 + \frac{(n+1)}{2n(n-1)}\sigma\pi\right.$$
$$\left. + \frac{(3n+2)}{8n}\pi^2 + \frac{n^2}{8(n-1)^2}\right] \quad (7.18)$$

Calling the difference between the reciprocal value of $s'$ for the marginal ray and its value for a paraxial ray, *i.e.*, the spherical aberration, $\Delta(1/s')$, we have

$$\Delta\left(\frac{1}{s'}\right) = \frac{\rho^2}{(f')^3}(A\sigma^2 + B\sigma\pi + C\pi^2 + D) \quad (7.19)$$

where

$$A = \frac{n+2}{8n(n-1)^2} \quad (7.20)$$

$$B = \frac{n+1}{2n(n-1)} \quad (7.21)$$

$$C = \frac{3n+2}{8n} \quad (7.22)$$

$$D = \frac{n^2}{8(n-1)^2} \quad (7.23)$$

If the difference between the value of $s'$ for the marginal ray and its value for a paraxial ray is $\Delta(s') = $ L.S.A., then it is seen from Eq. (7.11) that

$$\Delta(s') = -(s')^2 \Delta \left( \frac{1}{s'} \right) \qquad (7.24)$$

where $s'$ is given by Eq. (7.15) or by the thin-lens first-order equation. Equation (7.19) is the required spherical-aberration equation in the more simplified notation. The coefficients $A$, $B$, $C$, $D$ involve only the index of refraction and are therefore constant for a given type of glass. The equation may be used to calculate the spherical aberration of any thin lens for any position of the object. As will become evident with use, it is much simpler to deal with the reciprocal-aberration function $\Delta(1/s')$ than with the longitudinal-aberration function $\Delta(s')$.

In the development above, we have considered an axial object point. The general case of the consideration of oblique refraction from an extra-axial point object is a great deal more involved, and we shall not go into it here. However when this is carried through, it proves to be true that the spherical aberration is just about the same as for points on the axis, varying as the square of the radius of the aperture defining the oblique pencil of rays. Thus the spherical aberration of a lens is essentially constant over its entire field and for simplicity, in practice, is determined for an axial object point rather than for an extra-axial point.

Similar spherical aberration expressions may be obtained for the spherical mirror.

**7.4. Reduction or Elimination of Spherical Aberration.** We first observe that the spherical aberration may be reduced by limiting the size of the greatest lens zone that may be employed. This entails the use of a stop with a consequent reduction in the amount of light that is transmitted.

Spherical aberration can be eliminated by giving the reflecting or refracting surfaces the proper curvature. In the case of mirrors, we have seen that all the rays originating at one focus of an ellipsoidal surface are imaged at the other focus so that such a surface is free from spherical aberration for its foci. Likewise the paraboloidal surface has no spherical aberration for reflection of parallel rays.

The characteristics of spherical aberration for a lens can be obtained directly from Eq. (7.19). In order that the lens be free from spherical aberration, it is necessary that the quadratic form in the equation be zero,

$$A\sigma^2 + B\sigma\pi + C\pi^2 + D = 0 \qquad (7.25)$$

Solving for $\sigma$,

$$\sigma = \frac{-B\pi \pm \sqrt{B^2\pi^2 - 4A(C\pi^2 + D)}}{2A} \qquad (7.26)$$

It is helpful to set $Y$ equal to the quadratic function,

$$Y = A\sigma^2 + B\sigma\pi + C\pi^2 + D \qquad (7.27)$$

and to keep in mind the graph of $Y$ as a function of $\sigma$, shown in Fig. 7.3. With $\pi$ as a parameter there results a family of parabolas, one of which is shown. From analytical geometry, the coordinates $(\sigma_m, Y_m)$ of the minimum, or vertex, are given by

$$\sigma_m = -\frac{B\pi}{2A} \qquad (7.28)$$

and

$$Y_m = \pi^2\left(-\frac{B^2}{4A} + C\right) + D \qquad (7.29)$$

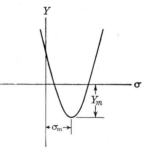

FIG. 7.3. Graph of spherical aberration as a function of shape factor.

A change in the value of $\pi$ then is reflected in a concomitant change in $\sigma_m$ and $Y_m$. Where the parabola cuts the $\sigma$ axis indicates the real roots of Eq. (7.26), and when $Y_m > 0$, which leads to the same expression as setting $4A(C\pi^2 + D) > B^2\pi^2$ from the discriminant of Eq. (7.26), the roots of $\sigma$ are imaginary. Only when the solution leads to values of $\sigma$ that are real can Eq. (7.25) be satisfied, thus leading to no spherical aberration. By setting $Y_m = 0$, we can obtain the least value of the absolute value of $\pi$, for a given index of refraction, that will lead to real values of $\sigma$ such that Eq. (7.25) is satisfied. This leads to

$$\pi = \frac{\sqrt{n(n+2)}}{n-1} \qquad (7.29a)$$

The corresponding value of $\sigma$, by substituting in Eq. (7.25) or using Eq. (7.28) directly, is

$$\sigma = 2(n+1)\sqrt{\frac{n}{n+2}} \qquad (7.29b)$$

Equations (7.29a) and (7.29b) yield pairs of values for the position and shape factors that will make the spherical aberration zero. Larger values of $\pi$ than those given by Eq. (7.29a) will also yield values of $\sigma$ such that the spherical aberration may be made zero. For large enough values of $\pi$, $Y$ can be made negative, thus making the lens overcorrected. Of course, since all the terms in Eq. (7.25) are necessarily positive except the second, $\pi$ and $\sigma$ must be of opposite sign to make $Y = 0$. If we take $n = 1.50$ as the value representative of the glass of a lens, $\pi = 4.58$ ($\sigma = -3.27$) and for real objects this leads to virtual images. The case of importance is when the object and image are both real. From Eq. (7.13), in general, this corresponds to values of $\pi$ that are, in absolute value, less

than 1 for finite object and image distances. When the object is at
infinite distance, $\pi = -1$; and when the image is at infinite distance,
$\pi = +1$. For $\pi$ less than 1 in absolute value, Eq. (7.29a) leads to
$n < 0.25$, and for $\pi$ in absolute value equal to 1, the result is $n = 0.25$.
This shows that spherical aberration cannot be eliminated from a single
lens when the object and image are both real.

A single lens may be designed, however, to give the minimum amount
of spherical aberration under any conditions. As usual, the left column
of the following is the geometric treatment, and the right column carries
the calculus treatment.

Minimum spherical aberration
corresponds to the lowest point of
the curve in Fig. 7.3, and this is
given by Eq. (7.28),

$$\sigma = -\frac{B\pi}{2A}$$

or                                  (7.30)

$$\sigma = -\frac{2(n + 1)(n - 1)}{n + 2}\pi$$

Differentiating the expression for
$Y$ partially, with respect to $\sigma$,
gives

$$\frac{\partial Y}{\partial \sigma} = 2A\sigma + B\pi$$

and equating this to zero for an
extreme gives

$$\sigma = -\frac{B\pi}{2A}$$

which is a minimum and is the
result shown in Eq. (7.28). Substituting the values of $A$ and $B$
yields

$$\sigma = -\frac{2(n + 1)(n - 1)}{n + 2}\pi \quad (7.30)$$

For an infinitely distant object and $n = 1.50$, $\sigma = 0.71$. Substituting
this value into Eq. (7.12) gives $R_2 = -5.90R_1$. This condition is realized with either a double-convex lens, as in Fig. 7.4a, or with a double-

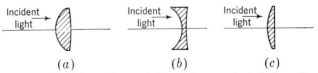

$$(a) \qquad\qquad (b) \qquad\qquad (c)$$

FIG. 7.4. Lenses (a) and (b) have shapes giving minimum spherical aberration. Lens (c)
has slightly more aberration.

concave lens, as in Fig. 7.4b. In each case the surface of greater curvature is turned toward the incident light. For a plano-convex lens with
the curved surface toward the object (Fig. 7.4c), the spherical aberration
is very nearly that of a lens designed for minimum spherical aberration.
On the other hand, if the plano-convex lens, or the lenses shown in Fig.
7.4a, b, is reversed, the aberration is very large. We can see why this is

so: when the parallel rays first fall on the plane face, all the refraction occurs at the curved surface, but when they fall first on the curved surface, the refraction is divided between the two surfaces. Therefore it is not necessary to have such a large angle of incidence. In other words, when a great deal of aberration is present, the parallel rays that are farther removed from the axis are bent too much toward the axis. Just as with a prism, in which the angle of minimum deviation occurs when the incident and emergent rays make equal angles with the faces, so here the least aberration occurs when the total bending is equally divided between the incident and emergent surfaces.

By combining a positive lens and a negative lens it is possible to eliminate spherical aberration for a single zone. The lenses are shaped so that the spherical aberration of the negative component nullifies that of the positive component. If the positive and negative elements are cemented and the combination acts as a positive lens, the focal length of the positive element will be smaller than that of the negative element. The spherical aberration of the positive element would be greater than that of the negative element since the spherical aberration varies inversely as the cube of the focal length. The positive element is shaped to have minimum spherical aberration, and the negative element is shaped to increase its aberration by just an amount to make the total spherical aberration zero. Combinations of this type are usually made in such a way as to eliminate both spherical aberration and chromatic aberration. We shall develop the expressions for a combination free of spherical aberration and chromatic aberration after we have discussed chromatic aberration for lenses.

When the lens system employed is of so large an aperture that the slope angle $u$ is large enough to require the use of the fifth-order term in Eq. (7.1), the optical designers resort to what is known as the trigonometrical ray calculation and tracing. This method is fairly exact and consists in choosing certain rays and tracing their courses through the system by calculating the refraction at each surface using Snell's law and the trigonometrical relationships between the sines of the angles and sides of a triangle (see Prob. 7.5). In this way, by trial and error, the best form and arrangement of lenses giving the least amount of aberration are found.

**7.5. Coma.** The aberration called coma occurs for the rays that come from object points that are off the lens axis. Figure 7.5 illustrates, in a lens, the effect of coma on a pencil of rays from an extra-axial object point $Q$. In order to discuss the character of one aberration, it is assumed that all other aberrations are absent, thus avoiding the confused picture that the various superposed aberrations would produce. Therefore it is assumed that the only aberration present is coma. The principal ray of the pencil through the center of the lens is brought to a focus in the image plane at $Q'$, which represents the paraxial image of $Q$. Rays 11 from an inner zone of the lens come to a focus in the image plane at $Q'_1$; rays 22 focus at $Q'_2$; and rays 44, refracting through the outer lens zone, are imaged at $Q'_4$. The rays, refracting through the different zones, focus at different places in the image plane and give the images $P'Q'$, $P'Q'_1$, . . . , $P'Q'_4$. This shows that the equivalent focal length varies for the different zones. The lateral magnification for the different zones, illustrated in Fig. 7.5, is an account of the effect of coma on the rays in the *primary*, or *meridional*, *plane*, i.e., the plane containing the principal axis and the oblique principal, or chief, ray (the plane of the diagram). There

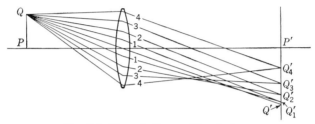

Fig. 7.5. Coma in the meridional plane.

are also skew rays from $Q$ incident on the lens; and the plane at right angles to the meridional plane and containing $Q$ is called the *secondary*, or *sagittal, plane;* the meridional plane is sometimes called the *tangential plane*. The totality of skew rays has a much more pronounced effect on the nature of the image due to coma than the meridional rays. This is illustrated in Fig. 7.6, which shows, in perspective, an object plane with object $PQ$, the image plane with image $P'Q'$, and a lens with principal axis $PP'$. The ray through the center of the lens falls at the paraxial image $Q'$. The action of one of the zones of the lens on meridional and skew rays from $Q$ is described as follows: The meridional rays $Qa$, incident on the lens at $aa$, are imaged at the point $a$ in the image plane. The rays $Qc$ in the sagittal plane, incident at $cc$ on the lens zone, are imaged at $c$ in the image plane. The skew rays $Qb$ (not drawn), incident on the lens zone at $bb$, strike the image plane at $b$. The skew rays $Qd$ (not drawn), incident at $dd$, strike the image plane at $d$. Thus the cone of rays through the lens zone comes to a focus in a circle $abcd$ rather than in a point. This circle $K_1$ is known as the *comatic circle*, and every point of it is the mutual meeting place of two rays which come from two diametrically opposite points of the lens zone. Notice how the striking points are distributed around the comatic circle in relation to their corresponding positions of origin on the lens zone. Starting with the lower point $a$ on the zone and the striking point $a$ on the comatic circle, a point *b* on the zone removed 45° from *a* on the zone is imaged at *b* removed 90° from *a* on the comatic circle. The point *c* removed 90° from *a* on the lens zone is imaged at *c* removed 180° from *a* on the comatic circle, etc. Every ray that is incident on the lens zone at some angle from the low

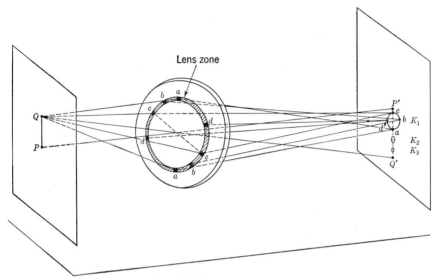

Fɪɢ. 7.6. The comatic circles.

point *a* strikes the comatic circle at twice this angle from the corresponding point *a* on the comatic circle. There is thus introduced on the comatic circle a torsional displacement in zonal angle. The radius of a comatic circle is proportional to the square of the zone radius, and the distance of the comatic circle from the paraxial image point $Q'$ also is proportional to the square of the zone radius. Therefore smaller zones will produce comatic circles of smaller radii with centers displaced downward from $K_1$. Comatic circles of the innermost zones are shown at $K_2$ and $K_3$. There is thus produced an expanding series of overlapping comatic circles as shown in the greatly magnified diagram of Fig. 7.7. The greatest intensity is at the apex corresponding to the paraxial point $Q'$ with the intensity decreasing toward the flare end upward in the direction of $P'$.

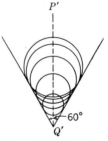

Fɪɢ. 7.7. Comatic flare.

This gives the over-all appearance similar to that of a comet; hence the name *coma*. When the paraxial image $Q'$ lies farthest from the principal axis, forming the comatic flare end nearest the axis with the bright apex away from the axis as in Figs. 7.5 and 7.7, the coma is designated as *negative*. In this case the magnification of the outer zones is smaller than that for the central zone.    When $Q'$ lies nearest the principal axis, so that the comatic flare extends outward, or away from the axis, the coma is *positive*.    In this case the magnification for the outer zones is larger than for the central zone.

By straightforward geometric and algebraic methods, similar to those used in the derivation of the spherical-aberration equations, an expression for the length of the comatic flare $Q'Q'_4$ in Fig. 7.5 may be obtained for a thin lens.    The expression obtained is

$$Q'Q'_4 = \frac{3\rho^2 \tan \beta}{2f'n(n-1)} [(n+1)\sigma + (2n+1)(n-1)\pi] \frac{1}{1-\sigma} \qquad (7.31)$$

where $\rho$ is the radius of the lens zone, $\beta$ is the angle that the chief ray makes with the principal axis, and the other quantities have the same significance as in Sec. 7.3.    An expression for the angular value of coma is desirable in dealing with the practical problem of the elimination of coma in lens combinations.    The value of angular coma is

$$\psi = \frac{\rho^2 \tan \beta}{(f')^2} (E\sigma + G\pi) \qquad (7.32)$$

where $\psi$ is the angle subtended at the center of the lens by $Q'Q'_4$ and the constants $E$ and $G$ have the values

$$E = \frac{3(n+1)}{4n(n-1)} \qquad (7.33)$$

$$G = \frac{3(2n+1)}{4n} \qquad (7.34)$$

Thus coma varies directly as the square of the lens-zone radius and the tangent of the angle of skewness.    The length of the comatic flare varies inversely as the first power of the focal length, while its angular value subtended at the lens center varies inversely as the square of $f'$.

Coma gives the image very poor definition and differs from spherical aberration in several respects.    First, instead of being measured longitudinally, it is measured laterally, the amount being given by Eqs. (7.31) and (7.32).    Second, as we have seen, a point object is imaged in overlapping comatic circles and not as a circle in spherical aberration.    Third, the expression for comatic aberration is a function of the angle of obliquity of the skew rays, resulting in an asymmetric enlargement of the image and being zero on the axis.    Fourth, we shall show that coma may be eliminated completely for a single thin lens for one pair of object and image points by the proper choice of the curvature of the lens surfaces.

The coma that we have described corresponds to the type that arises when the aperture stop is in the plane of the lens and when there is no spherical aberration present.    This type is termed *pure coma*.    In the presence of spherical aberration, and when the aperture stop is not in the plane of the lens, thus causing eccentric refraction, the comatic image becomes a great deal more confused.   A discussion of this type is beyond the scope of the present treatment, and the student interested is referred to Taylor listed at the end of this chapter.   In general when refraction is eccentric, there is present additional coma which is a result of the effect of spherical aberration and eccentric refraction.

**7.6. Coma and the Sine Condition.**   We see that coma is a result of the difference of lateral magnification for rays that refract through different lens zones.   We have also seen in Sec. 2.5 [Eq. (2.12)] that the lateral magnification for a thin lens in air is given by $y'/y = \sin u/n \sin u'$, so that the lateral magnification will be constant for all zones if

$$\frac{\sin u}{\sin u'} = \text{constant} \qquad (7.35)$$

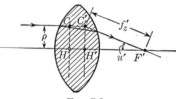

Fig. 7.8.

which is Abbe's sine condition previously referred to.   Therefore coma will be absent for a thin lens if Abbe's sine condition is satisfied.   Also from Eq. (2.3), if Abbe's sine condition is satisfied, the lens is free from spherical aberration.

When there are no other aberrations present, the sine condition is used to indicate the amount of coma present.   In practice, an object is assumed to be at a very large distance from the lens.   Then $\sin u \propto \rho$, and the sine condition reduces to

$$\frac{\rho}{\sin u'} = \text{constant} \qquad (7.36)$$

By trigonometrical ray tracing the sine condition expressed by Eq. (7.36) may be tested.   To see how this is done, let us return momentarily to the course of a parallel ray through a lens in relation to its principal planes. We recall our earlier development (Sec. 5.5) that when a parallel ray is incident onto a lens, as shown in Fig. 7.8, it refracts in such a way as to appear to come from a point $C'$ on the second principal plane $H'C'$, where $C'$ is at the same height as $C$, the point of intersection of the incident ray on the first principal plane $HC$.   The axial distance $H'F'$ was defined as $f'$ for the lens.   Actually $C'H'$ (and also $CH$) is the locus of the principal points which are determined by the rays traced through the lens at different zone radii $\rho$.   $CH$ and $C'H'$ are really curved surfaces and assume the form of planes for small values of $\rho$, the former being called the *first principal surface* and the latter the *second principal surface*.   Now, if there is no spherical aberration, and also no coma, then $\sin u' = \rho/\text{constant}$ leads to the fact that the distance $C'F'$ must be constant and equal to the paraxial focal length $f'$. The points $C'$ would then lie on a spherical principal surface. However, if there is no spherical aberration and there is coma, then the focal lengths $f'_z$, measured along the rays $C'F'$, would be different for the different zones. The presence of coma, in the absence of spherical aberration, may therefore be determined by using the equation

$$\frac{\rho}{\sin u'} = f'_z \tag{7.37}$$

For any parallel ray at a zone height $\rho$, $u'$ may be determined by tracing and $f'_z$ computed from Eq. (7.37). Then $\rho$ is plotted against $f'_z$. If the lens has no coma, the plot is a straight line and the departure of such a plot from a straight line indicates the amount of coma present.

On the other hand, when spherical aberration is present, the sine condition does not indicate the amount of coma, since then all the rays do not intersect at a common point $F'$ in Fig. 7.8. Under these conditions the amount of coma for a given value of $\rho$ is obtained by subtracting from the paraxial focal length the longitudinal spherical aberration and comparing this value with the value obtained from Eq. (7.37). Thus as a measure of the amount of coma, we may use the expression $f' - $ L.S.A. $- f'_z$.

**7.7. Reduction or Elimination of Coma.** Setting the coefficient in the aberration equation (7.32) or (7.31) equal to zero yields

$$\sigma = -\frac{G}{E}\pi$$

or

$$\sigma = -\frac{(2n+1)(n-1)}{n+1}\pi \tag{7.38}$$

and since this can be satisfied physically, it is possible to eliminate coma for a simple lens for some given position of the object. The sine condition for no coma also leads to Eq. (7.38). With an object at infinite distance and $n = 1.5$, $\sigma = 0.80$. This does not differ very much from the value $\sigma = 0.71$ obtained for minimum spherical aberration, so that a lens designed for minimum spherical aberration will not have an excessive amount of coma. Solving Eqs. (7.30) and (7.38) simultaneously, we obtain $n = 0$ or $n = 1$, and if the first solution is excluded, then the only values which satisfy the equations are $\sigma = \pi = 0$. These are the values of $\sigma$ and $\pi$ for which the lens of minimum spherical aberration has no coma. This is an equiconvex or equiconcave lens with object and image positions equal. These conditions hold when the refraction is central, but when eccentric refraction is considered, the diaphragm acting as an entrance pupil can be so positioned that the coma due to the spherical aberration may have the correct magnitude and sign to nullify the normal coma.

Coma may be eliminated from a doublet composed of two thin lenses in contact. The coma aberration for this combination is

$$\psi_1 + \psi_2 = \frac{\rho_1^2 \tan \beta}{(f_1')^2} (E_1\sigma_1 + G_1\pi_1) + \frac{\rho_2^2 \tan \beta}{(f_2')^2} (E_2\sigma_2 + G_2\pi_2) \quad (7.39)$$

where the subscripts 1 and 2 are for the first and second lenses, respectively. For no coma,

$$\frac{E_1\sigma_1 + G_1\pi_1}{(f_1')^2} + \frac{E_2\sigma_2 + G_2\pi_2}{(f_2')^2} = 0 \quad (7.40)$$

where, for thin lenses in contact, $\rho_1 = \rho_2$. If the compound lens is to have a focal length $f'$, then

$$\frac{1}{f'} = \frac{1}{f_1'} + \frac{1}{f_2'}$$

If $s_1'$ is the image of the first lens and the object for the second lens, $\pi_1 = (-2f_1/s_1') + 1$, $\pi_2 = (-2f_2/s_1') - 1$ so that

$$\frac{\pi_1 - 1}{\pi_2 + 1} = \frac{f_1'}{f_2'} \quad (7.41)$$

The three equations (7.40), (7.41), and $\frac{1}{f'} = \frac{1}{f_1'} + \frac{1}{f_2'}$ for a known focal length contain the independent variables $n_1$, $n_2$, and the four radii of curvature. If the doublet is cemented, as is often done, the second surface of the first lens and the first surface of the second lens have the same radius. There are then four equations to determine six variables, and this presents the possibility of imposing conditions for the elimination of other aberrations.

**7.8. Aplanatism.** In Sec. 1.6 we discussed the aplanatic refracting surface, the Cartesian oval, that gives rise to an axial point image of an axial point object. A lens is aplanatic when it is free of spherical aberration and coma. Solving the equations for no spherical aberration and no coma simultaneously, there results

$$\sigma = \pm(2n + 1) \quad (7.42)$$

and

$$\pi = \mp \frac{n + 1}{n - 1} \quad (7.43)$$

Substituting the values $\sigma = -(2n + 1)$ and $\pi = (n + 1)/(n - 1)$ into Eqs. (7.12) to (7.17) yields

$$f' = \frac{n+1}{1-n} R_2 \tag{7.44}$$

$$s = \frac{n+1}{n} R_2 \tag{7.45}$$

$$s' = (n+1)R_2 = ns \tag{7.46}$$

$$R_1 = \frac{n+1}{n} R_2 \tag{7.47}$$

which stipulate the conditions for an aplanatic lens shown in Fig. 7.9. From Eqs. (7.46) and (7.47), $s = R_1$ so that with the object point $P$ placed at the center of curvature of the first surface, the refraction occurring at the second surface forms the image point $P'$ with spherical aberration and coma missing. The points $P$ and $P'$ are known as the aplanatic points of the spherical surface of radius $R_2$.

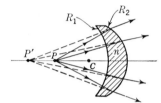
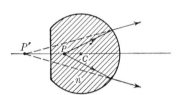

Fig. 7.9. Aplanatic lens.  Fig. 7.10. Aplanatic points of a sphere.

Since the rays from $P$ suffer no refraction at the front surface of radius $R_1$, the point $P$ may be considered as situated in the medium of index $n$ and radius $R_2$ as shown in Fig. 7.10. With the surrounding medium air, the points $P$ and $P'$ are aplanatic for the spherical surface and the distance $PC$ is given by

$$PC = \frac{n+1}{n} R_2 - R_2 = \frac{R_2}{n} \tag{7.48}$$

These principles of aplanatism are utilized to extreme advantage in microscope objectives. There it is desirable to permit as wide a pencil of light from the object being viewed as is possible but without aberration. How this is accomplished is illustrated in Fig. 7.11. Some oil of the same refractive index as the hemispherical glass is placed in contact with the latter, and the specimen $P$ to be viewed is immersed in

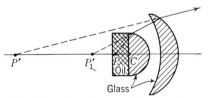

Fig. 7.11. The oil-immersion objective.

the oil as shown. The distance $PC$ is made to satisfy Eq. (7.48) for the sphere so that $P_1'$ is the aplanatic point conjugate to $P$. The virtual image $P_1'$ is made to coincide in position with the radius of curvature of the first surface of the following aplanatic lens so that the final image free from spherical aberration and coma appears at $P'$. In this way the divergence of the rays is effectively reduced, with the result that optical elements lying farther to the right of the objective may be corrected in accordance with pencils of smaller effective opening. Such an objective is known as an oil-immersion objective.

It proves to be true that it is not possible to arrange for a system to be aplanatic for more than just one position of the object so that if the system is to be corrected for spherical aberration for more than one object position, coma will be present.

**7.9. Astigmatism and Curvature.** Even if spherical aberration and coma are completely eliminated, there will be present in general two other

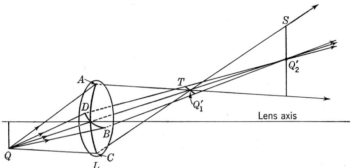

Fig. 7.12. Astigmatic images of a point object.

aberrations, astigmatism and curvature of the field. These aberrations affect object points that are removed from the axis, and we shall consider them jointly here since they are the two aspects of the same phenomenon; these aberrations depend approximately on $\tan^2 \beta/f'$, where $\beta$ is the angle of obliquity of the chief ray as defined in Sec. 7.5 and $f'$ is the lens focal length. We assume of course that spherical aberration and coma are absent.

We have seen (Fig. 7.6) that when a pencil of rays from an extra-axial object point falls onto a lens there are introduced different amounts of convergence in the meridional plane and in the sagittal plane. As a consequence of this, the rays lying in the primary plane come to one focus, and those lying in the secondary plane come to another focus. This is illustrated in Fig. 7.12, where $Q$ is an object point off the axis of the lens $L$. The rays in the primary plane $QAC$ come to a focus at $Q'_1$, and those in the secondary plane $QDB$ focus at $Q'_2$. When all the rays of the emergent bundle are considered, they pass through a line at $T$ lying in the secondary plane and perpendicular to the principal ray $QQ'_1Q'_2$ and also pass through the line at $S$ lying in the primary plane and perpendicular to the lens axis. This phenomenon, characterized by the fact that a point object is imaged in two focal lines in planes perpendicular to each other and to the principal ray, is known as *astigmatism*.  The image at $T$ is called the primary image, or the *tangential focus*.  The image at $S$ is called the secondary image, or the *sagittal focus*.  The character of the emergent pencil is such that its cross section in general is elliptical, degenerating into lines at $T$ and $S$.  If a spoked wheel is considered to be used as an object, the axis of the wheel coinciding with the lens axis, then only the spokes will be imaged sharply at the secondary focus, while only the rim will be imaged sharply at the tangential focus.

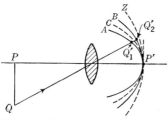

FIG. 7.13. The primary image surface $A$, the secondary image surface $B$, the surface of best definition $C$, and the Petzval surface $Z$.

This is why the term tangential is employed.  Somewhere between $T$ and $S$ the major and minor axes of the ellipse are equal, forming a circle; at this position the image is best and is known as the *circle of least confusion*.  The astigmatism is reckoned positive when the sagittal focus is to the right of the tangential focus.  The primary and secondary focal lines are straight lines only in the sense of the third-order theory that we are considering.  For instance, the primary focal line is actually a short arc of a circle in a plane perpendicular to the lens axis.

So far we have considered only one point on the object.  Each point of a plane object will form its corresponding primary image, secondary image, and circle of least confusion.  In correspondence to the totality of points on the object, the locus of the primary images, the locus of the secondary images, and the locus of the circles of least confusion are curved surfaces which come together or touch on the lens axis at the point which is the paraxial image of the conjugate axial object.  These surfaces are shown in Fig. 7.13, the locus of the primary images being called the *primary image surface* (paraboloidal), that of the secondary images the *secondary image surface* (paraboloidal), and that of the circles of least confusion the *surface of best focus*, or *definition*.  $PQ$ is the object plane, $P'$ the paraxial image point of $P$, $Q'_1$ and $Q'_2$ the primary and secondary images of $Q$, $A$ the primary image surface, $B$ the secondary image surface, and $C$, midway between $A$ and $B$, the surface of best definition.  In general the surface of best focus $C$ is therefore not a plane, and this gives rise to the aberration known as *curvature of the field*.  On the other hand, the presence of astigmatism is indicative of the fact that $A$ and $B$ are separated.  For images on the axis there is no astigmatism.  If $A$ and $B$ are brought into coincidence by some manner of correction, $C$ is likewise coincident, and if the resultant surface is curved, then there is present curvature of the field but with no astigmatism.  In such a case, it is not possible to bring to a sharp focus all parts of the field simultaneously.  If the surface $B$ is equal in curvature to $A$ and concave to the right, then $C$ may lie along a vertical plane passing through the paraxial image point $P'$. In this case the curvature is absent, *i.e.*, the field is flat, but astigmatism is present. In general, the problem of optical design is to bring the surfaces $A$, $B$, and $C$ into coincidence with the plane through $P'$ as much as possible.

**7.10. Elimination of Astigmatism and Curvature.** The amount of astigmatism and curvature in an optical system is ascertained usually by tracing several principal, or chief, rays through the system and locating the positions of the primary and secondary images. For this purpose

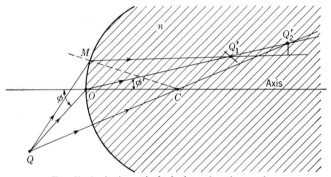

FIG. 7.14. Astigmatic foci of a refracting surface.

two equations are employed, a spherical-surface refraction equation involving the object distance and the primary image, and one involving the object distance and the secondary image. Figure 7.14 shows an object point $Q$ off the axis of a convex refracting surface whose refractive index is $n$ with respect to the object space and whose radius of curvature is $R$. The primary astigmatic focus due to meridional rays is at $Q_1'$, and the secondary astigmatic focus due to sagittal rays is at $Q_2'$. If the position of the object point $Q$ from $O$ is $s$, the position of $Q_1'$ from $O$ is $s_1'$, and that of $Q_2'$ from $O$ is $s_2'$, then it is not difficult to show (see Appendix ID) that, for the primary focus,

$$\frac{n \cos^2 \phi'}{s_1'} - \frac{\cos^2 \phi}{s} = \frac{n \cos \phi' - \cos \phi}{R} \qquad (7.49)$$

and, for the secondary focus,

$$\frac{n}{s_2'} - \frac{1}{s} = \frac{n \cos \phi' - \cos \phi}{R} \qquad (7.50)$$

where $\phi$ and $\phi'$ are as usual the angles of incidence and refraction, respectively, and all the quantities follow the established sign convention. These equations will yield the astigmatic difference $s_2' - s_1'$. It can be shown, and this is left as a problem, that the vanishing of this astigmatic difference leads to the condition for the aplanatic points of a sphere as discussed in Sec. 7.8.

By placing $n = -1$ and $\phi' = -\phi$, Eqs. (7.49) and (7.50) are converted into the corresponding ones for a mirror, and in that case the astigmatic difference is

$$s_2' - s_1' = \frac{2s_1's_2'}{R} \sin \phi \tan \phi \qquad (7.51)$$

Equations (7.49) and (7.50) for the refracting surface and Eq. (7.51) for the reflecting surface show that the astigmatic difference increases with the angle of obliquity.

For a thin lens in air with a small central stop close to the lens, Coddington has shown that the primary astigmatic image from the lens is given by

$$\frac{1}{s_1'} - \frac{1}{s} = \frac{1}{\cos \beta} \left( n \frac{\cos \beta'}{\cos \beta} - 1 \right) \left( \frac{1}{R_1} - \frac{1}{R_2} \right) \qquad (7.52)$$

and for the secondary astigmatic image

$$\frac{1}{s_2'} - \frac{1}{s} = \cos \beta \left( n \frac{\cos \beta'}{\cos \beta} - 1 \right) \left( \frac{1}{R_1} - \frac{1}{R_2} \right) \qquad (7.53)$$

where $s_1'$ and $s_2'$, measured along the principal, or chief, ray, are the positions of the primary and secondary foci, respectively, and $\beta$ is the angle of obliquity of the chief ray which refracts at the first lens surface at an angle $\beta'$, so that $\sin \beta = n \sin \beta'$. Subtracting Eq. (7.53) from Eq. (7.52) there results the expression for the astigmatic difference,

$$s_2' - s_1' = s_1's_2' \left( \frac{1}{R_1} - \frac{1}{R_2} \right) \left( n \frac{\cos \beta'}{\cos \beta} - 1 \right) \sin \beta \tan \beta \qquad (7.54)$$

The object distance affects the astigmatic difference somewhat but does not affect the curvature of the field.

Equations (7.49) and (7.50) for refracting surfaces, Eq. (7.51) for a mirror, or Eq. (7.54) for a lens may be used to determine the astigmatic difference for several angles of obliquity. The corresponding positions of best definition can then be compared with the paraxial focus, and the curvature of the field can then be ascertained.

We have indicated that the method of eliminating the astigmatism resolves itself into bringing the primary and secondary image surfaces into coincidence. When this is done, the surfaces fall in general on a curved paraboloidal surface known as the *Petzval surface*, resulting in what is known as *Petzval curvature*. The Petzval surface is shown at Z in Fig. 7.13 and is a surface whose form is fixed for a given lens and on which, in the absence of astigmatism, the image is formed. The shapes of the image surfaces are a function of the lens shape and the location of the axial stops. For a thin lens it is not possible to eliminate both the astigmatism and the curvature of the field. However, by positioning the stop favorably, the astigmatism may be reduced, or the field may be made more flat. For instance, if we consider placing a vertical screen through $P'$ (Fig. 7.13), the central part of the field would be sharply in focus, while the area more remote from the center would be out of focus owing to the presence of astigmatism and curvature of the field. If the screen is moved to the left, the outermost parts of the field, although focusing more sharply, would still suffer from astigmatism and the central part of the field would be out of focus. With the screen to the left of $P'$ and with no astigmatism, there would be Petzval curvature present, and the edge of the field would be sharply in focus, but the center would be out of focus. Now the primary image surface is always three times as far from the Petzval surface as the secondary image surface is from the Petzval surface. Thus by introducing a sufficient amount of negative astigmatism, surfaces $A$ and $B$ of Fig.

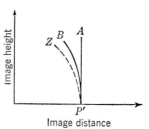

Fig. 7.15. A compromise correction for astigmatism and curvature of the field.

7.13 may be made to fall to the right of the Petzval surface, in which case $A$ will be to the right of $B$, as shown in Fig. 7.15. With a screen placed somewhat to the left of $P'$, it will be found that a compromisingly good focus can be obtained throughout the field. Of course, a flatter field can be obtained by introducing more negative astigmatism so that $A$ curves more to the right, but the amount of astigmatism is thereby also increased. Such a flat field is obtainable by using a concavo-convex lens with a central stop placed as much in front of it as will make the rays passing through the lens form the primary and secondary image surfaces in opposite directions. Figure 7.16 shows the type of correction that is employed in the better quality photographic objectives. The astigmatism is zero at one point of the field, and the curvature of the Petzval surface is made relatively small. The objective is used in the vicinity of the point of zero astigmatism. A system having these characteristics with zero astigmatism at one point is called an *anastigmat*. To obtain this degree of correction it is generally necessary to design a complex lens such as the Zeiss Sonnar lens that contains a negative component between two positive ones with a stop between the last two as shown in Fig. 7.17.

In addition to producing a compromise field that is relatively flat and possesses a tolerable amount of astigmatism, it is possible to eliminate astigmatism and curvature of the field by using two separated elements, positioning the stop properly, and satisfying the *Petzval condition*, which states that

$$n_1 f_1' + n_2 f_2' = 0$$

where $n_1$ and $f_1'$ are the refractive index and focal length of one lens and $n_2$ and $f_2'$ are those for the second lens. By utilizing a positive and negative lens and satisfying the Petzval condition, the curvature of the field may be eliminated, resulting in a flat field. If $f_1'$ is that of the positive lens, then $f_1' < f_2'$, requiring that $n_1 > n_2$.

We note that both coma and astigmatism cause the definition of the image to become poorer as the angle of obliquity $\beta$ becomes larger. However, astigmatism depends on $\tan^2 \beta$ and coma on $\tan \beta$, so that for small angles $\beta$ coma is the more important.

It is to be realized that the astigmatism we have considered is due to the asymmetrical location of the object with respect to a symmetrical

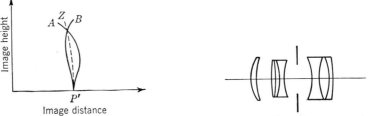

Fig. 7.16. Image surfaces for an anastigmat.    Fig. 7.17. The Zeiss Sonnar anastigmat.

optical surface. The term astigmatism is also used to describe the type of image that obtains when an astigmatic lens is employed. A lens of this type could have one of its faces spherical and the other face cylindrical. Consider the left half of such a lens to be plano-spherical and the right half to be plano-cylindrical, with their plane faces coinciding, and with the cylindrical axis vertical. A point object situated on the spherical axis to the left of the lens would converge more in the horizontal plane than in the vertical plane, the focus in the horizontal plane being closer to the lens. The emergent pencil possesses two line foci, so that it is astigmatic, the astigmatism being due to the asymmetry of the lens surfaces. The cylindrical surface forms a line image of a point. If a screen with vertical and horizontal lines is used as an object, the vertical lines will be in focus at one of the foci and the horizontal wires will be in focus at the other of the foci. The best image is between the two at the position of the circle of least confusion. The astigmatism of the eye is due to the fact that the cornea has different curvatures in different planes, thus behaving as an astigmatic lens. A person suffering from astigmatism of the type above described will focus either the vertical lines or the horizontal lines of a rectangular lattice network but is unable to focus both sets simultaneously. His best focus is at the position of the circle of least confusion.

**7.11. Distortion.** With spherical aberration, coma, astigmatism, and curvature of the field absent, there will be a sharply imaged point in the image plane corresponding to every point in the object plane. These aberrations control the quality of definition of the image point. In addition, for an ideal optical system, it is desired to have the totality of points in the image plane in the same geometric relationship to each other as their corresponding object points have in the object plane. In general this metric relationship between object and image is not preserved, owing to the fact that the magnification for all rays traversing the lens is not constant, thus giving rise to the phenomenon of *distortion*. Distortion does not affect the definition of the image but affects the location of an image point in the image plane. The way in which distortion occurs is illustrated in Fig. 7.18*a, b*, where we assume that all other aberrations are absent. In both figures, $P'$ and $Q'$ are the paraxial images of $P$ and

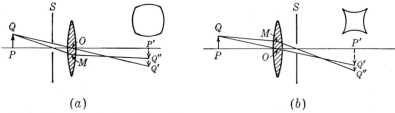

(a)                                        (b)

FIG. 7.18. Illustrating (*a*) barrel-shaped, or negative, and (*b*) pincushion-shaped, or positive, distortion.

$Q$, respectively. $S$ is the aperture stop, and $QM$ is the chief ray which falls, on the image plane, at $Q''$ nearer to the axis in (*a*) and farther from the axis in (*b*) than the paraxial image $Q'$. Because of the position of the stop, a different cone of rays is utilized in the formation of the point $Q''$. When the aperture stop is in front of the lens, as in (*a*), the outermost parts of a plane object, as the corners of a square, are magnified less than the object points situated nearer the axis. The resulting distorted image is shown above the ray diagram and is called *negative*, or *barrel-shaped, distortion*. In Fig. 7.18*b* the outermost parts of the object are magnified more than the inner ones, and this gives rise to the type of image distortion shown and is called *positive*, or *pincushion-shaped, distortion*. The magnitude of the distortion, measured by the distance $Q'Q''$, decreases as the stop is brought nearer to the lens. The student is urged to draw the corresponding figures using a diverging lens. Where must the stop be to form positive distortion? For a sufficiently thin lens there is no distortion, but we have seen that it is desirable to employ stops in optical systems. The position of a stop determines the amount and type of distortion present and, if correct, may be instrumental in reducing distortion as well as some of the other aberrations.

Let us now look into the conditions for freedom from distortion. We have seen that the entrance pupil limits the size of the beam entering the system in the object space, and it is so situated that the chief ray passes through its center. Likewise the exit pupil limits the beam in the image space and has the chief ray, on emergence, pass through its center.

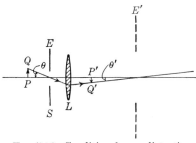

In Fig. 7.19 is shown a lens $L$, in front of which is a stop $S$ acting as aperture stop and as entrance pupil $E$ whose image in the lens $L$ is the exit pupil $E'$. $PQ$ is the object plane, and $P'Q'$ is the image plane. The ray shown from $Q$ and passing through the system is a chief ray which intersects the centers of entrance and exit pupils. Such a ray is representative of all principal

Fig. 7.19. Condition for no distortion.

rays from any point of the object plane. The magnification is given by Eq. (6.6), which we here repeat,

$$m = \frac{1}{m_{EE'}} \frac{p'}{p}$$

where $p$ is the position of the object plane from the entrance-pupil plane and $p'$ is the position of the image plane from the exit-pupil plane. The magnification $m_{EE'}$ of the exit pupil with respect to the entrance pupil is readily seen to be given by $\tan \theta / \tan \theta'$, so that

$$m = \frac{p' \tan \theta'}{p \tan \theta} \tag{7.55}$$

where $\theta$ and $\theta'$ are the angles that the chief ray makes with the principal axis in the object and image planes, respectively. From Eq. (7.55) we

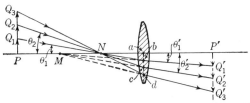

Fig. 7.20. Illustrating the formation of an image free of distortion. The intersections of the chief rays before and after refraction lie in a plane *abcd* normal to the principal axis. The centers of the entrance and exit pupils, $N$ and $M$, are free from spherical aberration.

see that the magnification of all object points will be constant if, for all values of $\theta$, $p'/p$ is constant and $\tan \theta'/\tan \theta$ is constant. A little thought will show that the constancy of $p'/p$ requires that the system be corrected for spherical aberration with respect to the entrance and exit pupils. The constancy of $\tan \theta'/\tan \theta$ requires that the points of intersection of the incident and refracted chief rays lie in a plane normal to the principal axis. These two conditions are illustrated in Fig. 7.20. Rays from different points $Q_1$, $Q_2$, $Q_3$ in the object plane are imaged, respectively, at $Q'_1$, $Q'_2$, $Q'_3$. The centers of the entrance and exit pupils are, respectively, at $N$ and $M$, which are considered to be corrected for spherical aberration. The incident ray $Q_1b$ meets the corresponding refracted ray $bQ'_1$ in the point $b$. In the same way, point $c$ is the intersection of the incident ray $Q_2c$ and refracted ray $Q'_2c$, etc. In general points $a$, $b$, $c$, $d$ form a curve. In the special case where they lie in a plane perpendicular to the principal axis, as drawn in the illustration, we have

$$\tan \theta_1 = \frac{ab}{Na}$$

$$\tan \theta_2 = \frac{ac}{Na}$$

$$\tan \theta'_1 = \frac{ab}{Ma}$$

$$\tan \theta'_2 = \frac{ac}{Ma}$$

$$\therefore \quad \frac{\tan \theta'_1}{\tan \theta} = \frac{Na}{Ma} = \frac{\tan \theta'_2}{\tan \theta_2} = \text{a constant}$$

showing that there is no distortion under these conditions. On the other

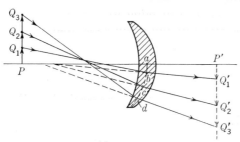

Fig. 7.21. Illustrating the curved locus *abcd* of the formation of the intersection points of the incident and refracted chief rays. The entrance and exit pupils are afflicted with aberration, and the image is distorted.

hand, in Fig. 7.21 is shown a situation in which the intersections of the chief rays before and after refraction lie along a curve and the centers of the entrance and exit pupils are afflicted with aberration. In general this situation gives rise to distortion.

As in the other types of aberrations, ray tracing may be used to ascertain the amount of distortion present. For any point in the object plane the image points corresponding to paraxial magnification and zonal, or true, magnification are obtained. The difference between these gives the amount of distortion.

Some distortion in optical instruments that are employed for visual purposes is tolerable. However, in aerial photography or where metrical relationships are to be preserved, as in the photography of geometrical diagrams, it is essential that distortion be eliminated.

By using a symmetrical arrangement of two similar meniscus convex lenses placed with their concave surfaces facing each other and with a stop midway between them, the positive distortion of the first element may be nullified by the negative distortion of the second element. For such a lens, distortion is absent only when object and image are symmetrically positioned. When used at other object-image distances some distortion is present. A symmetrical lens that corrects for distortion and spherical aberration is called *orthoscopic*, or *rectilinear*.

We shall not consider the equation giving the coefficients of distortion since it is rather complicated and of very little practical value. However, the distortion turns out to be proportional to $\tan^3 \beta$, and the coefficient of distortion is a function of the lens shape factor and a position factor with respect to entrance- and exit-pupil positions.

**7.12. The Seidel Theory.** We have already indicated that Seidel's theory for producing an aberrationless system is embodied in the conditions inherent in his five equations. His theory takes into consideration approximations only to the third order, and the formulas developed are to be used as correcting terms which must be added to the terms of the first-order theory in cases where, in addition to paraxial rays, oblique rays also contribute to the formation of the image. The student who is interested in the derivation of these equations will find them developed in the appropriate references at the end of the chapter. We shall here indicate their meaning and thus point out their relationship to the developments so far presented. Each equation is in the form of a summation, the summing index extending over each refracting surface comprising the system. If we designate the five expressions by $\Sigma_1$, $\Sigma_2$, $\Sigma_3$, $\Sigma_4$, $\Sigma_5$, then their nature is such that if $\Sigma_1 = 0$ there will be no spherical aberration at the center of the field. If $\Sigma_1 = 0$ and $\Sigma_2 = 0$, there will be no coma and Abbe's sine condition is satisfied. If $\Sigma_1 = \Sigma_2 = 0$ and $\Sigma_3 = 0$, there is no astigmatism of oblique rays. If $\Sigma_1 = \Sigma_2 = \Sigma_3 = 0$ and $\Sigma_4 = 0$, there is no curvature of the field and the condition is equivalent to satisfying the Petzval condition for removal of curvature. If $\Sigma_1 = \Sigma_2 = \Sigma_3 = \Sigma_4 = 0$ and $\Sigma_5 = 0$, there is no distortion. Thus the form of the equations is such that each has meaning only when all those preceding it are zero. When all five conditions are fulfilled, the optical system is aberrationless. In practice, however, to produce a perfectly aberrationless system would require an unusual number of refracting surfaces.

We shall indicate the form and applications of the equations by illustrating with the first of the Seidel sums which, for spherical refracting surfaces, may be stated as

$$\sum_1 = \frac{1}{2} \sum l_i^4 \left[ n_i \left( \frac{1}{R_i} - \frac{1}{\xi_i} \right) \right]^2 \left( \frac{1}{n_i' \xi_i'} - \frac{1}{n_i \xi_i} \right) \tag{7.56}$$

in which, corresponding to the $i$th refracting surface, $R_i$ is the radius of curvature and $\xi_i'$ and $\xi_i$ are the conjugate-image and -object distances, respectively. The quantity $n_i$ is the refractive index to the left and the quantity $n_i'$ that to the right of the $i$th refracting surface. The quantity $l_i$ is the ratio of the height of incidence, above the principal axis, of a ray on the $i$th refracting surface to the height of incidence of the same ray on the plane of the entrance pupil of the optical system. Let us apply Eq. (7.56) to the situation depicted in Fig. 7.1. Since there is only one refracting surface, we have $R_1 = R$, $\xi_1 = s$, $\xi_1' = s'$, $n_1 = 1$, $n_1' = n$, and

$$\sum_1 = \frac{l_1^4}{2} \left( \frac{1}{R} - \frac{1}{s} \right)^2 \left( \frac{1}{ns'} - \frac{1}{s} \right)$$

From the first-order equations, the value of $s'$ is given by $\dfrac{1}{s'} = \dfrac{n-1}{nR} + \dfrac{1}{ns}$

so that

$$\sum_1 = \frac{n-1}{n^2} \left( \frac{1}{R} - \frac{1}{s} \right)^2 \left( \frac{1}{R} - \frac{n+1}{s} \right) \frac{l_1^4}{2} \tag{7.57}$$

Except for the quantity $l_1$, we see that this expression is identical with the spherical-aberration correction in Eq. (7.5). The quantity $l_i$ is dimensionless so that it is not directly comparable with our previous $\rho$. However $l_i$, as defined above, has an advantage when one wishes to obtain expressions for the angular values of the aberrations, which then come out in rather simple forms.

In the same way, Eq. (7.56) may be directly applied to a thin lens, thus obtaining the spherical-aberration coefficient given in Eq. (7.9). We leave this as an exercise in the problems.

In the event that all five aberrations are satisfied, the optical system will produce an aberrationless image of an object located in a plane some distance away. However, if the object plane is shifted toward or away from the system, the image will again suffer from aberrations. The formation of aberrationless images of objects at various distances is subject to other conditions involving fifth-order theory. Sir John Herschel formulated the condition that must be satisfied if a system is to be corrected for spherical aberration for two object distances near each other. This condition is in contradiction to the second of Seidel's conditions. Thus the Herschel condition and the sine condition cannot be satisfied simultaneously. Therefore, if the lens is to be free from distortion and curvature of the field for a range of object distances, it will be necessary to endure a slight coma at every distance, or if it is required to have precise definition of the image, the lens will not be usable for a range of object distances.

**7.13. Chromatic Aberration.**  In our study of the aberrations thus far considered it has been assumed that the light is monochromatic, or of one color or wavelength.  In fact, the monochromatic aberrations are usually corrected for only one color since they are affected only very slightly with wavelength.  Sometimes spherical aberration is corrected for more than one wavelength.  However, since the index of refraction of a lens varies with wavelength, causing the different constituent colors of a polychromatic beam to bend by different amounts, the image produced suffers from color effects, thus giving rise to the phenomenon of *chromatic aberration*.  Figure 7.22 illustrates what is termed *axial*, or *longitudinal*,

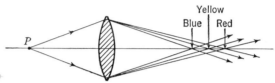

Fig. 7.22. Longitudinal chromatic aberration.

*chromatism.*  White light from a source at $P$ is incident on a lens which disperses the light, bringing the blue to a focus nearest to and the red to a focus farthest from the lens.  The other colors present are spread out axially as shown.  A screen placed at the violet focus will show a central blue image surrounded by a colored halo.  Nowhere along the axis is the image in perfect focus, the best focus occurring at the position of the circle of least confusion.  The linear distance, measured along the axis, between the extreme foci, as between the blue and red image points, is taken as a measure of the longitudinal chromatic aberration.  The aberration is *positive* when the blue focus lies to the left of the red focus as in Fig. 7.22.  That produced by a diverging lens is in the opposite direction.

Since the positions of the principal planes are a function of the index of refraction (see Sec. 5.1), the different colors will have different focal lengths, thus giving rise to a difference in magnification with wavelength.  Hence in addition to longitudinal chromatic aberration there is present *lateral chromatic aberration*.  Lateral chromatic aberration is measured in terms of the difference in image sizes.  The aberration is *positive* when the image formed by the red color is more magnified than that formed by the violet color.

Longitudinal chromatic aberration has the same magnitude over the entire field and increases with increase in aperture.  Lateral chromatic aberration does not depend on aperture.

In order to make a system entirely *achromatic*, say for blue and red, *i.e.*, corrected for longitudinal and lateral chromatic aberration for these colors, both the focal lengths must be made the same, and the principal planes must be made to coincide for the two colors. Usually only one or the other of the corrections is sufficient. Thus if an optical system has a large aperture and small field of view, it is more urgent to correct for longitudinal chromatic aberration. In this case the correction would make the rays of all colors come to a focus in the same plane, but the magnification would not be constant. On the other hand, if the system has a small aperture and large field of view, it is best to correct for the lateral chromatic aberration. Here the focal length for the colors would be made the same, with the result that the magnification would be constant but the images would not all lie in one plane.

The important cases are when thin lenses are combined to produce an achromatized system. For a cemented combination made of a thin biconvex and a thin biconcave lens, the principal planes lie within the glass so that the lateral chromatic difference may be negligible. The system could therefore be made almost perfectly achromatic by arranging for the focal lengths to be the same.

**7.14. Achromatic Combinations.** In correcting a system for the chromatic aberrations it is sufficient to employ the first-order-theory equations. Consider the "achromatic doublet," two thin lenses combined to correct for the chromatic aberrations. As is customary for instruments that are used for visual purposes, the system is achromatized for the $C$ (red) and $F$ (blue) colors, as discussed in Sec. 1.10 for achromatic prisms.

In general when two thin lenses, of focal lengths $f_1'$ and $f_2'$, are coaxially placed a distance $d$ apart, their combined focal length $f'$ is given by Eq. (5.22),

$$\frac{1}{f'} = \frac{1}{f_1'} + \frac{1}{f_2'} - \frac{d}{f_1'f_2'}$$

Using $1/f_1' = k_1(n_1 - 1)$ and $1/f_2' = k_2(n_2 - 1)$, where $k_1$ and $k_2$ represent the differences in the reciprocals of the radii of curvature of the surfaces, respectively, of lens 1 and lens 2, we have

$$\frac{1}{f'} = k_1(n_1 - 1) + k_2(n_2 - 1) - k_1k_2(n_1 - 1)(n_2 - 1)d \quad (7.58)$$

Equation (7.58) indicates that the focal length of the lens combination is a function of the wavelength since both $n_1$ and $n_2$ are functions of the wavelength. In discussing the achromatic doublet two important cases present themselves: when the doublet has its elements separated by some amount $d$, and when the elements are cemented so that $d = 0$. These are below given parallel considerations, the left-hand column without the calculus, the right-hand column using the calculus.

Let us write Eq. (7.58) for the two colors, blue and red, for which the focal length $f'$ is to be achromatized. We shall call $n_{1b}$ and $n_{2b}$ the values of the refractive indices, respectively, of the first and second lenses corresponding to blue light, and $n_{1r}$ and $n_{2r}$ those corresponding to red light. Then

$$\frac{1}{f'_b} = k_1(n_{1b} - 1) + k_2(n_{2b} - 1)$$
$$- k_1k_2(n_{1b} - 1)(n_{2b} - 1)d$$

and

$$\frac{1}{f'_r} = k_1(n_{1r} - 1) + k_2(n_{2r} - 1)$$
$$- k_1k_2(n_{1r} - 1)(n_{2r} - 1)d$$

To achromatize for the focal length for these two colors, we must have $f'_b = f'_r$ or

$$(n_{1r} - n_{1b})k_1 + (n_{2r} - n_{2b})k_2$$
$$+ [(n_{1b} - 1)(n_{2b} - 1)$$
$$- (n_{1r} - 1)(n_{2r} - 1)]k_1k_2d = 0$$
$$(7.58a)$$

Now consider the situation in which both lenses are made of the same glass. Using $n_{1b} = n_{2b} = n_b$ and $n_{1r} = n_{2r} = n_r$, Eq. (7.58a) reduces to

$$(n_r - n_b)[(k_1 + k_2)$$
$$- k_1k_2(n_b + n_r - 2)d] = 0$$

Since $n_r \neq n_b$, we have

$$d = \frac{1}{n_b + n_r - 2}\left(\frac{1}{k_1} + \frac{1}{k_2}\right)$$
$$(7.58b)$$

Substituting for $k_1$ and $k_2$ the values $1/k_1 = f'_1(n_y - 1)$,

$$\frac{1}{k_2} = f'_2(n_y - 1),$$

Using the symbol $\lambda$ for wavelength, and differentiating Eq. (7.58) with respect to $\lambda$, gives

$$\frac{d}{d\lambda}\left(\frac{1}{f'}\right) = [k_1 - k_1k_2(n_2 - 1)d]\frac{dn_1}{d\lambda}$$
$$+ [k_2 - k_1k_2(n_1 - 1)d]\frac{dn_2}{d\lambda}$$
$$(7.58A)$$

The quantities $dn_1/d\lambda$ and $dn_2/d\lambda$ are the slopes to the curves of the variation of refractive index with wavelength and are known as the *dispersions* of the respective media (see Chap. 15). They are also functions of the wavelength. Equating Eq. (7.58A) to zero will determine the condition for which $1/f'$ is an extreme. Thus we have

$$[k_1 - k_1k_2(n_2 - 1)d]\frac{dn_1}{d\lambda}$$
$$+ [k_2 - k_1k_2(n_1 - 1)d]\frac{dn_2}{d\lambda} = 0$$
$$(7.58B)$$

Now consider the case in which both lenses are made of the same glass so that $n_1 = n_2 = n_y$ and $dn_1/d\lambda = dn_2/d\lambda = dn/d\lambda$. Then

$$[k_1 + k_2 - 2k_1k_2(n - 1)d]\frac{dn}{d\lambda} = 0$$

and since $dn/d\lambda \neq 0$,

$$d = \frac{k_1 + k_2}{2k_1k_2(n - 1)} \quad (7.58C)$$

Substitute for $k_1$ its value $1/f'_1(n - 1)$ and for $k_2$ its value $1/f'_2(n - 1)$. Then

$$d = \frac{f'_1 + f'_2}{2} \quad (7.58D)$$

Therefore if the elements are separated in accordance with Eq.

where $n_y$ is the refractive index corresponding to some intermediate color $y$, then

$$d = \frac{(f'_1 + f'_2)(n_y - 1)}{n_b + n_r - 2} \quad (7.58c)$$

We can simplify the value for $d$ if we choose the intermediate color so that $n_y = (n_b + n_r)/2$; then

$$d = \frac{f'_1 + f'_2}{2} \quad (7.58d)$$

Therefore if two lenses, made of the same material, are separated in accordance with Eq. (7.58$d$), the system will be achromatic for two colors. The indices of refraction corresponding to these colors will be equally spaced on either side of the index of refraction corresponding to the color for which the focal lengths in Eq. (7.58$d$) are computed. We can perhaps see more of what is meant if we set

$$n_1 = n_2 = n$$

in Eq. (7.58). This yields

$$\frac{1}{f'} = (k_1 + k_2)(n - 1)$$
$$- dk_1k_2(n - 1)^2 \quad (7.58e)$$

which shows that the reciprocal of the focal length is a parabolic function of $n$. The graph shown in Fig. 7.23 corresponds to both lenses being convex. [At least one of them must be converging and must also be of larger focal length as seen from Eq. (7.58$c$), since $d$ is positive.] By satisfying Eq. (7.58$d$), it is seen that the wavelength corresponding to $n_y$ is the one for which the focal

(7.58$D$), the reciprocal of the focal length will exhibit an extreme at the wavelength for which $f'_1$ and $f'_2$ are computed. The second derivative with respect to $\lambda$ leads to

$$\frac{d^2}{d\lambda^2}\left(\frac{1}{f'}\right) = [k_1 + k_2 - 2k_1k_2$$
$$(n - 1)d]\frac{d^2n}{d\lambda^2} - 2k_1k_2\left(\frac{dn}{d\lambda}\right)^2 d$$

and the value of this, corresponding to Eq. (7.58$C$), is $-2k_1k_2(dn/d\lambda)^2 d$, which is negative for two converging lenses. Thus $1/f'$ as a function of $\lambda$ exhibits a maximum, the exact form of the curve depending on the function that is employed to express the relationship between $n$ and $\lambda$ (see Chapter 15). The focal length has a corresponding minimum, and its rate of change is zero at the wavelength for which $f'_1$ and $f'_2$ are computed. By setting $n_1 = n_2 = n$ in Eq. (7.58) and differentiating it with respect to $n$, the characteristics of the symmetrical curve in Fig. 7.23 may

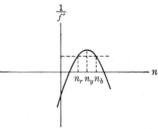

FIG. 7.23. Graph of the reciprocal of the combined focal length of two lenses separated achromatically, as a function of the refractive index of the lenses.

be obtained. The achromatization then is for two points on either side of the minimum value for $f'_1$,

length is a minimum, and at that region the rate of change of $f'$ with respect to the wavelength is zero. For some achromatized value of $f'$, as indicated by the horizontal dotted line, the two colors for which the system is achromatic are those corresponding to the indices $n_r$ and $n_b$. These are the two values of $n$ that satisfy Eq. (7.58e). The sum of these roots is

$$n_r + n_b = \frac{k_1 + k_2 + 2k_1k_2d}{k_1k_2d}$$

and putting in the values of $k_1$, $k_2$, and $d$, there results

$$\frac{n_r + n_b}{2} = n_y$$

as it should be. As we have already remarked, the $C$ and $F$ Fraunhofer lines are the ones with respect to which doublets in certain optical instruments are often achromatized. The intermediate color employed is the $D$ line of sodium. These three lines are usually employed in the measurement of refractive index because of the convenience of a hydrogen-discharge tube and a sodium flame. With this choice $n_D$ does not quite fall midway between $n_C$ and $n_F$ (see Table 1.3), but the amount of dissymmetry present is so small as not to affect the degree of achromatism appreciably. For visual work it is more effective to use for the intermediate value that wavelength to which the eyes have the greatest visibility. Thus many visual instruments are corrected around the value 5500 A.

and since the profile is rather flat, the achromatization is approximately good for a whole band of wavelengths.

For the case of two thin lenses in contact, Eq. (7.58B) yields the condition

$$k_1 \frac{dn_1}{d\lambda} + k_2 \frac{dn_2}{d\lambda} = 0 \quad (7.58E)$$

or

$$\frac{k_1}{k_2} = -\frac{dn_2}{dn_1}$$

Considering the increments

$$dn_2 = n_{2F} - n_{2C}$$

and $dn_1 = n_{1F} - n_{1C}$, and

$$k_1 = \frac{1}{f_1'(n_{1D} - 1)}$$

and $k_2 = 1/f_2'(n_{2D} - 1)$, we have

$$\frac{f_2'}{f_1'} = -\frac{(n_{2F} - n_{2C})/(n_{2D} - 1)}{(n_{1F} - n_{1C})/(n_{1D} - 1)}$$

or

$$\frac{f_2'}{f_1'} = -\frac{\omega_2}{\omega_1} \quad (7.58F)$$

where $\omega_1$ and $\omega_2$ are the dispersive powers of the lenses.

This last equation may also be obtained by taking the total differential of the equation

$$\frac{1}{f'} = \frac{1}{f_1'} + \frac{1}{f_2'}$$

This yields

$$-\frac{df'}{f'^2} = -\frac{df_1'}{f_1'^2} - \frac{df_2'}{f_2'^2}$$

Now in general $1/f' = k(n - 1)$, so that

$$-\frac{df'}{f'^2} = k\,dn = \frac{dn}{f'(n - 1)} = \frac{\omega}{f'}$$

By achromatizing in the fashion outlined above, the profile around the minimum of the graph of $f'$ as a function of wavelength is so relatively flat that the system is approximately achromatic for a good portion of the visible spectrum. Actually the system is truly achromatic for only two colors. The system is thus corrected for lateral chromatic aberration, but it suffers from longitudinal chromatic aberration. We shall see in the next chapter that oculars of microscopes and telescopes, of the Huygens or Ramsden types, are corrected in the above fashion.

The other important case is the condition of achromatism for the cemented doublet with components of different glass. Setting $d = 0$ in Eq. (7.58a) and using the $C$, $F$, and $D$ colors, we obtain

$$\frac{k_1}{k_2} = -\frac{n_{2C} - n_{2F}}{n_{1C} - n_{1F}}$$

which reduces to

$$\frac{f_2'}{f_1'} = -\frac{(n_{2F} - n_{2C})/(n_{2D} - 1)}{(n_{1F} - n_{1C})/(n_{1D} - 1)}$$

where the right-hand member is a ratio of the dispersive powers of the two lenses (see Sec. 1.9). Thus

$$\frac{f_2'}{f_1'} = -\frac{\omega_2}{\omega_1} \qquad (7.58f)$$

Thus in terms of dispersive powers

$$-\frac{df'}{f'^2} = \frac{\omega_1}{f_1'} + \frac{\omega_2}{f_2'}$$

and equating this to zero leads to Eq. (7.58F).

Equation (7.58f), or Eq. (7.58F), shows that since $\omega_1$ and $\omega_2$ are always positive, one of the lenses must be convex and the other concave in order to form an achromatic doublet. Also, if the lens of focal length $f_1'$ is convergent and the combination is to be convergent, then $f_1' < f_2'$ and $\omega_1 < \omega_2$. A common form of an achromat is a converging lens of crown cemented to a diverging lens of flint, and the doublet achromatizes for the

*C and F lines.* The four radii of curvature of such a combination have three conditions: Eq. (7.58*f*), or Eq. (7.58*F*), the equation

$$\frac{1}{f'} = \frac{1}{f'_1} + \frac{1}{f'_2}$$

and the common radius of curvature of the cemented pair. This permits a fourth condition to be imposed such as one for minimizing spherical aberration. In the next section we take up the achromat corrected for spherical aberration.

When a system has been achromatized for two colors, some chromatic error remains and gives rise to a diffuse area of colors surrounding the image. These are called the *secondary spectrum*. The secondary spectrum may be reduced by achromatizing for three colors for which three lenses must be employed.

As we have pointed out, if the cemented lens may be considered thin, then achromatizing for the focal length also produces a system that is relatively free from longitudinal aberration. When the elements are separated, it is not possible to achromatize longitudinally as well as laterally unless each of the two separated elements consists of an achromatic pair (see Prob. 7.35). When the elements are single lenses and they are achromatized laterally, longitudinal aberration is present since the principal planes are not the same for different colors.

**7.15. Achromatic Doublet Free of Spherical Aberration.** Given the focal length of a cemented doublet, the types of glasses, and the position of the object, what must be the lens shapes so that the images are free from chromatic aberration and axial spherical aberration? The solution to this is obtained by referring to Eqs. (7.19) and (7.27). For two thin lenses in contact, the condition for no spherical aberration is

$$\rho^2 \left[ \frac{Y_1}{(f'_1)^3} + \frac{Y_2}{(f'_2)^3} \right] = 0 \tag{7.59}$$

For the doublet to be additionally achromatic, $f'_2 = -f'_1(\omega_2/\omega_1)$, so that Eq. (7.59) yields the condition

$$Y_1 = \left(\frac{\omega_1}{\omega_2}\right)^3 Y_2 \tag{7.60}$$

where $Y_1$ and $\omega_1$ refer to the crown element and $Y_2$ and $\omega_2$ refer to the flint element. In addition, the relationship in Eq. (7.41) holds here,

$$\pi_1 - 1 = -\frac{\omega_1}{\omega_2}(\pi_2 + 1) \tag{7.61}$$

For a known value of $\pi_1$, say $\pi_1 = -1$ giving parallel rays incident on a telescope objective, $\pi_2$ is determined. Since $Y_1$ and $Y_2$ are functions of the shape factors and position factors, by using curves showing the variation of $Y_1$ and $Y_2$ as a function of their respective shape factors, the possible solutions for the shape factors satisfying Eq. (7.60) may be obtained. In this way, an achromatic doublet free of chromatic and spherical aberration may be designed.

**7.16. Chromatic Aberration and the Petzval Condition.** It is possible to form two lenses in contact so that the system will be achromatic and have a flat field free of curvature. For this purpose the equations that must simultaneously be satisfied are

$$\frac{f_1'}{f_2'} = -\frac{\omega_1}{\omega_2}$$

and

$$\frac{f_1'}{f_2'} = -\frac{n_2}{n_1}$$

These lead to the condition

$$\frac{\omega_1}{\omega_2} = \frac{n_2}{n_1} \qquad (7.62)$$

requiring that the lens of greater dispersive power have the smaller refractive index. In general for ordinary crown and flint glasses, the glass of greater dispersive power is the more refracting. It was only after 1886 that there was made commercially available glasses that would satisfy Eq. (7.62). Achromats made of ordinary crown and flint are known as *old achromats*, and the achromats made from the newer glasses, such as the barium glasses, are called *new-type achromats*. The new achromats also give much less secondary spectrum. When a system is achromatic with no secondary spectrum and is also aplanatic, it is termed *apochromatic*.

**7.17. Summary.** We have seen how the monochromatic and chromatic aberrations affect both the definition and position of the image. It should be clear, however, that it is not possible to eliminate simultaneously the five monochromatic and two chromatic aberrations for a lens. However, it is possible to reduce the aberrations to a degree which in general is consistent with the requirements of an optical system. For this purpose compound lenses, made of a number of elements, can be designed to give an image that is relatively free from aberrations. The requirements of an optical system, whether it is to cover a small or large angular field, whether it is to be used for visual or photographic purposes, whether it is to be used for high magnifications in which metrical relationships are to be preserved, etc., will determine which of the seven aberrations it is most important to eliminate, and then the system can be designed so that it accordingly functions in a highly satisfactory manner.

## REFERENCES

Born, Max: "Optik," Verlag Julius Springer, Berlin, 1933.

Coddington, Henry: "A Treatise on the Reflection and Refraction of Light," Simpkins and Marshall, London, 1829.

Drude, Paul: "Theory of Optics," Longmans, Green & Co., Inc., New York, 1933.

Gardner, I. C.: "Applications of the Algebraic Aberration Equations to Optical Design," *Natl. Bur. Standards (U.S.) Sci. Paper* 550.

Hardy, A. C., and F. H. Perrin: "The Principles of Optics," McGraw-Hill Book Company, Inc., New York, 1932.

Lummer, Otto: "Photographic Optics," The Macmillan Company, New York, 1900.

Smith, T. Townsend: "Spherical Aberration of Thin Lenses," *Natl. Bur. Standards (U.S.) Sci. Paper* 461.

Taylor, H. Dennis: "A System of Applied Optics," The Macmillan Company, New York, 1906.

Whitaker, E. T.: "The Theory of Optical Instruments," *Cambridge Tracts Math. Mathematical Phys.* 7, 1907.

## PROBLEMS

**7.1.** Derive Eq. (7.8) for the spherical aberration of a mirror from elementary considerations, following the method employed for obtaining Eq. (7.5), and show that the marginal rays focus closer to the mirror than the paraxial rays.

**7.2.** Using Eq. (7.8), show that the value for the longitudinal spherical aberration of the mirror is given approximately by $\left(\dfrac{R - s}{R - 2s}\right)^2 \dfrac{\rho^2}{R}$.

**7.3.** A concave spherical mirror has a radius of curvature of 30.0 cm. A point object is located 60.0 cm from the mirror surface. Compute the spherical-aberration effect for rays that strike the mirror surface at 2.00 cm and at 10.0 cm from the axis.

**7.4.** A thin biconvex lens with a refractive index of 1.50 and radii of curvature 50.0 and 20.0 cm has a diameter of 3.00 cm. An object is placed axially a distance of 100 cm from the lens. Compute the longitudinal spherical aberration (*a*) when the surface of larger radius of curvature is nearer the object, (*b*) when the smaller radius surface is nearest the object.

**7.5.** A convex spherical surface of 5.00 cm radius and refractive index 1.50 is to the right of an object axially situated 15.0 cm from it. Find the longitudinal spherical aberration for a ray incident on the surface at a distance 2.00 cm from the axis, (*a*) by computation, (*b*) by trigonometrical ray tracing; (*c*) what is the aberration if the ray is incident at 0.500 cm from the axis? For part *b* observe that from Eqs. (2.1) to (2.4) we have $\sin \phi = [(-s + R)/R] \sin u$, $\sin \phi' = (n/n') \sin \phi$,

$$u' = -|u'| = -(\phi - \phi' - u)$$

$s' = R + \dfrac{R \sin \phi'}{\sin (\phi - \phi' - u)}$. The first equation determines $\phi$, the second $\phi'$, the third $u'$, and the fourth $s'$ for the marginal ray. The quantities are shown in Fig. 2.2. In applying these equations, five-place logarithms should be employed.

**7.6.** An equiconvex lens has the following constants: radius of curvature 100 cm, axial thickness 2.00 cm, diameter 20.0 cm, refractive index 1.50. Find the longitudinal spherical aberration, by ray tracing, for a parallel ray distant 10.0 cm from the axis. HINT: Apply the equations shown in Prob. 7.5 to each surface in turn.

Observe that instead of the first equation the expression $\sin \phi = \rho/R$ holds for the first surface.

**7.7.** Obtain an expression for the longitudinal value of the spherical aberration for a spherical mirror corresponding to Eq. (7.11) for the lens.

**7.8.** For what mirror shapes and under what corresponding conditions is there nc spherical aberration? Explain fully.

**7.9.** (a) Plot the shape factor $\sigma$ as a function of $R_1/R_2$ for a thin lens. (b) Plot the position factor $\pi$ as a function of $f'/s$. Interpret these graphs with reference to the characteristics of $\sigma$ and $\pi$.

**7.10.** Draw to scale principal sections of lenses having the following ratios of $R_1/R_2$, and indicate the corresponding shape factors: $1/1$, $1/\infty$, $1/-1.5$, $1/1.5$, $-5/1$, $\infty/1$, $1/5$.

**7.11.** On the same graph paper plot the constants $A$, $B$, $C$, and $D$ as a function of $n$, from $n = 1.50$ to $n = 1.70$. Of what value are these curves?

**7.12.** On the same piece of graph paper plot $Y$ and separately $(s'/f')^2Y$ as a function of the position factor $\pi$ for an equiconvex lens whose refractive index is 1.50 in the range $\pi = -5$ to $\pi = 5$. Note that $Y$ is proportional to the spherical aberration $\Delta(1/s')$, while $(s'/f')^2Y$ is proportional to the longitudinal value of the spherical aberration $\Delta(s')$. On the basis of the plot, which function is the easier to deal with?

**7.13.** Parallel rays fall on a thin lens whose radii of curvature are $R_1 = 15.0$ cm and $R_2 = -10.0$ cm. If the lens has a refractive index of 1.52 and its diameter is 5.00 cm, find the spherical aberration and longitudinal value of the spherical aberration for the rim rays.

**7.14.** Show that $\sigma$ in Eq. (7.26) has real roots when $n < \dfrac{-(1 + \pi^2) + \sqrt{1 + 3\pi^2}}{1 - \pi^2}$.

Discuss the physical significance of this.

**7.15.** A convex lens of refractive index 1.70 is to be designed to have minimum spherical aberration for parallel rays. Find the ratio of the required radii of curvature, and draw a principal section of one possible lens.

**7.16.** Compute the spherical aberration, for a distant object, of lenses (a) and (c) in Fig. 7.4. For each, the convex surface receiving the parallel light has a radius of curvature of 20.0 cm, the refractive index is 1.50, and the diameter is 10.0 cm. Also compute the spherical aberration for lens (c) with the plane surface receiving the incident light.

**7.17.** An equiconvex lens of refractive index 1.60 forms an image that is the same distance from the lens as the object. Find the spherical aberration. The radius of curvature of the surfaces is 50.0 cm, and the diameter is 20.0 cm.

**7.18.** The trigonometric calculation of the longitudinal spherical aberration for a telescope objective, made of a cemented double-convex crown lens and a plano-concave flint lens, yielded the following data:

| $\rho$, mm | 0 | 2 | 4 | 6 | 8 | 10 | 12 | 14 |
|---|---|---|---|---|---|---|---|---|
| L.S.A., mm | 0 | $-0.010$ | $-0.020$ | $-0.062$ | $-0.100$ | $-0.120$ | $-0.080$ | 0.030 |

Plot $\rho$ as a function of the longitudinal spherical aberration. These results are typical of the degree to which spherical aberration is corrected in practice. The plot shows that the negative aberration increases more rapidly with $\rho$ than the positive aberration and then diminishes after reaching a maximum. Owing to the thickness of the lens and use of larger apertures, the actual curves deviate in the manner shown from the ideal equations, which neglect terms of order higher than 3.

**7.19.** By differentiating $Y$ partially, find an expression that shows the effect of a variation in the shape of a lens on the spherical aberration. Discuss the resulting expression.

**7.20.** A thin convex lens has the following constants: $n = 1.50$, $R_1 = 10.5$ cm, $R_2 = -21.0$ cm. Light from an extra-axial distant object point falls on the lens. Find (a) the length of the comatic flare and (b) the angular coma for a zone 0.500 cm in radius. The angle that the chief ray makes with the principal axis is 10.0°.

**7.21.** Plot $E$ and $G$ [Eqs. (7.33) and (7.34)] as a function of $n$ from $n = 1.50$ to $n = 1.70$.

**7.22.** For the lens and conditions stated in Prob. 7.6 find the amount of coma present.

**7.23.** Using the figure, where $P$ and $P'$ are the aplanatic points of the sphere whose refractive index is $n$, prove that the sine condition holds for all zones of the sphere.

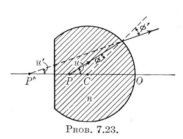

PROB. 7.23.

**7.24.** Find the positions of the aplanatic points of a spherical glass ball whose refractive index is 1.60 and whose radius of curvature is 6.50 cm.

**7.25.** Using the positive solution in Eq. (7.42) and the negative solution in Eq. (7.43), find the expressions for $s'$, $s$, and $R_2$. Interpret the results.

**7.26.** A thin double-convex lens has a refractive index 1.50 and radii of curvature 10.0 and 5.00 cm. On a line making an angle of 30° with the principal axis at the lens center there is a point object 10.0 cm from the lens. The lens diameter is 6.00 cm. Find (a) the position of the primary focus, (b) the position of the secondary focus, (c) the astigmatic difference, (d) the length of the primary line image, (e) the length of the secondary line image.

**7.27.** (a) Convert Eqs. (7.49) and (7.50) into the corresponding ones for a mirror, and obtain Eq. (7.51). (b) A concave mirror has a radius of curvature of 40.0 cm and a diameter of 8.00 cm. A point object is 50.0 cm from the principal axis, and its projection on the axis is 100 cm from the pole of the mirror. Find (1) the position of the primary-image focus, (2) the position of the secondary-image focus, (3) the astigmatic difference, (4) the length of the primary line image, (5) the length of the secondary line image.

**7.28.** From Eqs. (7.49) and (7.50) show that when the astigmatic difference vanishes, it leads to the condition for the two aplanatic points of a sphere.

**7.29.** A telescope is being examined to determine its state of correction. When the center of the field is focused sharply, the edge of the field is out of focus, but when the edge of the field is brought into focus, the center of the field goes out of focus. Draw an image-distance vs. image-height diagram indicating the type of affliction present.

**7.30.** Apply Eq. (7.56) to a thin lens of refractive index $n$ with respect to its surroundings, and obtain the spherical-aberration coefficient shown in Eq. (7.9).

**7.31.** A cemented doublet made of thin components is achromatic for the $C$ and $F$ colors and has a focal length of 25.0 cm. Using the dispersive powers for the silicate-crown- and silicate-flint-glass components from the constants of Table 1.3, find the focal lengths of the components.

**7.32.** If the common radius of curvature in the doublet of Prob. 7.31 is 20.0 cm, what are the other radii of curvature?

**7.33.** A thick lens is made of high-dispersion crown glass with refractive indices as given by Table 1.3. If $R_1 = 40.0$ cm, $R_2 = -30.0$ cm, and $t = 2.00$ cm, find (a) the positions of the principal planes for the different colors, (b) the longitudinal chromatic aberration for the $C$ and $F$ lines for paraxial rays. The lens is in air, and the object is very distant.

**7.34.** Two convex thin lenses made of light silicate crown have focal lengths, at 5500 A, of 200.0 and 60.00 mm. They are separated so that they form an achromatic combination in the sense discussed in Sec. 7.14, with the combined focal length a minimum at 5500 A. Using the table below and Eq. (7.58e), compute and plot the combined focal length $f'$ in millimeters as a function of the wavelengths indicated. Interpret the curve in the light of achromatism.

| Wavelength, A.......... | 4000 | 4500 | 5000 | 5500 | 6000 | 6500 | 7000 | 7500 |
|---|---|---|---|---|---|---|---|---|
| $n$...................... | 1.524 | 1.518 | 1.513 | 1.510 | 1.508 | 1.506 | 1.505 | 1.504 |

**7.35.** Using Eq. (5.21), $m = s_1's_2'/s_1s_2$, for the lateral magnification as applied to two lenses separated a distance $d = s_1' + s_2$, where $s_1$ and $s_1'$ are the object and image positions, respectively, for the first lens and $s_2$ and $s_2'$ are those, respectively, for the second lens, show that if it is desired to achromatize the system completely, *i.e.*, with respect to position and magnification of the image, then each of the separate lenses must be achromatized individually. HINT: $s_1$ is the same for all colors, and $s_2'$ must be the same for all colors. Hence $s_1'/s_2 = $ constant. The argument proceeds along similar lines if you wish to employ the calculus; then $d(s_1'/s_2) = 0$.

**7.36.** Three thin lenses of focal lengths $f_1'$, $f_2'$, and $f_3'$ are coaxially placed, with the second situated a distance $d_1$ to the right of the first, and the third a distance $d_2$ to the right of the second. Find an expression for the equivalent focal length $f'$ and the condition of zero variation in $1/f'$ when all lenses have the same refractive index. Interpret the result in the light of the correction for lateral chromatic aberration.

**7.37.** Write a summary of the significant conclusions and results of the developments of this chapter.

# CHAPTER 8

## OPTICAL INSTRUMENTS

We are now in a position to look into the formation of optical instruments whose image-forming characteristics are a consequence of the principles of geometrical optics which we have thus far established. Rather then attempt to present a great variety of instruments, we shall concern ourselves primarily with the coverage of general types such as the microscope and telescope. We shall see that these operate on similar principles: a unit known as the objective is used to gather the light and form an initial image, which in turn is magnified by another unit known as the ocular. We shall also find it necessary to study the different kinds of oculars that are employed, and we shall see how their construction affects the quality of the image.

In view of the fact that the eye is employed in the use of visual instruments whose designs are necessarily thereby influenced, it is best if we first go into the image-forming properties of the eye, which, in its own right, is an optical instrument whose complete visual mechanism involves the fields of psychology and physiology. We shall limit our discussion, however, to the physical principles, but we must keep in mind that the eye performs more than just one function: it is used to perceive and measure light, it is used to discriminate between different colors, and it determines object positions in the field of view.

**8.1. The Eye—Its Structure and Optical System.** In Fig. 8.1 is shown a section of the human eye, which is approximately a sphere of about 1 in. diameter, whose outer layer $S$ is called the *sclerotic*. This opaque coating is a membrane that is made of tough fibrous tissue. The front part of the sclerotic, and continuous with it, is a transparent section of smaller radius of curvature called the *cornea C*. The next layer inward is the *choroid ch,* which is a membrane composed of many blood vessels and lined internally with pigment cells. The *retina R*, a structure of fibers and cells, is the image receptor and is directly connected to the optic nerve $O$. Within the eyeball is the elastic *crystalline lens L*, which is held in place by the suspensory ligament $l$, extending from the lens edges to the *ciliary muscle M*. The ciliary muscle can vary the tension of the suspensory ligament, resulting in an alteration in the curvature of the lens surfaces. The cornea and the crystalline lens are the image-producing elements, the space between them containing a salt solution

126

known as the *aqueous humour A*. The space between the lens and the retina is filled with a transparent gelatinous substance called the *vitreous humour V* and consisting mostly of water. The *iris I*, a circular diaphragm limiting the aperture of the eye, is a pigmented membrane whose central hole, termed the *pupil*, permits light to enter the eye. The action of the iris is involuntary so that when its radiating fibers contract, the pupil dilates.

Light enters the eye through the cornea, which has an axial thickness of about 0.5 mm and an index of refraction of 1.35. It then passes through the aqueous humour, the lens, and the vitreous humour, whose

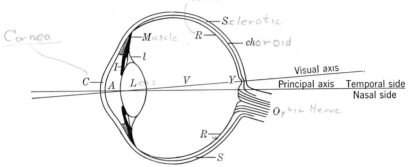

Fig. 8.1. Horizontal cross section of the right eye.

indices of refraction are 1.34, 1.44, and 1.34, respectively, and then falls on the retina. The retina contains two kinds of structures known as rods and cones; these act as the receptors of the optical image, which they transmit to the brain by way of the optic nerve. The point on the retina at *Y* is called the *yellow spot*, or the *macula lutea;* it is about 2 mm in diameter, and at its center is the *fovea centralis*, which is about 0.25 mm in diameter and contains practically only cones. The distribution of the rods and cones varies in the retinal regions removed from the fovea so that there are only about 10 per cent cones in the outer portions. The acuity of vision is greatest at the fovea and falls off toward the outer regions, which are sensitive to the observation of motion. Because of this, the muscles (not shown) attached to the sclerotic and holding the eye in position always rotate the eyeball until the image being examined falls on the fovea. This fact is indicated by the visual axis in the figure. At the point where the optic nerve extends through the eyeball, the retina is absent and there is no sensitivity to light. This is known as the *blind spot*.

Since the refractive indices of the media that the light rays traverse are all about the same, most of the refraction occurs at the outermost surface of the cornea, which has a radius of curvature of 7.83 mm.

For the normal or average eye when it is relaxed, the second principal focal point of the system falls at the retina, a distance of 22.8 mm from the vertex of the cornea.   The first principal focal point is at a distance of $-12.1$ mm from the vertex of the cornea.   Objects at infinity are thus in focus.   In order that the eye bring into focus objects that are closer to it, the ciliary muscles contract, relaxing the ligaments, and permitting the curvature of the lens faces to increase.   This decreases the focal length of the system and permits the eye to see near objects.   The ability of the eye to change its power in this way and thus focus for different object distances is known as *accommodation*.   The range over which the eye can

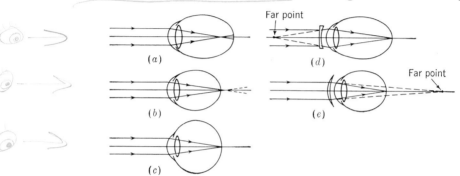

FIG. 8.2. (*a*) The myopic eye.   (*b*) The hyperopic eye.   (*c*) The emmetropic eye. (*d*) Myopic eye with correcting lens.   (*e*) Hyperopic eye with correcting lens.

bring objects in focus is represented by the distance between the *far point* and the *near point*, the former being the distance that an object can be brought into focus when the eye is relaxed, and the latter the distance of an object in focus when the eye is accommodating by the fullest amount. For a normal eye the far point is at infinity, and the near point is at 25 cm from the eye.   However, these values are a function of age, and the range of accommodation is greatest in young people and least in old persons. The near point regularly increases with age from a few years to age eighty, while the far point starts to decrease at about age fifty.   This loss of accommodation is known as *presbyopia* and is due to the fact that the ciliary muscles lose their effect and the crystalline lens becomes less elastic.   Convex spectacle lenses are used to compensate for loss of accommodation.

There are three common defects of the eye, *myopia*, or nearsightedness, *hyperopia* (also called hypermetropia), or farsightedness, and astigmatism.   The first two are due to the far point of an eye having normal accommodation not at infinity, while astigmatism is a result of the cornea having different curvatures in different meridian planes, as explained in Sec. 7.9.   Figure 8.2 shows (*a*) the myopic eye, (*b*) the hyperopic eye, and (*c*) the normal, or *emmetropic*, eye.   In (*d*) and (*e*) are shown the myopic and hyperopic eyes, respectively, with their corresponding correcting spectacle lenses. In (a) the eyeball is unusually long in comparison with the radius of curvature of the cornea so that parallel rays are brought to a focus in front of the retina. Therefore, with the eye relaxed, the position of the far point is finite, and rays diverging from this position will focus onto the retina. This means that the eye is too powerful for focusing parallel rays onto the retina. Therefore, to remedy this defect, a diverging spectacle lens must be employed as shown in (d). If the focal length of the correcting lens is chosen so that it coincides with the far point of the myopic eye, then parallel rays will converge down to a focus

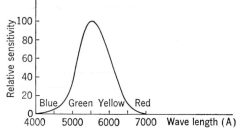

Fig. 8.3. Spectral sensitivity curve for a normal eye.

on the retina. Thus if a shortsighted person has his far point at 40.0 cm, then he needs lenses whose power is $-2.50$ diopters. In (b) the eyeball is shortened, so that the focus for parallel rays falls behind the retina. By similar reasoning it is seen that a converging spectacle lens is needed to remedy the hyperopic eye as shown in (e). Notice that the far point for this eye is to the right of the retina, so that the relaxed eye of a hyperope will focus onto the retina an incident beam converging to the far point.

Astigmatism is corrected by the use of a cylindrical lens that is made to neutralize the unequal curvatures of the cornea (see Sec. 7.10).

The sensitivity of the eye as a function of color is given by the visibility curve in Fig. 8.3. The ordinates represent, on a relative basis, the brightness as estimated by a normal eye of a given amount of energy throughout the visible spectrum. The ordinate value of 100 is arbitrarily assigned to the maximum. The abscissa is given in wavelength λ. The curve shows that the eye is not equally sensitive to all colors but has a maximum sensitivity at 5550 A corresponding to the yellow-green. This curve is for normal brightness. However, when the brightness is reduced to the amount that is just perceptible at each color, practically the same shaped curve is obtained, but it is shifted to the left, with the maximum occurring at about 5150 A. The curve starts at about the same position as for the normal brightness curve and has a long-wavelength cutoff at 6500 A, so that the width of the curve is somewhat reduced. This means that at low levels of brightness the sensitivity to red light is reduced and that to blue light is increased. This phenomenon is known as the *Purkinje effect*. The explanation given for such a shift is that the eye responds primarily by rod vision for low-level brightness. This is in keeping with the fact that the rods appear to be associated with night vision and that the cones are responsible for daylight (color) vision.

**8.2. Components of Telescopes and Microscopes.** The primary purpose of an optical instrument, such as a telescope or a microscope, is to bring into view for examination an object that would otherwise not be comparably observable with the unaided eye. In general there is no definite distinction between telescopes and microscopes. The telescope is generally used to magnify an object which is at a large distance away, such as a star, and is small to the naked eye by virtue of distance. On the other hand, the microscope is used to magnify objects that are too small to be seen by the eye even when placed at the near point. In either case the optical system is made up of two major elements represented schematically in block form in Fig. 8.4. The first element, known as the *objective*, forms a real

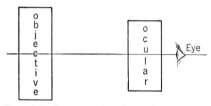

FIG. 8.4. Components of a telescope or a microscope.

image of the object. The second element, known as the *ocular*, is positioned so that it forms a final virtual magnified image of the intermediate image formed by the objective. The eye is positioned to observe this magnified image.

In the very simplest of the refracting instruments the objective and the ocular are each a single lens. For the better instruments the objective and ocular are compound elements designed to correct for aberrations; in addition the ocular is also constructed to perform other functions such as increasing the field of view or making possible measurements with the aid of cross hairs or scales which are included in the ocular. There are also usually included diaphragms, which are used to improve the character of the image.

When the objective is made of glass lenses, the instrument is designated a refracting type, such as a refracting telescope. However, if the objective is a concave mirror used to form the intermediate real image, then the instrument is of the reflecting type, such as a reflecting telescope.

We shall now undertake a study of the function of telescopes, microscopes, and their component parts.

**8.3. Magnifying Power.** The magnifying power of an optical instrument may be defined in a variety of ways, but it is usually considered with reference to its geometrical interpretation. Thus when an object of a given height is at some distance from the eye, there is formed a retinal image whose size depends not only on the height of the object but also on its distance from the eye. The ratio of the semiheight $y$ of the object to its distance from the eye defines the tangent of half the visual angle $2\theta_0$ as shown in Fig. 8.5. We now define the *magnifying power $M$* of an optical instrument as the ratio of the size of the retinal image when the object is viewed with the instrument to the size of the retinal image when

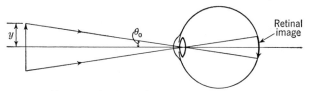

FIG. 8.5. Angle subtended by retinal image.

the object is viewed with the eye alone. Thus if $\theta_o$ is the semiangle subtended by the object when viewed with the unaided eye and $\theta_i$ is the semiangle subtended by the image when viewed with the optical instrument placed before the eye, then

$$M = \frac{\tan \theta_i}{\tan \theta_o} \tag{8.1}$$

This equation will be employed to obtain expressions for the magnifying power in terms of the constants of the optical system composing the instrument. The reader should be careful to distinguish the magnifying power from the linear lateral magnification, which was defined as a ratio of the length of the image to the length of the object.

**8.4. The Simple Microscope.** The simple microscope is nothing more than the ordinary magnifying glass or the simple magnifier. The magnifying power of such an instrument is readily obtainable with the aid of Fig. 8.6. In (a) is shown the retinal image formed by an object $PQ$ whose position is $d$ with respect to the eye, forming

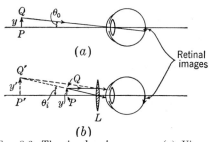

FIG. 8.6. The simple microscope. (a) Viewing the object with the unaided eye. (b) Viewing the object with the simple microscope.

the visual angle $2\theta_o$. The object cannot be placed closer than the near point of the eye so that there is a limit to the size of the retinal image formed in this manner. In (b) a simple microscope, lens $L$, is used to increase the size of the retinal image and hence the visual angle. With the lens, of short focal length, close to the eye the object $PQ$ may be placed closer to the lens than its focal length, producing a virtual image $P'Q'$ which subtends the visual angle $2\theta_i$. The object $PQ$ is now closer to the eye than in $(a)$. If the position of $PQ$ with respect to the lens is $s$, then, assuming the lens close to the eye,

$$M = \frac{y/s}{y/d} = \frac{d}{s}$$

or

$$M = d\left(\frac{1}{s'} - \frac{1}{f'}\right) \tag{8.2}$$

where $s'$ is the position of the image $P'Q'$ and $f'$ is the lens focal length. Since both $d$ and $s'$ are negative by our convention of signs, $M$ is positive, indicating an erect image. There are now two cases that may be considered for application of Eq. (8.2). When the object is positioned so that $s' = d$, then

$$M = 1 - \frac{d}{f'} \tag{8.3}$$

On the other hand, the object may be positioned so that the image falls at infinity with the eye in a relaxed state; then

$$M = -\frac{d}{f'} \tag{8.4}$$

Usually in specifying the magnifying power of optical instruments $d$ is taken to be the normal distance of distinct vision $-25$ cm; then

$$M = \frac{25}{f'} + 1, \qquad \text{for image at distance distinct vision, } -25 \text{ cm} \tag{8.5}$$

and

$$M = \frac{25}{f'}, \qquad \text{for image at infinity} \tag{8.6}$$

Note that the magnifying power is greater when the image is formed at the position of most distinct vision. However, if $f'$ is small, the small loss in magnifying power when the image is made to fall at infinity is compensated for by the fact that the vision is most comfortable. The student should have little difficulty in showing that the linear lateral magnification $s'/s$ leads to the same expression as the magnifying power for the case where the image is at the distance of most distinct vision.

The smaller the focal length of a magnifying glass, the higher the magnifying power. Since it is difficult to produce simple microscopes of very short focal length and corrected for aberration, there is a practical upper limit of about 20 for $M$. To obtain higher values of $M$, a compound microscope is employed as described in the next section.

**8.5. The Compound Microscope.** In Fig. 8.7 is shown the optical system of a compound microscope. In accordance with the schematic of Fig. 8.4, the objective with focal points $F_o$ and $F'_o$ is depicted by the lens

$L_o$, and the ocular with focal lengths $F_e$ and $F'_e$ is represented by the lens $L_e$ known as the *eyepiece*. The object $PQ$ is placed very close to $F_0$ so that an initial magnified image $P'_1Q'_1$ is produced. The eyepiece is positioned as a simple magnifier with respect to $P'_1Q'_1$, thus forming the enlarged final virtual image $P'Q'$. The ray construction, for simplicity of presentation, has been made for thin lenses. Actually the construction should be made using the two principal planes for the objective and the two principal planes for the ocular. The magnifying power of the microscope is given by the product of the magnifying powers of the objective and the

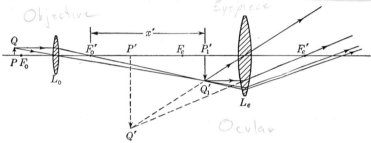

FIG. 8.7. The compound microscope.

ocular. The magnifying power of the objective $M_o$ is simply the magnification between $PQ$ and $P'_1Q'_1$ and given by Eq. (4.14) as $M_o = -x'/f'_o$, where $f'_o$ is the focal length of the objective. The magnifying power of the eyepiece $M_e$ is given by Eq. (8.5) or (8.6). Thus for the microscope,

$$M = M_o M_e = -\frac{x'}{f'_o}\left(\frac{25}{f'_e} + 1\right), \qquad \text{for image at distance of distinct vision, } -25 \text{ cm} \qquad (8.7)$$

and

$$M = -\frac{x'}{f'_o}\frac{25}{f'_e}, \qquad \text{for image at infinity} \qquad (8.8)$$

where $f'_e$ is the focal length of the eyepiece. For most comfortable vision the intermediate image falls very close to the first focal point $F_e$ of the eyepiece so that the final image is very distant. Furthermore, in commercial microscopes, the distance from $F'_o$ to $F_e$ is standardized to a value of 18 cm, thus making it more practical to correct the objective for aberrations for only a single image distance. This distance from the second focal point of the objective to the first focal point of the ocular is known as the *optical tube length* and must not be confused with the *mechanical tube length*, which is the distance from the lower end to the upper end of the microscope tube. We now have, for a microscope with a standardized optical tube length of 18 cm,

$$M = -\frac{18}{f'_o}\frac{25}{f'_e} \qquad (8.9)$$

Since $M$ in Eqs. (8.8) and (8.9) is negative, the final image is inverted with respect to the object. For a large magnification both the objective and ocular should be of small focal length.

**8.6. Microscope Objectives and Resolving Power.** The microscope is usually provided with several objectives and several eyepieces or oculars. We shall consider the ocular types in a later section. The objective is usually an achromatic combination correcting for two colors for spherical aberration, for coma, and for other aberrations. To bring out the very finest detail, an apochromatic objective, achromatized quite perfectly for three colors and corrected for spherical aberration for two colors, is employed, thus permitting a higher magnification. An objective is designated by several numbers, one of which is its focal length usually stated in millimeters. Figure 8.8 shows the components of two typical microscope objectives, (*a*) an achromat of 16 mm focal length, and (*b*) an apochromat of 2 mm focal length. Since the objective is usually corrected for one working distance, it can be designed to satisfy optimum conditions. The apochromat eliminates practically all color fringe and is used also in the making of photographs with a microscope, or, as the process is known, in *photomicrography.*

(*a*)                    (*b*)

Fig. 8.8. Microscope objectives. (*a*) Achromatic 16 mm. (*b*) Apochromatic 2 mm. The lenses are made of different kinds of crown and flint components.

It is found that additional detail is obtained only up to a certain limiting magnifying power; a greater magnification will show no more detail, the image thereafter becoming coarser or fuzzier. This limitation in bringing out the fine structure of an object is inherent in one of the most important properties of an optical instrument, known as *resolving power.* We shall study the subject of resolving power in greater detail in Chap. 14, but we shall here present those facts which are pertinent to an understanding of the microscope. In the chapter on Diffraction it is shown that a perfect optical system cannot give rise to a point image of a point object but instead always gives rise to a diffraction disk made up of a system of concentric light and dark rings. For two point sources there are two such diffraction disks. As the object points are made to approach each other, their diffraction disks get closer until they start to overlap. When the disks overlap sufficiently, they are no longer separately distinguishable. For the disks to be resolved, their diffraction patterns must be separated by a distance at least equal to the radius of the central diffraction ring. If they are any closer, the two points appear as one and increasing the magnification does not increase the ability of the instrument to resolve the two points since both the separation and size of the disks increase at the same rate. However, if the diameter of the objective is increased, the sizes of the diffraction disks are decreased so that they can be closer together and still be seen as separated.

As shown in Sec. 14.4, the separation $z$ of two object points that can just be resolved by a lens with a circular outline in monochromatic light of wavelength $\lambda$ is

$$z = \frac{0.61\lambda}{n \sin u} \tag{8.10}$$

where $n$ is the index of refraction in the object space and $u$ is half the angle formed by the extreme rays from the axial point through the object plane, i.e., the angle subtended at $P$ by the rim of the objective in Fig. 8.7. The result shown in Eq. (8.10) is based on the assumption that the objects are self-luminous. The object points seen with a microscope, however, are not self-luminous and are always illuminated by light from an external source, which is focused on the object by means of an optical system known as a condenser. Under these conditions, Abbe showed that the finest detail that can be resolved by the objective of a microscope, when the value of $n \sin u$ for the illuminating condenser is the same as that for the objective, is

$$z = \frac{\lambda}{2n \sin u} \tag{8.11}$$

The quantity $n \sin u$ is called the *numerical aperture* (N.A.) so that the smallest distance between two points in the object that can be resolved by the objective of a microscope is

$$z = \frac{\lambda}{2\text{N.A.}} \tag{8.12}$$

When the illuminating condenser (substage) is not employed, the resolving power of the microscope is half as much as that given by Eq. (8.12). The numerical aperture is a true measure of the resolving power of the objective; the larger the numerical aperture, the finer can be the structure of a microscope object and still be resolved. When the object is in air, the numerical aperture cannot be greater than unity and ranges in practice from values as low as 0.08 to as high as 0.95. By using an oil-immersion microscope, as discussed in Sec. 7.8, the numerical aperture is increased in practice to higher values. The apochromat of Fig. 8.8b is of the oil-immersion type. We can now calculate the limiting useful magnifying power obtainable with the compound microscope for visible light. Taking the largest practical value obtainable for numerical aperture as 1.60, then for $\lambda = 5550 \times 10^{-8}$ cm, $z = 1.73 \times 10^{-5}$ cm. The resolving power of the eye at this wavelength is 1.16 min of arc, which, at the distance of distinct vision 25 cm, subtends a length of

$$(1.16 \times 25)/(60 \times 57.3) = 8.4 \times 10^{-3} \text{ cm}$$

Therefore, if the full resolving power of the objective is to be realized, the magnifying power is $(8.4 \times 10^{-3})/(1.73 \times 10^{-5}) = 485$. Increasing the magnification beyond this will bring out no more detail, and for a given objective there is a limiting eyepiece magnification that will just be sufficient to make visible the detail produced by the objective. The resolving power may be increased further by using light of lower wavelength in the violet and ultraviolet region of the spectrum. Since ordinary glass does not and quartz does transmit this low-wavelength radiation, the optical elements are usually made of quartz. Of course it is possible to obtain higher microscope magnifications, of the order of 1000, but this is done at the expense of other features, as explained in the next section.

Microscope objectives have marked upon them their equivalent focal length (or the initial magnification) and their numerical-aperture number. Sometimes the mechanical tube length and the cover-glass thickness for which the objective is corrected are stated. If the focal length and numerical aperture are not marked, they may easily be determined experimentally. The microscope usually has a draw tube which may be set for two different values. At each draw-tube setting the magnification of a stage micrometer (a slide containing a very small engraved scale and placed on the micrometer stage) is determined with a micrometer eyepiece (see Sec. 8.15). Then the absolute values of the magnifying powers corresponding to the draw-tube settings 1 and 2 are $M_{o1} = x'_1/f'_o$ and $M_{o2} = x'_2/f'_o$. Therefore $f'_o = (x'_2 - x'_1)/(M_{o2} - M_{o1})$, where $x'_2 - x'_1$ represents the difference between the draw-tube extensions. This determines the equivalent focal length, which may now be used to obtain $x'_1$, and from this can be obtained the position of the second focal point of the objective by observing the location of the micrometer eyepiece. For dry objectives the numerical aperture may be determined by removing the eyepiece and orienting the microscope tube horizontally. Then, at a distance of about ½ m from the incident side of the objective, two small light bulbs are set up and separated in a direction transverse to the principal axis. By sighting down the microscope tube, the positions of the light bulbs, when their images are on the point of disappearing at diametrically opposite edges of the objective, may be determined. If lines from these positions of the lights are drawn to the focal point of the objective, the angle formed at the focal point is $2u$. For oil-immersion objectives one uses an Abbe apertometer to determine the numerical aperture.

**8.7. Normal Magnifying Power and Entrance and Exit Pupils.** With the magnifying power and resolving power of an instrument are intimately related the light-gathering power and the field of view. For instance, as shown in Chap. 9, the illumination in the image is directly proportional to the square of the numerical aperture and inversely pro-

portional to the square of the lateral magnification.   Thus by increasing
the magnifying power the illumination is decreased for a given numerical
aperture.   The relationship to the field of view is brought out by Fig. 8.9,
which is a reproduction of Fig. 8.7 using the entire object $PQ$ and representing the objective and eyepiece by vertical planes.   The objective is
the aperture stop of the system, and since there are no lenses to the left
of $L_o$, it also serves as the entrance pupil $E_1E_2$.   By following the rays
through the system it is seen that $E'_1E'_2$ is the exit pupil, which of course
is conjugate to $E_1E_2$.   Therefore the exit pupil is the image of the objective formed by the eyepiece.   The eye must be placed at the exit pupil,

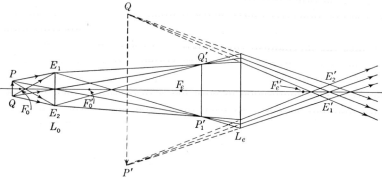

FIG. 8.9.  Ray diagram for compound microscope showing the entrance pupil $E_1E_2$ and exit
pupil $E'_1E'_2$.

or the eye ring as it is sometimes called, in order to observe the largest
field of view; when the eye is placed either to the left or to the right of
$E'_1E'_2$, the outer bundle of rays will not be observable.   The design of
microscopes is such that the exit pupil is of the order of 1 cm or so from
the emergent side of the eyepiece so that it is convenient to place the eye
there.   Now all the light flux that enters the entrance pupil emerges from
the exit pupil and will fall upon the retina if the entrance pupil of the eye
is at least as large as the exit pupil of the instrument.   When the magnifying power of an instrument is such that its exit pupil coincides in
diameter and position with the entrance pupil of the eye, it is called the
*normal magnifying power*.   For this magnifying power the inherent resolving power of the instrument is realized, and the brightness of the object is
equal to what it would be if the object were observed with the unaided
eye (neglecting reflection and absorption losses).   When the magnifying
power is greater than normal, the diameter of the exit pupil of the microscope is decreased below the diameter of the entrance pupil of the eye,
with the result that the illumination of the retinal image is decreased.
Somewhat larger magnifying powers than normal are ordinarily used in
microscopes, and the loss of light is compensated for by increasing the

external illumination. This results in better seeing conditions. When the magnifying power of the microscope is less than normal, the exit pupil is greater than the entrance pupil of the eye and all the light passing through the instrument cannot enter the eye. Thus in general the optimum condition for a microscope with reference to its magnifying power, resolving power, brightness of retinal image, and field of view obtains when the exit pupil of the instrument is made to coincide in position and size with the entrance pupil of the eye.

No discussion of a microscope would be complete without mention of depth of field, depth of focus, and working distance. The *depth of field* is the magnitude of the change in object distance that can be produced

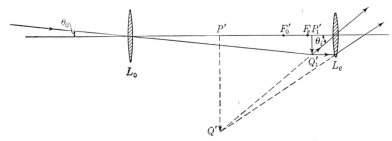

FIG. 8.10. Astronomical refracting telescope.

without causing an intolerable blurring of the image. The *depth of focus* is the magnitude of the change in the position of the plane on which the image is received without causing an intolerable lack of sharpness in focus. The *working distance* is the distance between the objective and the microscope cover glass when the objective is in focus. The depth of field varies inversely as the numerical aperture so that if one is interested primarily in a large depth of focus, it may be obtained at the expense of resolving power. The working distance increases as the numerical aperture decreases and as the magnifying power decreases.

**8.8. Telescopes.** Telescopes are employed to form an image at infinity of an object which is at an infinite distance. They may also be employed to form an image at a finite distance of an object which is at a finite distance. Telescopes may be divided into refracting telescopes, which employ a glass refractor as the objective, and into reflecting telescopes, which employ a mirror as the telescope objective. These may further be divided into astronomical telescopes, in which the final image is inverted with respect to the object, and into terrestrial telescopes, in which the final image is erect.

**8.9. The Astronomical Refracting Telescope.** The characteristics of a telescopic system can be ascertained from the astronomical refracting type shown in Fig. 8.10. The lens $L_o$ represents the objective whose second focal point is $F'_o$, and the lens $L_e$ represents the eyepiece whose first focal point is $F_e$. In actual practice the thin-lens objective is replaced by a corrected compound system, and the eyepiece is in general replaced by an ocular. The ray shown incident on the objective is from the top $Q$ of a distant object $PQ$ (not shown). The objective forms the intermediate image $P'_1Q'_1$, which acts as a real object for the eyepiece that forms the final magnified inverted virtual image $P'Q'$. For a distant object the angle $\theta_o$, subtended at the objective, is essentially the same as would be subtended at the unaided eye, and the angle $\theta_i$ is very nearly that subtended at the eye placed near the eyepiece. If the position of $P'_1Q'_1$ is $s'_1$ with respect to the objective and $s_2$ with respect to the eyepiece, then the magnifying power is

$$M = \frac{\tan \theta_i}{\tan \theta_o} = \frac{P'_1Q'_1/s_2}{P'_1Q'_1/s'_1}$$

$$M = \frac{s'_1}{s_2} \tag{8.13}$$

As is the more usual case, the object is at an infinite distance, and the telescope is adjusted so that the final image is thrown out to infinity. Then $s'_1 = f'_o$, and $s_2 = -f'_e$, so that

$$M = -\frac{f'_o}{f'_e} \tag{8.14}$$

Since $M$ is negative, the final image is inverted with respect to the object. It is seen that a long-focal-length objective and a short-focal-length eyepiece are essential to producing a large magnifying power.

The objective is ordinarily the aperture stop of the telescope so that it also functions as the entrance pupil. The exit pupil is the image of the entrance pupil formed by the lenses to the right of it; hence the exit pupil is the image of the objective formed by the eyepiece. Since the objective is relatively distant from the eyepiece whose focal length is short, the exit pupil falls near the second focal point of the eyepiece. Thus for a telescope that images at infinity an infinitely distant object the magnifying power is

$$M = \frac{D}{D'} \tag{8.15}$$

where $D$ and $D'$ are the diameters of the entrance and exit pupils, respectively. Equation (8.15) provides a conveniently rapid method of measuring the magnifying power of a telescope. By focusing the telescope for parallel rays, $D'$ may be observed; and $D$ is the diameter of the objective. The objective is a compound lens corrected for aberrations.

As discussed in the sections on the microscope, the useful magnifying power of a telescope is limited by its resolving power. For visual use, as there explained, the most desirable situation is when the exit pupil of the telescope coincides in position and size with the entrance pupil of the eye. Under these conditions the inherent resolving power of the telescope is completely realized, full illumination of the retinal image is obtained since the pupil of the eye is filled with light, and the greatest field of view is achieved. When $M$ is increased beyond the normal magnifying power, $D'$ is proportionately decreased so that the diameter of the exit pupil is smaller than that of the entrance pupil of the eye, resulting in a decrease in the illumination of the retinal image and a decrease in the field of view. As with the microscope it is practical to employ a somewhat larger magnifying power to increase the ease of observation at the expense of some loss in illumination and field of view.

The limiting angle of resolution $\alpha$ subtended at the objective by two object points whose position is $s$ relative to the objective can be obtained from Eq. (8.10). Thus

$$\alpha = \frac{z}{s} = \frac{0.61\lambda}{sn \sin u}$$

Since $s$ is very large in comparison with the radius of the entrance pupil, $\sin u \doteq D/2s$; and with $n = 1$,

$$\alpha = \frac{1.22\lambda}{D} \tag{8.16}$$

which shows that the resolving power increases as the diameter of the objective increases.

A telescope may be used to view an extended object such as the moon, or it may be used to view point objects such as the stars. When it is used to view an extended object and the diameter of the objective is large enough so that the exit pupil is equal in position and size to the entrance pupil of the eye, then all the light gathered by the objective enters the pupil of the eye. Under these conditions the amount of light entering the eye is $M^2$ times that entering the unaided eye where $M$ is the normal magnifying power. However, this light falls on an image whose area is $M^2$ times as large; the brightness of the image is then the same as that of the source. With an objective diameter larger than that corresponding to the normal magnifying power there is no gain in image brightness. On the other hand, if the exit pupil of the telescope is smaller than the entrance pupil of the eye, the brightness of the image is less than the natural brightness of the object. Hence for extended objects the brightness of the image can never appear greater than the object appears to the unaided eye. When the telescope is used to view a point source, the image is brighter than when the unaided eye views the object since the objective of the telescope, because of its greater diameter, has a larger light-gathering power than the pupil of the eye.

**8.10. The Terrestrial Refracting Telescope.** One way of converting an astronomical telescope into one which forms an upright image of the object being viewed is by inserting a lens system known as an *erector* between the objective and the ocular. The function of an erector is illustrated by the simple single lens shown in Fig. 8.11; however, lens combinations corrected for aberration are more often employed as telescope erectors than are single lenses. $I_1$ represents the real inverted image formed by the objective. The lens forms the real erect image $I_2$, which

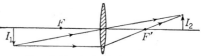

FIG. 8.11. A single-lens erector.

is then magnified by the eyepiece or ocular in the usual manner. The distance between $I_1$ and $I_2$ is either equal to or greater than four times the focal length of the lens according as there is not or there is introduced magnification between $I_1$ and $I_2$. Hence the disadvantage of such an erector is that it requires the telescope tube to be rather long.

Galileo devised a terrestrial telescope in which the inverted image formed by the objective is reinverted by the use of a diverging lens as

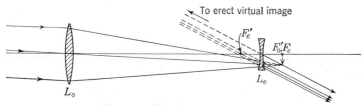

FIG. 8.12. The Galilean telescope.

the eyepiece. The Galilean telescope, or opera glass as it is commonly known, is shown in Fig. 8.12, which is drawn to illustrate the formation of an image at infinity of an infinitely distant object. Rays from the top of the object are shown incident on the objective $L_o$, which forms the real inverted image at the second focal point $F'_o$ in the absence of the eyepiece $L_e$. With the eyepiece placed so that its first focal point $F_e$ coincides with $F'_o$ the rays from the objective are intercepted, forming an image at infinity. As can be seen from the figure, the magnifying power is again given by Eq. (8.14), $M = -f'_o/f'_e$, which is positive, indicating an erect image. This telescope has the advantage of being considerably shorter. However, it has the disadvantage that the exit pupil falls to the left of the eyepiece. With the objective as the aperture stop and entrance pupil, the exit pupil falls near $F'_e$. Since it is not possible to place the eye at the exit pupil, the field of view is reduced. The best one can do here is to place the eye very close to the eyepiece. The

Galilean telescope is limited to the use of low powers, about 2 or 3.   We leave it as an exercise to show that the field of view depends on the relative aperture of the objective (see Prob. 8.20).

The prism binocular is a terrestrial telescope that embodies the features of having a large field of view, of having a small length, and of permitting magnifying powers as high as 10.   The image is both inverted and reversed from right to left by means of two Porro prisms combined as shown in Fig. 1.15 and positioned between objective and ocular.   Since the light rays traverse the distance between the two right-angle prisms three times, it is possible to shorten the telescope by separating the prisms.   The prisms are arranged so that the separation of the objectives is greater than that of the oculars.   The stereoscopic effect, *i.e.*, the depth perception, is thus increased.   In binocular vision the retinal images from both eyes are somewhat dissimilar, owing to the slightly different angle at which each eye sights, making it possible for the brain to perceive an image in three dimensions, or to determine depth.   The distance beyond which no relief is obtained is called the *radius of stereoscopic vision*.   The radius of stereoscopic vision is proportional to the ratio of the distance between the entrance pupils of the binoculars to the interpupillary distance (see Prob. 8.24).   Thus by increasing the separation between the binocular objectives the stereoscopic radius is increased.   Of course an increase in the magnifying power of the binocular telescope also proportionately increases the radius of stereoscopic vision.

**8.11. The Reflecting Telescope.**   A reflecting telescope operates on the same principle as a refracting astronomical telescope.   In the reflecting telescope a large concave mirror is employed to gather the light and form the real inverted image.   The different methods of observing this image have given rise to the types of so-called "reflecting" telescopes shown in Fig. 8.13.   In all diagrams $T$ represents the telescope tube, $M$ the light-gathering mirror, and $L$ the eye lens or ocular.

In the Herschel telescope (*a*), the mirror axis is inclined to the incoming parallel rays, thus forming the real image $I$ to one side of the telescope tube axis.   In this way, when the image is observed with the eyepiece, the observer's head obstructs a minimum amount of incoming light. Obviously this kind of mounting is not suitable for small telescopes.

In the Newtonian mounting (*b*), the light is reflected to one side by a reflecting prism.   The mirror axis is parallel to the axis of the telescope tube.

In (*c*) is shown the Gregorian mounting, which consists of a concave light-gathering mirror $M$ and a smaller concave mirror $m$.   The mirrors face each other and are separated by a distance somewhat greater than the sum of their focal lengths so that the image $I_1$ formed by $M$ falls between the focal point and center of curvature of $m$, which forms the real image $I_2$. This image is examined by the eyepiece $L$ through a circular aperture which has been cut in $M$. The effective focal length of this telescope is very much increased. The focus $I_1$ is known as the *prime focus*.

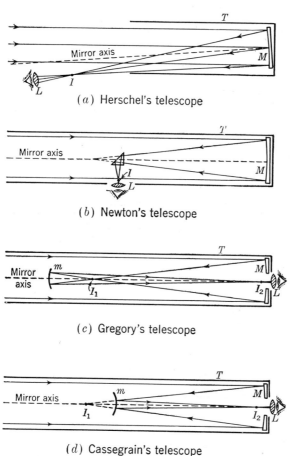

( *a* ) Herschel's telescope

( *b* ) Newton's telescope

( *c* ) Gregory's telescope

( *d* ) Cassegrain's telescope

Fig. 8.13. Reflecting telescopes.

The Cassegrainian telescope shown in (*d*) is similar to the Gregorian type but with a convex hyperboloidal mirror for $m$ rather than a concave mirror. The image $I_1$ falling between the position of the focal point and pole of $m$ acts as a virtual object so that a real image is formed at $I_2$. This telescope is advantageous in that it is shorter than the Gregorian type, and the spherical aberrations of both mirrors, being in opposite directions, tend to neutralize each other.

Reflecting telescopes are inherently free from chromatic aberration, and spherical aberration is entirely eliminated on the axis by making the light-gathering mirror a paraboloid of revolution. The central part of the field is then very clear, but the presence of coma and astigmatism causes the field to be less sharp even at short distances from the center. The light-gathering power of a reflecting telescope can be made very much larger than for a refracting telescope since mirrors can more easily be made of large diameter than can lenses. Since the light does not have to pass through a reflector, the problem of forming a large annealed glass disk to be used for reflection purposes is less critical than if it were to be employed for refraction. Nevertheless the difficulties encountered in forming very large diameter reflectors are also of painstaking magnitude.

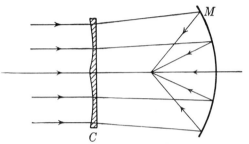

FIG. 8.14. The Schmidt reflector.

The parabolized glass surface is formed into a mirror by evaporating a deposit of aluminum onto its concave surface in a high vacuum. In this way the metal is prevented from tarnishing since the oxide formed in the air acts as a protective transparent coating. The metal aluminum also has the property of high reflectance into the ultraviolet region of the spectrum.

If the light-gathering mirror is spherical, it has the advantage of being free from the blurring aberration coma. However, it suffers from spherical aberration, for which it may be corrected by utilizing the Schmidt arrangement shown in Fig. 8.14. The correction is effected by placing a diverging correcting refraction plate $C$ at the center of curvature of the reflecting mirror $M$. The correction plate is so shaped that it corrects for spherical aberration for each zone of the mirror. Astigmatism is also thus eliminated. This arrangement makes possible a sharp focus over a much larger area as compared with that obtainable from large paraboloidal reflecting telescopes. Of course the Schmidt principle may be used with the Cassegrainian and other mountings shown in Fig. 8.13.

**8.12. The 200-in. Telescope.** The largest astronomical telescope in the world is the 200-in. Hale telescope atop Mount Palomar in southern California. As with the other large modern telescopes, the instrument is in reality a 200-in. camera since it is primarily used for photographic observations. A photographic plate possesses the property of building up an image through prolonged exposure so that stars which are far beyond eye vision can be recorded even if they have a high degree of faintness.

The light-gathering mirror of the Mount Palomar telescope is a disk of pyrex glass whose diameter is 200 in. The concave surface has a few molecular layers of an aluminum reflecting coating, and the reflecting surface is paraboloidal to an accuracy of about one-millionth of an inch. An error of a few millionths of an inch would cause an intolerable amount of image distortion. The glass mirror, which has a hole cut from its center, for use in a Cassegrainian mounting, weighs about 15 tons. This mirror is supported in a massive steel structure known as the camera body, which also contains the photographic plate. The camera body is itself supported by a very large steel cradle so that the camera may be directed to different points of the sky. Although the mirror, body, and cradle weigh over 500 tons, the mechanism as a whole operates with clockwork precision and delicacy. The camera is

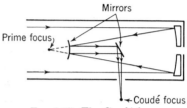

FIG. 8.15. The Coudé focus.

kept pointed at a given star by precision-controlled adjustments that compensate for the earth's rotation. The prime focus of the telescope is 666 in., resulting in an $f$ number equal to $f/3.33$. It is at this focus that most direct photography on stars is done. The focal length may be increased to the value 3200 in. by using the Cassegrainian mounting, resulting in an $f$ number equal to $f/16$. For much higher magnifications the Coudé focus shown in Fig. 8.15 may be used. The corresponding focal length is 6000 in., and the relative aperture is $\frac{1}{30}$.

As compared with the 100-in. camera at Mount Wilson, the 200-in. camera has twice the diameter, hence four times the area, and so four times the light-gathering power. Therefore the 200-in. camera is capable of photographing faint stars twice as distant from the earth, thus increasing the observable space by eight times. The 200-in. camera can reach out to a distance of 1 billion light-years. A light-year is the distance light travels in 1 year, or 5870 billion miles.

Since the 200-in. camera is unable to photograph, into well-defined focus, areas that are greater than a fraction of a degree in angular diameter, a 48-in. Schmidt camera is used as a scout to photograph much larger areas. The 48-in. Schmidt camera reaches out only about 300 million light-years.

**8.13. Components of an Ocular.** We have seen that the prime function of an eyepiece or ocular is to enlarge or magnify the real image formed by the objective of the optical instrument. The single lens eyepiece performs this function exclusively, and we have used it in our diagrams to illustrate this function.  The more general form of eyepiece, known as the ocular, is composed usually of two lens components illustrated in Fig. 8.16.  The three rays labeled 1, 2, and 3 represent those from the top of an object and passing through the top of the image *I* as formed by the objective (not shown).  If the lens marked *FL* were absent, the rays marked 1 and 2 would miss the eye lens *EL* completely, with a consequent reduction in the field of view.  By intercepting another lens *FL* the rays from the outer part of the field are collected and refracted into the eye lens, thus increasing the field of view.  The ocular thus consists of two components; the one nearest the eye is designated as the *eye lens*, whose principal function is to act as a magnifier and enlarge the image formed by objective, and the component farther from the eye is called the *field lens*, whose principal function is to improve the field of view.  Obviously the best location for the field lens is in the plane of

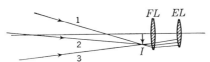

FIG. 8.16.  The ocular.  *FL* is the field lens, and *EL* is the eye lens.

the real image since there it would have no effect on the magnification and would function solely to improve the field of view.  If this were done, however, any dust particles or scratches present on the field lens would be magnified into view.

The two most widely used oculars are the Huygens type and the Ramsden type.  These are considered in the following section.

**8.14. The Huygens and Ramsden Oculars.**  In Fig. 8.17a is shown the Huygens ocular, which consists of two plano-convex crown lenses disposed as shown and separated by a distance equal to half the sum of the individual lens focal lengths.  In the figure we have drawn the Huygens ocular whose field lens has a focal length $3f'$ and whose eye lens has a focal length $f'$.  (Ratios of focal lengths other than 3 may also be employed.)  The ocular is positioned so that the image *I* formed by the objective (not shown) falls in the first focal plane of the ocular, which then directs the rays as a parallel beam through the exit pupil into the eye.  The image *I* may be considered as a virtual object of the field lens, which forms a diminished real image *I'* which is at the first focal point of the eye lens.  In the case shown *I'* is midway between the lenses, and *I* is midway between *I'* and the eye lens.  With the lenses separated by half the sum of the focal lengths the system, as we have seen in Sec. 7.14, is corrected for lateral chromatic aberration.  However, the ocular does possess longitudinal aberration.  Furthermore, if cross hairs or a scale is to be used, it must be placed in the plane of the real image *I'* and that involves some mechanical difficulties.  Also in this case, the eye lens alone magnifies the scale so that there would be present distortion and other aberrations since the eye lens alone is not corrected. The ocular suffers from curvature of the field and must therefore be used with scales that are not very long. Huygenian oculars containing short scales placed at the center of the field are used with microscopes. A field stop should be placed at the position occupied by $I'$ to bring into effect a sharply defined final image.

The Ramsden ocular shown in Fig. 8.17$b$ is composed of two plano-convex crown lenses each of focal length $f'$. In order to correct for lateral

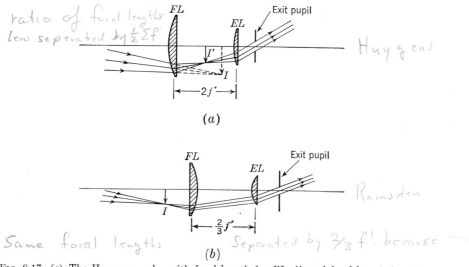

*ratio of focal lengths*
*lens seperated by $\frac{1}{2}\cdot\frac{2}{3}f'$*

*Huygens*

(*a*)

*Same focal lengths*

*Ramsden*

*Seperated by $\frac{2}{3}f'$ because*

(*b*)

FIG. 8.17. (*a*) The Huygens ocular with focal length for *EL*, $f'$, and focal length for *FL*, $3f'$. (*b*) The Ramsden ocular. The focal length of either lens is $f'$.

chromatism, they must be separated by a distance equal to $f'$. This, however, would position the field lens in the plane of the real image $I$ formed by the objective, and as we have seen, such an arrangement would bring into view dust particles and scratches on the field lens. By moving the field lens somewhat toward the eye lens the ocular does not correct fully for lateral chromatic aberration, but it has the advantage of having the real image formed by the objective in front of the field lens. The usual practice is to separate the lenses by a distance equal to $\frac{2}{3}f'$ as shown. The ocular is then positioned so that $I$ falls at its first focal plane. The field lens may be considered to form an image of $I$ at the first focal plane of the eye lens so that parallel rays pass through the exit pupil and then the eye. A simple application of the lens equation shows that $I$ is distant $f''/4$ in front of the field lens. The field stop and cross hairs or scale must be positioned in the plane of the real image $I$. This *Ramsden,* type of ocular is better adapted for use with cross hairs or scales since it possesses a much flatter field. The lateral chromatism is greater for the

Ramsden than for the Huygens ocular, but the longitudinal chromatic aberration is only about half as great as in the Huygens ocular.

The field of view for either ocular may be made as high as 50°. The Ramsden ocular is called a *positive ocular*, while the Huygenian type is called a *negative ocular*. Since a Ramsden ocular acts truly as a magnifier, it is a simple matter to distinguish it from the Huygenian ocular in practice. To correct the Ramsden ocular further for chromatic aberration, the eye lens is made in the form of an achromatic doublet, and the ocular is then called a *Kellner*, or *achromatized Ramsden*, *ocular*.

By positioning a thin plate of glass between the field lens and the eye lens of a Ramsden ocular and inclining it at 45° with the principal axis the system is known as a *Gauss ocular*. Light directed onto the glass plate through an aperture in the side of the ocular is reflected down its axis, illuminating the cross hairs in its path. A Gauss ocular is most useful in the laboratory when it is desired to align the different components of a spectrometer. For instance, when used with a telescope which is being focused for parallel light, a plane reflecting surface may be placed before the objective. The reflected image of the cross hairs is then brought into view by adjustment of the draw tube in which the Gauss ocular is contained. When the reflected image of the cross hairs is in the same plane of the cross hairs, as tested by the absence of parallax, the telescope is focused for parallel rays.

**8.15. The Micrometer Ocular.** For the precise measurement of small distances the micrometer eyepiece or ocular is employed. The type known as the *filar micrometer eyepiece* is illustrated in Fig. 8.18. In the field of view are seen a horizontal fixed cross hair, a vertical fixed cross hair $C_1$, and a pair of vertical movable cross hairs $C_2$ (about 0.05 mm apart), all of which are in the focal plane of the ocular. The movable

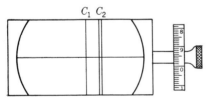

FIG. 8.18. The micrometer ocular.

cross hairs are driven perpendicular to the ocular axis by the fine micrometer screw. At the bottom of the field of view is a saw-toothed index (not shown) to indicate the whole revolutions of the micrometer head. The ocular is generally used with the microscope and has a standard sleeve to fit into the microscope tube. In use the cross hairs are first brought into focus by sliding the ocular; then the object is brought into focus by moving the microscope tube. When there is no parallax between the image and the cross hairs, the readings of a length may be taken. The micrometer ocular must always be calibrated by comparison with a standard scale since the micrometer constant changes with the change of focal length. Once the micrometer microscope is focused for measurement, it should be left that way for the entire series of measurements.

**8.16. The Spectrometer.** In this section we shall describe one of the most important of optical instruments. In Sec. 1.8 it was pointed out how the index of refraction of a prism may be determined by placing the prism on a spectrometer table and measuring the prism angle and the angle of minimum deviation. The spectrometer is useful also in studying spectra and making observations on the phenomena of interference, diffraction, and polarization, all of which we shall study in subsequent

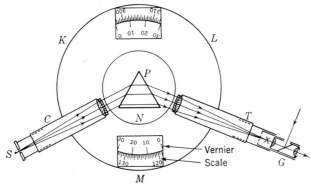

FIG. 8.19. The spectrometer.

chapters. From a quantitative point of view its function is to measure angles. A spectrometer (Fig. 8.19) consists essentially of a collimator $C$, a telescope $T$, a turntable $KLM$ to which the diametrically positioned verniers, shown through the viewing windows, are attached, a platform $N$, and a divided circular scale marked off in degrees and also shown through the viewing windows.

The collimator is a tube at one end of which is a slit $S$ perpendicular to the plane of the figure and at the other end of which is a well-constructed achromatic lens. The width of the slit and its position relative to the collimator lens are independently adjustable. When the slit is illuminated and positioned at the first focal point of the collimator lens, the light rays emerging from the collimator are parallel. If a prism $P$ is positioned on the table, the beam of light is refracted into the telescope achromatic objective in whose second focal plane are mounted the cross hairs shown. The telescope is shown equipped with a Gauss ocular $G$ whose distance, and that of the cross hairs, from the objective may be varied by mechanical adjustments such as a rack and pinion. In this way the telescope may be set for parallel rays. In some instruments the collimator and telescope objectives are mounted in tubes that can slide within $C$ and $T$, respectively. The rays shown in the figure are for a monochromatic beam.   The ocular magnifies the real image of the slit formed in its focal plane.   For a polychromatic beam the observer sees an image of the slit corresponding to each component color or wavelength.

The telescope and turntable are mounted so that they can be independently rotated about a common axis that passes through the center of the divided circle and is normal to the plane of the figure.   The collimator is generally fixed to the spectrometer framework so that its optical axis passes through this same center, and in some instruments it, too, is free to rotate about this common axis.   The circular scale is attached to the telescope so that a relative angular displacement between turntable and telescope is indicated by the verniers.   The platform, on which a prism or other object may be placed, is adjustable for height and may be either rotated independently of the turntable or rigidly attached to the turntable.   The platform is provided with leveling screws, and the collimator and telescope units are provided with leveling, fine-adjustment, and locking screws.   In making a reading the average of both verniers should be used to compensate for any slight off-centering that may be present in the divided circular scale.

We shall not go into a detailed account of the adjustments of a spectrometer before it can be put to use, since the procedures are given in standard laboratory manuals and it is assumed that such procedure will be covered by the student in the laboratory course.   However, it should be realized that complete adjustment of a spectrometer entails (1) focusing the telescope for parallel light, (2) focusing the collimator for parallel light, (3) adjusting the collimator and telescope so that their principal axes are coincident and perpendicular to the axis of rotation, and (4) causing the refracting edge of the prism, if one is employed, to be parallel to the axis of rotation.   The author has found that the student gains a great deal if, at this point, he figures out a procedure for each one of these adjustments and then checks these with those given in laboratory manuals.

In using Eq. (1.16) to measure the refractive index of a prism, the angle of the prism may be measured by using the Gauss ocular and observing two readings: first, one of the prism faces forming the angle is set perpendicular to the telescope axis and the vernier reading noted; then either the turntable or the telescope is rotated into position to enable the other prism face to be set perpendicular to the telescope axis and the vernier reading noted.   The angle of the prism is then given by the difference between 180° and the angle turned through as determined from the two readings.   If the spectrometer is not equipped with a Gauss ocular, the angle of the prism may be determined by positioning the prism on the platform so that part of the light from the collimator bathes one of the faces and the remaining light bathes the other of the faces forming the refracting angle. The telescope is turned to receive the light reflected from one of the faces, and the cross hairs are positioned on the faint image of the slit that can be seen. The vernier reading is taken, and the telescope is rotated so that the image of the slit is obtained by reflection from the other face. Again the vernier reading is recorded. The angle of the prism is half the angle through which the telescope has been turned, the latter being ascertained from the recorded vernier readings. The student should draw a figure and prove this to himself.

The angle of minimum deviation may be obtained by setting the cross hairs on the image of the slit when the prism is set for minimum deviation as shown in Fig. 8.19, and recording the reading. Then the prism is removed, and the telescope is rotated into position to sight the undeviated beam. The angle through which the telescope has been rotated is the angle of minimum deviation. For a more precise determination and, at the same time, to avoid removing the prism, the method illustrated in Fig. 8.20 may be used. With the prism in some minimum-deviation position I, as in Fig. 8.19, the telescope is set to receive the emergent beam; call this reading $R_1$. Now rotate the turntable, say clockwise,

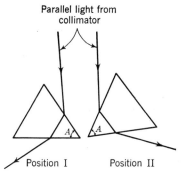

Parallel light from collimator

Position I    Position II

FIG. 8.20. Determination of angle of minimum deviation.

until the prism is in the minimum-deviation position II. The telescope is rotated counterclockwise and again set to receive the emergent beam; call this reading $R_2$. Then it can be shown that the angle through which the turntable rotates is $180 - \delta_m$, where $\delta_m$ is the angle of minimum deviation; $\delta_m = R_2 - R_1 - 180$ when the vernier zero has effectively not crossed the 360° scale mark, and $\delta_m = R_2 - R_1 + 180$ when the vernier zero has effectively crossed the 360° mark. It is to be noted that when the zero of the vernier crosses the 360° scale mark during a rotation and then recrosses it in the opposite sense in a subsequent rotation, it effectively is considered as no crossing. Observe that these relationships correspond to the scale numbering shown in Fig. 8.19 so that, in rotating the turntable clockwise or the telescope counterclockwise, the zero of the vernier passes the scale markings in increasing sequence. The proof of the above relationships as well as their modification when the zero of the vernier passes the scale markings in decreasing sequence is taken up in the problems.

When the spectrometer is used for visual examination of spectra, it is called a *spectroscope*, and when the telescope is made to record the spectrum photographically in camera fashion, it is called a *spectrograph*.

## PROBLEMS

**8.1.** Why does the pupil of an eye look black to an observer?

**8.2.** A person with presbyopic eyes has his far point at infinity and his near point at 60.0 cm from the eyes. (*a*) What kind and power of spectacle lenses should be given the person for reading purposes to restore his near point to 16.0 cm? (*b*) Where is his new far point? Neglect the distance between the back surface of the spactacle lens and the corneal vertex.

**8.3.** A myopic subject has his far point at 30.0 cm from the vertex of the cornea. (*a*) Find the kind and power of spectacle lenses required, neglecting the distance from the lens to the cornea. (*b*) Find the focal length and power of the lenses if the back surfaces of the thin lenses are distant 1.00 cm from the vertex of the cornea. These are known as vertex focal length and vertex power, respectively.

**8.4.** A farsighted person is unable to see objects distinctly when they are closer than 80.0 cm. What are the kind and power of the spectacle lenses that will enable him to see objects at the normal distance of 10.0 in.?

**8.5.** A person has his near point at 15.0 cm and a range of distinct vision of 85.0 cm. What is his range of distinct vision when he wears close-fitting spectacles with $-0.800$ diopter?

**8.6.** It is desired to use a camera to photograph objects at a distance of 50.0 cm. If a lens of 1.50 diopters is positioned in front of and close to the camera objective, for what distance must the camera be set to bring the objects into focus?

**8.7.** Show that when a simple microscope is adjusted to cause the image to fall at the distance of distinct vision, the linear lateral magnification is equal to the magnifying power of the instrument.

**8.8.** Would a person with myopic eyes get as much aid from a simple microscope as one with emmetropic eyes? Explain.

**8.9.** The ratio of the magnifying power of a converging lens when it is used to throw an image at the distance of distinct vision to that when it is used to throw an image at infinity is 1.20. (*a*) What is the distance of distinct vision for the eye if the focal length of the lens is 4.80 cm? (*b*) At what distance from the lens must an object be positioned so that the image falls at the distance of distinct vision found in (*a*)?

**8.10.** A compound microscope has an objective of focal length 2.50 mm and an eyepiece of focal length 20.0 mm. If the optical tube length is 18.0 cm, find the magnifying power of (*a*) the objective, (*b*) the eyepiece, and (*c*) the microscope. The microscope forms the final image at infinity.

**8.11.** How far must the eyepiece be moved toward the objective in the microscope of Prob. 8.10 in order that the image be formed at the normal distance of distinct vision? What is the magnifying power of the microscope now?

**8.12.** Make a ray construction similar to Fig. 8.7 for a compound microscope using the principal planes for objective and ocular.

**8.13.** A 16-mm-focal-length-microscope achromatic objective has a numerical aperture of 0.250. (*a*) Find the smallest separation between object points that can be distinguished when the microscope is used with a substage condenser of numerical aperture 0.250 for light of maximum visual spectral sensitivity. (*b*) Find the normal magnifying power corresponding to a 2.00-mm diameter of the pupil of the eye. (Hint: Note that the normal magnifying power of an instrument is given by the ratio of the numerical aperture of the objective to the numerical aperture of the eye. Compute the latter for the normal distance of distinct vision.) (*c*) Specify the ocular that will ensure this magnifying power.

**8.14.** When the draw tube of a microscope is set at 15.0 cm, 1 unit on the stage micrometer is abserved to cover 8 similar units in the ocular, and when the draw tube is set at 20.0 cm, the ocular reading is 11.5 units. Compute the focal length of the objective.

**8.15.** (a) How much more light do the following binoculars gather than the unaided eye whose pupil has a diameter of 5 mm: $7\times, 30; 7\times, 35; 7\times, 40$. The first number in the designations represents the magnifying power of the binocular, such as $7\times$, and the second number represents the diameter of the objective in millimeters. (HINT: The amount of light passing through a circular lens is proportional to the square of its diameter.) (b) For each of the binoculars find the ratio of the illumination on the retina (amount of light incident per unit area) using the binocular to that with the unaided eye.

**8.16.** The figure shows the entrance and exit pupils $E$ and $E'$, respectively, of an optical system which forms an image $P'$ of an object $P$. If a screen is considered to

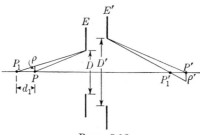

PROB. 8.16.

be in the plane of $P'$ and the object is shifted a distance $d_1$ to $P_1$, then the image point will shift to $P_1'$ so that the image will be out of focus on the screen, producing a circle of confusion of radius $\rho'$. From the figure show that $d_1 = 2\rho p/(D - 2\rho)$, where $D$ is the diameter of the entrance pupil, $\rho$ is the conjugate in the object space of $\rho'$, and $p$ is the position of $P$ with respect to $E$. Show also that if $P_1$ is considered to be shifted to the right of $P$, then the corresponding distance $d_2$ is given by $d_2 = 2\rho p/(D + 2\rho)$. The sum $d_1 + d_2$ is the depth of field and may also be expressed as

$$d_1 + d_2 = \frac{2p\rho'}{mD - 2\rho'} + \frac{2p\rho'}{mD + 2\rho'}$$

where $m$ is the linear lateral magnification. Show this, and interpret the result when $mD = 2\rho'$.

**8.17.** Obtain Eq. (8-14) by regarding the magnifying power as the product of the magnifying powers of the objective and ocular.

**8.18.** The objective of an astronomical telescope has a focal length of 45.0 cm and a relative aperture of $\frac{1}{3}$. For parallel rays the exit pupil has a diameter of 2.00 cm. Find (a) the magnifying power of the telescope and (b) the focal length of the eyepiece.

**8.19.** A telescope with an objective of focal length 50.0 cm is used to bring into view an object 150 cm distant. When the ocular is adjusted to throw the image to infinity, the magnifying power is 5. (a) Find the focal length of the ocular. (b) What is the magnifying power if the ocular is adjusted to view an object at infinity?

**8.20.** With the eye placed close to the ocular of the Galilean telescope (Fig. 8.12) the pupil of the eye is the aperture stop of the system. Find the exit pupil, entrance and exit windows, and the field stop. Then show that the angular field of view in the image space is given by $\tan^{-1} d_o/2(f_o' + f_e')$, where $d_o$ is the diameter of the objective. Show that, for large magnifying powers, the angular field of view is given approximately by $\tan^{-1} d_o/2f_o'$ so that it is a function of the relative aperture of the objective.

**8.21.** The objective and eyepiece of an opera glass are separated by 10.0 cm. What are their focal lengths if the magnifying power is 5?

**8.22.** A terrestrial telescope has a magnifying power of 8. The objective and eyepiece have focal lengths of 20.5 cm and 2.80 cm, respectively. What is the magnification of the erecting system?

**8.23.** Show that Eq. (8.14) is true for the Galilean telescope.

**8.24.** Given that the radius of stereoscopic vision is $R_e$ for unaided eyes whose interpupillary separation is $d_e$, show that when binoculars of magnification $M$ are employed the radius of stereoscopic vision $R_b$ is given by $R_b = R_e M d_b / d_e$, where $d_b$ is the separation of the entrance pupils of the binoculars.

**8.25.** If the field lens (Fig. 8.16) were exactly in the plane of the real image, what would be the effect (a) on the magnifying power, (b) on the position and size of the exit pupil?

**8.26.** Prove that the image $I$ (Fig. 8.17a) is distant $f/2$ from $EL$ in the Huygens ocular.

**8.27.** Prove that $I$ (Fig. 8.17b) is distant $f/4$ from $FL$ in the Ramsden ocular.

**8.28.** The objective of a telescope has a focal length of 40.0 cm and a relative aperture of $1/7.50$. The ocular is of the Ramsden type, the focal length of the field and eye lens being 6.00 cm. (a) What is the angular resolving power of the telescope for light of wavelength 5550 A? (b) Find the position and size of the exit pupil. (c) Find the magnifying power of the instrument. (d) The telescope is used to view an extended object with the eye (pupil diameter is 4 cm) placed in the plane of the exit pupil. Discuss the effectiveness of the telescope in relation to resolving power, brightness of image, and normal magnifying power.

**8.29.** Write out a procedure for each of the adjustments of a spectrometer enumerated in Sec. 8.16.

**8.30.** Prove the relationships $\delta_m = R_2 - R_1 - 180$ and $\delta_m = R_2 - R_1 + 180$ corresponding to the conditions given in Sec. 8.16.

**8.31.** How do the relationships for $\delta_m$ in Prob. 8.30 change when the first reading is taken in position II and the second reading in position I of Fig. 8.20? What change is involved if the vernier and scale are constructed so that the scale numbers decrease as the turntable is rotated clockwise and the telescope is rotated counterclockwise?

## CHAPTER 9

## PHOTOMETRY

The successful design of an optical instrument generally involves a knowledge of the quantity of light passing through the optical system. The science of measuring and comparing light quantities is known as *photometry*. In the field of photometry a group of concepts and a system of units suitable to the field of illuminating engineering have been developed. In considering these concepts and units we shall see that there are four fundamental photometric quantities, called luminous flux, luminous intensity, luminance or brightness, and illuminance. Many instruments have been developed for the measurement and comparison of photometric quantities, and we shall limit our discussion to a few of these in order to illustrate their usefulness and principles of operation.

**9.1. Luminous Flux.** When a solid or liquid is at a temperature above 500°C, the radiant energy that it emits is in the visible region of the spectrum. The radiant energy which a source emits per unit time is called *radiant flux* and represents a time rate of flow of energy. This radiation is inhomogeneous and is functionally related to the color or wavelength of the radiation by a curve such as is shown in Fig. 9.1, where $P_\lambda$ represents the radiant flux per unit wavelength interval $d\lambda$ so that the total radiant flux $P$ is given by

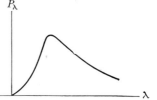

FIG. 9.1. Radiant flux per unit wavelength interval as a function of wavelength.

$$P = \int_0^\infty P_\lambda \, d\lambda \qquad (9.1)$$

Radient flux is in watts

The unit of $P$ is of course that of power, ordinarily expressed in watts. When a sample of radiant flux is evaluated with respect to its ability to produce a visual sensation, it is termed *luminous flux*, which again designates a flow of energy expressed in watts. Now if equal quantities of different colors, say red, blue, and green, all appeared to have the same brightness to the eye, then the radiant flux would provide a method of measuring the luminous flux. But, as we have seen in Sec. 8.1, Fig. 8.3, the human eye is not equally sensitive to radiation of different colors or wavelengths but has a maximum sensitivity at 5550 A and very low sensitivity at 4000 and 6500 A. To express quantitatively the visual

155

effect of the radiant flux, an arbitrary unit of luminous flux is chosen so that the relative visibility of the radiation is included in the definition. The name of this unit is the *lumen;* it is defined as the luminous flux in a sample of radiant flux at a wavelength of 5550 A and of amount 0.00146 watt. In other words, if the radiant flux in a sample of 5550 A is 1 watt, the corresponding luminous flux is 685 lumens. If the radiant flux in a sample at another wavelength $\lambda$ is 1 watt, then the luminous flux is $685V_\lambda$, where $V_\lambda$ is the relative luminosity at this wavelength as given by the curve in Fig. 8.3. Thus for a light source radiating energy of many wavelengths, the total number of lumens, or the luminous flux $F$, is given by

$$F = 685 \int_0^\infty V_\lambda P_\lambda \, d\lambda \qquad \text{lumens} \qquad (9.2)$$

For a sample of radiant flux, the luminous efficiency is a ratio of the luminous flux to the radiant flux or

$$\text{Luminous efficiency} = \frac{685 \int_0^\infty V_\lambda P_\lambda \, d\lambda}{\int_0^\infty P_\lambda \, d\lambda} \qquad (9.3)$$

and is expressed in lumens per watt. It should be clear that in Eq. (9.2) the factor $685V_\lambda$ represents the luminous efficiency in lumens per watt at the wavelength $\lambda$ and $P_\lambda \, d\lambda$ represents the number of watts, giving for the entire expression the number of lumens. In practice the integrations are performed graphically or numerically. For instance, in evaluating Eq. (9.2) the curves $V_\lambda$ and $P_\lambda$ are plotted as a function of $\lambda$; then the sum of the products of the ordinates corresponding to selected wavelengths is computed.

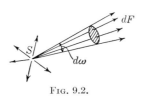

Fig. 9.2.

For a light source such as a lamp, the term luminous efficiency is often used to represent the ratio of the output luminous flux to the power consumed by the source. This of course represents the over-all efficiency since not all the power consumed goes into producing radiant flux.

**9.2. Luminous Intensity.** Consider a so-called point source of light $S$ emitting luminous flux in all directions (Fig. 9.2). We wish to know the amount of flux radiated per unit solid angle in a given direction. The flux $dF$ per unit solid angle $d\omega$ defines the *luminous intensity* $I$ of the source in a given direction, or

$$I = \frac{dF}{d\omega} \qquad (9.4)$$

The unit of $I$ is the *lumen per steradian,* or the *candle.* The term *candle-power* is often employed to represent the luminous intensity expressed in candles, but it should be realized that the term is a misnomer since luminous intensity is not power. If a sphere of radius $R$ is drawn about the point $S$ as center, then the magnitude of a solid angle in steradians is equal to the area on the surface of the sphere subtending the solid angle divided by $R^2$. A unit solid angle or 1 steradian is subtended by an area on the spherical surface equal to $R^2$. Since the total surface area of a sphere is $4\pi R^2$, the total solid angle about the point $S$ is $4\pi$ steradians. Thus for a source radiating uniformly in all directions the flux, from Eq. (9.4), is

$$F = 4\pi I \tag{9.5}$$

Therefore a point source emitting light uniformly in all directions radiates $4\pi$ lumens per candle. If the source radiates nonuniformly in different directions, as is exemplified by a filament lamp whose luminous intensity in a direction at right angles to the filament length is greater than that along a line with the filament length, then the total amount of flux radiated is equal to $4\pi$ times the mean of the luminous intensities in the different directions, designated as mean spherical candlepower.

Although the lumen is the fundamental photometric unit and the candle is the quantity of flux radiated by a point source in some specified direction, it is more practical to provide and maintain a laboratory standard of luminous intensity since measurements of intensity are simpler to perform than those of flux. The original photometric standard was a candle of sperm wax weighing ⅙ lb and burning at a specified rate of 120 grains/hr. This standard was abandoned because its luminous intensity varies with the length of the wick, the height of the flame, the air temperature, and other factors. It was superseded by the Vernon-Harcourt pentane-lamp standard burning a mixture of air and pentane vapor. The standard has a luminous intensity of 10 candles. Corresponding to this, one defines a point source of luminous intensity radiating uniformly in all directions at one-tenth the rate of the Vernon-Harcourt pentane lamp burning in air at 76 cm Hg pressure containing 8 parts in 1000 of water vapor. To avoid setting up and maintaining the Vernon-Harcourt lamp the U.S. Bureau of Standards employs secondary standards in the form of electric lamps operated at a specified wattage. The luminous intensities of these lamps are periodically checked against the standard pentane lamp.

The present international standard, called the *new international candle*, is defined as one-sixtieth of the luminous intensity of one square centimeter of a black body at the freezing temperature of platinum. A surface that absorbs all the incident radiant energy and reflects none is an ideally black surface, and the surface referred to in the definition of the standard is one that appears perfectly black when cold since the luminous intensity of a surface at a given temperature is a function of how black the surface is when cold. Corresponding to this standard of luminous intensity the luminous efficiency of monochromatic radiant flux at 5550 A is obtained as 685 lumens per watt.

**9.3. Luminance, or Brightness.** The concept of luminous intensity as discussed in the previous section is applicable only to point sources or to sources whose dimensions are small enough in relation to the distance involved so that they can be considered as point sources. If the source cannot be treated as a point source, *i.e.*, if it has a finite area, the term *luminance*, or *brightness*, is used to specify, in an analogous manner, the luminous intensity, in a given direction, of unit area of the extended surface. The unit area is the projected area of the source on a plane normal to the given direction. Thus if *da* (Fig. 9.3) is an element of area of the light source, then the luminance $B$ in a direction making an angle $\theta$ with the normal to the elemental area is

FIG. 9.3.

$$B = \frac{dI_\theta}{da \cos \theta} \tag{9.6}$$

where $dI_\theta$ is the luminous intensity of the elemental source in the direction $\theta$. The units of $B$ are candles per square centimeter or candles per square foot. In the case of diffuse surfaces (radiating or reflecting) $dI_\theta$ is a simple function of the angle $\theta$ and is given by

$$dI_\theta = dI_n \cos \theta \tag{9.7}$$

where $dI_n$ is the luminous intensity along the direction of the normal to the surface. The law expressed by Eq. (9.7) is known as *Lambert's law* and is closely obeyed by reflectors, such as blotters or freshly fallen snow, and radiators, such as tungsten and carbon sources. For surfaces that obey Lambert's law the luminance becomes

$$B = \frac{dI_n}{da} \tag{9.8}$$

so that $B$ is independent of $\theta$ and the source appears equally bright from all directions of observation.

Since the brightness of a diffusely reflecting (or radiating) surface is the same at all angles of observation, another unit for brightness may be employed. The unit is the *lambert*, which is defined as the brightness of a perfectly diffusing surface that is emitting or reflecting 1 lumen/cm². For a surface that reflects all the light incident upon it, the number of lumens incident per unit area, or *illuminance* (see Sec. 9.4), is equal to the number of lumens reflected per unit area, and its brightness in lamberts is equal to its illuminance in lumens per square centimeter. It is left as an exercise in the problems to show that a brightness of 1 candle/cm² is equivalent to $\pi$ lamberts. If not all the incident light is reflected, then the brightness in lamberts is equal to the product of illuminance and a reflectance coefficient. Table 9.1 lists some typical luminance values.

TABLE 9.1. VALUES OF LUMINANCE

| Source | Luminance, candles/cm² |
|---|---|
| Sun | $2.3 \times 10^5$ |
| High-intensity arc | $8.5 \times 10^4$ |
| Tungsten at 2800°K | 1000 |
| Electric-lamp filament | 500 |
| Laboratory mercury arc | 10 |
| Clear blue sky | 0.35 |

**9.4. Illuminance.** *Illuminance* refers to the amount of light flux that is incident *upon* a unit area of a surface. If $dF$ is the elemental light flux incident on an element of area $dA$, then the illuminance $E$ is defined as

$$E = \frac{dF}{dA} \qquad (9.9)$$

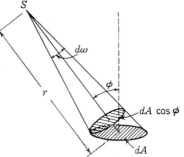

In Fig. 9.4 is illustrated the case where the elemental area $dA$ is illuminated by a point source $S$. The distance of the source from $dA$ is $r$, which makes an angle $\phi$ with the normal to $dA$. The light flux reaching the area is

$$dF = I\, d\omega = \frac{I\, dA\, \cos\phi}{r^2}$$

FIG. 9.4. Illuminance produced by a point source.

where $I$ is the luminous intensity of the source. Thus

$$E = \frac{I \cos\phi}{r^2} \qquad (9.10)$$

which is the illuminance of $dA$ and is the well-known inverse-square law for oblique incidence. The total illuminance due to several point sources is obtained by adding the illuminances due to each of the sources.

The unit of illuminance, as can be seen from Eq. (9.9), is the lumen per square centimeter, the lumen per square meter, or the lumen per square foot. In the engineering field the unit employed for illuminance is the *meter-candle*, if $r$ is measured in meters, and the *foot-candle*, if $r$ is in feet. For instance a foot-candle is the illuminance produced by a point source of 1 candle whose light falls normally on a surface at a distance of 1 ft. The use of the units foot-candle and meter-candle are not wise since they imply a quantity which is dimensionally not that of illuminance. However, their use is becoming less frequent. Sometimes the term *lux* is used in place of meter-candle and *phot* in place of centimeter-candle.

If the source is not a point source but is of finite size, the illumination on an area can be obtained by dividing the source into elemental regions of such size that the inverse-square law may be applied to each. The

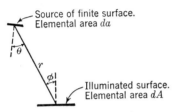

Fig. 9.5. Illuminance of a surface by an extended source.

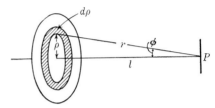

Fig. 9.6. Illuminance due to a flat circular disk.

total illumination is then computed by integration. The illumination $dE$ at $dA$ (Fig. 9.5) due to an element of area $da$ of the source is

$$dE = \frac{dI \cos \phi}{r^2}$$

where $dI$ is the luminous intensity of the elemental area in the direction of $dA$ and is given by Eq. (9.6). Thus

$$dE = \frac{B \cos \theta \cos \phi \, da}{r^2} \tag{9.11}$$

As an example of the application of the differential expression (9.11), we shall compute the illuminance of a flat circular disk of radius $R$ at a point $P$ (Fig. 9.6) on the central axis perpendicular to the plane of the disk and situated in a surface that is parallel to the disk. Every point of the ring-shaped element of radius $\rho$ and area $da = 2\pi\rho \, d\rho$ is at the same distance $r$ from $P$. Here $\theta = \phi$, and the illuminance at $P$ is given by

$$dE_P = \frac{2\pi B l^2 \rho \, d\rho}{(l^2 + \rho^2)^2}$$

If the source obeys Lambert's law, then $B$ is independent of $\theta$ and

$$\begin{aligned} E_P &= 2\pi B l^2 \int_0^R \frac{\rho \, d\rho}{(l^2 + \rho^2)^2} \\ &= \frac{\pi B R^2}{l^2 + R^2} \end{aligned} \tag{9.12}$$

The numerator is simply the luminous intensity of the source, and the denominator is the square of the distance of the rim of the disk to the axial point $P$. If $R$ is small compared with $l$, the expression reduces to that given by the inverse-square law for a point source. In other words, if the ratio of $R$ to $l$ is sufficiently small so that $R^2$ may be neglected, the circular disk may be considered a point source. For instance if a circular disk of 1 cm diameter is distant $\frac{1}{2}$ m, then $(R/l)^2 = 0.0001$ so that by neglecting $R$ the disk may be considered a point source with an error of 0.01 per cent.

**9.5. Luminance and Illuminance of Optical Images.** The photometric principles that have thus far been discussed may be employed to determine the luminance and illuminance of optical images. In Fig. 9.7 is

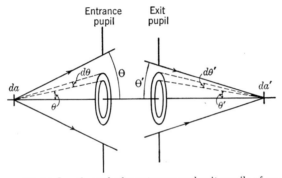

Fig. 9.7. Passage of light flux through the entrance and exit pupils of an optical system.

shown an element of area $da$ of the object and the conjugate area element $da'$ in the image. The light flux is shown passing through the entrance and exit pupils of the optical system. To obtain an expression for the total flux from $da$ entering the entrance pupil, consider an annular element in the plane of the entrance pupil formed by two cones whose generating lines make angles $\theta$ and $\theta + d\theta$ with the normal to $da$. The flux from $da$ into this element is given by $dF = B \, da \cos \theta \, d\omega$. The solid angle $d\omega$ subtended by the ring is given by the area of a sphere of unit radius contained in the ring, or $d\omega = 2\pi \sin \theta \, d\theta$. Therefore

$$dF = 2\pi B \, da \sin \theta \cos \theta \, d\theta$$

If the source obeys Lambert's law, then $B$ is the uniform brightness of the surface when viewed from all directions and the total flux through the entrance pupil is

$$F = 2\pi B \, da \int^\Theta \sin \theta \cos \theta \, d\theta$$

which yields

$$F = \pi B \, da \sin^2 \Theta \tag{9.13}$$

In the same way, the luminous flux passing through the exit pupil is given by

$$F' = \pi B' \, da' \sin^2 \Theta' \tag{9.14}$$

where $B'$ is the illuminance of the image $da'$ and $\Theta'$ is the angle subtended at $da'$ by the exit-pupil radius. Neglecting losses due to absorption and reflection, $F$ and $F'$ are equal so that

$$\pi B \, da \sin^2 \Theta = \pi B' \, da' \sin^2 \Theta'$$

or

$$\frac{B'}{B} = \frac{da}{da'} \frac{\sin^2 \Theta}{\sin^2 \Theta'} \tag{9.15}$$

Using Abbe's sine condition $ny \sin \Theta = n'y' \sin \Theta'$ and remembering that $da \, y'^2 = da' \, y^2$, there results

$$\frac{B'}{B} = \left(\frac{n'}{n}\right)^2 \tag{9.16}$$

where $n$ and $n'$ are the refractive indices of the object and image spaces, respectively. Hence if $n' = n$, the luminance of the image is at best equal to that of the object.

The illuminance of the image $E'$ is obtained from Eq. (9.14),

$$E' = \pi B' \sin^2 \Theta' \tag{9.17}$$

and again using Abbe's sine condition,

$$E' = \frac{\pi B'(n \sin \Theta)^2}{n'^2 m^2} = \frac{\pi B(n \sin \Theta)^2}{n^2 m^2} \tag{9.18}$$

where $m$ is the linear lateral magnification. Since $n \sin \Theta$ is the numerical aperture, Eq. (9.18) may be written

$$E' = \frac{\pi B'(\text{N.A.})^2}{n'^2 m^2} = \frac{\pi B(\text{N.A.})^2}{n^2 m^2} \tag{9.19}$$

showing that the image illuminance is directly proportional to the square of the numerical aperture and inversely proportional to the square of the linear lateral magnification.

**9.6. The Photometer and Illuminometer.** An instrument that is employed for the measurement of the luminous intensity of light sources is called a photometer. The measurement of luminous intensity is based on the inverse-square law, and the principle employed is illustrated by Fig. 9.8. Two point sources $S_1$ and $S_2$ are placed one on either side of the photometer head represented by the prism $ABC$. The diffusely reflecting surfaces $AC$ and $BC$ have the same reflection ratio and are equally inclined to the incident light. The illuminance of the surface $AC$ by the source $S_1$ of intensity $I_1$ is

$$E_1 = \frac{I_1 \cos \phi}{r_1^2}$$

Likewise the illuminance of surface $BC$ by source $S_2$ of intensity $I_2$ is

$$E_2 = \frac{I_2 \cos \phi}{r_2^2}$$

By moving the photometer head along the line $S_1 S_2$ it is possible to adjust for the case where both surfaces appear equally illuminated. Then

$$\frac{I_1}{r_1^2} = \frac{I_2}{r_2^2} \tag{9.20}$$

and the luminous intensity of an unknown source may thus be determined if the other source is a standard. The method holds strictly for

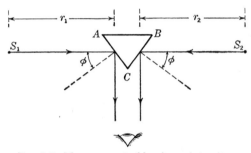

FIG. 9.8. Measurement of luminous intensity.

point sources, but as we have seen, the conditions of a point source may be satisfied to a good approximation by utilizing such distances in relation to the dimensions of the sources that the error involved in employing the inverse-square law is kept to a tolerable value. Of course the accuracy of such a visual method is a function of how well the eye can estimate the relative brightness of the two illuminated surfaces. A photometer head that permits high precision in measurement settings is the one employed in the Lummer-Brodhun photometer illustrated in Fig. 9.9a. The photometer head contains a screen $B$ whose surfaces, illuminated by the two sources $S_1$ and $S_2$, are made of a white diffusing substance such as plaster of paris. The totally reflecting prisms $M_1$ and $M_2$ reflect the light onto the opposite faces of a specially constructed photometric "cube" $C$. The cube consists of two right-angled prisms with their hypotenuses in contact. The hypotenuse of the left-hand prism is ground away in part so that it forms the pattern shown in Fig. 9.9b. The unshaded portions of the pattern represent the parts of the two prisms that are in contact. The light from $S_1$ is transmitted through the cube by the portions of the hypotenuses that are in contact, while light from $S_2$ is totally reflected as shown. The observer then sees the pattern (*b*) in which the shaded portion corresponds to light from the right-hand side of *B*, while the white portion corresponds to light from the left-hand side of *B*. When the two sides of *B* have equal illuminance, the pattern is not discernible. In order to facilitate the judgment of the disappearance of the pattern, and thus improve the accuracy of setting, the pieces of glass $G_1$ and $G_2$ are inserted. This makes the trapezoidal patches somewhat darker than the surrounding field, and the observer

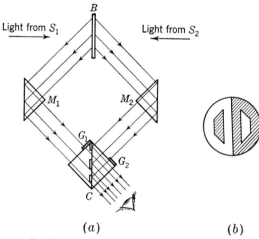

(*a*)            (*b*)

FIG. 9.9. The Lummer-Brodhun photometer. (*a*) The photometer head. (*b*) The field of view.

strives to equalize the contrast between the patches and the surrounding field. To average out any differences that may be present in the reflectance of both sides of *B*, another set of readings is made with the sides of *B* reversed. For this purpose the photometer head may be rotated through 180°, and when the two sets of readings are averaged, other errors due to dissimilarities in the photometer head are also eliminated.

In discussing the principle of the ordinary photometer we have assumed that the sources $S_1$ and $S_2$ had the same color. However, if the two halves of the field of a photometer are illuminated by lights of different colors, the accuracy of the settings is considerably reduced because the eye is incapable of judging when two different colors produce equal brightness. When the two sources do not differ in color to a large degree, the Lummer-Brodhun photometer gives reliable results if the photometer balance is made by matching contrasts as described above. When the color difference is very large, a *flicker photometer* may be employed. Here the field presented to the eye is illuminated alternately by the light from the two sources. There is a frequency of the alternations at which the color difference disappears owing to persistence of vision. However, the flicker due to brightness difference is present. The photometer head may now be adjusted to minimum flicker corresponding to equal illuminance. A flicker photometer can of course be used to compare the luminous intensities of two sources of the same color.

Other methods of comparing two beams of light of different colors are dealt with in the specialized field of *heterochromatic photometry*. For instance, in *spectrophotometry*, the two beams are dispersed into their respective spectra and then are compared by wavelength steps in which both parts of the photometer field are illuminated by a single wavelength at each setting.

Instruments that are used to measure the illuminance on a surface are known as *illuminometers*. The *Weber illuminometer*, shown in Fig. 9.10, is an example of the operation of this class of instruments. A Lummer-Brodhun cube $C$ receives light on one of its faces from the surface whose illuminance is to be determined and on the other face from the ground glass $G$, which is

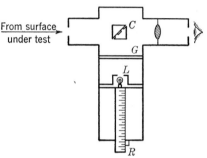

FIG. 9.10. The Weber illuminometer.

illuminated by the lamp $L$. The distance of $L$ from $G$ may be altered and the corresponding setting read on the scale marked on the supporting rod $R$. With the scale calibrated in lumens per square foot or foot-candles the illuminance of the surface under test may be readily determined after a photometric balance is made.

In addition to the physiological photometers in which the comparison of the photometric fields is made by the human eye there are the physical photometers that employ light-sensitive detectors such as the selenium cell, the photoelectric cell, and the radiometer. The selenium cell is representative of the class of detectors whose electrical properties change when illuminated, the photoelectric cell operates on the principle of electron emission from metal surfaces under the action of light, and the radiometer involves the measurements of very small electric currents resulting when light radiation falls on a thermopile. For more detailed information on the relative merits of these physical detectors the student is urged to resort to standard texts in these fields.

## PROBLEMS

**9.1.** (*a*) In a sample of radiant flux there is 15.0 watts of monochromatic light of wavelength 5460 A. Find the luminous flux and luminous efficiency of this radiation. For relative luminosity values see the table in Appendix II. (*b*) If the radiant sample also contains 10.0 watts of light of wavelength 6000 A, find the total radiant flux, the total luminous flux, and the efficiency.

**9.2.** Two small lamps are mounted 8.00 ft above a table top. The lamps have a luminous intensity of 100 candles and are 10.0 ft apart. Find the illuminance on the table at a point that is between the lamps, 6.00 ft from one lamp, and vertically below the line joining the lamps.

**9.3.** A chandelier contains five small lamps, each of 200 candles, situated at the vertices of a pentagon of side 30.0 cm. The plane of the pentagon is 80.0 cm above a table top. Find the illuminance at a point on the table directly below the center of the pentagon.

**9.4.** A point source of light is distant 100 cm from a circular aperture of 4.00 cm diameter. The luminous intensity of the source in the direction of the aperture is 50.0 candles. Find the luminous flux passing through the aperture.

**9.5.** A diffusing reflector has a reflectance coefficient of 0.80. What is its brightness in lamberts if it has an illuminance of 50.0 lumens/ft²? Express the result also in candles per square centimeter.

**9.6.** A point source of light is placed 5.00 m from the window of a photoelectric cell which supplies a current of 10.0 microamperes/lumen of light flux. What photoelectric current will flow if the source has a luminous intensity of 50.0 candles and the photoelectric cell window has an opening 5.00 cm² in area?

**9.7.** A small lamp of 150 candles is 4.00 ft above the center of a table 6.00 ft square. How much less illumination is there at the table corners than at the mid-points of the edges?

**9.8.** A point source of luminous intensity $I$ is mounted $h$ ft above the center of a circular table of radius $R$. Find an expression for the illuminance at the table rim. Show that this illuminance is a maximum when $h = R/\sqrt{2}$.

**9.9.** The Bunsen grease-spot photometer consists of a sheet of opaque white paper which reflects all the radiant energy incident upon it. The sheet is rendered translucent over a small circular region by means of paraffin wax. The translucent spot transmits a large amount of the incident light, reflects the rest, and appears dark with respect to the surrounding white sheet when observed by reflected light. At a balance the spot is indistinguishable from the surrounding area, and the amount of light coming from unit area of spot and surroundings is the same. If the illuminances by the two sources on either side of the photometer head are $E_1$ and $E_2$, and if $f$ is the fraction of the light reflected by the spot, show that at a balance $E_1 = E_2$.

**9.10.** Compute the value of $E_p$ when $R = 1.00$ cm and $l = 10.0$ cm, (a) using Eq. (9.12), and (b) assuming a point source. Compute the percentage difference.

**9.11.** A high-intensity arc lamp, whose illuminance is 80,000 candles/cm², is in air in front of a converging lens whose diameter is 3.00 in. The lens forms a real image of the arc at a distance of 12.0 in. from the lens. Find the illuminance in the image of the arc, neglecting reflection and absorption losses. [HINT: Apply Eq. (9.17).]

**9.12.** Two point sources of 10.0 candles and 30.0 candles luminous intensities are separated by 100 cm. Find where on the line joining them the illuminance produced by each is the same.

**9.13.** The two sides of the screen of a photometer head reflect unequally. A balance is obtained when a source of luminous intensity $I_1$ is distant $x_1$ from one side of the screen and a second source of luminous intensity $I_2$ is distant $x_2$ from the other side of the screen. The photometer head is rotated through 180°, and a balance is again obtained when the screen is distant $X_1$ from the first source and $X_2$ from the second source. Show that $I_1/I_2 = x_1X_1/x_2X_2$. (HINT: Let $C_1$ and $C_2$ be the corresponding transmission coefficients of the two sides of the screen.)

**9.14.** Show that for a very distant object $E'$ in Eq. (9.19) varies inversely as the square of the $f$ number. Such a relationship holds for telescopes and camera objectives.

**9.15.** Show that 1 candle/cm² is equivalent to $\pi$ lamberts. (Hint: In the accompanying figure $S$ is a source 1 cm² in area radiating according to Lambert's law. Let $B$

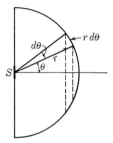

PROB. 9.15.

be the brightness of the source in candles per square centimeter; then $I = B \cos \theta$. The total flux radiated by $S$ can be found from $dF = E\,dA$, where the illuminance $E = I/r^2$ is to be integrated over the area of a hemisphere. Employ the area

$$dA = 2\pi r \sin \theta\, r\, d\theta$$

of the indicated zone. The result obtained by integration will reveal the required relationship.)

# CHAPTER 10

## NATURE OF LIGHT AND WAVE MOTION

In the field of geometrical optics which we have thus far studied, we have been concerned with the establishment of principles which govern the formation of images by optical elements. As we have seen, it is possible to accomplish this by adopting the concept of a ray of light coupled with the experimental laws of reflection and refraction. We have said nothing about the nature of light that would explain the phenomena of reflection, of refraction, of the fact that light undergoes reflection and refraction simultaneously, and of the fact that light apparently travels in straight lines. These and other well-known facts such as that light carries energy, that light travels through empty space, and that it has a definite velocity of $3 \times 10^{10}$ cm/sec must also be taken into consideration in the formulation of a theory of what light is. In addition there are the important phenomena of *interference, diffraction*, and *polarization*, all of which play a significant role in any concepts concerning the nature of light. In this and subsequent chapters we shall be concerned with these facts and phenomena, their study and discussion constituting what is called physical optics.

In this chapter we shall first discuss the corpuscular and wave theories of light that have arisen. This will be followed by a presentation of the characteristics of wave motion and some sections on the measurement of the velocity of light.

In the next few chapters we shall study the subjects of interference, diffraction, absorption, scattering, dispersion, and polarization, always being aware of those observational results which are or are not in harmony with theories concerning the nature of light.

**10.1. Corpuscular and Wave Theories of Light.** From the fact that energy may be transmitted from one point of space to another by means of a light beam it is evident that there are only two general theories that may be invoked, corresponding to the two general ways in which energy may be transmitted, *viz.*, either by a stream of moving particles or by means of a wave disturbance. Accordingly in the seventeenth century there arose, on the one hand, the *corpuscular theory*, which was strongly supported by Newton, and, on the other hand, the *wave theory*, which was defended by Huygens, Descartes, and others.

Newton imagined that light consists of a stream of swiftly moving

168

particles emitted by the source, the different colors being due to different-sized corpuscles. The particles or corpuscles follow straight-line motion in empty space and were assumed to suffer an elastic impact when impinging on a mirror, so that there result equal angles of incidence and reflection. Reflection and refraction at an interface, such as air-glass, Newton explained as due to the presence of forces of repulsion and attraction, and whether a corpuscle is repelled or reflected by a surface, or whether it is attracted and so refracted, depends on the "state" of the corpuscle when it arrives at the interface, *i.e.*, whether it is in a "fit of easy reflection" or a "fit of easy transmission." The mechanism for throwing a corpuscle into one of these "fits" is the assumed production of vibrations in an "etherlike" medium at the interface. The waves so produced, as when small objects thrown on a water surface produce ripples, give rise to regions of varying density, thus occasioning a corpuscle to be in a fit of easy reflection or a fit of easy transmission. By considering that different media have different attractions for the corpuscles, the law of refraction, that the ratio of the sine of the angle of incidence to the sine of the angle of refraction is a constant, may be obtained. Thus, if corpuscles traveling in a medium $a$ with velocity $v_a$ are incident at an angle $\phi$ with the normal at the refracting surface of a denser medium $b$, they experience only a normal component of acceleration toward medium $b$ and therefore bend toward the normal as they enter medium $b$ with velocity $v_b$, making an angle $\phi'$ with the normal. Since the component of velocity parallel to the refracting surface is unaltered, it follows that $\sin \phi / \sin \phi' = v_b / v_a = $ constant. We see, however, that this result specifies that the light has a greater velocity in the denser medium, a prediction that was found to be at variance with the observed facts when Foucault, in the early part of the nineteenth century, experimentally showed that the velocity of light in water is less than in air (see Sec. 10.8). Some of the merits of a theory lie in the extent to which its predictions are borne out by experiment. As we shall see in the chapters on Interference and Diffraction, there were other predictions of the corpuscular theory that were not in harmony with experiment. Newton stuck tenaciously to his corpuscular theory primarily because he believed in the rectilinear propagation of light and the waves with which he was familiar, those of sound and water, bent around ordinary obstacles. But light rays do produce diffraction patterns which cannot be explained by the corpuscular theory. Newton's arguments for the corpuscular theory were extremely ingenious, but his theory finally gave way in favor of the wave theory, which met with uncontestable success in its explanations and predictions.

The wave theory stipulated that a light source sets up a disturbance in an all-pervading medium called the *ether* and that this disturbance travels in all directions through the medium, the various colors being represented by different wavelengths. The succeeding sections deal with the characteristics of wave motion, and in what follows we shall see how the wave theory successfully explains the different kinds of experimental evidence. We shall see that some of the evidence demands the additional hypothesis that light is a transverse wave motion. But it must be realized that this earlier wave theory considers that all space is filled with the luminiferous ether, a medium capable of transmitting waves with a velocity of $3 \times 10^{10}$ cm/sec. As a consequence, such a medium must be imagined to possess an elasticity that is far greater than that of steel and a density that is indeed very close to zero, thus offering negligible resistance to the passage of the planets in their motion around the sun. There were certainly some objections to the early wave theory! In 1860 Clerk Maxwell introduced his electromagnetic theory of light according to which the light wave is composed of varying coupled electric and magnetic fields, each transverse to the other and both transverse to the direction of propagation of the wave. Maxwell's theory replaced the elastic ether medium by an electromagnetic one possessing the requisite electrical properties rather than mechanical ones. Maxwell's theory predicts the observed speed of travel of the electromagnetic waves. At present the state of affairs is that we consider the electric and magnetic fields as the fundamental entities, and it is not necessary to invoke and look into the nature of an ether.

Although the wave theory of light is successful in explaining a large class of optical phenomena, it fails to explain other phenomena such as those which are a result of the interaction of light with matter, or the origin of spectra. An outstanding illustration of the interchange of energy between radiation and matter is the phenomenon of the photoelectric effect: when light of the right frequency is incident on a metal plate, electrons are ejected with a definite velocity which is a function of the frequency of the light and is independent of the light intensity, which determines the number of electrons that are emitted. Phenomena such as this find their explanation in the *quantum theory* of the twentieth century, which asserts that light consists of small bundles of energy called *photons*. The energy of each photon is given by $h\nu$, where $h$ is Planck's constant, $6.62 \times 10^{-27}$ erg sec, and $\nu$ is the frequency of the light in vibrations per second. The photons move with the speed of light in free space. We shall have more to say about the quantum theory in a later chapter.

There appear to be, then, two classes of phenomena; for one class, such as the photoelectric phenomenon, it is necessary to consider light as possessing a corpuscular nature in which there is a discontinuous distribution of energy, and for the other class, such as interference and diffraction, the wave nature of light is adequate for an explanation. Light then appears to have a dual nature, and at times a photon mechanism is employed, while at other times a wave mechanism is used for analysis. We shall also see that a material particle such as an electron behaves under certain conditions as if it had a group of waves associated with it. For our discussion of the phenomena of interference, diffraction, and polarization it is not necessary to concern ourselves with the existence of photons, and we shall employ the wave nature of light, which is completely adequate in dealing with these phenomena.

**10.2. Wave Types.**     The student is no doubt familiar with the existence of water waves, knows that sound is transmitted by a wave motion, and is perhaps aware of the fact that electromagnetic waves transmit radio waves, X rays, light, γ rays, and other radiation.     The common prerequisite for the production of a wave is a vibrating or oscillating source. The vibrations of the water particles responsible for the wave disturbance are initiated by some such act as the dropping of a stone onto a quiet surface; waves along a stretched rope are set up by mechanically vibrating one end of the rope transverse to its length; a mechanically vibrating source, as the prongs of a tuning fork, sets up disturbances in the air which reach our ears and produce the sensation of sound; and the electrically charged particles surging back and forth in the antenna of a radio transmitter set up in space changing electrical and magnetic conditions which manifest themselves as electromagnetic waves.

Most waves are either longitudinal or transverse.     A *longitudinal* wave is characterized by the fact that the particles of the medium in which the wave disturbance progresses vibrate parallel to the direction of propagation of the wave.     In sound the particles move, at one instant, in the direction and, in the next instant, opposite to the direction of wave travel, thus forming the familiar regions of condensation and rarefaction. In a *transverse* wave the particles vibrate perpendicular to the direction of wave propagation, as in the wave along the stretched rope.     We shall see later in our study of the phenomenon of polarization that all electromagnetic waves are transverse in character.     It should be kept in mind that the significant property of any wave is its ability to transfer energy.

**10.3. Simple Periodic Wave Motion.**     The type of motion performed by the source of the wave motion determines the characteristics of the resulting disturbance.     For instance, if a small section of a stretched string is given a sharp impulse, a single wave pulse is propagated along the string.     On the other hand, if one end of the string is attached to a vibrating source performing simple harmonic motion, the resulting periodic waves will be simple harmonic.     One of the most important types of wave motions is this so-called "simple" periodic disturbance since it is frequently met with in actual wave disturbances and, as we shall see, is fundamental in the production of more complex types of wave motions.

It will be remembered that when a particle $P$ (Fig. 10.1) rotates with uniform speed in a circle of reference, the oscillatory linear motion of the projection $Q$ of this particle on a diameter is simple harmonic. For the straight-line periodic motion along the $y$ axis, the displacement $y$ of $Q$ from the center $O$ is given by

$$y = A \sin (\omega t + \epsilon) \tag{10.1}$$

where $A$ is the radius of the circle, $\omega$ is the angular speed of $P$ in radians per second, $t$ is the time, $\omega t + \epsilon$ is the *phase angle*, and $\epsilon$ is the *epoch*, sometimes called the *phase constant*, and represents the value of the phase angle for $t = 0$. Point $Q$ performs simple harmonic motion, reaching a maximum displacement equal to $A$, the amplitude of the motion, and having an instantaneous velocity equal to $\omega \sqrt{A^2 - y^2}$ and an instantaneous acceleration equal to $-\omega^2 y$. $Q$ then performs a to-and-fro motion, experiencing zero velocity and maximum acceleration at the end points of its path and maximum velocity and zero acceleration at $O$, called its equilibrium position. The motion is characterized by the statement that $Q$ has an acceleration proportional to its distance from the equilibrium position and opposite in direction to it. Such motion occurs whenever the forces present follow Hooke's law such as with the vibrations of an elastic medium. The motion is periodic, repeating itself in successive time intervals corresponding to one complete rotation of the reference particle and having a period $T = 2\pi/\omega = 1/f$, where $f$ is the frequency in vibrations per second.

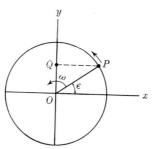

Fig. 10.1. Simple harmonic motion.

Equation (10.1) is the general expression for the simple periodic motion of a single particle. Let us now see how this vibratory motion may be transmitted through a medium. For this purpose consider a line of the particles of a medium that are equally spaced and elastically connected, numbered 0, 1, 2, 3, . . . , in Fig. 10.2a. Let particle 0 be subjected to simple harmonic motion with an amplitude $A$ as indicated in (b), which shows particle 0 at its maximum downward displacement after a time of one-quarter period. The motion of particle 0 has been transmitted to particles 1, 2, and 3, and at the end of this quarter period it is assumed that the disturbance has reached particle 4. In (c) is shown the configuration after the second quarter period, when particle 0 is at its equilibrium position, particle 4 has its downward maximum displacement, and the disturbance has reached particle 8. In (d) particle 0 has its upward maximum displacement corresponding to the third quarter period, with the disturbance reaching particle 12, and in (e) particle 0 has returned to its starting position, thus completing one period of vibration, the disturbance now reaching particle 16, which is the first particle in phase with particle 0. Thus each particle performs the same simple harmonic motion as the source particle 0, but there is a constant progressive phase difference from particle to particle. The simultaneous motion of all the particles gives rise to a wave form or disturbance which is propagated through the medium and is what is called a simple harmonic wave. We notice that it is not the particles but a wave form or configuration that advances through the medium. The wave disturbance

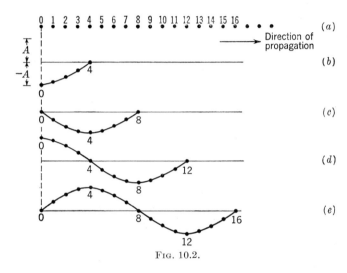

FIG. 10.2.

travels a distance equal to one wavelength λ during the time $T$ of one vibration of any particle, giving for the velocity $v$ of the wave propagation

$$v = \frac{\lambda}{T} = f\lambda \qquad (10.2)$$

which is the simple harmonic wave equation relating the wave velocity, the period, or frequency, and the wavelength.

Equation (10.1) gives the displacement of a single oscillating particle at any time $t$. We can obtain a more generalized expression giving the displacements of all the particles situated along the path of the disturbance at any one instant. Thus, in Fig. 10.2a, let the position of any particle be represented by its distance $x$ from 0. Then a disturbance started by particle 0 reaches a particle, distant $x$ from it, in the time $x/v$, and its displacement is

$$y = A \sin\left[\frac{2\pi}{T}\left(t - \frac{x}{v}\right) + \epsilon\right] \qquad (10.3a)$$

where we have included the phase constant $\epsilon$ for generality. Equation (10.3) may have the useful alternate forms

$$y = A \sin\left[ 2\pi \left( \frac{t}{T} - \frac{x}{\lambda} \right) + \epsilon \right] \tag{10.3b}$$

and

$$y = A \sin\left[ \frac{2\pi}{\lambda} (vt - x) + \epsilon \right] \tag{10.3c}$$

Equations (10.3) give $y$ as a function of $x$ and $t$ for a wave disturbance moving toward the right. For a wave disturbance moving to the left the expressions remain the same, with $-x$ substituted for $x$. Any particle in the path of the wave disturbance has a given value of $x$, and as the wave configuration passes this point, the particle moves up and down with simple periodic motion. With $x$ taking on successive values corresponding to the different positions of the particles, we see that the motions of all the particles are identical except that they are progressively out of phase by a constant amount. The curve drawn through all the particles at any time $t$ yields the wave form of the disturbance. The equations yield real values for $x$ between $-\infty$ and $+\infty$ so that the equations represent an infinite train of harmonic waves whose wavelength is the distance between any one particle and the very next one that is in phase.

It is very useful to obtain an expression for the difference in phase between any two particles in a wave train. Let the positions of two particles be designated $x_1$ and $x_2$; then their respective displacements $y_1$ and $y_2$ are

$$y_1 = A \sin\left[ \frac{2\pi}{\lambda} (vt - x_1) + \epsilon \right] \quad \text{and} \quad y_2 = A \sin\left[ \frac{2\pi}{\lambda} (vt - x_2) + \epsilon \right]$$

The phase difference $\delta$ at any time $t$ is

$$\delta = \left[ \frac{2\pi}{\lambda} (vt - x_1) + \epsilon \right] - \left[ \frac{2\pi}{\lambda} (vt - x_2) + \epsilon \right]$$

$$\delta = \frac{2\pi}{\lambda} (x_2 - x_1) \tag{10.4}$$

In this equation it must be remembered that $\lambda$ is the wavelength in the medium. In view of Eq. (10.2), since the frequency of vibration remains unchanged when a wave passes from one medium into another, the wavelength is proportional to the speed of the wave. Hence if $\lambda_0$ is the wavelength in vacuum, which is the value customarily employed, then $\lambda_0 = n\lambda$, where $n$ is the absolute index of refraction of the medium. Equation (10.4) now becomes

$$\delta = \frac{2\pi}{\lambda_0} \Delta \tag{10.5}$$

where $\Delta = n(x_2 - x_1)$ is the optical-path difference. This equation, stating that the phase difference is $2\pi/\lambda_0$ times the optical-path difference, is of extreme importance, and we shall frequently have occasion to make use of it.

We have considered the form of the wave to depend on the vibratory motion transmitted to the particles of a medium, and although now we do not think of a light wave as a disturbance in an elastic-solid medium, as indicated in Sec. 10.1, the conclusions carry over into light and all electromagnetic waves which are characterized by different ranges of wavelengths. The electromagnetic spectrum ranges from the long electromagnetic waves with wavelengths of the order of hundreds of miles to $\gamma$ rays as low as 5XU($1$XU $= 10^{-11}$ cm). The visible wavelengths to which the human eye is sensitive stretches from the violet region around 3800 A to the red region around 7200 A. On the long-wavelength side of the visible band are the infrared and heat waves, stretching to about $0.7\ \mu$ ($1\ \mu = 10^{-4}$ cm), beyond these the micro- and short electromagnetic waves, and then the wireless and long electromagnetic waves. On the short-wavelength side of the visible spectrum are the ultraviolet and far-ultraviolet waves, going down to about 45 A, below that the X rays with wavelengths down to about 100X units, and shorter than these are the $\gamma$ rays from radioactive substances. The visible region covers a small fraction of the entire electromagnetic range.

Looking at Eqs. (10.3) from the electromagnetic point of view, $y$ is identified as the electric field strength or the magnetic field strength, with $A$ recognizable as the amplitude, or maximum value of $y$. The equation then represents a plane wave of electric intensity (or magnetic intensity) propagated in the positive $x$ direction with velocity $v = 3 \times 10^{10}$ cm/sec, period $T$, and wavelength $\lambda$. The harmonic variation of electric intensity occurs in a plane at right angles to the direction of propagation, and the accompanying harmonic variation of the magnetic intensity is in the plane perpendicular to that containing the electric variation and also transverse to the direction of propagation. In general if the plane wave is not propagated in the $x$ direction but in a direction whose direction cosines are $L$, $M$, and $N$, then the wave equation takes the form

$$Y = A \sin \left[ \frac{2\pi}{T} \left( t - \frac{Lx + My + Nz}{v} \right) + \epsilon \right] \qquad (10.6)$$

where we have used $Y$ for the displacement and $x$, $y$, $z$ for the mutually orthogonal axes.

A surface through which a wave disturbance is traveling and in which all the particles are vibrating in phase is called a *wave front*. For the plane wave given by Eq. (10.6) this locus is defined by

$$Lx + My + Nz = \text{constant}$$

which is the equation of a plane and therefore signifies a plane wave front. For Eqs. (10.3) the surface defining the wave front is $x = $ constant, which signifies a plane wave front parallel to the $yz$ plane. Another wave front, with which we shall have occasion to deal, is the *spherical* wave front that surrounds a point source. A small portion of a spherical wave front of large radius of curvature approximates a plane wave front.

Let us see how the energy carried by a simple harmonic wave is related to the amplitude of the waves. We have seen that the instantaneous velocity of a simple harmonic vibration is $\omega \sqrt{A^2 - y^2}$, and the maximum value of this is $\omega A$, which a vibrating particle possesses as it passes through its equilibrium position. The corresponding kinetic energy of the particle is then proportional to $A^2$. This, however, represents the total energy since the motion is such that it possesses all potential and no kinetic energy at the end points of its motion and all kinetic and no potential energy at its equilibrium position. Therefore the energy given to a particle is proportional to the square of the amplitude. Now the time rate of flow of this energy per unit area normal to the direction of propagation is called the *intensity*, which is therefore proportional to the square of the amplitude. For a point source of light producing spherical waves, we have seen (Sec. 9.4) that the intensity is inversely proportional to the square of the distance from the source. For spherical waves, then, the amplitude falls off inversely as the first power of the distance from the source. It is of course assumed that the wave is passing through perfectly transparent media with no loss in intensity due to absorption. If absorption be present, then the amplitude will decrease on this account by an additional factor which is an exponential involving the first power of the distance, due to the law of absorption.

**10.4. Composition of Simple Harmonic Motions.** In our studies of wave motion we shall have occasion to consider the addition of several simple harmonic motions, and we shall here consider those combinations which will be applicable in the study of light waves. When two or more sets of waves are made to cross the same region of a medium and then are examined, it is found that the individual waves have come through unaltered. This illustrates the well-known *principle of superposition* according to which the resultant displacement of any point at any instant is the sum of the displacements of the individual waves. This result is characteristic of all wave motion, and we shall use the principle to obtain the resultant disturbance due to two or more superimposed waves.

First consider finding the resultant displacement due to two simple periodic motions acting along the same line and having the same frequency and different amplitudes. According to Eq. (10.1) the individual displacements are

$$y_1 = A_1 \sin (\omega t + \epsilon_1) = A_1(\sin \omega t \cos \epsilon_1 + \cos \omega t \sin \epsilon_1)$$

and $\qquad\qquad\qquad\qquad\qquad\qquad\qquad\qquad\qquad\qquad$ (10.7)

$$y_2 = A_2 \sin (\omega t + \epsilon_2) = A_2(\sin \omega t \cos \epsilon_2 + \cos \omega t \sin \epsilon_2)$$

The resultant displacement $y$ is the algebraic sum of the individual displacements, giving

$$y = (A_1 \cos \epsilon_1 + A_2 \cos \epsilon_2) \sin \omega t + (A_1 \sin \epsilon_1 + A_2 \sin \epsilon_2) \cos \omega t \quad (10.8)$$

Now let

$$A_1 \cos \epsilon_1 + A_2 \cos \epsilon_2 = A \cos \epsilon \qquad \text{and} \qquad A_1 \sin \epsilon_1 + A_2 \sin \epsilon_2 = A \sin \epsilon$$
$$(10.9)$$

Then

$$A^2 = A_1^2 + A_2^2 + 2A_1A_2 \cos (\epsilon_2 - \epsilon_1) \qquad\qquad (10.10)$$

and

$$\tan \epsilon = \frac{A_1 \sin \epsilon_1 + A_2 \sin \epsilon_2}{A_1 \cos \epsilon_1 + A_2 \cos \epsilon_2} \qquad\qquad (10.11)$$

Equation (10.7) now becomes

$$y = A \cos \epsilon \sin \omega t + A \sin \epsilon \cos \omega t$$
$$y = A \sin (\omega t + \epsilon) \qquad\qquad (10.12)$$

The resultant displacement then is a simple harmonic motion of the same frequency as the original individual motions but with a resultant amplitude given by Eq. (10.10) and a new phase constant given by Eq. (10.11). A third harmonic motion may be combined with this motion to give the expression for the resultant displacement due to three simple harmonic motions, and so on for any number of superposed motions. When two light waves are made to combine, or, as we say, *interfere*, the intensity $I$ of the light at any point is proportional to the square of the amplitude. We see from Eq. (10.10), if the phase difference $(\epsilon_2 - \epsilon_1) = 0, 2\pi, 4\pi,$ . . . , then the disturbances are in phase, the case is that of constructive interference, and the intensity is proportional to $(A_1 + A_2)^2$. On the other hand, if $(\epsilon_2 - \epsilon_1) = \pi, 3\pi, 5\pi,$ . . . , the disturbances are 180° out of phase and the case is one of destructive interference with the intensity proportional to $(A_1 - A_2)^2$. When the amplitudes are equal and the phase difference is an integral multiple of $2\pi$, the intensity is proportional to four times the square of the amplitude of either wave, and when the phase difference is an odd integral multiple of $\pi$, the intensity is zero. We shall make use of these results in our study of interference.

There is a very useful graphical method of obtaining the resultant amplitude and phase constant of the two or more simple harmonic motions discussed above. It follows the polygonal method of adding vectors. Equation (10.10) is readily recognizable as the well-known law of cosines in trigonometry giving the value of one side of a triangle in

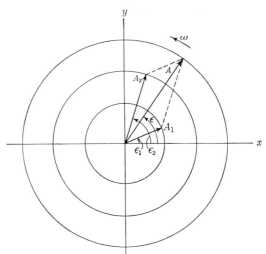

FIG. 10.3. The vector addition of amplitudes.

terms of the other two sides and the included angle between them. The amplitudes may then be represented as vectors, as shown in Fig. 10.3. The amplitudes $A_1$ and $A_2$ are represented as vectors having phase constants $\epsilon_1$ and $\epsilon_2$, respectively, and rotating with an angular speed $\omega$. By vector addition the resultant amplitude $A$ is given by the diagonal of the parallelogram and leads to Eq. (10.10). The vertical components of $A_1$ and $A_2$ are seen to be $y_1 = A_1 \sin(\omega t + \epsilon_1)$ and $y_2 = A_2 \sin(\omega t + \epsilon_2)$, and that of $A$ is $y = A \sin(\omega t + \epsilon)$; all three vectors rotate with the same angular velocity $\omega$, and the resultant displacement $y = y_1 + y_2$ is satisfied at all instants. The phase constant $\epsilon$ of the resultant motion is seen to be given by Eq. (10.11). The

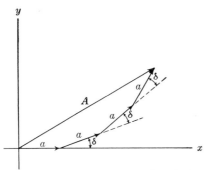

FIG. 10.4. Resultant amplitude of four equal amplitudes having the constant phase difference δ.

equivalent polygonal method of forming the resultant amplitude of many amplitudes with corresponding phase constants is very useful, as we shall see in our study of diffraction. Figure 10.4 illustrates the vector construction for the resultant amplitude $A$ of four equal amplitudes $a$ with corresponding equal phase differences δ. Clearly, the resultant intensity, proportional to $A^2$, will depend for its value on $a$ and δ.

Let us now consider the addition of two simple harmonic motions of the same frequency but with displacements at right angles to each other. This kind of superposition has important applications in the study of light. Consider the two harmonic motions to be executed along the $y$ and $z$ axes with corresponding amplitudes $A$ and $B$. Then the two motions are expressed by

$$y = A \sin (\omega t + \epsilon_1)$$
$$z = B \sin (\omega t + \epsilon_2) \tag{10.13}$$

where $\epsilon_1$ and $\epsilon_2$ are the phase constants corresponding to the two motions. Both equations are related parametrically by $t$, which may be eliminated to give the resultant motion. From Eqs. (10.13) we obtain

$$\frac{y^2}{A^2} - \frac{2yz}{AB} \cos (\epsilon_2 - \epsilon_1) + \frac{z^2}{B^2} = \sin^2 (\omega t + \epsilon_1) + \sin^2 (\omega t + \epsilon_2)$$
$$- 2 \sin (\omega t + \epsilon_1) \sin (\omega t + \epsilon_2) \cos (\epsilon_2 - \epsilon_1) \tag{10.14}$$

By suitable trigonometric substitutions it can easily be shown that the right-hand member of Eq. (10.14) is identical with $\sin^2 (\epsilon_2 - \epsilon_1)$. Thus the resultant motion is given by

$$\frac{y^2}{A^2} - \frac{2yz}{AB} \cos (\epsilon_2 - \epsilon_1) + \frac{z^2}{B^2} = \sin^2 (\epsilon_2 - \epsilon_1) \tag{10.15}$$

Equation (10.15) is one of second degree, and the student will remember, from analytical geometry, that the locus type is determined by the character of the indicator formed by subtracting four times the product of the coefficients of the $y^2$ and $z^2$ terms from the square of the coefficient of the product term $yz$. Here the indicator is

$$\frac{4}{A^2B^2} \cos^2 (\epsilon_2 - \epsilon_1) - \frac{4}{A^2B^2} = -\frac{4}{A^2B^2} \sin^2 (\epsilon_2 - \epsilon_1)$$

which is less than zero for all values of $\epsilon_2 - \epsilon_1$ other than $0$, $\pi$, $2\pi$, $3\pi$, . . . and thus represents an ellipse with center at the origin. For $\epsilon_2 - \epsilon_1 = \pi/2$ $3\pi/2$, $5\pi/2$, . . . , Eq. (10.15) becomes

$$\frac{y^2}{A^2} + \frac{z^2}{B^2} = 1$$

which is an ellipse oriented with its axes $2A$ and $2B$ parallel to the axes of $y$ and $z$, respectively. For all values of $\epsilon_2 - \epsilon_1$ other than an integral multiple of $\pi$ the ellipse is rotated with respect to the $y$ and $z$ axes. When $\epsilon_2 - \epsilon_1 = 0$, $\pi$, $2\pi$, $3\pi$, . . . , the equation yields the straight lines

$$y = \pm \frac{A}{B} z$$

the positive slope corresponding to $\epsilon_2 - \epsilon_1 = 0$, $2\pi$, $4\pi$, . . . and the negative slope corresponding to $\epsilon_2 - \epsilon_1 = \pi$, $3\pi$, $5\pi$, . . . . We have here considered the two motions to have equal frequencies, and this is the case of primary interest in the study of light. The curves obtained are examples of the more general class of resultant motions known as Lissajous figures, and some very interesting motions may be achieved by combining two motions with different frequencies. However, we shall be primarily concerned with component vibrations of the same frequency in the study of polarized light.

**10.5. Coherence and Incoherence of Waves.** Let us consider the sum of a large number of simple harmonic wave trains of the same frequency and having amplitudes $A_1$, $A_2$, $A_3$, . . . , $A_N$. If the phases of all the waves are the same, then by the method of Fig. 10.4 all the vectors point in the same direction, the resultant amplitude is the sum of the individual amplitudes, and the intensity is proportional to $(A_1 + A_2 + A_3 + \cdots + A_N)^2$. If in addition all the amplitudes are equal, then the intensity is proportional to $N^2$ times the intensity of a single wave. This result is illustrative of the fact that when all the waves have fixed phases relative to each other, the waves are said to be *coherent* and amplitudes add to give the resultant amplitude.

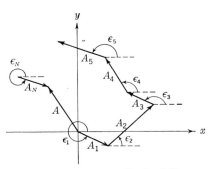

Fig. 10.5. Resultant amplitude of $N$ waves having random phases.

On the other hand, suppose that all the phases have completely random values. In other words the $\epsilon$'s are independent of each other, and each may arbitrarily take on any value from 0 to $2\pi$. In this case the method of Fig. 10.4 would yield an $N + 1$ polygon whose individual $N$ vectors have arbitrary directions as shown in Fig. 10.5. The square of the resultant amplitude $A$ forming the $(N + 1)st$ side is given by

$$A^2 = \left( \sum_{k=1}^{N} A_k \cos \epsilon_k \right)^2 + \left( \sum_{k=1}^{N} A_k \sin \epsilon_k \right)^2 \qquad (10.16)$$

where the first expression on the right-hand side of the equation represents the square of the summation of all the horizontal components of each vector amplitude and the second expression is the square of the summation of the vertical components of each vector. The squares of the summations lead to square terms of the type $\sum_k A_k^2 \cos^2 \epsilon_k$ and $\sum_k A_k^2 \sin^2 \epsilon_k$ and to product terms of the type $\sum_{k \neq m} A_k A_m \cos \epsilon_k \cos \epsilon_m$ and $\sum_{k \neq m} A_k A_m$

$\sin \epsilon_k \sin \epsilon_m$. Since the $\epsilon$'s are strictly random, so that each $\epsilon$ has the same likelihood of having any value between 0 and $2\pi$, the summations must be averaged with respect to the phases from 0 to $2\pi$. The computation of such an average gives for the product terms $\cos \epsilon_k \cos \epsilon_m$ or $\sin \epsilon_k \sin \epsilon_m$, zero, while the square terms $\cos^2 \epsilon_k$ or $\sin^2 \epsilon_k$ each averages to $\frac{1}{2}$ (see Prob. 10.14). Therefore the average of the square amplitude is

$$\sum_{k=1}^{N} A_k^2 = A_1^2 + A_2^2 + A_3^2 + \cdots + A_N^2,$$ or the average intensity is pro-

portional to the sum of the intensities of the individual waves. If all the amplitudes are equal, then the average intensity is proportional to $N$ times the intensity of a single wave. Thus when the waves have random phase relations, they are said to be *incoherent* and the intensities add to give the resultant mean intensity. This conclusion implies that $N$ is very large, for otherwise the cancellation of waves will not be complete, since in the analysis it is implied, for instance, that with random phases there will be just as many terms with positive values as there will be with negative values of $\cos \epsilon_k$ and the terms will cancel.

Optical electromagnetic waves, such as the light from a sodium flame, are due to the source atoms emitting wave trains which have random phases that are changing many times per second. The radiation then is incoherent. When two waves from two different sources are brought together, they never can be made to interfere because, as discussed in the next section, two sources are sufficiently different so that there is no systematic phase relation between the light of a given frequency from one source and that of the corresponding frequency from the other source. The resultant mean intensity is then the sum of the individual intensities. Interference effects would therefore not be possible. To get interference, it is necessary to divide the light from a single source into two parts, or beams, and then permit these two beams to superimpose. In this way a constant phase difference is preserved at all times, the waves are coherent, and interference effects may be produced. We shall see how this is done in the next chapter.

**10.6. Complex Waves and the Fourier Theorem.** We have seen that when any number of simple harmonic waves, with equal frequencies but different amplitudes and phases, are compounded they superpose in such a way as to give a resultant wave that is also simple harmonic of the same frequency. It may therefore be represented by a simple sinusoidal function having the proper resultant amplitude and phase constant. The more general case of superposing simple periodic waves having different frequencies gives rise to resultant waves that cannot be represented by a simple periodic function and are called complex waves. In Fig. 10.6 are shown three examples of a complex wave synthesized in (a) from two simple periodic sine waves traveling in the same direction, with the frequencies in the ratio of 3/1, amplitudes in the ratio 2/1, and in phase, in (b) from the same component waves but out of phase by $\pi/4$, and in (c) from one sine and one cosine curve having frequency and amplitude relations as in (a). In each case the two component waves are shown on the lower level, and the resultant complex form, obtained by adding

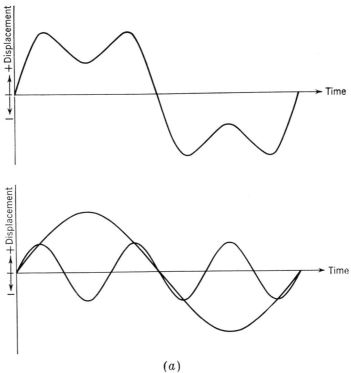

(a)

Fig. 10.6. Complex wave forms.

the displacements due to the individual waves, is shown on the upper level. It is clear that none of the complex waves is representable by a single sinusoidal function. The complex forms are periodic, and as a comparison between all three illustrates, the resultant amplitude depends on the phase difference.

The reverse process, that of decomposing a complex wave into a number of simple ones, is also possible according to a theorem by the French mathematician Fourier (1768–1830). The theorem states that any periodic function can be represented by a sum of sine and cosine terms of the form

$$y = A_0 + A_1 \sin \omega t + A_2 \sin 2\omega t + A_3 \sin 3\omega t + \cdots$$
$$+ B_1 \cos \omega t + B_2 \cos 2\omega t + B_3 \cos 3\omega t + \cdots \quad (10.17)$$

where $y$ is the displacement of the complex wave at any time $t$. Equation (10.17) is known as a Fourier series and represents the complex wave $y$ whose given form is employed mathematically to determine the amplitudes $A_k$ and $B_k$. Many complex forms may be exactly reproduced by employing a limited number of components such as the complex wave in Fig. 10.6$a$, which has the Fourier form $y = 2A \sin \omega t + A \sin 3\omega t$. For

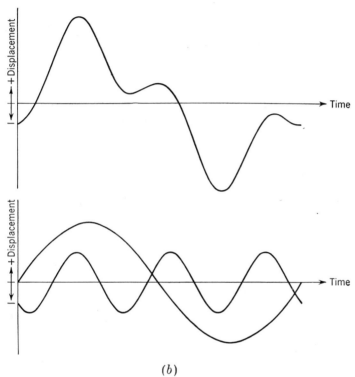

(b)

FIG. 10.6. (*Continued*)

other complex wave forms as high as 20 or 30 components may be required, while for certain arbitrary complex forms a finite number of components is insufficient and an infinite series of components must be employed to give an exact reproduction.

A light beam is really a complex wave in which there are superposed a multitude of elementary wave trains emitted by the atoms composing the light source. No physical wave is perfectly sinusoidal, and even a highly monochromatic light wave must be considered as containing a finite range of frequencies. It is therefore often desirable to find the spectrum components of a light wave, and this may be done by the Fourier methods.

**10.7. Huygens' Principle.** When the original wave theory was first proposed, one of the objections raised against it was its inability to account for the rectilinear propagation of light. The arguments followed the reasoning that if light consists of a wave motion it should behave in a manner similar to water and sound waves, which obviously bend around corners. As we have already mentioned, light waves do show the phenomenon of diffraction and, as we shall point out, when the wavelength of the wave is very small in comparison with the dimensions of an

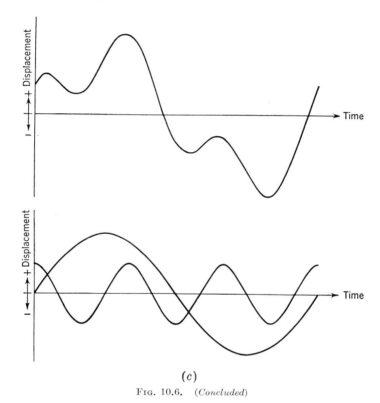

(c)

FIG. 10.6. (*Concluded*)

obstacle or aperture, the amount of bending or diffraction is extremely small. That such is the case with light waves was not realized even though Grimaldi had succeeded in obtaining some diffraction effects. Nevertheless rectilinear propagation is approximately followed for light waves, and to overcome the difficulties that the wave theory experienced in explaining rectilinear propagation, Huygens proposed that all points on a wave front may be considered as centers of new disturbances, thus creating secondary wavelets which travel with a speed equal to that of propagation of the wave; the envelope to these secondary wavelets at any subsequent time locates the form and position of the new wave front. As an illustration, in Fig. 10.7 are shown two wave fronts *W*, in

(a) of the spherical type originating from a point source S and in (b) of the plane type. A wave front, it will be recalled, is a surface all points of which are vibrating in the same phase. For each, the points 1, 2, 3, . . . 6 have been chosen as secondary sources of disturbance, and, with each point as center, a wavelet of radius $vt$ has been drawn, where $v$ is the

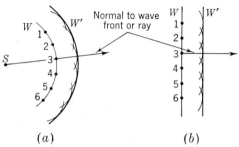

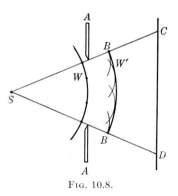

FIG. 10.7. Huygens' construction. (a) Spherical wave front. (b) Plane wave front.

velocity of propagation of the wave and $t$ is any subsequent time. The envelope, or common tangent, to all the wavelets locates the new wave front $W'$, which is spherical in (a) and plane in (b). That the Huygens construction explains the apparent formation of sharp shadows, or the rectilinear propagation, is shown by Fig. 10.8, which shows a light source S, an aperture $AA$, and a screen $CD$. The lines $SC$ and $SD$ are normals to the spherical wave front $W$ and represent light rays that we have employed in our study of geometrical optics. The points $C$ and $D$ then represent the positions where a sharp shadow should be cast, if the rectilinear propagation were strictly true, producing light on the screen that is inside the cone $CSD$ and perfect darkness above $C$ and below $D$. By using Huygens' construction there is obtained the wave front $W'$, which is limited by the points $BB$ lying on the rays $SC$ and $SD$. Light will therefore be present at $C$ and $D$ and between $C$ and $D$ and will be absent in the regions of the geometrical shadows. We know, however, that light does bend into the geometrical shadow to a very slight extent, indicating that something about this simple conception of secondary wavelets is not quite valid. A little thought shows that the principle assumes that only one point on the secondary wavelet is effective in producing light, *viz.*, the point lying on the envelope to the wavelets. Such a view cannot be reconciled with experiment. In addition the construction predicts a backward wave, since each source

FIG. 10.8.

of secondary disturbance sends out a spherical wavelet and, by Huygens' construction, another series of wave fronts moving toward the light source is obtainable.  This of course is never observed experimentally.

Fresnel, making use of the principles of interference, was able to resolve the difficulties and provide a satisfactory explanation.  In the chapter on Diffraction we shall see how the principles of interference explain the phenomenon of the bending of light around obstacles and also lead to approximate rectilinear propagation.  The method of interference considers that the secondary wavelets have amplitudes and simple harmonic vibrations.  The wavelets are then treated as many interfering sources,

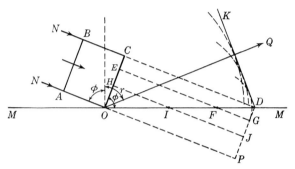

Fig. 10.9. Reflection by Huygens' principle.

and the disturbance at any point is found by combining the various wave trains to yield the resultant.  In this mathematical study of Huygens' principle, which is beyond the scope of this text, it proves to be true that the spherical wavelets have an amplitude that depends on the factor $\cos \theta + 1$, where $\theta$ is the angle between the outward normal to a spherical wave front and the line drawn from the intersection point of the normal with the wave front to the point at which the resultant disturbance is being computed.  The intersection point of the normal with the wave front represents a source of secondary wavelets.  In the forward direction $\theta = 0$, and the amplitude exists, but in the backward direction $\theta = 180°$, and the amplitude is zero.  This means that the wavelets do not travel backward, thus doing away with the difficulty in Huygens' original principle.  The quantity $\cos \theta + 1$ is called the *obliquity* factor, and we shall have other occasions to refer to it.

We have seen how Huygens' construction locates the position of the wave front after a given time, and we shall now see how it may be employed to prove the laws of reflection and refraction.

In Fig. 10.9 is shown a portion of a plane wave front $AB$ bounded by the wave normals $N$ advancing in the direction shown, making an angle $\phi$ with the plane reflecting surface. $MM$.  To make the Huygens construction and locate the new wave front after reflection, consider the instant when point $A$ is at $O$ in contact with the reflecting surface and point $B$ is at $C$. All the points along $OD$, such as $I$, $F$, and $D$, will be struck in succession by the corresponding point on the advancing wave front, such as $H$, $E$, and $C$, respectively, and by Huygens' principle they will become centers of secondary wavelets. If there were no reflecting boundary and the medium were homogeneous, the wave front $OC$ would be at position $DP$ in the time it takes $C$ to reach $D$. After this time the wavelet from $O$ as center has a radius $OP$, that from $I$ as center has a radius $IJ$, and that from $F$ as center has the radius $FG$. The new wave front is $DK$ and moves in the direction of its wave normal $Q$, making an angle of reflection

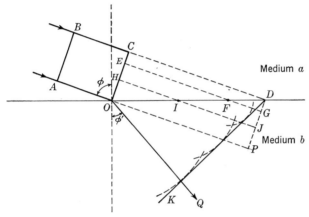

Fɪɢ. 10.10. Refraction by Huygens' principle.

$r$ with the perpendicular to the reflecting surface at $O$. It is readily seen that the angle of incidence $\phi$ is equal to the angle of reflection $r$.

In Fig. 10.10 is shown the Huygens construction for the refraction of a plane wave front $AB$. The velocities of the wave disturbance in the upper and lower media are $v_a$ and $v_b$, respectively, where $v_a > v_b$. The incident wave front, whose normal makes an angle $\phi$ with the perpendicular to the refracting surface at $O$, gives rise to secondary disturbances at all points along $OD$. In the time it takes the disturbance to travel from $C$ to $D$, the wavelet from $O$ is at a distance equal to $(v_b/v_a)OP$, that from $I$ is at a distance $(v_b/v_a)IJ$, etc. The refracted wave front is $DK$ propagated in the direction $OQ$, making an angle $\phi'$ with the perpendicular to the refracting surface. It is left as an exercise for the student to show that $\sin \phi / \sin \phi' = v_a / v_b$.

**10.8. The Velocity of Light.** A very fundamental property of light, and of all electromagnetic radiations, is its finite velocity of propagation. It is a quantity which has been measured with extremely high precision since its determination was first attempted by Galileo and represents one of the most significant constants in our physical universe. We shall here review some of the methods that were employed to measure the velocity of light.

The very first attempt was made in the year 1667, the method being that proposed by Galileo. Two men with lanterns were stationed atop two hills a large distance apart (about 1 mile). At the start of the experiment each lantern was covered. Then one man uncovered his lantern and the other man uncovered his lantern the instant he saw the light from the first man's lantern. The first man measured the time from the instant he uncovered his lantern to the instant he observed the light from the other man's lantern. The velocity of light is then calculable by

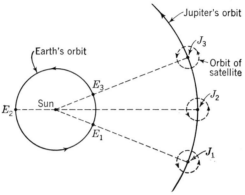

FIG. 10.11. Römer's observations leading to the determination of the velocity of light.

dividing twice the separation of the men by the recorded time. The experiment failed, however, since the velocity is so large that it demanded the time to be measured to the order of $10^{-5}$ sec, which of course was lacking in the experiment.

The first successful determination was made by a Danish astronomer, Römer in 1675, using astronomical observations. To understand the method, it is necessary to recall that the planet Jupiter has several satellites, or moons, that revolve about it as does the earth's moon about the earth. The satellites revolve in orbits that are nearly parallel to the orbital plane of Jupiter and the earth, so that each satellite becomes eclipsed once in each revolution. Jupiter itself has a period around the sun which is somewhat under 12 years, while the average period of revolution of the inner satellite of Jupiter is a little less than 42.5 hr. Römer was engaged in studying the time of occurrence of the eclipses of this inner satellite, and he noted, from data accumulated over a long period of observations, that the time between successive eclipses varied throughout the year, an eclipse occurring earlier than the expected time while the earth was approaching Jupiter and later than the calculated time while the earth was receding from Jupiter. The facts are illustrated by Fig. 10.11. At some period in the earth's revolution, the earth will be in position $E_1$ closest to Jupiter's position $J_1$. Considering the orbits as circular, the earth will be in position $E_2$ farthest away from Jupiter's position $J_2$ after a time $t$ given by $\omega_E t = \pi + \omega_J t$, where $\omega_E$ and $\omega_J$ are the angular velocities of the earth and Jupiter, respectively. Taking $\omega_J = 12\omega_E$, $t = 0.545$ year, so that again after this time the earth will be in position $E_3$ nearest to Jupiter's position $J_3$. The light signal of an eclipse will reach the earth, when in position $E_2$, at a later time than when the earth is at $E_1$ or $E_3$. Römer concluded that this increase is the time required for light to traverse the diameter of the earth's orbit and obtained a value of 192,000 miles/sec for the velocity of light. This value is high owing to the fact that the diameter of the earth's orbit was known only approximately in Römer's time. If we use the value 16.5 min as the time taken for light to traverse the diameter of the earth's orbit, about 185,600,000 miles, the velocity of light is about 187,000 miles/sec.

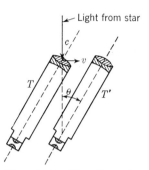

FIG. 10.12. The aberration of light.

The second determination for the velocity of light was made by Bradley in 1728 in connection with his astronomical discovery that there is an apparent shift in the position of a fixed star due to the motion of the earth in its orbit. This effect is known as the *aberration of light* and can be understood from Fig. 10.12. A telescope $T$ is used to view a star's light which is moving in the direction of the downward arrow with velocity $c$. If the telescope were stationary, its axis would have to be pointed vertically in the true direction of the star, whose image would then be brought into view. Now consider that the earth's orbital motion results in the telescope's moving with velocity $v$ at right angles to $c$. In order to permit the light to travel down the axis of the instrument as it moves from position $T$ to position $T'$, the telescope must now be inclined in the direction of its motion at an angle $\theta$ with the vertical as shown. The relationship between the *angle of aberration* $\theta$, the velocity of the earth $v$, and the velocity of light $c$ is seen to be $\tan \theta = v/c$. By measuring $\theta$ and using the value known to be the orbital velocity of the earth Bradley found a value of $c$ which agreed within experimental error to that obtained by Römer in the previous method. The aberration is a maximum when the direction of the motion of the earth is at right angles to the direction of the star as in Fig. 10.12 and is zero when the earth's motion is along the direction of the star. For a star whose direction is perpendicular to the plane of the earth's orbit and passing through the sun, the apparent motion of the star when the observations are extended for a year is a circle, while for a star whose direction is in the plane of the earth's orbit, the apparent motion of the star is a straight line. For a star whose direction makes an angle between 0 and 90° with the earth's orbital plane, the apparent motion of the star is an ellipse. The student should illustrate these cases with diagrams.

The first laboratory method for measuring the velocity of light was devised by Fizeau in 1849. In principle the method resembles that of Galileo but was developed with apparatus that made it possible to measure a short time interval with good precision. Light from an intense source $S$ (Fig. 10.13) is introduced into the tube $T$ through the lenses $L_1$, which focus the light at $F$ with the aid of a glass plate $P$. $W$ is a large, many-toothed wheel, free to rotate in a vertical plane around the horizontal

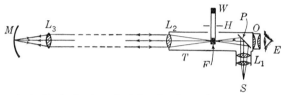

Fig. 10.13. Fizeau's toothed-wheel method for the determination of the velocity of light.

axis $H$ and positioned so that $F$ comes at one of the spaces of the toothed wheel. With $F$ at the principal focus of lens $L_2$ the light is rendered parallel outside the optical tube. After traveling several miles the light is brought to a focus on the concave spherical mirror $M$ by lens $L_3$. The center of curvature of $M$ is made to coincide with the center of $L_3$ so that the light is returned as a parallel beam over the same path and passes through $P$ and into the ocular $O$. When the wheel is rotated, the light beam is broken up into short wave trains, and if the speed is appropriate, the flash that passes through the space between two teeth returns to $F$ when the next tooth occupies the position formerly occupied by the space through which the light has passed. The image of $S$ is therefore eclipsed. At twice this speed the image of $S$ is again visible since the next space falls into position at $F$. Knowing the distance from the wheel to the mirror, the number of cogs on the wheel, and the speed of rotation of the wheel, the velocity of light can be determined. In one of Fizeau's determinations twice the distance from $F$ to $M$ was 10.72 miles, the wheel had 720 teeth, and the first eclipse occurred at a rotational speed of 12.6 rev/sec. This gives for the velocity of light

$$c = (10.72)(1440)(12.6) = 194,500 \text{ miles/sec}$$

That this value is much higher than those obtained from astronomical observations is explained by the fact that Fizeau's determinations lacked the comparable precision, owing principally to the difficulty encountered in ascertaining the exact speed of rotation at the time of an eclipse. Also, the light reflected from the teeth of the wheel caused a general illumination of the field. Fizeau's experiments were improved upon by subsequent investigators, principally Cornu in 1874 and Young and Forbes several years later. The rotations of the wheel were automatically recorded, the distance from wheel to mirror was increased, an improved technique for observing the condition of eclipses was employed, the teeth were beveled so as to reduce the presence of general illumination, and other improvements[1] were utilized. Cornu obtained a value of 300,400 km/sec, or about 186,700 miles/sec, and Forbes obtained a value somewhat higher.

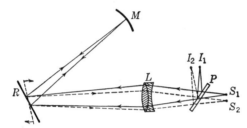

Fig. 10.14. The rotating-mirror method of Fizeau and Foucault.

In the year 1850 both Fizeau and Foucault, although collaborating for a while, independently made public their measurements of the velocity of light by what is known as the rotating-mirror method. Light from a well-defined source $S_1$ (Fig. 10.14) falls on a lens $L$, which converges the beam onto a mirror $R$, free to rotate about an axis normal to the paper. The light is brought to a focus on the fixed concave mirror $M$, whose center of curvature coincides with the axis of rotation of $R$. Since the central ray of the convergent pencil is normal to $M$, the light will retrace its path and come to a focus at $S_1$. With a glass plate $P$ interposed between the lens and the light source an image of $S_1$ is formed at $I_1$. The central ray of the pencil, reflected from $R$, is always normal whatever the position of $R$ so that if $R$ is rotated slowly, then as long as light falls on the mirror $M$ the light is returned over the same path and forms an image at $I_1$. But if $R$ is rotated rapidly enough so that it turns through an appreciable angle while the light traverses the path from $R$ to $M$ and back to $R$, then the returning light will traverse a new path after reflection at $R$. With the mirror rotating in the direction shown the rays will follow the dotted path and form the image at $S_2$ or at $I_2$ after reflection from $P$. The shift in the position of the image $I_1 I_2$ is a function of the angle turned through by the rotating mirror, the distance $RM$, the dis-

---

[1] For more details the reader is referred to W. M. Preston, "The Theory of Light," 5th ed., The Macmillan Company, New York, 1928.

tance $RL$, and the distance $LS_1$.   By measuring the image shift, the angle turned through by $R$ in the time it takes light to traverse the distance $2RM$ is determined, and knowing the angular velocity of rotation of $R$ the velocity of light is calculable.   In Foucault's measurements, $RM$ was effectively 20 m, and the mirror was rotated at a speed to give an image deflection of 0.7 min which was measured with a micrometer eyepiece.   He obtained the value $2.98 \times 10^{10}$ cm/sec, or 185,200 miles/sec.   The small image shift limited the precision of the experiment, but with his apparatus Foucault was able to prove that the velocity of light in water is less than that in air by introducing a tube of water between $R$ and $M$.   We have seen that the Newtonian corpuscular theory of light

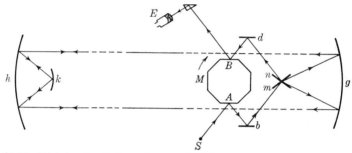

Fɪɢ. 10.15.  Michelson's rotating-mirror method for measuring the velocity of light.

demanded that light have a greater velocity in water, and Foucault's result was decisive evidence against the corpuscular theory.   It is to be noted that the precision of Foucault's determination was limited by his inability to increase the distance $RM$ since an increase in this distance resulted in an intolerable loss in intensity in the image.   This is so because light is returned from $M$ only during a small fraction of the time required for a rotation of $R$ and this fraction gets smaller as RM is increased. Michelson (1852–1931) modified the Fizeau-Foucault apparatus, removing the lens from the position shown in Fig. 10.14, and placing a lens of very long focal length between the two mirrors and close to $R$.   With this arrangement he was able to increase the distance $RM$ by about a factor of 30 and suffer practically no loss in intensity of the image, obtaining a shift in the image $I_1I_2$ amounting to 133 mm.   Newcomb further increased the brightness of the image and thus was able to use larger distances $RM$ by employing a rotating mirror made of four reflecting surfaces rather than just one.

The most precise series of measurements of the velocity of light, with apparatus based on the Foucault method, were made by Michelson and his associates.   Figure 10.15 shows a diagrammatic sketch of the apparatus used by Michelson in 1924.   Light from a high-intensity-arc source

$S$ is incident on one of the reflecting faces $A$ of an octagonal mirror $M$, which directs it with the aid of mirrors $b$ and $m$ to the concave mirror $g$. Mirror $g$ reflects the light into a parallel beam to the concave mirror $h$, which brings it to a focus at the concave mirror $k$. As in the Fizeau apparatus the beam retraces its path to $g$, converges to the mirror $n$, and, by way of mirror $d$, is incident on the opposite face of the octagonal mirror. From there it passes to the micrometer ocular $E$, which is used to indicate with precision the position of the image. When the mirror $M$ is rotated at the appropriate speed, it completes ⅛ rev in the time it takes the light to travel from $A$ to $g$ to $h$ and back to $B$. In this time one face of $M$ exactly replaces the next one adjacent to it, and the position of the image in $E$ remains unaltered. Knowing the distance of the total light path and the angular speed of the rotating mirror, the speed of light is readily obtainable. Thus if $l$ is the total distance traversed by the light beam and $N$ is the number of revolutions of $M$, then the velocity of light $c$ is given by $c = 8lN$. In Michelson's determinations the light traveled from the observation station on Mount Wilson to a station on Mount San Antonio, both in California, a distance of about 22 miles, or 35.4 km. This distance was determined by the U.S. Coast and Geodetic Survey to an accuracy of better than $14 \times 10^{-6}$ per cent. The speed of rotation of the mirror, amounting to about 529 rev/sec, was measured by comparison with standard tuning forks and standard pendulums. The mean of more than 1700 individual determinations, corrected to vacuum, was $c = 299,796 \pm 4$ km/sec. The correction to vacuum was made for air having an effective refractive index of 1.000225, corresponding to the conditions of temperature and pressure prevailing in Michelson's determinations. The correction here amounts to an increase of a little over 67 km/sec, obtained by $(0.000225)(299,796)/1.000225$ (why?). (The values quoted for the previous determinations were also corrected to vacuum.)

In order to eliminate the uncertainty of the exact conditions of the atmosphere through which the light was traveling and, at the same time, improve the quality of the image, Michelson and his coworkers Pease and Pearson in 1929 set for themselves the task of determining the velocity of light in vacuum directly. For this purpose a tube 1 mile long and about 3 ft in diameter was constructed, and the optical path was made to occur within the tube which could be evacuated to about 0.5 mm Hg. A rotating mirror of 32 faces was employed, and the actual light path, by repeated reflections within the tube, amounted to about 10 miles. The measurements were completed, after Michelson's death (1931), by Pease and Pearson, who obtained the value $c = 299,774$ km/sec with a probable error of a few tenths kilometers per second, the value being a mean of nearly 3000 determinations.

A method similar in principle to the toothed-wheel method of Fizeau was employed by Karolus and Mittelstaedt in 1925 to yield a very accurate value for the velocity of light. The method permits the interruption of a light beam several millions of times per second, using Kerr cells and the principles of polarized light. The principles of polarization are taken up in Chap. 16, and we shall here merely include as much in our discussion as is necessary to give an over-all view of the method. Figure 10.16 shows a schematic outline of the apparatus, which contains two Kerr cells $K_1$, $K_2$ and three nicol prisms $N_1$, $N_2$, and $N_3$. The Kerr cells

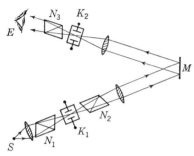

are essentially condenser plates containing nitrobenzene between them, and when a cell, such as $K_1$, is placed between two crossed nicols $N_1$ and $N_2$, the light from the source $S$ passes through to the mirror $M$ when there is a voltage across the plates of $K_1$. When there is no voltage across the plates of $K_1$, no light gets through $N_2$. By placing a high-frequency alternating potential across the plates of $K_1$ the light beam from $S$ may accordingly be interrupted. After reflection from $M$ the light passes through another Kerr cell $K_2$, which is followed by the nicol prism $N_3$, which is crossed in relation to $N_2$. Thus $K_2$ has the same relationship between $N_2$ and $N_3$ as $K_1$ had between $N_1$ and $N_2$. Therefore light will get through to the eye $E$ only when there is a voltage across the plates of $K_2$. The light beam is thus chopped up electrically, as was done mechanically by the toothed wheel of Fizeau, but at a much greater rate depending on the frequency of the voltage wave impressed on the plates of $K_1$. With the same voltage wave supplying $K_1$ and $K_2$, consider the instant when a voltage maximum is present on the Kerr cells, permitting a light flash to emerge from $N_2$. If, in the time it takes the light to reflect from $M$ and reach $K_2$, the voltage wave across $K_2$ passes through its zero value, the light will be eclipsed and the eye will see no light. This state of affairs corresponds to an eclipse occurring with the Fizeau apparatus when a tooth occupies the position previously occupied by a space in the time it takes the light to travel outward and return again. With an effective light path of somewhat under 333 km and known frequency of the voltage variations Karolus and Mittelstaedt obtained, as a mean value of their determinations, $c = 299,778$ km/sec. This result, corrected to vacuum, has an error of $\pm 20$ km/sec and is seen to have very good agreement with the precise determinations of Michelson, Pease, and Pearson. Anderson

Fig. 10.16. Measurement of the velocity of light by the Kerr cell method.

in 1941 used a Kerr cell arrangement and reported for the velocity of light in vacuum $c = 299,776 \pm 14$ km/sec.

The suggested value for the best value of the velocity of light in vacuum is $c = 299,776$ km/sec, and this agrees closely with the value predicted on the basis of Maxwell's theory of electromagnetic waves and with the experimentally determined value for the velocity of these waves in free space. It is now a generally accepted fact that light is an electromagnetic radiation.

**10.9. Group and Wave Velocity.** Let us consider two sine waves $W$ and $W'$ (Fig. 10.17$a$), having equal amplitude $A$, with corresponding wavelengths $\lambda$ and $\lambda'$, and traveling to the right with velocities $v$ and $v'$,

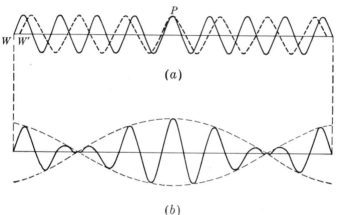

(a)

(b)

Fɪɢ. 10.17. (a) Two waves, differing slightly in wavelength and velocity, moving to the right. (b) Illustrating the group formation of the two waves.

respectively. The resultant wave displacement $y$ as a function of the horizontal distance $x$ and time $t$ is given by

$$y = A \sin \frac{2\pi}{\lambda} (vt - x) + A \sin \frac{2\pi}{\lambda'} (v't - x)$$

which, from the trigonometric relation

$$\sin a + \sin b = 2 \sin \left[ \frac{(a + b)}{2} \right] \cos \left[ \frac{(a - b)}{2} \right]$$

may be written

$$y = 2A \sin \pi \left[ \left( \frac{v}{\lambda} + \frac{v'}{\lambda'} \right) t - \left( \frac{1}{\lambda} + \frac{1}{\lambda'} \right) x \right] \cos \pi \left[ \left( \frac{v}{\lambda} - \frac{v'}{\lambda'} \right) t - \left( \frac{1}{\lambda} - \frac{1}{\lambda'} \right) x \right]$$

Now consider that $\lambda$ differs from $\lambda'$ and $v$ differs from $v'$ by slight amounts $d\lambda$ and $dv$, respectively; then

$$y = 2A \, \sin \pi \left[ \frac{2v\lambda + v \, d\lambda + \lambda \, dv}{\lambda(\lambda + d\lambda)} \, t - \frac{2\lambda + d\lambda}{\lambda(\lambda + d\lambda)} \, x \right]$$

$$\cos \pi \left[ \frac{v \, d\lambda - x \, dv}{\lambda(\lambda + d\lambda)} \, t - \frac{d\lambda}{\lambda(\lambda + d\lambda)} \, x \right]$$

and taking $d\lambda$ small compared with $\lambda$ and $dv$ small compared with $v$,

$$y = 2A \, \cos \frac{\pi \, d\lambda}{\lambda^2} \left( \frac{v \, d\lambda - \lambda \, dv}{d\lambda} \, t - x \right) \sin \frac{2\pi}{\lambda} \, (vt - x) \qquad (10.18)$$

which is the equation of a sine wave of the same velocity and wavelength as one of the original waves $W$ but with an amplitude that is modulated in accordance with the cosine factor. This resultant wave for a given instant is shown by the solid curve in Fig. 10.17$b$. The figure also shows the envelope (dotted curve), whose wavelength is greater and can be seen to have the value $2\lambda^2/d\lambda$. The superposition of the two waves shown in ($a$) produces the wave group illustrated by ($b$), and the velocity with which the maximum of the group moves, *i.e.*, the *group velocity* $u$, is given by the coefficient of $t$ inside the first parentheses of the cosine factor of Eq. (10.18), or

$$u = v - \lambda \frac{dv}{d\lambda} \qquad (10.19)$$

Therefore the group velocity, also called the signal velocity, is less than or greater than the wave velocity $v$, also called the phase velocity, according as $v$ in the medium increases or decreases with $\lambda$. In other words, with the longer waves $W'$ moving at a greater speed than those of $W$, at some time later the amplitude will build up to a maximum somewhat to the left of point $P$ and the group will have a smaller velocity than that of the individual waves, while if the shorter waves $W$ have the greater velocity, the amplitude will build up somewhat to the right of $P$ and the group will have a greater velocity than that of the waves. A train of waves advancing over the surface of water affords a visual illustration. There the individual waves may be seen to run forward through the group and die out as they arrive at the front, and fresh waves, replacing them, appear at the rear. The group as a whole moves more slowly than the waves. Although Eq. (10.19) was derived for a special group of waves, it can be shown it is quite general for any group of waves. It is important to realize that the energy belongs to the group rather than to the waves. The group velocity is equal to the wave velocity when $dv/d\lambda = 0$, that is, when all the individual waves have the same velocity or when there is no dispersion in the medium. As we have seen, a light beam is not strictly monochromatic, so that in the experimental determination of the velocity of light, many wavelengths are present. Furthermore, what is measured in the methods outlined in the previous section is an isolated wave train or a group of waves representable as a Fourier series of individual waves of different wavelengths, so that what is really determined is the group velocity rather than the wave velocity of the waves. But when it is said that the relative index of refraction is the ratio of the velocities in the two media, then what is referred to are the wave velocities. For transparent media in the optical region (see Sec. 15.7) the refractive index decreases with increase in wavelength; hence the wave velocity of light in these media increases with wavelength, and the group velocity is less than the wave velocity. The amount by which $u$ and $v$ differ depends on the dispersion curve for the particular medium. For air there is negligible difference between the measured group velocity and the actual wave velocity, amounting to a little over 2 km/sec. When Foucault measured the velocity of light in water, he also obtained a value for the group velocity that was nearly the value for the wave velocity, since water is not a highly dispersive liquid. On the other hand the measurement by Michelson on the velocity of light in carbon disulfide showed that the velocity of light in air is 1.76 times that in the liquid. From the indices of refraction for air and carbon disulfide, the velocity in air should be 1.64 times that in carbon disulfide. The difference between the group and wave velocities in carbon disulfide is just the amount to explain the apparent discrepancy.

## PROBLEMS

**10.1.** (*a*) Give explanations of the occurrence of simultaneous reflection and refraction, using (1) the Newtonian corpuscular theory and (2) the wave theory. (*b*) To what are the different colors due in white light, (1) on the basis of the corpuscular theory, (2) on the basis of the quantum theory?

**10.2.** Prove the harmonic relation $\omega \sqrt{A^2 - y^2}$ for the instantaneous velocity and $-\omega^2 y$ for the instantaneous acceleration given in Sec. 10.3.

**10.3.** Plot the equation $y = 5 \sin (2\pi x/6)$.

**10.4.** A particle performs the simple periodic motion given by

$$y = 10 \sin \left[ \frac{2\pi t}{T} + \alpha \right]$$

If the period is 30.0 sec/cycle and the particle has a displacement of 5 units at $t = 0$, find (*a*) the phase angle at $t = 7.50$ sec, (*b*) the phase difference between two positions of the particle 6 sec apart.

**10.5.** At a time $t = 0$ a train of waves has the form $y = 4 \sin (\pi x/50)$. The velocity of the wave is 30.0 cm/sec. Find the equation giving the wave form at a time $t = 2$ sec.

**10.6.** Plot the equation $y = 5 \sin \left( \frac{2\pi t}{8} - \frac{\pi}{6} \right)$.

**10.7.** A simple periodic wave disturbance having an amplitude of eight units traverses a line of particles in the positive $x$ direction. At a given instant the displacement of a particle 10.0 cm from the origin is six units, and that of a particle 25.0 cm from the origin is four units, both particles in positive displacement. What is the wavelength of the disturbance?

**10.8.** Draw up a chart of the electromagnetic spectrum, and tabulate the wavelengths or wavelength ranges of the various rays or wave regions in centimeters, angstroms, millimicrons, and X units.

**10.9.** Show that the resultant wave produced by the two waves

$$y_1 = A \sin 2\pi \left( \frac{t}{T} - \frac{x}{\lambda} \right)$$

and $y_2 = A \sin 2\pi \left( \frac{t}{T} - \frac{x + \Delta}{\lambda} \right)$ is given by $y = 2A \cos \frac{\pi \Delta}{\lambda} \sin 2\pi \left( \frac{t}{T} - \frac{x + \frac{\Delta}{2}}{\lambda} \right)$.
Interpret the result, and find what the resultant intensity is when the path difference is an integral number of wavelengths and when it is an odd integral number of half wavelengths.

**10.10.** When two similar wave trains travel through the same medium at the same time but in opposite directions, a pattern of "standing waves" is produced. Using the waves $y_1 = A \sin 2\pi \left( \frac{t}{T} - \frac{x}{\lambda} \right)$ and $y_2 = A \sin 2\pi \left( \frac{t}{T} + \frac{x}{\lambda} \right)$, find the resultant, and show that the antinodes, where the motion is a maximum, occur at the points $x = \lambda/2, \lambda, 3\lambda/2, 2\lambda, \ldots$, with the nodes occurring midway between a pair of antinodes.

**10.11.** Two periodic motions are given by $y_1 = 4 \sin (\omega t - 30°)$ and

$$y_2 = 6 \sin (\omega t - 60°)$$

Find the resultant amplitude and phase constant (a) graphically, (b) by calculation.

**10.12.** Find the resultant amplitude and phase constant of the three motions $y_1 = \sin (\omega t + 30°)$, $y_2 = 3 \sin (\omega t + 75°)$, $y_3 = 6 \sin (\omega t - 110°)$, (a) graphically, (b) by calculation.

**10.13.** Reduce the right-hand side of Eq. (10.14) to the value given in Eq. (10.15).

**10.14.** Show that the value of $\cos^2 \epsilon$ averaged over all angles from 0 to $2\pi$ is $\frac{1}{2}$. (HINT: Integrate the function between the limits 0 to $2\pi$, and divide by $2\pi$.)

**10.15.** Using Huygens' principle, construct the refracted wave front for a plane wave making an angle of 30° with the refracting surface. The ratio of the velocity of light in the incident medium to that in the refracting medium is $\frac{4}{3}$.

**10.16.** Using 18.5 miles/sec for the velocity of the earth in its orbit and 20.48 sec for the angle of aberration, find the value for the velocity of light.

**10.17.** Give an explanation of why the light retraced its path, in the Fizeau apparatus, after reflection from the mirror $M$.

**10.18.** In the Fizeau apparatus the speed of rotation of the wheel is adjusted until the $k$th eclipse occurs. Show that the velocity of light is given by $c = 4lnN/(2k - 1)$, where $l$ is the distance from the toothed wheel to the mirror $M$, $n$ is the number of revolutions of the wheel, and $N$ represents the number of teeth of the wheel. The widths of the teeth and open spaces are equal.

**10.19.** (a) Express Eq. (10.19) in the form $c/u = n - \lambda_0 \, dn/d\lambda_0$, where $c$ is the velocity of light in vacuum, $n$ is the index of refraction, and $\lambda_0$ is the wavelength in vacuum. Remember that $c = nv$ and $\lambda_0 = n\lambda$. (b) Show that in terms of the wavelength in the medium the expression takes the form

$$c/u = n^2/(n + \lambda \, dn/d\lambda) \doteq n - \lambda \, dn/d\lambda$$

# CHAPTER 11

## INTERFERENCE

We have seen in the last chapter (Secs. 10.4 and 10.5) that when two wave trains superimpose they may combine in such a way as to reinforce each other and produce a resultant intensity that is greater than what is to be expected from the separate intensities, exemplifying what is termed _constructive interference._ On the other hand, the combination may be such as to produce a resultant intensity that is less than what is to be expected from the separate intensities, exemplifying what is termed _destructive interference;_ if the resultant intensity is zero, it is termed _complete destructive interference._ There are two classes of interference phenomena, those arising from the superposition of waves that have undergone only reflection or refraction, and those arising from the superposition of waves that have experienced bending due to diffraction. We shall consider the former in this and the following chapter and treat the latter in Chap. 13.

Interference provides a criterion as to whether any phenomenon possesses wave properties. We shall see that certain fundamental conditions, some inherent in the nature of light and others necessary for experimental observations, must be satisfied in order to produce interference effects. We shall also see how interference affords a means of measurement of wavelengths.

**11.1. Interference from a Double Slit.** Thomas Young, in 1800, performed the first experiment revealing an interference pattern due to the superposition of wave trains from two separate light sources. Young permitted sunlight to pass through a pinhole $S$ (Fig. 11.1) and then through two pinholes $S_1$ and $S_2$. The spherical waves emerging from $S_1$ and $S_2$ interfere to form a pattern on the screen $MON$. In accordance – with the laboratory techniques employed today we shall consider the pinholes replaced by narrow parallel slits, thus giving rise to cylindrical wave fronts. The source is considered to be monochromatic so that only light of one wavelength is employed. A typical pattern of interference fringes from such a double-slit arrangement is shown in Fig. 11.2. The pattern shows evenly spaced light and dark bands, or fringes, running parallel to the plane of the double slits and symmetrical about the line through $O$. Let us see how the wave theory of light accounts for such a pattern. In Fig. 11.1 are drawn two sets of waves from $S_1$ and $S_2$ in accordance with Huygens' principle. In each set of waves a solid semicircle represents the region of maximum displacement, or crest of the wave, and midway between these are the broken semicircles representing the regions of minimum displacement, or wave troughs. The figure is drawn for some instant and reveals places where crests and crests fall

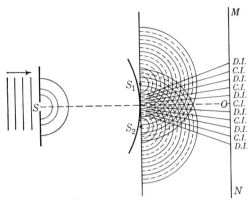

Fig. 11.1. Young's arrangement for interference from a double slit.   C.I., region of constructive interference.   D.I., region of destructive interference.

together and regions where crests and troughs fall together. Wherever a crest falls on a crest, the intensity is a maximum leading to regions of constructive interference (C.I.), while the meeting places of crest and trough lead to the regions of destructive interference (D.I.). These

Fig. 11.2. Interference fringes from a double slit.   (*By permission from "Fundamentals of Optics," by F. A. Jenkins and H. E. White.   Copyright, 1950, Second Edition.   McGraw-Hill Book Company, Inc.*)

regions of constructive and destructive interference are the alternate bands of brightness and darkness of Fig. 11.2.

Now consider Fig. 11.3 for a quantitative analysis. We are interested in the resultant disturbance at some point $P$ due to the superposition of the wave vibrations from the sources $S_1$ and $S_2$. With the slits $S_1$ and $S_2$ of equal width, very close together, and equidistant from the source slit $S$, the vibrations at $S_1$ and $S_2$ are of the same frequency and equal amplitude. The superposition of two such periodic motions was developed in Sec.

10.4, and the resultant amplitude at $P$ is given by Eq. (10.10), which here becomes

$$A_P^2 = 2A^2(1 + \cos \delta) = 4A^2 \cos^2 \frac{\delta}{2} \qquad (11.1)$$

where $A_P$ is the resultant amplitude at $P$, $A$ is the amplitude of either disturbance, and $\delta$ is the phase difference between the two disturbances at $P$. Using the relationship [Eq. (10.4)] between the phase difference and path difference, there results

$$\delta = \frac{2\pi}{\lambda} (S_2P - S_1P) \qquad (11.2)$$

Thus when

$$S_2P - S_1P = k\lambda,$$
$$k = 0, 1, 2, \ldots \qquad (11.3)$$

the intensity, proportional to the square of the amplitude, is a maximum, and when

$$S_2P - S_1P = (k + \tfrac{1}{2})\lambda$$
$$k = 0, 1, 2, \ldots \qquad (11.4)$$

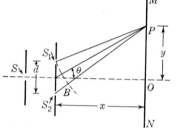

FIG. 11.3. Interference from a double slit showing the paths $S_1P$ and $S_2P$ from the slit sources to a point $P$.

the intensity is a minimum. There are therefore alternate regions of constructive and destructive interference on the screen $MN$, with the region at $O$ one of constructive interference. A plot of $A_P^2$ as a function of $\delta$ shows the intensity variation in the interference pattern. This is an oscillating function having periodic maxima with periodic intermediate minima in correspondence with the experimentally observed bright and dark fringes. The energy of the two beams redistributes in the interference pattern so that there is represented the same average intensity as would be present if there were no interference. For proof of this see Prob. 11.3.

It is very useful to express the path difference in terms of the distance $y$ that $P$ is from the central point $O$. This entails finding the locus of points having a given path difference which, from Eqs. (11.3) and (11.4), we see to be hyperbolas, since a hyperbola is a curve that is formed by a point that moves so that the difference in its distances from two fixed points ($S_1$ and $S_2$) is a constant. From Fig. 11.3,

$$(S_1P)^2 = x^2 + \left(y - \frac{d}{2}\right)^2 \quad \text{and} \quad (S_2P)^2 = x^2 + \left(y + \frac{d}{2}\right)^2$$

where $d$ is the separation of the slits and $x$ is the distance of the slits to the screen. The path difference $\Delta$ is

$$\Delta = S_2P - S_1P = \left[ x^2 + \left( y + \frac{d}{2} \right)^2 \right]^{1/2} - \left[ x^2 + \left( y - \frac{d}{2} \right)^2 \right]^{1/2} \quad (11.5)$$

and this equation reduces to

$$4(d^2 - \Delta^2)y^2 - 4\,\Delta^2 x^2 = \Delta^2(d^2 - \Delta^2) \quad (11.6)$$

or

$$\frac{y^2}{\Delta^2/4} - \frac{x^2}{(d^2 - \Delta^2)/4} = 1 \quad (11.7)$$

which is the equation of a hyperbola in standard form with the foci on the $y$ axis. The curves in Fig. 11.1 connecting points of constant path difference are therefore hyperbolas. The eccentricities of the hyperbolas are given by $\left( \dfrac{\Delta^2}{4} + \dfrac{d^2 - \Delta^2}{4} \right)^{1/2} \div \dfrac{\Delta}{2} = \dfrac{d}{\Delta}$. For the optical region, corresponding to the conditions of constructive or destructive interference, the path difference is of the order of $10^{-8}$ cm, and with $d$ of the order of $10^{-2}$ cm it is seen that the eccentricity is very large. This results in hyperbolas that are very flat and for practical purposes are taken to be straight lines as shown in Fig. 11.1. In view of the fact that both $d$ and $y$ are small compared with $x$ when the fringes are under observation, Eq. (11.6) may be approximated by

$$y = \frac{x\Delta}{d}$$

so that for the bright fringes

$$y = \frac{k\lambda x}{d} \quad (11.8)$$

and for the dark fringes

$$y = \frac{(k + \frac{1}{2})\lambda x}{d} \quad (11.9)$$

Equation (11.8) gives the positions for the intensity maxima, and Eq. (11.9) gives the positions where the intensity is zero. Both the maxima and the minima are uniformly spaced, and the integer $k$ is called the order of interference. The separation on the screen between the $k$th and $(k + 1)$st bright fringe is given by

$$y_{k+1} - y_k = \frac{(k + 1)\lambda x}{d} - \frac{k\lambda x}{d} = \frac{\lambda x}{d} \quad (11.10)$$

which is also the separation between the dark fringes. Equation (11.10) shows that the separation of the fringes is constant for given values of $\lambda$, $d$, and $x$ and varies directly with the wavelength and distance from the slits and inversely with the slit separation. These facts are in agreement with the observed interference patterns. In practice the separation of the fringes, $d$, and $x$ are measurable, thus affording a direct method of determining the wavelength of light.

**11.2. Conditions for Interference.** In order to have a well-defined observable interference pattern, the intensity at a region corresponding to destructive interference must remain zero, and that at a region corresponding to constructive interference must remain a maximum. To realize such a state, it is necessary that the following conditions be fulfilled:

1. The phase difference between the two vibrating sources must remain constant so that the difference in phase between the waves at any point is not changing with time.

2. The waves from each source must have the same period and wavelength and must have equal or very nearly equal amplitudes.

3. The light must be of a single wavelength or very nearly monochromatic; otherwise, the optical-path difference between the interfering beams must be small.

4. The wave fronts of the interfering wave trains must be traveling in the same direction or make only a very small angle with each other.

5. The waves from the two sources must possess the same state of polarization.

Condition 1 is demanded by the requirement that there be sustained maxima and minima. To bring about condition 1 requires that the two sources ($S_1$ and $S_2$ in Young's experiment) must be derived from a single source. Light from two different sources never produce interference patterns due to the incoherent nature of light, as explained in Sec. 10.5. With two independent sources there are present phase changes which occur very rapidly, of the order of $10^8$ sec$^{-1}$. Any interference fringes present would change with each phase change and there would be no sustained maxima or minima.

Condition 2 follows from the development given in Sec. 10.4. With the amplitudes equal there would be complete destructive interference at the dark-fringe regions and maximum intensity at the bright-fringe regions.

Condition 3 is necessary in order to avoid the masking of all interference due to the presence of more than one wavelength in the interfering light sources. The effect is illustrated in Fig. 11.4, showing two plane wave fronts traveling as indicated and making a small angle with each other. Consider that the waves have originated from a single source and that they contain many wavelengths. Let $M$, where the wave fronts intersect, be a point that is the same optical distance from each source. Therefore at $M$ there is constructive interference for all the wavelengths present in the beams. Now consider some position $N$ where the optical-path difference for some wavelength is $\lambda/2$, resulting in destructive interference for this wave component.   For neighboring wave components there will be partial constructive interference at $N$.   If $NN$ is large enough and there is still destructive interference for the waves of wavelength $\lambda$, there will be complete constructive interference for the neighboring components.   This causes a masking of the interference effect for the wavelength $\lambda$.   If white light is used, only a few fringes are seen on either side of the central position $M$ owing to the fact that, even though at a point on either side of $M$ there is darkness for some wavelength, there is partial or complete brightness for the neighboring wavelengths.

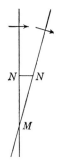

Fig. 11.4. Interference of waves having a mixture of many wavelengths.

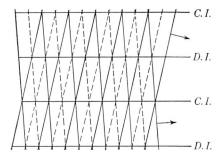

Fig. 11.5. Illustrating two interfering plane wave fronts making a small angle with each other.

Condition 4 may clearly be seen with the aid of Fig. 11.5, which shows two plane wave fronts making a small angle with each other and traveling in the directions shown.   The solid lines represent crests and the dotted lines represent troughs of the waves.   The regions of constructive and destructive interference are indicated.   It is clear that increasing the angle between the wave fronts decreases the spacing between the interference fringes.   The fringes may thus get so close together as to be unobservable even under high magnification.

We shall postpone a discussion of condition 5 until we take up the study of polarization in Chap. 16 (see Sec. 16.13).

We shall consider in the following section various other devices that may be utilized in the production of interference phenomena.   The method of the double slit employed by Young belongs to one class of devices which, by reflection or refraction, changes the directions of two parts of the same wave front so that they subsequently reunite at a small angle.   In addition there is a second class of devices that divides the amplitude of a portion of a wave front into two parts which later reunite to produce interference, as exemplified by the interference in thin films or plates.   In the former class, small portions of a wave front are utilized, giving rise to diffraction effects as well as interference effects. In the latter class, large portions of a wave front may be employed, resulting in interference fringes with a minimum degree of superimposed diffraction effects.

**11.3. Fresnel's Biprism and Double Mirrors, Lloyd's Mirror, and Billet's Split Lens.** The bright and dark fringes obtained by Young were not regarded as proof that they were caused by the interference of the two beams of light. The objections lay in the thought that the bands were due to a modification of the light produced by passing through the two slits (or two holes), *i.e.*, a modification due to diffraction at the edges.

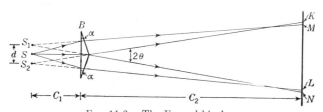

FIG. 11.6a. The Fresnel biprism.

FIG. 11.6b. Interference fringes obtained with a Fresnel biprism. (*By permission from "Fundamentals of Optics," by F. A. Jenkins and H. E. White. Copyright, 1950, Second Edition. McGraw-Hill Book Company, Inc.*)

To show that the bands were due to true interference, Fresnel devised his biprism experiment, employing refraction to obtain two coherent sources, and his double-mirror arrangement, employing reflection to obtain two coherent sources.

In Fig. 11.6a is shown a biprism $B$, in front of which is a light source $S$. The biprism is essentially two prisms of very small refracting angle $\alpha$ placed base to base. The slit passing through $S$ perpendicular to the plane of the figure is accurately parallel to the refracting edge of the biprism. As can be seen from the figure, the refracting edge of the biprism divides the incident light into two portions. The one passing through the upper half of the biprism appears to come from the virtual image $S_1$, and that passing through the lower half of the biprism appears to come from the virtual image $S_2$. The virtual images $S_1$ and $S_2$, coplanar with, close to, and equidistant from $S$ ($\alpha$ is small), now act as coherent sources giving rise to interference bands in the overlapping region $KN$. As with the double-slit arrangement, the separation between the fringes is given by Eq. (11.10), which here becomes

$$y_{k+1} - y_k = \frac{\lambda(C_1 + C_2)}{d} \tag{11.11}$$

where $C_1$ and $C_2$ are the distances of the source and screen from the prism, respectively, and $d$ is the distance between the virtual sources $S_1$ and $S_2$. A photograph of the resulting interference fringes is shown in Fig. 11.6b. The superimposed rhythmic variation in the brightness of the fringes is due to diffraction arising from the presence of the straight edges at the apex and vertices of the biprism (see the chapter on Diffraction). The fringes may be measured with a micrometer eyepiece and so determine the wavelength $\lambda$. The determination of $d$ may be effected in one of several ways. Since the biprism has a small refracting angle, the light passes through the prism at minimum deviation so that the angle of deviation $\theta$ is given by $\theta = (n - 1)\alpha$, where $n$ is the refractive index of the prism. Since $d = 2C_1\theta$, then Eq. (11.11) becomes

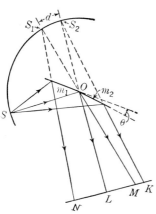

$$y_{k+1} - y_k = \frac{\lambda(C_1 + C_2)}{2C_1(n - 1)\alpha} \tag{11.12}$$

which may be used to find $\lambda$ if $n$ and $\alpha$ for the prism are known. On the other hand, $d$ may be determined by measuring $\theta$ directly on the spectrometer, using incident parallel light. For another method of measuring $d$, see Prob. 11.6.

The second device of Fresnel for obtaining the interference between the two sections of a wave front is illustrated in Fig. 11.7, which shows two mirrors $m_1$ and $m_2$ inclined at a small angle $\theta$. Light from an illuminated slit at $S$ is incident on the mirrors, whose line of intersection through $O$ is parallel to the source slit. Two virtual images $S_1$ and $S_2$ are formed by reflection from the mirrors as shown. The light at the screen $KN$ appears to come from the virtual sources, and interference fringes are formed in the overlapping regions of $KL$ and $MN$, that is, in the region of $ML$. The formations of the fringes are similar to those in the double-slit and biprism arrangements. Since $\angle S_1OS_2 = 2\theta$, the separation of the fringes is given by

$$y_{k+1} - y_k = \frac{\lambda(C_1 + C_2)}{d} = \frac{\lambda(C_1 + C_2)}{2C_1\theta} \tag{11.13}$$

where $C_1 = OS_1 = OS_2$ and $C_2 = OL$. It can be seen that $S$, $S_1$, and

$S_2$ lie on a common circle with $O$ as center. The fringes have the same general appearance as those obtained from a biprism, and there is also usually present a superposed diffraction pattern.

Lloyd's method (1834) for producing interference fringes makes use of a single mirror $m$ disposed with respect to the slit source $S_1$ as shown in Fig. 11.8. The mirror may be a piece of plate glass the top surface of which is silvered, and the slit is adjusted so that it is parallel to the reflecting surface. The virtual image $S_2$, formed by reflection, acts as a light source coherent with $S_1$ to produce the characteristic interference fringes in the overlapped region $MN$. A photograph of the fringes

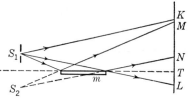

Fig. 11.8. Lloyd's single mirror.

formed by Lloyd's mirror is shown in Fig. 11.9, and the spacing of the fringes is again given by $\lambda C/d$, where $C$ is the distance from the sources to the screen, $\lambda$ is the wavelength, and $d$ is the distance from $S_1$ to $S_2$. Point $T$, lying on the perpendicular bisector of $S_1S_2$, marks the central fringe of zero path difference and is not visible since no reflected light can reach it. It may be brought into view by inserting a thin film of mica in the path of the direct rays. This increases the path of the direct

Fig. 11.9. Interference fringes obtained with the Lloyd mirror. (*By permission from "Fundamentals of Optics," by F. A. Jenkins and H. E. White. Copyright, 1950, Second Edition. McGraw-Hill Book Conpany, Inc.*)

beam and displaces the central fringe upward toward $K$. When this is done, it is found that the central fringe of zero path difference is dark. The only way this can occur with a zero path difference is for one of the beams in Fig. 11.8 to have suffered a $\pi$ change of phase. Obviously it must be the reflected beam that has suffered this $\pi$ change of phase upon reflection, with the result that the fringe of zero path difference is one of destructive interference. We shall have more to say in the next section about the conditions under which a light wave suffers a change of phase upon reflection. In accordance with the discussion in Sec. 11.2, if white light is used, a system of fringes corresponding to each component wavelength is produced, with the result that the central fringes, or fringes of zero path difference, for all wavelengths are superposed. With the double slit, the biprism, and double-mirror arrangements the central fringe is white, while with Lloyd's mirror the central fringe is dark. As we go out from the central fringe, the various interference bands corresponding to the different wavelengths fall on different positions, causing confusion due to the overlapping of the different colors. Next to the central fringe there are then a few colored fringes, and then general illumination. Lloyd's mirror arrangement makes it possible to realize achromatic fringes, *i.e.*, black and white fringes, when the illuminant of the source slit is white light. This may be accomplished by causing the violet end of the spectrum illuminating the slit source to be nearest the reflecting mirror. The violet sources are then closer than the red sources, and with proper adjustment the fringes due to the violet sources will have the same width as those due to the red sources. With this arrangement the distance between two consecutive bright fringes is the same for all wavelengths, or $\lambda/d$ is constant. The experimental arrangement is realized by employing a diffraction grating (see Sec. 13.4) and a lens to form a narrow spectrum used to illuminate the slit.

FIG. 11.10. The Billet split lens.

Billet's method for producing two interfering sources from a single source is shown in Fig. 11.10. A lens split into two parts, as shown, is used to form two real images of the slit source $S$. The light from the coherent sources $S_1$ and $S_2$ interferes to produce fringes as with the double-slit arrangement. The halves of the lens are separated by a short distance which can be very accurately adjusted. By displacing the two halves of the lens horizontally rather than vertically the images $S_1$ and $S_2$ are separated horizontally.

**11.4. Phase Change upon Reflection.** We have already stated that electromagnetic waves are transverse, and we shall study the transverse

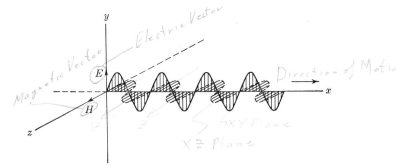

FIG. 11.11. Electric and magnetic variations in a light wave.

character of light waves in the chapter on Polarization. In accordance with the electromagnetic theory, a plane light wave traveling in the $x$ direction is represented as shown in Fig. 11.11. The sinusoidal wave form in the $xy$ plane corresponds to periodic electrical vibrations along the $y$ axis, and the sinusoidal wave form in the $xz$ plane represents the accompanying magnetic periodic vibration along the $z$ axis. The electric and magnetic variations are in mutually perpendicular planes both of which are transverse to the direction of propagation of the wave. The electric and magnetic character of the light wave may be represented, respectively, by the electric vector $E$ and magnetic vector $H$ shown in Fig. 11.11. The electromagnetic waves from a light source have their origin in the source molecules, which are oriented in all possible directions, giving rise to light whose electric vector takes on all possible vibration directions in the $yz$ plane. Such light is known as *unpolarized*, possessing symmetry around the direction of propagation. It is possible (see Chap. 16) to quench all directions of vibration except one and obtain light that is called *linearly polarized* or *plane-polarized*. The wave depicted in Fig. 11.11 is plane-polarized with the electric vector in the vertical plane. It is helpful to consider unpolarized light (ordinary light) as consisting of two orthogonal vibrations $E_y$ and $E_z$ (with their accompanying magnetic vibrations). Each of the $E$ vectors in the $yz$ plane is equivalent to two components along the $y$ and $z$ directions, leading to two net orthogonal vibrations along the $y$ and $z$ directions whose electric amplitudes are $E_y$ and $E_z$. The electric vector is the one generally employed to represent the light vector (see Sec. 11.8).

Now consider that a plane wave is incident upon the boundary separating two media of different optical densities. Let the angle of incidence be $\phi$ in the medium of refractive index $n_1$, and let the refracted angle be $\phi'$ in the medium of refractive index $n_2$. The fractions of the light reflected and refracted depend on $\phi$, $_1n_2 = n_2/n_1$, and the state of polarization or vibration of the incident light. The analysis is made by considering two cases: (1) the incident light is considered to be plane-polarized with the electric vector in the plane of incidence, and (2) the incident light is considered to be plane-polarized with the electric vector perpendicular to the plane of incidence. These cases are illustrated, respectively, by Fig. 11.12a,b. The electric amplitudes of the incident, reflected, and refracted or transmitted light vibrating parallel to the plane of incidence are represented, respectively, by $E_{pi}$, $E_{pr}$, and $E_{pt}$, which are assumed to act in the directions shown in Fig. 11.12a. The magnetic vector accompanying each electric vector is oriented perpendicular to and out of the plane of the figure. The electric amplitudes of the incident, reflected, and refracted or transmitted light vibrating normal to the plane of incidence are represented, respectively, by $E_{Ni}$, $E_{Nr}$, and $E_{Nt}$, which are assumed to act out of the plane of Fig. 11.12b. The corresponding magnetic vectors are $H_i$, $H_r$, and $H_t$, which are taken to have the directions shown in the figure. By applying the principles of electromagnetic theory to each of these cases, expressions giving the fraction of the light reflected and refracted are obtained. We postpone the details of derivation of these equations to Sec. 16.1 but shall state the expressions at this time in order to draw some conclusions which are of immediate interest. The expressions are known as the Fresnel[1] equations and are given by

$$\frac{E_{pr}}{E_{pi}} = \frac{\tan(\phi - \phi')}{\tan(\phi + \phi')} \tag{11.14}$$

$$\frac{E_{pt}}{E_{pi}} = \frac{2 \cos\phi \sin\phi'}{\sin(\phi + \phi') \cos(\phi - \phi')} \tag{11.15}$$

$$\frac{E_{Nr}}{E_{Ni}} = -\frac{\sin(\phi - \phi')}{\sin(\phi + \phi')} \tag{11.16}$$

$$\frac{E_{Nt}}{E_{Ni}} = \frac{2 \sin\phi' \cos\phi}{\sin(\phi + \phi')} \tag{11.17}$$

Equations (11.14) and (11.15) give, respectively, the ratios of the reflected and refracted electric amplitudes to the incident electric amplitude when

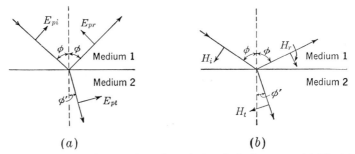

$(a)$ $\qquad\qquad\qquad\qquad$ $(b)$

FIG. 11.12. Reflection and refraction of a plane-polarized wave. (*a*) Electric vector parallel to the plane of incidence. (*b*) Electric vector perpendicular to the plane of incidence.

the incident light is polarized with the electric amplitude in the plane of incidence. Equations (11.16) and (11.17) give, respectively, the ratios of the reflected and refracted electric amplitudes to the incident electric amplitude when the incident light is polarized with the electric amplitude normal to the plane of incidence. It is very instructive to graph the equations and make some general observations. The student is asked to do this in the problems. We here wish to point out the meaning of the minus sign in Eq. (11.16). When $\phi > \phi'$ or when $n_2 > n_1$, the direction of the amplitude in the reflected wave is opposite to that in the incident wave. In other words, in the case of reflection from a rarer to a denser

---

[1] These equations were first derived by Fresnel using the elastic-solid theory of light. When the correct boundary conditions are applied to the passage of an elastic wave from one medium into another in accordance with this theory, the refracted wave must be assumed to have a longitudinal component with a displacement parallel to the propagation direction. The existence of such a component is at variance with experimental evidence. We shall later derive the Fresnel equations, using the electromagnetic-wave theory of light.

medium there is a phase change of $\pi$, or 180°, on the reflection of the vibrations perpendicular to the plane of incidence. For the vibrations parallel to the plane of incidence, Eq. (11.14) shows there is no change of phase for $\phi + \phi' < 90°$ and a $\pi$ change of phase for $\phi + \phi' > 90°$. The angle of incidence $\phi$ for which $\phi + \phi' = 90°$ is called the *polarizing angle* since $E_{pr} = 0$ and the reflected light is plane-polarized. We shall later have occasion to make use of this conclusion.

The special and important case of normal incidence can be ascertained by noting that as $\phi$ and $\phi'$ approach zero, $\phi$ approaches the value $n_2\phi'$, and in the limit we obtain for the reflected light

$$\frac{E_{Nr}}{E_{Ni}} = -\frac{{}_1n_2\phi' - \phi'}{{}_1n_2\phi' + \phi'} = -\frac{{}_1n_2 - 1}{{}_1n_2 + 1} \tag{11.18}$$

and

$$\frac{E_{pr}}{E_{pi}} = \frac{{}_1n_2\phi' - \phi'}{{}_1n_2\phi' + \phi'} = \frac{{}_1n_2 - 1}{{}_1n_2 + 1} \tag{11.19}$$

showing again that there is a $\pi$ change of phase when ${}_1n_2 > 1$. The ratio of the reflected to the incident intensity is given by the square of the ratio of the amplitudes and is called the *reflecting power*. For normal incidence the reflecting power for both the vibrations normal and parallel to the plane of incidence is $[({}_1n_2 - 1)/({}_1n_2 + 1)]^2$.

**11.5. The Thin Film.** Consider a thin film of transparent substance such as a film of oil floating on water, a thin soap film, or a film of air between two glass surfaces. Figure 11.13 shows a ray of light $SA$ from the source $S$ incident at an angle $\phi$ on one face of a thin film whose sides form a small angle $\theta$. After refraction at an angle $\phi'$ the ray reflects at $C$ and then emerges at $B$ in the direction $BM$. Another ray leaving the source $S$ reflects at $B$ in the direction $BN$. Rays $BM$ and $BN$ are coherent since they have originated from the same source, and interference effects may be observed in the vicinity of $B$. In deriving an expression for the difference in path between the rays $SBM$ and $SACBN$ it must be realized that the film has an extremely small angle $\theta$ and that the distance $AB$ is small compared with the distance of $S$ from the film. The optical-path difference $\Delta$, considering $S$ in air and the refractive index of the film as $n$, is given by

$$\Delta = SA + (AC + CB)n - SB \tag{11.20}$$

If $AP$ is constructed perpendicular to $BS$ and $BQ$ is constructed perpendicular to $AC$, then $AP$ and $BQ$ are wave fronts with respect to the incident and refracted rays $BP$ and $AQ$, respectively. Hence $BP = nAQ$. Also, since angle $ASP$ is small, we can take $AS = PS$. The above equation now becomes $\Delta = (QC + CB)n$. In the figure, $QC$ has been extended to $D$ so as to make $CD = CB$ and

$$\Delta = QDn = nBD \cos \alpha$$

The lines $KC$ and $KA$ are drawn normal, respectively, to the back and front faces of the film. This construction readily reveals that $BD$ is perpendicular to the back surface of the film at $E$. Hence $BD = 2d$,

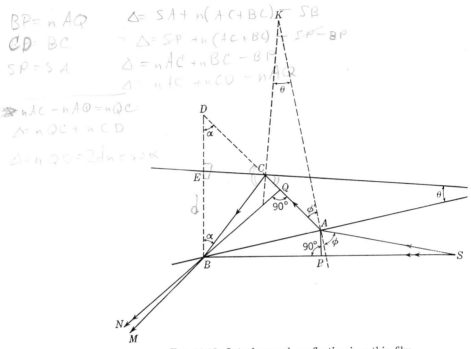

FIG. 11.13. Interference by reflection in a thin film.

where $d = BE$ is the so-called "thickness" of the film at $B$. We now have for the path difference, using $\alpha = \phi' + \theta$,

$$\Delta = 2nd \cos(\phi' + \theta) \tag{11.21}$$

In practice we deal with films that are so small that $\theta$ may be neglected in comparison with $\phi'$. Thus

$$\Delta = 2nd \cos \phi' \tag{11.22}$$

For a given film, the path difference then depends on the film thickness at the point $B$ and the angle $\phi'$. One must keep in mind the fact that Eq. (11.22) is an expression for the optical-path difference only and that there must additionally be taken into consideration the fact that either ray $SA$ or ray $SB$ suffers a $\pi$ change of phase upon reflection, as explained in the last section. Which one it is is determined by whether the refractive index of the film is greater or less than that of the surrounding medium. If we are dealing with an oil film on water, then ray $SB$ would suffer a $\pi$ change of phase on reflection. Therefore, as far as rays $BM$ and

*BN* are concerned, there will be interference minima when

$$2nd \cos \phi' = k\lambda, \qquad k = 0, 1, 2, 3, \ldots \tag{11.23}$$

and interference maxima when

$$2nd \cos \phi' = (k + \tfrac{1}{2})\lambda, \qquad k = 0, 1, 2, 3, \ldots \tag{11.24}$$

where $\lambda$ is the wavelength of the incident light.

Equation (11.22) may now be applied to some special cases:

1. Suppose parallel light is incident on a film of small wedge angle $\theta$. Then $\phi'$ is constant and $d$ is variable. For monochromatic light, where the film has a thickness $d$ satisfying Eq. (11.23) the light will interfere to produce minimum intensity, and at the positions where $d$ satisfies Eq. (11.24) there is maximum intensity in the reflected light. There are then present dark interference bands which are parallel to the edge of the wedge, each band lying where $d$ satisfies Eq. (11.23). To perceive these fringes, not only must the wedge angle be small, but also the source must be broad or extended in order to see an extended system of fringes, since the light from a single point source will reach the eye, which is focused for parallel rays from a small region of the film, at some one point. An extended source supplies many points. Any one band of the alternate dark and bright fringes is the locus of constant film thickness, which is why such fringes are called *fringes of constant thickness*.

With white light, the fringes are colored since those colors whose wavelengths satisfy Eq. (11.23) are absent because of destructive interference. The minimum for each color occurs at a different value of $d$, with the result that at any position the path difference is such as to remove completely one color and partly other colors, resulting in colored fringes. The reader has no doubt witnessed the beautiful colors exhibited by a thin film of oil on water or a soap bubble.

We recall that the thin edge of a film appears black by reflected light. This may be observable at the top of a vertical soap film just before it breaks. The path difference for $d = 0$ is zero here, but the two interfering disturbances are 180° out of phase, causing destructive interference.

2. Now consider that parallel light is incident on a film whose bounding faces are plane and parallel so that $\theta = 0$. With the light monochromatic, $\Delta$ is the same all along the film so that if $\phi'$ has the value satisfying Eq. (11.23) the film will appear dark, while if Eq. (11.24) is satisfied the film will appear uniformly bright. For any other value of $\phi'$ the film will at all points be uniformly illuminated.

With white light, the colors whose wavelengths satisfy Eq. (11.23) will be absent, resulting in a film that appears uniformly colored. How interference fringes may be obtained with a plane-parallel film is taken up in the next section.

**11.6. Interference Fringes from a Plane-parallel Film or Plate.** The plane-parallel film may be employed to give interference fringes by causing $2nd \cos \phi'$ to vary over the face of the film. This in turn means a variation in $\phi'$. It is worth while to consider this case in some detail. In Fig. 11.14 is shown a series of rays multiply reflected from a plane-parallel film or plate $KLMN$ with thickness $d$ and refractive index $n$. A ray $R$, from a source $S$, incident on the film at an angle $\phi$ reflects in part as ray (1) and refracts in part with angle $\phi'$. Multiple reflection occurs within the film, and there results a set of parallel rays (1), (2), (3), etc., on one side of the film, called the reflected rays, and a set of

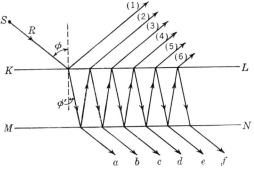

Fig. 11.14. Multiple reflections in a plane-parallel film.

parallel rays $a$, $b$, $c$, $d$, $e$, etc., on the other side of the film, called the transmitted rays.

The path difference between rays (1) and (2) is easily seen to be given by

$$\Delta = \frac{2nd}{\cos \phi'} - 2d \tan \phi' \sin \phi$$

which becomes, using $\sin \phi = n \sin \phi'$, $\Delta = 2nd \cos \phi'$. Since one of the rays, ray (1), here suffers a $\pi$ change of phase upon reflection, we again have the conditions that $\Delta = k\lambda$ results in a minimum and $\Delta = (k + \frac{1}{2})\lambda$ results in a maximum for rays (1) and (2). Now rays (2), (3), (4), etc., do not suffer any change in phase so that when $\Delta = k\lambda$ is satisfied, rays (1) and (2) interfere destructively but rays (2), (3), (4), etc., are all in phase. The amplitude of (2) is less than that of (1), and the destructive interference is not complete. However, it proves to be true that the sum of (3), (4), (5), etc., is just enough to nullify the excess between (1) and (2) and thus produce complete destructive interference. The student is asked to show this in Prob. 11.20. On the other hand, if $\Delta = (k + \frac{1}{2})\lambda$ is satisfied, then rays (1) and (2) interfere to produce a maximum, while there is 180° phase difference between rays (3) and (2), (5) and (4), (7) and (6), etc. Since each reflected ray is smaller in amplitude than its predecessor, there is not complete destructive interference between these pairs and there will thus remain a maximum intensity. Note that the conditions for maxima and minima so obtained are the same as when rays (3), (4), (5), etc., are not considered. For this reason, often only rays (1) and (2) are employed to obtain the conditions of interference.

Just as the rays proceeding from the top of the film may be brought together with a lens and made to interfere, so also may this be done with the transmitted rays $a, b, c, d, \ldots$. None of these rays suffers a phase change because of reflection, so that the condition for a maximum is $2nd \cos \phi' = k\lambda$ and the condition for a minimum is

$$2nd \cos \phi' = (k + \tfrac{1}{2})\lambda$$

However, the fringes due to reflected light have a greater contrast between maxima and minima.

Hence with an extended source and monochromatic light the film will be crossed by bright and dark interference fringes, each bright fringe corresponding to a fixed value of $\phi'$ that satisfies the equation $\Delta = (k + \tfrac{1}{2})\lambda$ for reflected light and $\Delta = k\lambda$ for transmitted light. The fringes then are concentric circles having as center the point of intersection with the film of the perpendicular drawn from the eye to the film. With films that are very thin such bands may be readily observed, but if the film is thick, the angle $\phi$ must be kept down to small values corresponding to nearly normal reflectance; otherwise the reflected rays become separated by so much that no interference can be seen because of the limited aperture of the eye. The fringes due to a variation in $\cos \phi$ are known as fringes of *constant inclination*, or Haidinger's fringes. We shall have occasion to refer to them again in dealing with interferometers.

The conditions of maxima and minima here discussed show that for normal incidence $\cos \phi = 1$, and there is no reflection for an optical thickness that is given by $nd = k\lambda/2$, or an even integral multiple of a quarter wavelength. The so-called "invisible" glass is made in accordance with this principle, accomplished by evaporation of thin transparent films on the glass. If a film whose refractive index $n_f$ is made to adhere to glass of refractive index $n_g$ so that $n_g > n_f$, then for normal incidence there is minimum reflection for an optical film thickness given by

$$n_f d = (k + \tfrac{1}{2})\lambda/2$$

or an odd integral multiple of a quarter wavelength. There will be no reflection or complete destructive interference if the fraction of the amplitude reflected at the air-film boundary is the same as that at the film-glass boundary (see Prob. 11.20). Thus, using the expression for the reflecting power at normal incidence obtained in Sec. 11.4, we have the equality

$$\left(\frac{_a n_f - 1}{_a n_f + 1}\right)^2 = \left(\frac{_f n_g - 1}{_f n_g + 1}\right)^2$$

where $_a n_f$ is the index of the film with respect to air and $_f n_g$ is the index of the glass with respect to the film. Using $_a n_f = n_f$ and $_f n_g = n_g/n_f$, the expression leads to the condition $n_f = \sqrt{n_g}$. *Coated* lenses and optical parts are made in accordance with these interference principles. It must be remembered that the thickness of the film is made to effect destructive interference for only one wavelength, and this is chosen in the spectral region to which the eye is most sensitive. Hence a coated lens looks purple because of the reflection occurring in the red and violet ends of the spectrum.

Fringes of equal inclination are formed at infinity, and the eye must be focused for parallel rays, whereas the fringes of constant thickness discussed in the preceding section are localized at a finite distance from the eye, the exact location being a function of the film thickness for films of a given wedge angle. For thin films the fringes of constant thickness are localized at the film.

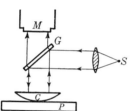

Fig. 11.15. Experimental arrangement for observing Newton's rings.

**11.7. Newton's Rings.** The interference rings that are well known as Newton's rings are circular interference fringes of the constant-thickness variety. An air wedge is formed by positioning the convex side of a converging lens on a plane glass plate. The experimental arrangement for the production and observation of the fringes is shown in Fig. 11.15. Light from the source $S$ is rendered parallel by a lens and then falls on a thin glass plate $G$, which partially reflects the light so that it falls normally on the air film formed by the curved surface of the converging lens $C$ in contact with the glass plate $P$. After reflection from the film the rays enter either the eye or a low-power microscope $M$, which is focused on the region about the point of contact between $C$ and $P$. The air film possesses radial symmetry about the point of contact, so that a locus of constant film thickness is a circle and the fringes are therefore concentric rings. Figure 11.16$a$ shows a photograph of Newton's rings obtained by reflected monochromatic light. We shall now obtain the expressions that relate the radii of the fringes, the wavelength of the light, and the radius of curvature of the converging lens $C$. Figure 11.17 shows an enlarged diagram of the curved surface $AOB$ of the converging lens in contact at $O$ with the upper surface $MN$ of the glass plate. Let $R$ be the radius of curvature of the lens and $\rho$ the radius of a Newton ring corresponding to the constant film thickness $d$, and formed by interference of two beams, one reflected from $AOB$ and the other from $MN$. Then

$$R^2 = \rho^2 + (R - d)^2$$

or $\rho^2 = d(2R - d)$. Since $d$ is small compared with $R$, we have, for all practical purposes,

$$\rho^2 = 2Rd \tag{11.25}$$

Using this value of $d$ in Eqs. (11.23) and (11.24) and cos $\phi' = 1$ for normal

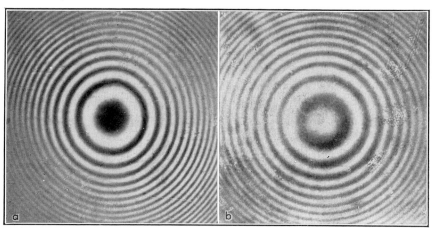

FIG. 11.16. Newton's rings by (a) reflection, (b) transmission. λ 5160 A. [*After D. Etter and J. Morgan (T.C.U. Laboratories).*]

incidence, we have the radii of the dark rings for monochromatic light, given by

$$\rho_k^2 = k\lambda R, \qquad k = 0, 1, 2, \ldots \tag{11.26}$$

and the radii of the bright rings, given by

$$\rho_k^2 = (k + \tfrac{1}{2})\lambda R, \qquad k = 0, 1, 2, \ldots \tag{11.27}$$

where the subscript $k$ is employed to indicate the $k$th ring. For a film of refractive index $n$, the right-hand members of Eqs. (11.26) and (11.27) are to be divided by $n$. We see that the radii of the dark rings are proportional to the square root of the natural numbers so that they get closer together with increasing $\rho$. This of course is evident in Fig. 11.16. For $k = 0$, $\rho_0 = 0$ in Eq. (11.26), and the center of the fringe system, as seen by reflected light, is dark. On the other hand, if the fringes are observed

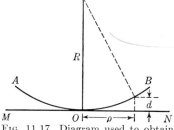

FIG. 11.17. Diagram used to obtain an expression for the radii of Newton's rings.

by transmitted light, the central spot will be bright, and the radii of the bright fringes are given by Eq. (11.26). This is illustrated by the photograph in Fig. 11.16b. When white light is used as the source, the rings are colored, and as already pointed out, the coloring of a ring, seen by reflected light, is complementary to that of the corresponding ring seen by transmitted light.

Equation (11.26) may be employed to determine the wavelength of a monochromatic source. In practice a plano-convex lens of large focal length is used to form the rings, and a traveling microscope is employed to determine the radii of the dark rings by reflection. A good procedure to follow is to measure the radii of some 15 or 20 rings and then plot $\rho_k^2$ as a function of $k$. The slope of the resulting straight line is $\lambda R$, and if $R$ is known or measured by a spherometer or other means, then $\lambda$ may be determined. However, it is possible to measure $R$ to a higher order of precision by using a known wavelength. It is well to point out here that the lens or plate may be deformed at the point of contact, or there may be dust particles present, so that the point of contact is not complete. In these cases there is an unknown constant quantity to be added or subtracted from the value for the thickness $d$. This would result in a straight line with the same slope $\lambda R$ and a $\rho^2$ intercept which is also determinable from the above plot.

It was Robert Hooke who first observed such circular interference rings, but it was Newton who studied and measured their radii with some precision. However, their first successful explanation was given by Young, who showed they were a consequence of the wave theory of light and are formed by interference. Newton attempted to explain the rings by his corpuscular theory and with the concept of "fits of easy transmission" and "fits of easy reflection." The explanation by the phenomenon of interference attributes the dark center to the $\pi$ change in phase that the wave suffers when it reflects from the upper surface of the glass plate forming the air film. That this is truly the case is further verified by using a lens of refractive index less than that of the glass plate and filling the space within with oil of an intermediate refractive index. Now the reflection of the light from both the top and bottom of the film suffers a $\pi$ change of phase, and the interference theory requires that the central spot be bright by reflected light. This was first observed to be true by Young.

Fringes of constant thickness are used to indicate the accuracy of a plane surface or the parallelism of surfaces, since the interference fringes form a map of contour lines. The optical part to be examined for flatness is brought in contact with a known optical flat which is plane to a fraction of a wavelength of light. If the surface being tested is not flat, a variable-thickness air film is formed and fringes of irregular form are observable. Each band is the locus of points where there is the same film thickness which changes by half a wavelength between neighboring bands. If the surface being tested is flat, then the fringes are straight.

**11.8. Wiener's Experiment.** The student is familiar with the interference pattern known as standing waves when a direct and a reflected wave traveling in opposite directions through the same medium superpose. The interference patterns characterized by nodes and loops are readily demonstrated in vibrating strings, vibrating air columns, and electrical transmission lines and resonators. Standing waves produced by interference between direct and reflected light waves were demonstrated by Wiener in 1890. Wiener's apparatus is illustrated in Fig. 11.18. A parallel beam of monochromatic light waves, traveling in the

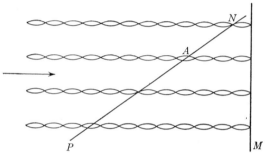

Fig. 11.18. Wiener's experiment showing the existence of standing light waves.

direction of the indicated arrow, falls normally on a mirror $M$. The stationary wave patterns produced and illustrated in the figure were recorded on a very thin film of photographic emulsion $P$ which was positioned at an angle as shown. The developed film showed an interference pattern of parallel dark and light bands corresponding, respectively, to the nodes and antinodes of the standing light waves. Where the emulsion coincided with antinodes, as at $A$, the photographic plate was affected, while at a node, such as at $N$, there was no developable image. A very significant fact brought out by the experiment is that there is a node at the reflecting surface. The electromagnetic theory of light shows that the electric vectors of the two interfering waves interfere destructively and give rise to a node at the reflecting surface, while the magnetic vectors give rise to an antinode at the reflecting surface. Therefore it is the electric vector which is considered as giving rise to the photographic action; in other words, the electric vector is the one which is responsible for the optical effects.

A process of color photography, based on the phenomenon of standing light waves, was devised by Lippman, necessitating specially prepared photographic plates.

## PROBLEMS

**11.1.** Light of wavelength 6500 A falls from a narrow slit onto two parallel slits whose separation is 0.150 mm. How far apart are the interference bands at a distance of 80.0 cm?

**11.2.** Eight interference fringes on a screen 100 cm away from an illuminated double slit of 0.200 mm separation have a separation of 1.95 cm. Find the wavelength.

**11.3.** Plot Eq. (11.1), using $A_p^2$ as ordinate and $\delta$ as abscissa. Show that the average intensity is the same as would exist if there were no interference, so that there is no loss but only a redistribution of energy.

**11.4.** In Fig. 11.3 suppose the phase difference between $S_1$ and $S_2$ is a constant amount, different from zero. What difference, if any, is produced in the fringes?

**11.5.** The distance from the source to the screen in a Fresnel biprism setup is 90.0 cm, and the distance from the prism to the screen is 65.0 cm. If the refractive index of the prism is 1.50 and the fringe separation in light of wavelength 5500 A is 0.0220 cm, find the refracting angles of the biprism in degrees.

**11.6.** The separation of the sources $d$ in the Fresnel biprism may be obtained without a knowledge of the index of refraction of the prism by use of an auxiliary lens whose focal length is less than $(C_1 + C_2)/4$. By using the lens between the prism and the screen, two positions of the lens may be found for which real images of the slit are formed. If $d_1$ and $d_2$ are the separations of the images corresponding, respectively, to the two lens positions, show that $d = \sqrt{d_1 d_2}$.

**11.7.** When a very thin plate of glass of refractive index 1.54 is placed into one of two interfering beams, the central bright fringe shifts by six fringe widths. Find the thickness of the glass plate if the wavelength is 5000 A. (HINT: The path of the beam is increased by 0.54$t$, where $t$ is the thickness of the glass plate.)

**11.8.** In the Fresnel mirrors the distance from the sources to $O$ is 32.0 cm, and the distance from $O$ to the screen is 68.0 cm. If $d$ subtends an angle of 0.280° and the fringe separation is 0.0250 cm, what is the wavelength of the radiation?

**11.9.** On the same graph plot the amplitude ratios given by Eqs. (11.14) and (11.16) as a function of the angle of incidence $\phi$, in the range 0 to 90°. Take as the relative index of refraction 1.50. Interpret the results.

**11.10.** On the same graph plot the reflecting powers $r_N = E_{Nr}^2/E_{Ni}^2$ and $r_p = E_{pr}^2/E_{pi}^2$ in per cent, using Eqs. (11.14) and (11.16), as a function of the angle of incidence $\phi$ in the range 0 to 90°, taking as the relative index of refraction 1.50. Interpret the results.

**11.11.** Unpolarized light falls on glass whose refractive index is 1.50. Find the reflecting power for the normal and parallel vibration components for (a) normal incidence, (b) grazing incidence.

**11.12.** A soap film has an index of refraction of $\frac{4}{3}$. Light of wavelength 5000 A (in vacuum) falls normally on the film and produces strong reflection in the first order. (a) What is the film thickness? (b) What is the wavelength of the light in the film?

**11.13.** Two plane rectangular pieces of glass are in contact at one edge and separated by a hair at the opposite edge so that a wedge·s formed. When light of wavelength 6000 A falls normally on the wedge, nine interference fringes are observed. What is the thickness of the hair?

**11.14.** A very thin film whose thickness is small in comparison with the wavelength appears black by reflected light. Explain this for the cases where the film is (a) optically more dense and (b) optically less dense than the media above and below it.

**11.15.** Light of wavelength 6000 A falls normally on a thin, wedge-shaped film of refractive index 1.35, forming fringes that are 2.00 mm apart. Find the angle of the wedge.

**11.16.** The figure illustrates the use of a Johansson gauge $J$, in conjunction with a plane test glass plate $G$, for the measurement of the thickness of the unknown block $B$. Both $J$ and $B$ are wrung on the base plate $P$; the process consists in sliding $J$ and $B$ on $P$ in such a way that there is no air or dust between $P$ and either $J$ or $B$. When light of wavelength 5500 A is incident perpendicularly on the enclosed film, 12 fringes are seen above the gauge $J$. Find the difference in thickness between $B$ and $J$.

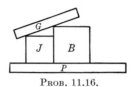

PROB. 11.16.

**11.17.** The distance between the fringes produced by illuminating a thin air wedge of $6 \times 10^{-3}$ degree of arc with light incident perpendicularly is 3.00 mm. Find the wavelength of the light.

**11.18.** Derive an expression for the path difference for the thin film, considering light from the source $S$ incident on the film in the direction of the converging end of the film, as shown in the accompanying figure rather than in Fig. 11.13.

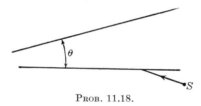

PROB. 11.18.

**11.19.** In Fig. 11.13, consider that $n_1$ is the refractive index in which $S$ is situated and $n_2$ is the refractive index of the film. Then show that the path difference is given by $2n_2d \cos (\phi' + \theta)$.

**11.20.** The figure shows the successive rays due to multiple reflections in a plane-parallel film. $A$ is the amplitude of the incident wave, $f_1$ the fraction that is reflected externally or internally, $f_2$ the fraction transmitted when refraction is into the film, and $f_3$ the fraction transmitted when refraction is out from the film. Show that the

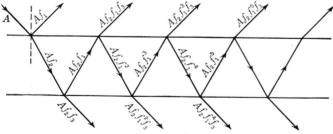

PROB. 11.20.

sum of the amplitudes of all the reflected rays on the upper side of the film, starting with the one for which the amplitude is $Af_2f_1f_3$, is equal to the amplitude of the first one whose value is $Af_1$. (HINT: Observe that $f_2f_3 = 1 - f_1^2$ by the principle of reversibility.)

**11.21.** Two plane-parallel glass plates contain an air film $4 \times 10^{-4}$ in. thick. White light is incident at an angle of 20°. Find the number of dark fringes observable in the reflected light in the spectral range 4000 to 6400 A.

**11.22.** An examination of Newton's rings in light of wavelength 5461 A reflected perpendicularly gives for the diameter of the tenth ring 0.512 cm. Find the radius of curvature of the convex surface in contact with the glass plate.

**11.23.** In Newton's ring experiment, the diameters of the fourth and twelfth dark rings are, respectively, 0.420 cm and 0.726 cm. If the radius of curvature of the convex surface forming the air film is 225 cm, what is the wavelength of the radiation? What is the radius of the fourth ring at this wavelength if the medium between the convex lens and glass plate is water of refractive index 1.33?

**11.24.** Light containing two wavelengths $\lambda_1$ and $\lambda_2$ falls perpendicularly on a Newton's ring arrangement composed of a plano-convex lens of radius of curvature $R$ in contact with a glass plate. If the $k$th dark ring corresponding to $\lambda_1$ coincides with the $(k + 1)$st dark ring corresponding to $\lambda_2$, show that the radius of the $k$th ring for $\lambda_1$ is given by $\rho_k^2 = \lambda_2 \lambda_1 R / (\lambda_1 - \lambda_2)$.

# CHAPTER 12

## INTERFEROMETERS AND INTERFEROMETRY

In the last chapter we have indicated how interference may be used to measure the wavelength of light. An instrument that is designed primarily to measure the wavelength of light in terms of some standard of length, or that is designed to measure an unknown length in terms of the wavelength of light, is known as an interferometer. We shall here see how some of the better known interferometers function, and we shall look into some of the more significant applications of interference methods to the field of measurement.

**12.1. The Michelson Interferometer.** One of the best known and most widely used interferometers is the one devised by Prof. A. A. Michelson. Figure 12.1 shows a photograph of the interferometer and Fig. 12.2 a diagram of the essential parts. The components are two excellent optically plane mirrors $M_1$ and $M_2$ and two plane-parallel optical flats $F$ and $G$, which are usually cut from a single plane-parallel plate so that they are identical. The surface of $F$ nearest $G$ may be half silvered in order that the light falling upon it be 50 per cent reflected and 50 per cent transmitted, although this is not necessary to the operation of the interferometer. As can be seen from Fig. 12.1, the mirror $M_1$ is mounted on a carriage so that it can be moved along a precision-machined track in the directions indicated by the double arrow shown at the left of $M_1$ in Fig. 12.2. The motion of $M_1$ is controlled by a very fine micrometer screw. Mirror $M_2$ is held by springs against adjusting screws so that $M_2$ may be made exactly perpendicular to $M_1$.

Light from the source $S$ is rendered parallel by the lens $L$. After entering $F$ the light is divided into two parts as shown: one part proceeds to the mirror $M_2$, which returns the light to the eye after reflection at $F$; the other part, reflecting inside $F$, proceeds to $M_1$, which reflects it back through $F$ to $E$. From a single source, by division of amplitude, there are thus produced two beams traveling toward $E$ and suitable for the production of interference. Plate $G$, known as the compensating plate, is inserted between $F$ and $M_2$ and aligned parallel to $F$ in order to equalize the optical paths of both interfering beams. In this way, the light reflected from $M_2$ has passed once through $F$ and twice through $G$, and the light reflected from $M_1$ has passed through $F$ an equivalent three times.

223

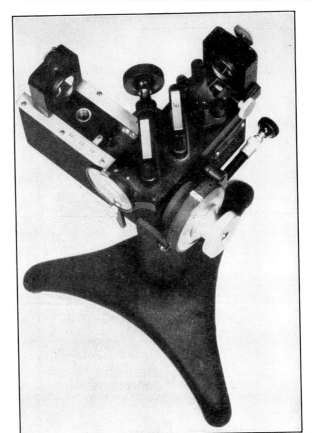

Fɪɢ. 12.1. The Michelson interferometer. (*Equipment by the Gaertner Scientific Corporation.*)

Sighting in the direction $M_1$ from $E$, the eye sees $M_1$ directly and a virtual image of $M_2$ formed by reflection in $F$. Therefore one of the interfering beams comes by reflection from $M_1$, and the other appears to come by reflection from the virtual image of $M_2$, which we shall call $M_2'$. The system then is essentially equivalent to the interference from an air film between $M_1$ and $M_2'$, with the difference that in a real film multiple reflections may occur, while here we have only two reflections. If $M_2$ is accurately perpendicular to $M_1$ and $F$ is at 45° to either, the film is one of constant thickness, while if $M_2$ is not perpendicular to $M_1$, $M_1$ and $M_2'$ are not parallel and we have the equivalent of a wedge-shaped film

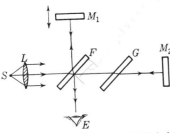

Fɪɢ. 12.2. Optical system of Michelson interferometer.

of variable thickness. The fringes may therefore take on different forms depending on how the interferometer is adjusted. The path difference introduced by reflection from $M_1$ and $M'_2$, when they are parallel, may be obtained by the following considerations:

The equivalent arrangement of the interferometer mirrors is as shown in Fig. 12.3. The situation illustrated is for $M_2$ closer to $F$ than $M_1$ by an amount $d$. The two interfering beams come to the eye at $E$ from the virtual images $S_1$ and $S_2$ of, say, the point source $S$ in Fig. 12.2, with the lens $L$ considered absent for the moment. The separation of the virtual sources is $2d$ since, when the eye sights normal to the mirrors, the total retardation of the beam reflected from $M_1$ must be $2d$. If the eye sights in the direction $E$(Fig. 12.3), making an angle $\alpha$ with the normal to the mirrors, then the path difference is $2d \cos \alpha$. The rays will interfere to produce fringes for those angles $\alpha$ that correspond to

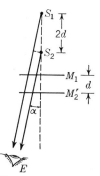

$$2d \cos \alpha = k\lambda, \qquad k = 0, 1, 2, \ldots \quad (12.1)$$

Now consider that the source $S$ is broadened by interposing the lens $L$ shown in Fig. 12.2 so that $S$ is at infinity. With monochromatic light, for a given $k$, $\alpha$ is a constant, and the locus of a fringe is a circle, or there are circular bright fringes separated by circular dark rings. By moving the mirror $M_1$ so that $d$ in Fig. 12.3 increases, a new fringe appears at the center of the field each time $M_1$ has been displaced by half a wavelength. This can be seen from Eq. (12.1), which shows that, for a given ring with a characteristic value of $k$, $\alpha$ must increase as $d$ increases in order to keep $d \cos \alpha$ constant. This means the rings appear at the center of the field and increase in radius as $d$ increases, gradually filling up the field with a multitude of interference rings. The inside rings with the smaller values of $\alpha$ have the larger values of $k$, while in Newton's rings the order of interference increases as the radii of the rings increase. Nevertheless, in both sets of rings, the rings get closer together as we go outward from the central fringe. Figure 12.4 shows photographs of the fringes (a) with $d = 5.1$ mm and (b) with $d = 2.1$ mm. In going from (a) to (b) the rings shrink in radius as $d$ is decreased, each ring vanishing at the center when $d$ has changed by half a wavelength. By decreasing $d$ the central fringe gets larger until when $d = 0$ and $M'_2$ coincides with $M_1$, there is no path difference and the whole field is dark, since the central fringe covers the whole field of view. By moving $M_1$ still more in the same direction, $M_1$ moves through the virtual image $M'_2$, and new fringes appear from the center. The eye must be focused for parallel rays to observe the circular fringes since they are formed at infinity.

When $M_2$ is not quite perpendicular to $M_1$, $M'_2$ makes a small wedge

FIG. 12.3. Coherent sources $S_1$ and $S_2$ in Michelson interferometer.

angle with $M_1$, forming an air film of variable thickness. If $d$ has a small value, so that the variation in path difference is due practically entirely to the variation in film thickness, the fringes are straight lines parallel to the edge of the wedge. But if $d$ is increased, some variation in angle is

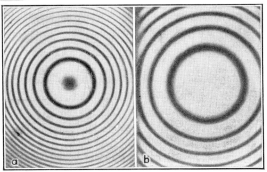

FIG. 12.4. Circular fringes with Michelson interferometer. Fringes taken with monochromatic sodium light. (a) $d = 5.1$ mm. (b) $d = 2.1$ mm.

also introduced and the fringes are curved as shown in Fig. 12.5$a$. As $d$ is decreased, the fringes move across the field of view, a new fringe moving across the center of the field each time $d$ is changed by half a wavelength. At the same time the fringes approach linearity until when $M_2'$ intersects $M_1$, so that there is zero path difference, the fringes are straight as shown in Fig. 12.5$b$. Ac-

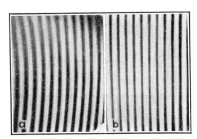

FIG. 12.5. Localized fringes in the Michelson interferometer. Fringes taken with monochromatic sodium light. (a) $M_1$ and $M_2'$ do not intersect. (b) $M_1$ and $M_2'$ intersect.

tually the central fringe is perfectly straight and in white light is achromatic. All other fringes are convex toward the central fringe. When $d$ is changed in the same direction, the fringes appear again with curvature opposite to that shown in Fig. 12.5$a$. To see localized fringes, the eye must be focused in the vicinity of the mirrors $M_1 M_2'$.

It is clear that by counting the circular fringes which disappear at the center of the field and having an accurate indication of the corresponding change in $d$, the wavelength of a monochromatic radiation is determinable. Conversely, by using a known wavelength, the change in $d$ may be determined with a very high degree of precision. In this way, as we shall see, Michelson found the length of the standard meter in terms of the wavelength of the highly monochromatic red cadmium waves.

When monochromatic waves are employed, the circular fringes can be seen even for very large path differences. However, we have seen that there is no such thing as a perfect monochromatic source, and the finite wavelength components give rise to their individual ring patterns, so that at large path differences the interference becomes masked.    With a good monochromatic source like the red cadmium line, visible circular fringes are possible up to $2d$ equal to about $\frac{1}{2}$ m.

The localized fringes shown in Fig. 12.5, on the other hand, are not visible beyond path differences of the order of several millimeters.    With monochromatic light the fringes number in the thousands, but with white light the number is limited to about 10 fringes in the neighborhood of the central fringe.    The white-light fringes are colored and are symmetrical with respect to the central fringe, which is dark (why?).    The fringes for the different wavelength components are in step at the point corresponding to the central fringe, but they get progressively more out of step as we go outward, so that after about 10 fringes the colors present at a given point add to yield essentially white light.

The Michelson interferometer possesses some significant inherent features.    First is the fact that the two beams are widely separated at right angles.    This permits the introduction of objects of relatively large size such as a gas-filled tube.    Second, since one of the reflecting planes $M_2'$ is virtual, it is possible to bring both planes into exact coincidence, or to cross them, or to effect the motion of one of the planes through the other.

We have mentioned above that when the source contains more than one wavelength the result is that due to the superposition of many fringe systems.    This we have seen limits the number of fringes observable with a polychromatic beam.    In other words, the visibility of the fringes is low where *visibility* is strictly defined as the ratio of the difference of the maximum and minimum intensities of two adjacent fringes to the sum of these intensities.    The Michelson interferometer is a very effective means of studying visibility curves, which are obtained by moving mirror $M_1$ (Fig. 12.2) and at chosen intervals estimating the visibility of the fringes. When the incident light consists of two or more wavelengths, it is found that the visibility of the fringes changes periodically with the separation $d$, so that there is a rhythmic change in the contrast between the bright and dark fringes.    The visibility curve of a spectral source yields information as to its degree of monochromaticity, and the greater the value of $d$ over which the fringes are visible, the more monochromatic the spectral source.

**12.2. The Jamin Interferometer.**    This interferometer (Fig. 12.6) is composed of two identical glass blocks $B_1$ and $B_2$, the back surfaces of which may be silvered.    Each ray of a monochromatic parallel beam, incident on $B_1$, partially reflects and partially refracts into two beams, which recombine after refraction in and reflection from $B_2$.    Since the beams originate from the same source, they are in a condition to interfere.    The interference fringes, known as Brewster's fringes, are observed in a telescope placed to receive the emergent beams at $E$. When the plates are parallel, the optical paths for both beams are the same. In a later section we shall see how this interferometer is suitable for the measurement of refractive index. A greater separation between the two parallel beams has been accomplished by modifications of the Jamin interferometer. One form of this due to Zehnder and Mach utilizes two half-silvered glass blocks $B_1$, $B_2$ and two plane reflectors $R_1$, $R_2$ positioned in a rectangular arrangement as shown in Fig. 12.7. Light incident on $B_1$, as

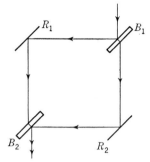

FIG. 12.7. The Zehnder-Mach modification of the Jamin interferometer.

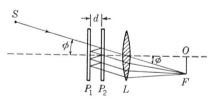

FIG. 12.6. The Jamin interferometer.

shown, partly reflects to $R_1$ and then goes on to $B_2$, through which it passes by refraction. That part of the original light which refracts through $B_1$ reflects at $R_2$ and reflects again at $B_2$. The two beams, proceeding downward from $B_2$, interfere to form fringes.

**12.3. The Fabry-Perot Interferometer.** This interferometer makes use of the fringes of constant inclination produced by the transmitted

FIG. 12.8. The Fabry-Perot interferometer showing multiply transmitted beams.

light after multiple reflection between two plane-parallel glass plates. The arrangement is shown in Fig. 12.8. The multiple reflections take place in an air film of constant thickness $d$ between two optical flats whose inside surfaces are silvered. The theory follows that developed in Sec. 11.6 on the interference fringes from a plane-parallel film. In Fig. 12.8, $S$ is a point in an extended source from which a ray of light is shown falling onto the interferometer plates at an angle $\phi$. The series of transmitted rays, arising from the internal multiple reflections, are brought to a focus $F$ by the lens $L$, which may be the eye lens. As shown in Sec. 11.6 the condition for maxima or reinforcement here is

$$2d \cos \phi = k\lambda, \qquad k = 0, 1, 2, \ldots \qquad (12.2)$$

where we have set $n = 1$ and $\phi' = \phi$. The fringes are concentric circles having $O$ as center, each circular fringe corresponding to a given value of

$\phi$, having a radius $OF$, and lying in a plane normal to that of the figure. The form of these fringes of constant inclination, or Haidinger fringes, is governed by means similar to those discussed for the Michelson interferometer. However, the parallel position of the plates is invariably used, the mounting of the plate nearest the observer being provided with the adjustment for obtaining parallelism. The other plate is movable by means of an accurate screw along a precision track in a direction perpendicular to its surface. As with the Michelson interferometer, when

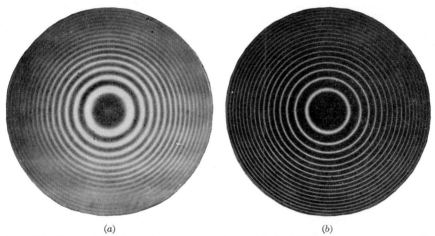

(a)                                                                        (b)

FIG. 12.9. Comparison of circular fringes obtained with (a) Michelson interferometer, (b) Fabry-Perot interferometer. (*By permission from "Fundamentals of Optics," by F. A. Jenkins and H. E. White. Copyright, 1950, Second Edition. McGraw-Hill Book Company, Inc.*)

$d$ is decreased for a given value of $\lambda$ and $k$, $\phi$ decreases so that the ring shrinks and vanishes at the center, a ring disappearing each time $d$ decreases by $\lambda/2$. The rings nearest the center have the largest values of $k$, so that the first ring corresponds to Eq. (12.2), the second to $2d \cos \phi_1 = (k - 1)\lambda$, and so on. The rings of maximum intensity are exceptionally sharp, as can be seen by comparing Fig. 12.9$b$, showing the fringes obtained with a Fabry-Perot interferometer, with those of Fig. 12.9$a$, obtained with a Michelson interferometer. The interferometer is thus very suitable for resolving very small wavelength differences. The fringes may be obtained with plate separations as large as 10 cm.

In general an interferometer based on multiple reflections yields fringes that are much sharper than the fringes obtained with two coherent beams. In the case of the Fabry-Perot interferometer the narrowness of the fringes produced by the transmitted light is improved when the reflecting power of the silvered plates is high. To understand why this is so, it is helpful to obtain an expression for the intensity of the transmitted fringes.

To do this, consider the figure associated with Prob. 11.20. The transmitted amplitudes are given by $C$, $Cr^2$, $Cr^4$, $Cr^6$, . . . , where we have set $r$ equal to the fraction of light that is reflected at both silvered surfaces and $C$ equal to the product of the original amplitude and the transmission coefficients. The successive transmitted beams have a constant phase difference which, by Eq. (10.4), is given by

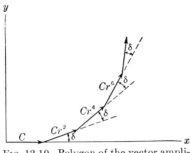

FIG. 12.10. Polygon of the vector amplitudes transmitted from a Fabry-Perot interferometer.

$\delta = (4\pi d/\lambda)\cos\phi$. In accordance with Sec. 10.4 the polygon of vector amplitudes is as shown in Fig. 12.10.

The intensity $I$ is proportional to the square of the resultant amplitude so that

$$I \propto (C + Cr^2\cos\delta + Cr^4\cos 2\delta + \cdot\cdot\cdot)^2$$
$$+ (Cr^2\sin\delta + Cr^4\sin 2\delta + Cr^6\sin 3\delta + \cdot\cdot\cdot)^2$$

or

$$I \propto C^2[(1 + r^2\cos\delta + r^4\cos 2\delta + \cdot\cdot\cdot)^2$$
$$+ (r^2\sin\delta + r^4\sin 2\delta + \cdot\cdot\cdot)^2]$$

We shall first evaluate each of the infinite series in the parentheses. Consider the equality

$$1 + r^2 e^{i\delta} + r^4 e^{i2\delta} + r^6 e^{i3\delta} + \cdot\cdot\cdot = \frac{1}{1 - r^2 e^{i\delta}}$$

which can be verified by performing the indicated division of the right-hand member. With $i = \sqrt{-1}$, the right-hand member may be rationalized, giving

$$1 + r^2 e^{i\delta} + r^4 e^{i2\delta} + r^6 e^{i3\delta} + \cdot\cdot\cdot = \frac{1 - r^2 e^{-i\delta}}{1 - r^2(e^{i\delta} + e^{-i\delta}) + r^4}$$

Now using the fact that $e^{\pm i\delta} = \cos\delta \pm i\sin\delta$, we have

$$(1 + r^2\cos\delta + r^4\cos 2\delta + \cdot\cdot\cdot) + i(r^2\sin\delta + r^4\sin 2\delta + \cdot\cdot\cdot)$$
$$= \frac{1 - r^2\cos\delta + ir^2\sin\delta}{1 - 2r^2\cos\delta + r^4}$$

Equating the real and imaginary parts,

$$1 + r^2\cos\delta + r^4\cos 2\delta + \cdot\cdot\cdot = \frac{1 - r^2\cos\delta}{1 - 2r^2\cos\delta + r^4}, \qquad r^2 < 1 \quad (12.3)$$

and

$$r^2\sin\delta + r^4\sin 2\delta + \cdot\cdot\cdot = \frac{r^2\sin\delta}{1 - 2r^2\cos\delta + r^4}, \qquad r^2 < 1 \quad (12.4)$$

Substituting Eqs. (12.3) and (12.4) into the expression for $I$,

$$I \propto C^2 \frac{(1 - r^2 \cos \delta)^2 + r^4 \sin^2 \delta}{(1 - 2r^2 \cos \delta + r^4)^2}$$

$$I \propto \frac{C^2}{1 - 2r^2 \cos \delta + r^4} = \frac{C^2}{(1 - r^2)^2 + 4r^2 \sin^2 (\delta/2)} \tag{12.5}$$

The intensity of the fringes is a maximum when $\delta = 0, 2\pi, 4\pi, \ldots$ and a minimum when $\delta = \pi, 3\pi, 5\pi, \ldots$ . This yields

$$I_{max} \propto \frac{C^2}{(1 - r^2)^2}, \qquad I_{min} \propto \frac{C^2}{(1 + r^2)^2}$$

and the visibility of the fringes $V$ is therefore

$$V = \frac{I_{max} - I_{min}}{I_{max} + I_{min}} = \frac{2r^2}{1 + r^4} \tag{12.6}$$

showing that $V$ is a function of the reflection coefficient only and increases with increase in $r$. We now have, from Eq. (12.5),

$$I = \frac{I_{max}}{1 + \frac{4r^2}{(1 - r^2)^2} \sin^2 \frac{\delta}{2}} \tag{12.7}$$

Equation (12.7) gives the intensity of the transmitted fringes as a function of the reflection coefficient $r$ and the phase $\delta$. A plot of $I$ as a function of $\delta$, using $r$ as a parameter, shows maxima at the positions $\delta = 2\pi$, $4\pi$, $6\pi$, . . . with relatively broad regions of minima between them; the sharpness of the decrease on either side of a maximum is a function of $r$, the intensity falling off more rapidly with increasing $r$. The student is asked to make such a graph in the problems.

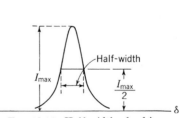

FIG. 12.11. Half-width of a fringe.

A measure of how rapidly the intensity falls on either side of the maximum, and hence a measure of the narrowness of a fringe, is the *half-width* illustrated in Fig. 12.11. The half-width is the width of the peak at the value $I = I_{max}/2$. Corresponding to this condition Eq. (12.7) gives

$$\delta = 2 \sin^{-1} \frac{1 - r^2}{2r} \tag{12.8}$$

which represents the distance from a point of maximum intensity to a point where the intensity has fallen to half the maximum. We shall use this value in Eq. (12.8) as a measure of the width of the fringes, and we see that it is a function of $r$ alone, decreasing as $r$ increases and approaching the value zero for $r = 1$. For example, if $r = 0.9$, $\delta = 0.211$ radian, which is to be compared with a total change of $2\pi$ radians between maxima. On the other hand, in the Michelson interferometer, two beams of equal intensity are brought together to form the interference fringes and, as we have seen, the intensity of the fringes is given by Eq. (11.1), or $I = I_{\max} \cos^2 (\delta/2)$, which, for $I = I_{\max}/2$, yields

$$\delta = 2 \cos^{-1} \left( \frac{1}{\sqrt{2}} \right) = \frac{\pi}{2} = 1.57 \text{ radians}$$

A Fabry-Perot interferometer is invariably used to obtain fringes in monochromatic light. When two such interferometers placed one after the other are used, fringes in white light may be observed and utilized to great advantage. When light is directed onto two such interferometers in tandem, the first transmits light to the second in certain directions only, and only if these directions coincide with the inclination directions of the rings of the second interferometer will the light be transmitted by it.

**12.4. The Lummer-Gehrcke Interferometer.** This interferometer, known as the Lummer-Gehrcke plate, makes use of the high internal reflecting power of glass at angles

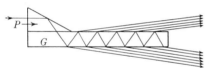

FIG. 12.12. The Lummer-Gehrcke plate.

close to the critical angle. It is also a less complicated type of interferometer and much easier to keep in adjustment. It consists of a long precision-made plane-parallel slab of optical glass or quartz $G$ with a prism $P$ cemented to it as shown in Fig. 12.12. The incoming parallel bundle of rays enters $P$, which reflects them into the interferometer. There they suffer many internal reflections, giving rise to two sets of emergent parallel bundles of rays as shown. Two sets of fringes are observable with a telescope either above or below the plate. The fringes are of the same nature as the Haidinger fringes of the Fabry-Perot interferometer, with the difference that in the latter the angle of incidence within the plate is nearly 90°, while here the multiple reflections occur at an angle just less than the critical angle. The fringes are bright, narrow maxima with wide minima between. When the plate is made of quartz, it can be used to advantage in the ultraviolet. The instrument is used often in the analysis of individual spectrum lines.

**12.5. Interferometric Applications.** *a. Measurement of the Standard Meter in Terms of Wavelength.* We have seen that the distance moved by the movable mirror in the Michelson interferometer is given by the observed number of fringes, say that vanish at the center of the field, times half a wavelength. Hence the distance moved is measurable to within a small fraction of the wavelength employed. Michelson set himself the task of determining the length of the standard meter bar in terms of an invariable unit which was chosen to be one of the wavelengths lying in the red portion of the spectrum of cadmium, since this wavelength was found to be extremely homogeneous. Michelson used his interferometer to effect the comparison and thus obtained a primary standard which is indestructible, permanent, and easily duplicated in any laboratory.

Since there are about 1,553, 164 cadmium red wavelengths in 1 m, it would not be possible to measure a displacement of the movable mirror through the entire length of 1 m, even if the source were able to give sharp fringes over so large a path difference.

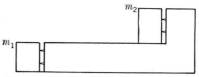

Fig. 12.13. Simplified diagram of etalons employed by Michelson.

Michelson used nine other standards, or *etalons* as they were called, of the type illustrated in Fig. 12.13, each a bronze metal bar with two silvered glass mirrors $m_1$ and $m_2$ fitted with adjusting screws for making them accurately parallel. The distance from $m_1$ to $m_2$ of the longest etalon was 10 cm, which was approximately twice the length of the next one, and so on down to the smallest, which was $10/2^8$, or about 0.391 mm. By using the shortest etalon in place of one of the mirrors, $M_2$ of Fig. 12.2, the mirror $M_1$ was adjusted, employing white light, until the central fringe appeared in the field of, let us say, the mirror $m_1$. Then, using the cadmium red light, the number of fringes passing the field of view was counted while the mirror $M_1$ was moved exactly the distance between $m_1$ and $m_2$, the end point being judged by the appearance of the central white light fringe in $m_2$. The distance $m_1m_2$ was thus determined in terms of the cadmium wavelength. This etalon was then compared with the next one by putting them both side by side in place of one of the Michelson interferometer mirrors, aligning mirror $m_1$ of the shorter etalon, which was movable, with $m_1'$ of the larger etalon, which was fixed, until they were coplanar. As before, $M_1$ was moved a distance equal to $m_1m_2$; then the smaller etalon was moved parallel to its length until $m_1$ occupied the plane previously occupied by $m_2$. From this position the number of fringes necessary to bring $m_2$ into the same plane of $m_2'$ was observed. The number of wavelengths contained in the longer etalon was thus determined. The second etalon was then compared with the third etalon, and so on, until the number of waves contained in the largest 10-cm etalon was obtained. The final operation involved placing the meter bar on the interferometer beside the 10-cm etalon, which was provided with a mark that was placed in coincidence with one of the end marks of the meter bar. The etalon was advanced in steps by bringing its front mirror into the plane previously occupied by its rear mirror until the entire length of the meter was stepped off. The total number of waves in the standard meter length was thus determined. The final result for the cadmium red wavelength was 1 m = 1,553, 163.5 wavelengths. Benoit, Fabry, and Perot repeated the determination of the length of the standard meter using the Fabry-Perot interferometer in conjunction with etalons consisting of two partially silvered mirrors facing each other and having fixed lengths of 100, 50, 25, 12.5, and 6.25 cm. It is now established that the international primary standard is the red cadmium line at 15°C and 760 mm Hg pressure having a wavelength $\lambda$ = 6438.4696 A.

  *b. Measurement of the Index of Refraction.* When a sample of glass of thickness $t$ and refractive index $n$ is inserted into the path of one of the beams of the Michelson interferometer, the increase in optical path is $2(n - 1)t$. For monochromatic light of wavelength $\lambda$, this path difference has introduced a displacement in the fringe system by $N$ fringes so that $2(n - 1)t = N\lambda$. By measuring $N$, $t$, and $\lambda$, the refractive index may be determined. The difficulty, however, is in ascertaining $N$, since in monochromatic light it is not possible to identify the same fringe in both the displaced and undisplaced systems. With white light, the center of the fringe pattern may be observed and so determine $N$, but

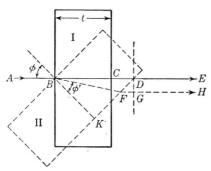

FIG. 12.14. Determination of the refractive index of a glass plate by a Michelson interferometer.

only for very thin samples because, as we have seen, for large path differences the white-light fringes become masked. A more successful method is to use two identical pieces of the sample. One is placed in front of and parallel to mirror $M_2$, and the other, fitted in a frame so that it can be slowly rotated about a vertical axis, is placed in front of mirror $M_1$ (Fig. 12.2). When this plate is slowly rotated through a desired angle, the optical path is lengthened and this change in optical path is a function of the thickness of the plate, the angle turned through, and the refractive index. This functional relationship is derived as follows:

  Figure 12.14 shows the glass plate of thickness $t$ and refractive index $n$, in position I normal to one of the beams $ABCDE$ of the Michelson interferometer. Position II shows the plate turned through an angle $\phi$, the light path now being $ABFGH$. The optical path from $B$ to $D$ in position I is $nt + CD$, and that corresponding to position II is $nBF + FG$. The increase in optical path, when the plate is rotated, gives rise to $N$ fringe counts. Hence

$$2(nBF + FG - nt - CD) = N\lambda$$

where the difference has been multiplied by 2 because the light travels twice over each path. Now

$$BF = \frac{t}{\cos \phi'}, \qquad FG = FD \sin \phi,$$

$$FD = KD - KF = t \tan \phi - t \tan \phi', \qquad \text{and} \qquad CD = \frac{t}{\cos \phi} - t$$

Substitution yields

$$\frac{nt}{\cos \phi'} + t \sin \phi \, (\tan \phi - \tan \phi') - nt - t \left( \frac{1}{\cos \phi} - 1 \right) = \frac{N\lambda}{2}$$

and using Snell's law, $n \sin \phi' = \sin \phi$, we have

$$\sqrt{n^2 - \sin^2 \phi} - \cos \phi = \frac{N\lambda}{2t} - 1 + n$$

which leads to

$$n = \frac{(2t - N\lambda)(1 - \cos \phi) + (N^2\lambda^2/4t)}{2t(1 - \cos \phi) - N\lambda} \tag{12.9}$$

Equation (12.9) shows that $n$ is determinable if $\lambda$ and $t$ are known and $\phi$ and $N$ are observed. To obtain $\phi$, a small auxiliary mirror is attached to the rotatable frame, and the angle of rotation is observed with telescope and scale. In practice the factor $N^2\lambda^2/4t$ is usually left off since it is small in comparison with the other terms.

For the measurement of the index of refraction of a gas, an interferometer like that of the Jamin type may be employed. By placing two similar evacuated glass cells in both paths of the Jamin interferometer and counting the number of fringes that cross the field of view as the gas under investigation is slowly admitted to one of the chambers, the refractive index of the gas at a known pressure and temperature is obtainable.

Another instrument that has been used for the determination of refractive indices of liquids and gases is the Rayleigh refractometer, which possesses some of the general features of Young's double-slit interferometer. Light from a slit source is rendered parallel by a lens, split into two interfering beams by a double slit, and, after passing through two identical cells, brought together again by another lens to form interference fringes. The displacement of the fringes is observed when a gas, for instance, is slowly admitted to one of the cells.

*c. Measurement of Wavelength.* We have seen that the Fabry-Perot instrument gives fringes that are exceptionally narrow. This makes the instrument superior to the Michelson interferometer for producing two sets of separated fringes due to the presence of two wavelengths. The Fabry-Perot instrument is most suitable then for comparing two wavelengths. Let us consider that a source emits two monochromatic radiations, such as the sodium $D$ lines, having wavelengths $\lambda_1$ and $\lambda_2$. Suppose the two mirrors have a separation so that the fringes due to the two wavelengths are exactly superposed near the center of the field, producing a condition of maximum distinctness. As the distance between the mirrors is gradually increased, the ring systems due to the two wavelengths gradually separate until the rings of one set are midway between those of the other set, producing a condition of minimum visibility. When the distance is increased further, the two systems again come into coincidence. The distance between successive maxima (or minima) represents a change of path difference of one wavelength more of one radiation than of the other. Therefore, if $N$ is the number of fringes for radiation $\lambda_1$ which appear or disappear at the center between successive maxima as the distance is altered, the change in the path difference for one wavelength is $N\lambda_1$ and the corresponding change for the other wavelength is $(N \pm 1)\lambda_2$, the plus or minus being determined by whether $\lambda_2 \lessgtr \lambda_1$. Thus the ratio of the wavelengths is given by

$$\frac{\lambda_1}{\lambda_2} = \frac{N \pm 1}{N} \tag{12.10}$$

and if one of the wavelengths is known, the other can be determined. The above is intended to show how the Fabry-Perot interferometer is suitable for a comparison of wavelengths.[1]

  *d. Determination of Spectral-line Structure.*   A spectral line may appear rather sharp and individual even though it may be composed of two or more wavelengths very close together. An ordinary prism spectrograph, for instance, does not have a large enough dispersion to separate the components, and there appears a single line. The Fabry-Perot interferometer is a powerful means of showing, and therefore making it possible to measure, the fine structure of a spectral line. When used with a prism spectrograph, the Fabry-Perot plates may be inserted between the collimating lens and the prism. With such an arrangement a spectral line of monochromatic purity has the appearance shown in Fig. 12.15.

---

[1] For more accurate methods and further experimental details the student is referred to:

  Joseph Valasek, "Introduction to Theoretical and Experimental Optics," John Wiley & Sons, Inc., New York, 1949.

  R. W. Wood, "Physical Optics," 3d ed., The Macmillan Company, New York, 1934.

The spectral line, or slit image *SL*, has superimposed on it small sections *a*, *b*, *c*, *d*, *e*, . . . , of the circular interference fringes indicated by the dotted curved lines, all of them belonging to the system that satisfies a single wavelength.   For a line that contains more than one wavelength

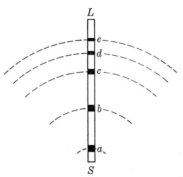

Fig. 12.15. Appearance of a spectral line with superimposed Fabry-Perot interference pattern for a monochromatic source.

the slit image has superimposed on it such a system of sections of interference fringes for each component wavelength.   Figure 12.16 shows two photographs of (*a*) a line with no fine structure and (*b*) a line with three components.   The international primary red-cadmium-line standard shows a Fabry-Perot pattern which indicates a very high monochromatic purity.   Recently Dr. W. F. Meggers has shown that one of the isotopes of mercury, mercury 198, manufactured by neutron bombardment of gold, provides a much more perfect standard of length.   The Fabry-Perot pattern rings of the green line of artificial mercury are many times sharper than those of cadmium.   The frontispiece shows a comparison of the Fabry-Perot pattern of green light from natural mercury with that from mercury 198.   The wavelength from mercury 198, 5460.7532 A, is more monochromatic than from any other known source and promises to replace the cadmium radiation as a primary standard.   We have already remarked that the Lummer-Gehrcke plate is also employed for the study of the fine structure of spectral lines.

Fig. 12.16. Photographs of a spectral line with Fabry-Perot fringes showing (*a*) no structure, (*b*) structure revealing three components. (*By permission from "Introduction to Physical Optics," Third Edition, by J. K. Robertson. Copyright, 1941, D. Van Nostrand Company, Inc.*)

  *e. Testing and Correcting Imperfections in Prisms and Lenses.*   Twyman and Green have adapted the use of the Michelson interferometer in a way that makes it possible to test optical systems with a high degree of perfection. A monochromatic point source $S$ (Fig. 12.2) is located at the principal focus of a very well corrected objective $L$ so that the interferometer is illuminated by plane waves. In one of the arms, say between $F$ and $M_1$, is placed the optical part under test and the mirror $M_1$ positioned so that the rays returning to $F$ are again parallel. Below $F$ is placed another objective, which focuses the plane waves on a small aperture in a screen. The eye is placed close to the aperture for making the observations. If the prism or lens under test has no imperfections,

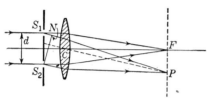

FIG. 12.17. Illustrating fringes formed by light from a star considered as a point source using the double-slit telescope.

the two wave fronts coming to the eye are truly plane and the field of view appears of uniform intensity. However, if there is a flaw in the specimen giving rise to regional differences in refractive indices, local variations in optical paths will result, thus producing corresponding localized fringe systems which are due to the deformed wave front. The individual areas that need to be polished to effect a correction are thus easily determined.

*f. Stellar Measurements.* The principle of the double-slit interferometer, as applied in the Rayleigh interferometer (*b*) above, may be employed in the measurement of the angular separation between the components of a double star or the measurement of the angular diameter of a single star. In principle the Rayleigh refractometer consists essentially of a double slit in front of a lens which may be considered as the objective of a telescope, as shown in Fig. 12.17. Consider that light from a star, of such small dimensions that it can be considered a point source, is incident on the system as shown. As with the Young's double slit, a series of fringes will be formed in the focal plane of the objective, the central bright maximum being at $F$, where the parallel rays, coming through the slit and heading onto the lens, come to a focus in phase. For rays in some other direction, such as those shown converging down to $P$, through which the central ray $CP$ passes, there is a path difference $S_1N$. The line $S_2N$ is normal to the rays. For small angles this path difference is proportional to the angle $S_1S_2N$ or to its equal angle $FCP$. Therefore the angular separation between $F$ and $P$ is given by $S_1N/d$, where $d$ is the slit separation. If $S_1N = \lambda$, $P$ is the next bright fringe and the angular separation between the fringes is $\lambda/d$.

Let us now assume that we have two similar stars acting as point sources. Then each gives rise to a system of fringes whose angular separation is $\lambda/d$. These systems will have their central fringes in different positions, so that the fringes will overlap and give rise to some form of intensity fluctuation. By increasing $d$ it is possible to obtain such a value that the maximum of one set of fringes falls at the minimum of the other set, with the result that the fringes disappear and there is uniform intensity in the field of view. The angular separation $\alpha$ between the central maximum due to one star and the adjacent central maximum due to the other star, when $d$ is such that the fringes are just not visible, is therefore $\lambda/2d$, which is also the angular separation of the stars or the angle subtended by the stars at the telescope. Therefore by varying the distance between the slit apertures until the fringes disappear the angular separation between the stars is determinable.

For a single star of finite dimensions, it may be considered as divided into a series of strip elements, each element acting as a source and producing its system of fringes. The resultant pattern is the sum of all these fringe systems, which are regularly displaced by very small amounts. By considering the star as a circular disk of uniform intensity, it can be shown that the interference fringes vanish when the angle subtended by the star is $1.22\lambda/d$,

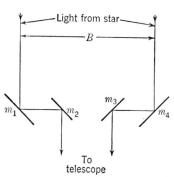

Fig. 12.18. Arrangement of mirrors in a Michelson stellar interferometer.

thus making it possible to determine the diameters of stars. For stars that subtend small angles, the value of $d$ is so great, of the order of 50 ft and larger, that it is impractical to have an adjustable slit in front of the telescope objective. Michelson solved this problem by devising the *stellar interferometer* the essentials of which are shown in Fig. 12.18. In the arrangement of the four mirrors, $m_2$ and $m_3$ are fixed, and the distance $B$ between $m_1$ and $m_4$ may be varied symmetrically. With this arrangement $m_1$ and $m_4$ serve as the apertures, and the fringes may be made to vanish by increasing $B$ to the value given by $1.22\lambda/B$. Michelson mounted such an arrangement of mirrors in front of the 100-in. reflecting telescope at Mount Wilson Observatory and made observations on the bright star Betelgeuse ($\alpha$ Orionis). The fringes vanished for a value $B = 306.5$ cm. With 5750 A as the effective wavelength he obtained

$$\text{Angular diameter of star} = \frac{1.22 \times 5.75 \times 10^{-5} \times 180 \times 3600}{306.5\pi}$$

$$= 0.0473 \text{ sec}$$

Using the known distance of the star, the diameter of Betelgeuse calculates to be $240 \times 10^6$ miles. In the same manner the diameters of other stars have been determined.

*g. Interference Filters.* The principle of the Fabry-Perot interferometer is used to advantage to form an *interference filter, i.e.,* an optical system that will transmit (or reflect) nearly monochromatic or small range of wavelengths when white light is incident upon it. Such a device, illustrated in Fig. 12.19, consists of two semitransparent silver films separated by a transparent dielectric such as a magnesium fluoride film. The films are deposited, by evaporation in vacuum, on a glass plate, and another glass plate is cemented over it for protection. When a parallel beam of white light is incident normally on the film, multiple reflections occur within the film, and if the film thickness is extremely small, say some particular wavelength for which the filter is intended, then maximum transmission in the visible region can be made to occur for this wavelength, so that the transmitted beams are reinforced for this wavelength or a small band of wavelengths around the chosen wavelength, the

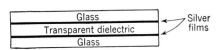

Fig. 12.19. The transmission-type interference filter.

rest of the light being reflected. For instance, the transmitted maxima for normal incidence are governed by Eq. (12.2), or $2nd = k\lambda$, where $n$ is the index of refraction of the dielectric. If the optical thickness of the dielectric is one wavelength, the maximum for this selected wavelength occurs for $k = 2$, while for $k = 1$, there is a maximum for $2\lambda$, which represents a large separation in the visible range of wavelengths. Thus with only two widely separated interference maxima, one of these may be suppressed by ordinary means such as a colored glass filter, which could be the protecting glass of Fig. 12.19. Some of the best filters available transmit light about 50 A on each side of the selected wavelength, with a transmission at the maximum of the band of about 40 per cent. When the light rays are incident obliquely on a filter made for a selected wavelength, the optical path of the rays within the film is increased and reinforcement for the original wavelength no longer occurs. There is also a reflection-type interference filter which is based on the same principle and constructed so that the reflected beam is very nearly monochromatic.

*h. The Michelson-Morley Experiment.* We have seen in a previous chapter, Sec. 10.1, that the earlier wave theory stipulated that a light source sets up a disturbance in an all-pervading medium, the *ether,* and that this disturbance travels in all directions through the medium. The student will recall that Bradley discovered the aberration of light in accordance with which the apparent direction of the stars was modified by the motion of the earth through space. The phenomenon of aberration (see Sec. 10.8) indicates that the medium (ether) which transmits electromagnetic vibrations, if one wishes to speculate on the possible existence of such a medium, must be at rest with respect to the telescope. This is so since if the ether in the telescope were not at rest, it would be carried along with it, the optical wave disturbance would also be carried along with the telescope tube, the place where the light rays would come to a focus would be independent of the motion of the tube, and in short there would be no aberration.   Hence, if there is an ether, it must be at rest with respect to the earth.   The most celebrated experiment designed to detect the motion of the earth through the ether was performed by Michelson and Morley in 1887 using the Michelson interferometer. To understand how the test was made, consider Fig. 12.20, which shows a simplified diagram of the light paths in the interferometer. The original beam from the light source at the left divides at $O$ (see Fig. 12.2 also) into two beams traveling with the velocity $c$, which after reflection from the mirrors $M_2$ and $M_1$ unite at $O$, forming fringes that are observable by a telescope placed below $O$.

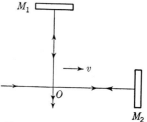

Fig. 12.20.  Use of the Michelson interferometer to detect an ether drift.

Consider that the two optical paths are the same and equal to $l$, and suppose that the earth is moving through space, in the direction $OM_2$, with a velocity $v$.   Then we may consider that the interferometer is at rest and the ether is moving past it with a velocity $-v$.   The time taken for the light to go from $O$ to $M_2$ and back to $O$ is

$$t_1 = \frac{l}{c+v} + \frac{l}{c-v} = \frac{2lc}{c^2-v^2} = \frac{2l}{c[1-(v/c)^2]}$$

For the other path we must remember that as the light travels from $O$ to $M_1$ and back to $O$, the interferometer is moving to the right with velocity $v$.   The path covered by the light beam forms the legs of an isosceles triangle whose apex is at $M_1$ and whose base is $vt_2$, where $t_2$ is the time for the light to go from $O$ to $M_1$ and back to $O$.   Thus

$$t_2 = \frac{2l}{\sqrt{c^2-v^2}} = \frac{2l}{c\sqrt{1-(v/c)^2}}$$

The difference in times is

$$t_1 - t_2 = \frac{2l}{c}\left\{\left[1-\left(\frac{v}{c}\right)^2\right]^{-1} - \left[1-\left(\frac{v}{c}\right)^2\right]^{-\frac{1}{2}}\right\}$$

Expanding each of the expressions in parentheses and retaining no terms higher than the quadratic in $v/c$, we get

$$t_1 - t_2 = \frac{2l}{c}\left(1 + \frac{v^2}{c^2} - 1 - \frac{v^2}{2c^2}\right)$$

$$t_1 - t_2 = \frac{lv^2}{c^3}$$

The path difference $\Delta$ is

$$\Delta = \frac{lv^2}{c^2}$$

If the interferometer were suddenly brought to rest, $\Delta = 0$ and a fringe shift, corresponding to $lv^2/c^2$, is to be expected. This can effectively be accomplished by rotating the entire apparatus through $90°$ so that the path $OM_1$ is in the direction of $v$. This introduces a path difference by the same amount but in the opposite direction. The total fringe shift should then correspond to $2lv^2/c^2$. The speed of the earth in its orbit around the sun is about 18.5 miles/sec so that $v/c$ is of the order of $10^{-4}$. To have an observable fringe shift, it is necessary to use an extremely large value of $l$. Michelson and Morley obtained an effectively large value of $l$ by reflecting the light back and forth many times. To ensure freedom from external influences, the interferometer was placed on a block of stone, which was floated on mercury. In one of the determinations $l = 11$ m so that for light of 5500 A the expected fringe shift is

$$\frac{(2 \times 1100) \times 10^{-8}}{5500 \times 10^{-8}} = 0.4$$

which can be detected. The results indicated that no significant shift occurred. This negative result, indicating the absence of an ether drift, led to a revision of our concepts concerning space and time and to the ingenious development of the theory of relativity by Einstein.

### PROBLEMS

**12.1.** In Michelson's determination of the standard meter in terms of the red cadmium wavelength, how many fringes had to be counted corresponding to the length of the shortest etalon?

**12.2.** When the movable mirror in the Michelson interferometer is displaced $1.8 \times 10^{-3}$ cm, 60 monochromatic fringes are counted at the center of the field. Find the wavelength of the light.

**12.3.** Circular fringes are observed in a Michelson interferometer illuminated with light of wavelength 5461 A. If the path difference between the reflecting mirrors is 0.300 cm, what is the angular diameter of the interference ring for $k = 6$?

**12.4.** Show that the path difference between the interfering beams in Jamin's interferometer is $2nd(\cos \phi_1' - \cos \phi_2')$, where $n$ and $d$ are, respectively, the refractive index and thickness of each glass plate and $\phi_1'$ and $\phi_2'$ are the angles of refraction in the glass plates.

**12.5.** Two identical 10-cm-long evacuated glass cells are placed in the two paths of a Jamin interferometer. When some gas is slowly admitted to one of the chambers at a known temperature and pressure, a shift of 80 fringes is observed with a wavelength whose value is 4000 A in the gas at the above temperature and pressure. What is the index of refraction of the gas?

**12.6.** When a thin piece of glass is inserted in one of the paths of a Michelson interferometer, a displacement of 18.5 fringes is observed in light of wavelength 5893 A. What is the thickness of the glass if its index of refraction is 1.60?

**12.7.** White light is incident normally on a Fabry-Perot etalon whose plate separation is $4 \times 10^{-4}$ cm. What are the wavelengths for which there are interference maxima in the transmitted beam in the range 4000 to 5000 A?

**12.8.** (a) Plot $V$ as a function of $r$, using Eq. (12.6), and find the value of $r$ for which $V$ is a maximum. (b) Find the maximum value of $V$ using the calculus.

**12.9.** Using Eq. (12.7), plot $I/I_{max}$ as a function of $\delta$ for $r^2 = 0.5$ and for $r^2 = 0.8$. What conclusions can you draw from the resulting curves?

**12.10.** Find the ratio of the transmitted maximum to the minimum intensity when the reflecting power of the metalized surfaces of a Fabry-Perot etalon is (a) 0.8 and (b) 0.5.

**12.11.** The index of refraction of a slab of glass of thickness 0.200 cm is determined in the manner outlined in Sec. 12.5b, using two identical such pieces in both beams of the Michelson interferometer. If 100 fringes pass the field of view in light of wavelength $5 \times 10^{-5}$ cm when one of the slabs is turned through an angle of $14°32'$, calculate the refractive index. What percentage error is involved in neglecting the term $N^2\lambda^2/4t$?

**12.12.** The components of the sodium $D$ doublet are $\lambda_1 = 5890$ A and $\lambda_2 = 5896$ A. By how much must the Fabry-Perot plates be separated so that, with the sodium light incident normally, a system of interference rings is present, with the $k$th-order rings of $\lambda_2$ falling on the $(k + 1)$st-order rings of $\lambda_1$? [HINT: $k\lambda_2 = (k + 1)\lambda_1$. Show that $d \doteq \lambda_1^2/2(\lambda_2 - \lambda_1)$.]

**12.13.** The dielectric of an interference filter has a thickness of $3 \times 10^{-5}$ cm and a refractive index of 1.35. (a) Find the wavelengths of the maxima transmitted when light is incident normally. (b) If the optical distance between the reflecting surfaces represents a wavelength for which a maximum is desired, to what interference order does this correspond? Assume the refractive index constant for the different wavelengths.

**12.14.** Devise an interferometric method of measuring the coefficient of thermal expansion of a sample of material.

# CHAPTER 13

# DIFFRACTION

We have already pointed out (Secs. 10.1 and 10.7) that light does not really travel in straight lines and that rectilinear propagation is only approximately followed. In Sec. 10.7 we have seen that Huygens proposed his principle of secondary wavelets in order to surmount the difficulties that the wave theory experienced in explaining apparent rectilinear propagation of light. It was there pointed out that light does bend into the geometrical shadow of an obstacle or aperture, illustrating the deviation of light travel from true rectilinear paths, or, as it is called, *diffraction*. The wave theory is successful in affording a satisfactory explanation of diffraction phenomena, and as will become evident, the amount of bending or diffraction is extremely small when the wavelength of the wave is very small in comparison with the dimensions of the obstacle or aperture. Such is the case with visible light waves and ordinary laboratory apertures, thus leading to approximate rectilinear propagation. On the other hand, when the wavelength of a wave is comparable with the size of the obstacle or aperture, the diffraction effect is much greater, as with water and sound waves. In Sec. 10.7 it was also pointed out that Fresnel was able to give a satisfactory explanation of diffraction effects by employing a combination of Huygens' wavelets with the principle of interference. In this chapter we shall see how, by treating the wavelets as many interfering sources, the disturbance and intensity at any point may be obtained, thus giving a quantitative account of observed diffraction patterns.

We shall divide the chapter into two parts, part I dealing with the general class of phenomena known as *Fraunhofer diffraction* and part II dealing with the general class of phenomena known as *Fresnel diffraction*. A Fraunhofer diffraction pattern is obtained when the light waves incident on the obstacle or aperture are plane (obtained by using a distant source or rendered parallel by a lens) and the screen, on which the diffraction pattern is observed, is effectively at an infinite distance from the obstacle or aperture or the pattern is observed by a telescope focused for parallel rays. A Fresnel diffraction pattern results when the light source or the screen or both are at a finite distance from the obstacle or aperture and no lenses are employed, so that the waves are spherical or cylindrical. We shall see that the analysis of Fraunhofer diffraction, in view of the fact that the diffracted wave is plane, is simpler than that of the Fresnel diffraction.

## PART I.   FRAUNHOFER DIFFRACTION

**13.1. The Single Slit.**   Figure 13.1 shows a section of a slit or rectangular aperture $AB$ whose length, running perpendicular to the plane of the figure, is large compared with its width $a$.   Plane monochromatic waves are shown incident on the slit perpendicular to its plane.   We wish to find an expression for the intensity of the diffraction pattern appearing at points $P_\theta$ in the focal plane of the lens.   By Huygens' principle each point of the wave in the plane of the slit acts as a source of secondary wavelets which interfere to produce a resultant disturbance at the points $P_\theta$ defined by the parallel rays incident on the lens at the diffraction angle $\theta$.   The point $P_0$ corresponds to the diffraction angle $\theta = 0°$.   In what follows we give, in accordance with our usual treatment, a noncalculus development on the left side of the double-column page and one using the calculus on the right side.

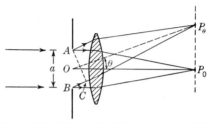

Fig. 13.1. The single-slit Fraunhofer diffraction.

Consider parallel rays in the direction $\theta$ interfering at the point $P_\theta$ in Fig. 13.1.   With $AC$ drawn perpendicular to $BC$, the optical path of all the parallel rays from $AC$ to $P_\theta$ are equal, and the path difference of the extreme rays from the ends of the slit is $BC = a \sin \theta$, the path differences of all the other intermediate rays varying from zero to this value.   To find the resultant disturbance of an infinite number of such parallel rays, it is helpful to use the polygon of vector amplitudes shown in Fig. 13.2, which represents $n$ equal vector amplitudes $A$ having the same phase difference $\gamma$.   The resultant intensity is proportional to the

Consider Fig. 13.1 without the lens so that the observation screen for the time being is at a finite distance from the slit, as shown in Fig. 13.4.   The center of the slit is the origin of the coordinate system chosen with $z$ as ordinate and $x$ as abscissa.   Consider that the slit is divided into the infinitesimal elements $dz$ each of which acts as a secondary source of disturbance emitting elementary waves which superpose to produce a resultant disturbance at $P_\theta$.   Let $r$ be the distance of $O$ from $P_\theta$ and $\rho$ be the distance from the element $dz$ to $P_\theta$.   A disturbance originating at $dz$ produces a displacement $du$ at $P_\theta$ given by [see Eq. (10.3$b$)],

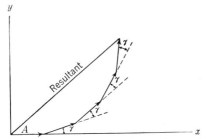

FIG. 13.2. Polygon of $n$ harmonic equal amplitudes with constant phase difference.

square of the resultant amplitude, or

$$I \propto A^2\{[1 + \cos \gamma + \cos 2\gamma + \cos 3\gamma + \cdots + \cos (n - 1)\gamma]^2 + [\sin \gamma + \sin 2\gamma + \sin 3\gamma + \cdots + \sin (n - 1)\gamma]^2\} \quad (13.1a)$$

Now the sums of each of the series

$$du = K \, dz \sin 2\pi \left(\frac{t}{T} - \frac{\rho}{\lambda}\right) \quad (13.1A)$$

where $t$ is the time, $T$ the period, and $\lambda$ the wavelength. The amplitude factor $K$ may be considered constant for all the elements $dz$ since we are interested in the limiting case of the screen being at infinite distance from the slit. Hence the angles are small, and any variation of amplitude with angle, with obliquity, or with slight differences in distance of element from $P_\theta$ may therefore be neglected. The waves from the elements $dz$ differ from one another essentially by the phase factor alone. The

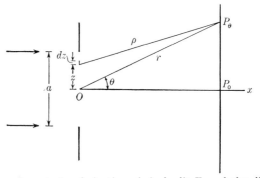

FIG. 13.4. Diagram for calculus derivation of single-slit Fraunhofer diffraction pattern.

in Eq. (13.1a) can be found as follows: Let

$$S_1 = 1 + \cos \gamma + \cos 2\gamma + \cdots + \cos (n - 1)\gamma$$

Multiplying by $2 \cos \gamma$, we have

$$2S_1 \cos \gamma = 2 \cos \gamma + 2 \cos^2 \gamma + 2 \cos \gamma \cos 2\gamma + \cdots + 2 \cos \gamma \cos (n - 1)\gamma$$

and using the trigonometric rela-

resultant disturbance at $P_\theta$ is then given by integrating Eq. (13.1A) over the width of the slit, or

$$u = K \int_{-a/2}^{a/2} \sin 2\pi \left(\frac{t}{T} - \frac{\rho}{\lambda}\right) dz \quad (13.1B)$$

Using for $P_\theta$ the coordinates $(x_0, z_0)$, and for $dz$ the coordinates $(0, z)$, then

$$\rho^2 = x_0^2 + (z - z_0)^2$$

tionship for the product of two cosines,

$$2S_1 \cos \gamma = 2 \cos \gamma + 1 + \cos \gamma$$
$$+ \cos 2\gamma + \cdots + \cos (n-2)\gamma$$
$$+ \cos 2\gamma + \cos 3\gamma + \cdots$$
$$+ \cos n\gamma$$

This takes the form

$$2S_1 \cos \gamma = 2S_1 + \cos \gamma - 1$$
$$+ \cos n\gamma - \cos (n-1)\gamma$$

or

$$S_1 = \frac{1}{2} + \frac{\cos n\gamma - \cos (n-1)\gamma}{2(\cos \gamma - 1)}$$
$$= \frac{1}{2} + \frac{\sin (2n-1)\dfrac{\gamma}{2}}{2 \sin \dfrac{\gamma}{2}}$$

which is easily seen to be equal to

$$S_1 = \frac{\sin \dfrac{\gamma}{2} + \sin (2n-1)\dfrac{\gamma}{2}}{2 \sin \dfrac{\gamma}{2}}$$

$$= \frac{\sin \dfrac{n\gamma}{2} \cos (n-1)\dfrac{\gamma}{2}}{\sin \dfrac{\gamma}{2}} \quad (13.1b)$$

In the same way, the sum $S_2$ for the sine series can be shown to be given by

$$S_2 = \frac{\sin \dfrac{n\gamma}{2} \sin (n-1)\dfrac{\gamma}{2}}{\sin \dfrac{\gamma}{2}} \quad (13.1c)$$

Equation (13.1a) now becomes

$$I \propto \frac{A^2 \sin^2 \dfrac{n\gamma}{2}}{\sin^2 \dfrac{\gamma}{2}} \quad (13.1d)$$

or

$$\rho^2 = r^2 \left(1 - \frac{2zz_0}{r^2} + \frac{z^2}{r^2}\right) \quad (13.1C)$$

and extracting the square root,

$$\rho = r \left[1 + \frac{1}{2}\left(\frac{z^2}{r^2} - \frac{2zz_0}{r^2}\right)\right.$$
$$\left. - \frac{1}{8}\left(\frac{z^2}{r^2} - \frac{2zz_0}{r^2}\right)^2 + \cdots \right]$$

Now passing to the case of Fraunhofer diffraction so that $r$ becomes very large, the quadratic and higher power terms in $z/r$ may be neglected, leading to

$$\rho = r - z \sin \theta \quad (13.1D)$$

Substituting into Eq. (13.1B) leads to

$$u = K \int_{-a/2}^{a/2} \sin \left[2\pi \right.$$
$$\left. \left(\frac{t}{T} - \frac{r}{\lambda} + \frac{z \sin \theta}{\lambda}\right)\right] dz \quad (13.1E)$$

Integrating,

$$u = \frac{-K\lambda}{2\pi \sin \theta}$$
$$\left[\cos 2\pi \left(\frac{t}{T} - \frac{r}{\lambda} + \frac{a \sin \theta}{2\lambda}\right)\right.$$
$$\left. - \cos 2\pi \left(\frac{t}{T} - \frac{r}{\lambda} - \frac{a \sin \theta}{2\lambda}\right)\right]$$

which reduces to

$$u = Ka \frac{\sin \alpha}{\alpha} \sin 2\pi \left(\frac{t}{T} - \frac{r}{\lambda}\right)$$
$$(13.1F)$$

where we have set

$$\alpha = \frac{\pi a \sin \theta}{\lambda} *$$

Equation (13.1F) shows that the

---

* If the plane wave in Fig. 13.1 is incident at an angle $i$ with the slit, it is necessary to replace $\alpha$ by the more general expression $\pi a(\sin i + \sin \theta)/\lambda$.

The phase $\alpha$ of the resultant amplitude is

$$\tan \alpha = \frac{S_2}{S_1} = \tan (n - 1) \frac{\gamma}{2}$$

so that the principal value of $\alpha$ is

$$\alpha = \frac{(n - 1)\gamma}{2} \qquad (13.1e)$$

[The student should think over and interpret the solution

$$\alpha = \frac{(n - 1)\gamma}{2} + \pi \Big]$$

Now consider that $n$ becomes infinitely large so that $nA$ and $n\gamma$

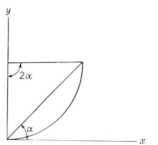

$y$

$2\alpha$

$\alpha$

$x$

FIG. 13.3. Graphical representation of resultant amplitude in the diffraction from a single slit.

remain finite. This corresponds to dividing the width of the slit $AB$ into an infinite number of infinitesimal strips or segments. The amplitude vectors of Fig. 13.2 now join to form the arc of a circle of length $nA$ as shown in Fig. 13.3. Also, from Eq. (13.1e), $\alpha$ approaches the value $n\gamma/2$, and Eq. (13.1d) becomes

$$I \propto A^2 \frac{\sin^2 \alpha}{\sin^2 \dfrac{\alpha}{n}} \qquad (13.1f)$$

resultant harmonic vibration at $P_\theta$ has an amplitude proportional to $\sin \alpha / \alpha$. Since the intensity is proportional to the square of the amplitude, we have, for the intensity $I_\theta$ at $P_\theta$,

$$I_\theta = I_0 \frac{\sin^2 \alpha}{\alpha^2} \qquad (13.1G)$$

where $I_0$ is the value of the intensity for $\alpha = 0$.

In the limit, $\sin \alpha / n$ may be replaced by $\alpha / n$, and we have

$$I_\theta = I_0 \frac{\sin^2 \alpha}{\alpha^2} \qquad (13.1g)$$

where $I_0$ is the value of the intensity when $\alpha = 0$, since

$$\frac{\sin \alpha}{\alpha} = 1$$

for $\alpha = 0$, and

$$\alpha = \frac{n\gamma}{2} = \frac{1}{2} \frac{2\pi}{\lambda} (a \sin \theta)$$

$$= \frac{\pi a \sin \theta}{\lambda} *$$

Equation (13.1g) or (13.1G) gives the variation of intensity as a function of position in the diffraction pattern. The intensity $I_0$ represents the intensity at the center of the pattern, *i.e.*, at $P_0$ (Fig. 13.1), where all the

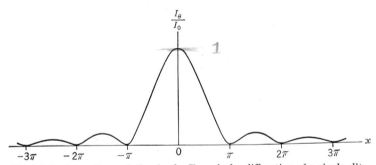

FIG. 13.5. Intensity variation in the Fraunhofer diffraction of a single slit.

wavelets arrive in phase to produce a maximum at all times. The significant characteristics of the intensity function are best obtained by examining the plot of Eq. (13.1G) shown in Fig. 13.5. In addition to the principal maximum at $\alpha = 0$, there are secondary maxima falling between the equally spaced zero-intensity minima which occur at the values $\alpha = \pm k\pi$, where $k = 1, 2, 3, \ldots$. The values of $\alpha$ for which the intensity is a maximum are given by the equation (see Prob. 13.6)

$$\tan \alpha = \alpha \qquad (13.2)$$

* If the plane wave in Fig. 13.1 is incident at an angle $i$ with the slit, it is necessary to replace $\alpha$ by the more general expression $\pi a (\sin i + \sin \theta)/\lambda$.

The values of $\alpha$ satisfying this equation are found by plotting the functions $y = \tan \alpha$ and $y = \alpha$ on the same graph and determining the intersection points of both graphs. When this is done (see Prob. 13.7), it becomes apparent that the maxima do not lie midway between the minima. We have seen that the minima occur for

$$\frac{a \sin \theta}{\lambda} = \pm k \tag{13.3}$$

so that as the slit width decreases, the value of $\theta$ for a given $k$ is larger and the diffraction pattern broadens. On the other hand, an increase in wavelength also broadens the pattern. Hence, if the wavelength is small compared with the dimensions of the slit, the diffraction pattern becomes

Fig. 13.6. Fraunhofer diffraction pattern of a single slit. (*By permission from "Light: Principles and Experiments," by G. S. Monk. Copyright,* 1937. *McGraw-Hill Book Company, Inc.*)

negligible in extent and we have light traveling approximately in straight lines. If white light is used, the principal maximum is white and the regions of secondary maxima are colored by the spectrum, with the red farther from the center of the pattern than the violet.

A photograph of Fraunhofer diffraction by a single slit, showing the general characteristics of intensity enumerated above, is given in Fig. 13.6. The diffraction bands of course are parallel to the slit.

We have seen from Eq. (13.3) that if $BC$ (Fig. 13.1) is one wavelength, then $P_\theta$ is a region of darkness. That this is as it should be is evident when we remember that not only the points $A$ and $B$ but every point between them sends rays of light to $P_\theta$. For each element in $AO$ there is a corresponding element in $BO$ whose ray differs in optical path length by half a wavelength, with the result that one-half of the wave front destroys the effect of the other half. If $BC$ is two wavelengths, $AB$ can be considered divided into four equal parts, the upper two interfering destructively and likewise for the lower two, resulting again in darkness. On the other hand if $BC = (\frac{3}{2})\lambda$, then the wave front may be considered as made up of three equal parts. Then the upper two-thirds cancel, and the effect of the lower third results in the first secondary maximum.

In deriving Eq. (13.1$g$) or (13.1$G$) an opening whose length was large compared with its width was employed. If the rectangular aperture has a width $a$ and comparable length $b$, say parallel to the $x$ and $y$ axes, respectively, with the $z$ axis normal to the aperture, and the origin of coordinates at the center of the aperture, similar analysis over both dimensions of the aperture leads to the equation

$$I_\theta = I_0 \frac{\sin^2 \alpha_1}{\alpha_1^2} \frac{\sin^2 \alpha_2}{\alpha_2^2} \qquad (13.4)$$

in which $\alpha_1 = (\pi a \sin \theta_1)/\lambda$, and $\alpha_2 = (\pi b \sin \theta_2)/\lambda$, where $\theta_1$ is the angle that the diffracted ray, drawn from the origin, makes with the $xz$ plane and $\theta_2$ is the angle it makes with the $yz$ plane. The intensity at the center of the pattern is $I_0$, corresponding to $\alpha_1 = \alpha_2 = 0$. The resultant intensity is zero if either $\alpha_1$ or $\alpha_2$ is an integral multiple of $\pi$. For all points $P_\theta$ in the $xz$ plane, $\theta_2 = 0$ and

$$I_\theta = I_0 \frac{\sin^2 \alpha_1}{\alpha_1^2}$$

while for points $P_\theta$ in the $yz$ plane, $\theta_1 = 0$ and

$$I_\theta = I_0 \frac{\sin^2 \alpha_2}{\alpha_2^2}$$

each expression resulting in a pattern corresponding to a slit, one of whose dimensions is long compared with the other, as before, but in mutually perpendicular directions. There are thus produced two systems of diffraction bands forming a rectangular intersecting network with a bright central maximum of rectangular shape whose sides, of course, are rotated through 90° with respect to those of the aperture (why?).

**13.2. The Circular Aperture.** The Fraunhofer diffraction through a circular aperture is of the utmost importance in view of the circular form of lenses and stops but is also much more complicated mathematically. The left side of the following double-column page contains an approximate but very simplified treatment of the diffraction pattern produced by a circular aperture, while the right side presents the more rigorous mathematical development.

Figure 13.7 shows the cross-section of a circular aperture $AB$ of diameter $a$, the plane of the aper-

FIG. 13.7. Simplified diagram illustrating Fraunhofer diffraction through a circular aperture.

Figure 13.8 shows one quadrant of a circular aperture of diameter $a$, with its plane in the $xz$ plane. Plane waves are incident on the aperture in the $y$ direction toward the reader. The circular aperture is considered to be divided into elemental diffracting areas $s\, ds\, d\varphi$, as shown, each acting as a secondary source of disturbance. We wish to find the resultant disturb-

ture being perpendicular to the plane of the figure. Parallel monochromatic rays are incident on the aperture from the left, and the point $P_0$ represents the place where the rays are brought to a focus by a lens (not shown) placed at the slit. Diffracted rays from the top and

ance at $P_\theta$ which we may choose in the $xy$ plane on account of the presence of the circular symmetry. The distance of $P_\theta$ from the center of the aperture is $r$, assumed finite for the present, and its distance from the elemental area is $\rho$. A disturbance originating at the ele-

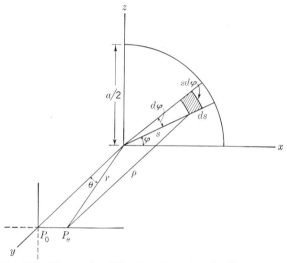

FIG. 13.8. Fraunhofer diffraction through a circular aperture.

bottom of the slit are shown meeting at $P$. If the distance of $P_0$ from the aperture is $c$ and the distance $PP_0$ is $y$, then it is clear that

$$BP^2 = c^2 + \left(\frac{a}{2} + y\right)^2$$

$$AP^2 = c^2 + \left(\frac{a}{2} - y\right)^2$$

Expanding each by the binomial expansion and neglecting higher powers of $(a/2 + y)/c$ and $(a/2 - y)/c$, we have

$$BP = c + \frac{(a/2 + y)^2}{2c}$$

$$AP = c + \frac{(a/2 - y)^2}{2c}$$

mental area produces a displacement $du$ at $P_\theta$ proportional to the area and given by

$$du = Ks\, ds\, d\varphi \, \sin 2\pi \left(\frac{t}{T} - \frac{\rho}{\lambda}\right)$$

$$(13.5A)$$

where the other symbols have the same meaning as in Eq. (13.1A). As before, the resultant disturbance at $P_\theta$ is given by

$$u = K \int_0^{2\pi} \int_0^{a_0} \sin 2\pi \left(\frac{t}{T} - \frac{\rho}{\lambda}\right) s\, ds\, d\varphi \quad (13\text{-}5B)$$

where we have designated the aperture radius as $a_0$. We see that since the coordinates of the eleso that the path difference is

$$BP - AP = \frac{ay}{c} \quad (13.5a)$$

By the same considerations as for the single slit in the latter part of the last section, if $ay/c$ is an integral multiple of a wavelength, there is a minimum of illumination at $P$, and if $ay/c$ is an odd multiple of a half wavelength, there is a maximum of illumination. The diffraction pattern of the circular aperture is obtained by considering Fig. 13.7 rotated about the central axis passing through $P_0$. There is thus formed a pattern characterized by a central bright disk, known as Airy's disk, surrounded by concentric bright and dark rings. Equation (13.5a) shows that the rings become smaller as the circular aperture is increased in size. The radius of the first diffraction minimum, or dark ring, is given by

$$y_1 = \frac{c\lambda}{a} \quad (13.5b)$$

which of course bounds the central maximum. The angle subtended at the center of the aperture by the radius of this first dark ring is

$$\theta_1 = \frac{\lambda}{a} \quad (13.5c)$$

We must remember that the above development is approximate, and the more accurate analysis gives for the angular radius of the first diffraction dark ring

$$\theta_1 = \frac{1.22\lambda}{a} \quad (13.5d)$$

mental area are $(s \cos \varphi, 0, s \sin \varphi)$ and those of $P_\theta$ are $(x_0, y_0, 0)$,

$$\rho^2 = (x_0 - s \cos \varphi)^2 + y_0^2 + s^2 \sin^2 \varphi$$
$$\rho^2 = r^2 - 2x_0 s \cos \varphi + s^2$$

Since $s$ is small compared with $r$, which is very large for Fraunhofer diffraction, we have, expanding by the binomial theorem,

$$\rho = r - s \sin \theta \cos \varphi$$

Substituting into Eq. (13.5B),

$$u = K \int_0^{2\pi} \int_0^{a_0} \sin 2\pi \left( \frac{t}{T} - \frac{r}{\lambda} \right. $$
$$\left. + \frac{s \sin \theta \cos \varphi}{\lambda} \right) s \, ds \, d\varphi$$

or

$$u = K \sin 2\pi \left( \frac{t}{T} - \frac{r}{\lambda} \right)$$
$$\int_0^{2\pi} d\varphi \int_0^{a_0} \cos 2\pi \left( \frac{s \sin \theta \cos \varphi}{\lambda} \right)$$
$$s \, ds + K \cos 2\pi \left( \frac{t}{T} - \frac{r}{\lambda} \right) \int_0^{2\pi} d\varphi \int_0^{a_0}$$
$$\sin 2\pi \left( \frac{s \sin \theta \cos \varphi}{\lambda} \right) s \, ds \quad (13.5C)$$

The second integral is an odd function so that its value is zero. This can be verified by integrating with respect to $s$ by parts and then carrying out the integration with respect to $\varphi$ in the series. The student is asked to do this in Prob. 13.8. Therefore

$$u = K \sin 2\pi \left( \frac{t}{T} - \frac{r}{\lambda} \right) \int_0^{2\pi} d\varphi \int_0^{a_0}$$
$$s \cos \left( \frac{2\pi}{\lambda} s \sin \theta \cos \varphi \right) ds$$

and integrating with respect to $s$ by parts,

This analysis, which is given in the right-hand column, considers dividing the circular aperture into many diffracting elements whose sum-total interference effect is found by the use of the calculus.

$$u = K \sin 2\pi \left( \frac{t}{T} - \frac{r}{\lambda} \right) \int_0^{2\pi}$$

$$\left[ \frac{\cos (ba_0 \cos \varphi)}{b^2 \cos^2 \varphi} + \frac{a_0 \sin (ba_0 \cos \varphi)}{b \cos \varphi} \right.$$

$$\left. - \frac{1}{b^2 \cos^2 \varphi} \right] d\varphi$$

where $b = (2\pi/\lambda) \sin \theta$.

Now using the series expansion for $\cos (ba_0 \cos \varphi)$ and $\sin (ba_0 \cos \varphi)$, we have

$$u = K \sin 2\pi \left( \frac{t}{T} - \frac{r}{\lambda} \right) \int_0^{2\pi}$$

$$\left[ \left( -\frac{a_0^2}{2!} + \frac{b^2 a_0^4}{4!} \cos^2 \varphi - \frac{b^4 a_0^6 \cos^4 \varphi}{6!} \right. \right.$$

$$\left. + \frac{b^6 a_0^8 \cos^6 \varphi}{8!} + \cdots \right)$$

$$+ \left( a_0^2 - \frac{b^2 a_0^4 \cos^2 \varphi}{3!} + \frac{b^4 a_0^6 \cos^4 \varphi}{5!} \right.$$

$$\left. \left. - \frac{b^6 a_0^8 \cos^6 \varphi}{7!} + \cdots \right) \right] d\varphi$$

Collecting terms and integrating termwise, we now obtain

$$u = K\pi a_0^2 \left( 1 - \frac{m^2}{1!2!} + \frac{m^4}{2!3!} \right.$$

$$\left. - \frac{m^6}{3!4!} + \cdots \right) \sin 2\pi \left( \frac{t}{T} - \frac{r}{\lambda} \right)$$

$$(13.5D)$$

where we have set

$$m = \frac{\pi a_0 \sin \theta}{\lambda}$$

By multiplying and dividing Eq. (13.5D) by $m$, we arrive at

$$u = \frac{Ka_0 \lambda}{\sin \theta} \left( m - \frac{m^3}{1!2!} + \frac{m^5}{2!3!} \right.$$

$$\left. - \frac{m^6}{3!4!} + \cdots \right) \sin 2\pi \left( \frac{t}{T} - \frac{r}{\lambda} \right)$$

$$(13.5E)$$

The infinite series in the first parentheses of Eq. (13.5*E*) is convergent for all values of $m$ and is known as the Bessel function

$$J_1(2m) = m - \frac{m^3}{1!2!} + \frac{m^5}{2!3!} - \frac{m^6}{3!4!} + \cdots$$

This function has an infinite number of zeros, going through positive and negative values alternately as $m$ increases, with diminishing maxima, like a damped sine wave. The intensity in the diffraction pattern is proportional to the square of $J_1(2m)/m$. When $m = 0$, corresponding to $\theta = 0$ or $P_0$ in Fig. 13.8, the intensity from Eq. (13.5*D*) is a maximum, giving rise to the central bright disk. The first minimum corresponds to the first zero of $J_1$ which, from tables, is at $2m = 1.22\pi$. This gives

$$\sin \theta_1 = \frac{0.61\lambda}{a_0}$$

or

$$\sin \theta_1 = \frac{1.22\lambda}{a} \quad (13.5F)$$

$a_0$ = aperture radius

$a$ = aperture diameter

Succeeding minima such as the second and third have, for the corresponding values of $m$, 1.116 and 1.619. The second and third secondary maxima, or bright bands, have the $m$ values 0.819 and 1.333. There is thus produced a circular diffraction pattern with a very bright central disk followed by a series of alternate dark and bright rings of decreasing intensity.

Figure 13.9 shows a photograph of the diffraction through a circular opening. When light from a distant star is observed through a lens, the light has essentially passed through a circular aperture and is imaged as a circular diffraction pattern having the above characteristics. The

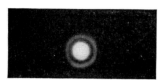

central maximum has an angular radius given by $\theta_1 = 1.22\lambda/a$, where $a$ is the diameter of the lens containing about 84 per cent of the energy transmitted, the rest going into the secondary maxima. This is of considerable importance in the subject of resolving power, which we treat in the next chapter.

FIG. 13.9. Fraunhofer diffraction pattern using a point source and a circular opening. (*By permission from "Fundamentals of Optics," by F. A. Jenkins and H. E. White. Copyright, 1950, Second Edition. McGraw-Hill Book Company, Inc.*)

If the light incident on a circular aperture is white, the image consists of superposed diffraction patterns each due to light of one wavelength, the shorter wavelengths corresponding to rings of smaller diameter.

**13.3. The Double Slit.** In Sec. 11.1 we discussed the interference fringes obtained from Young's double slit where it was assumed that the slits were extremely narrow and close together. We now see this was necessary in order that the central maxima of the diffraction patterns of each slit spread out over a relatively large region. With such an arrangement it was possible to consider that the resultant disturbance of the light emerging from the slits was due to a superposition simply of two interfering beams. We shall now investigate the Fraunhofer diffraction pattern when the width of the slits is comparable with that of the opaque region between them.

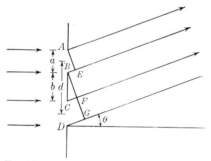

FIG. 13.10 Fraunhofer diffraction through a double slit.

Let us consider two parallel slits each of width $a$ separated by the opaque region $b$, the distance between slit centers being $d$ as shown in Fig. 13.10. The slit lengths are again large compared with their widths. The non-calculus and calculus developments are given, respectively, in the left- and right-hand columns.

The graphical representation of the superposition of amplitudes may be used to find the expression for the intensity in the double-slit diffraction pattern. As in Sec.

The integration here for the intensity in direction $\theta$ follows that given for the single slit but with the limits taken to extend over both slits. Taking the origin at

13.1, Fig. 13.3, the vector-amplitude diagram for each slit is the arc of a circle whose chord represents the resultant amplitude. Thus in

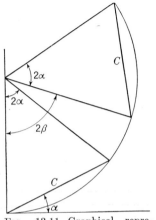

FIG. 13.11. Graphical representation of the resultant amplitude in the diffraction from a double slit.

Fig. 13.11, the chords $C$ represent the amplitudes of the waves through each slit. For the waves traveling in the direction $\theta$ we have

$$2\alpha = \frac{2\pi a \sin \theta}{\lambda}$$

which is the phase difference corresponding to the path difference $BE$ or $DG - CF$ in Fig. 13.10. At some point in the direction $\theta$ the amplitudes due to each slit combine to form a resultant whose square is proportional to the intensity at that point. From Fig. 13.11, the amplitudes from each slit differ in phase by $2\beta$, where

$$2\beta = \frac{2\pi (a + b) \sin \theta}{\lambda} = \frac{2\pi d \sin \theta}{\lambda}$$

which corresponds to the path difference $DG$ of Fig. 13.10. Ap-

the center of the slit $CD$ in Fig. 13.10, we have, using Eq. (13.1$E$),

$$u = K \left\{ \int_{-a/2}^{a/2} \sin \left[ 2\pi \right. \right.$$

$$\left. \left( \frac{t}{T} - \frac{r}{\lambda} + \frac{z \sin \theta}{\lambda} \right) \right] dz$$

$$+ \int_{d-(a/2)}^{d+(a/2)} \sin \left[ 2\pi \right.$$

$$\left. \left. \left( \frac{t}{T} - \frac{r}{\lambda} + \frac{z \sin \theta}{\lambda} \right) \right] dz \right\} \quad (13.6A)$$

Integrating

$$u = Ka \frac{\sin \alpha}{\alpha} \left[ \sin 2\pi \left( \frac{t}{T} - \frac{r}{\lambda} \right) \right.$$

$$\left. + \sin 2\pi \left( \frac{t}{T} - \frac{r}{\lambda} + \frac{d \sin \theta}{\lambda} \right) \right]$$

where $\qquad \alpha = \dfrac{\pi a \sin \theta}{\lambda}$

The quantity $2\alpha$ represents the phase difference corresponding to the path difference between the edges of a slit.

Reducing the last expression further yields

$$u = 2Ka \frac{\sin \alpha}{\alpha} \cos \beta \sin \left[ 2\pi \right.$$

$$\left. \left( \frac{t}{T} - \frac{r}{\lambda} + \frac{d \sin \theta}{2\lambda} \right) \right] \quad (13.6B)$$

where

$$\beta = \frac{\pi d \sin \theta}{\lambda}$$

The quantity $2\beta$ is the phase difference corresponding to the path difference between any point in one slit and the corresponding point in the other slit. The amplitude of the resultant disturbance represented by Eq. (13.6$B$) is proportional to $(2 \sin \alpha \cos \beta)/\alpha$, so

plying Eq. (10.10) to the amplitudes $C$ yields for the square of the resultant amplitude $A_r$,

$$A_r^2 = 4C^2 \cos^2 \beta \quad (13.6a)$$

Since $C^2$ is proportional to the intensity from a single slit, we have, for the resultant intensity in direction $\theta$,

$$I_\theta = 4I_0 \frac{\sin^2 \alpha}{\alpha^2} \cos^2 \beta \quad (13.6b)$$

where $4I_0$ is the intensity when $\alpha = 0$ and $\beta = 0$.

that the resultant intensity in the direction $\theta$ is given by

$$I_\theta = 4I_0 \frac{\sin^2 \alpha}{\alpha^2} \cos^2 \beta \quad (13.6C)$$

where $4I_0$ is the intensity corresponding to $\alpha = 0$ and $\beta = 0$.

We see that the intensity in the resultant pattern is given by the product of two functions: one, $(\sin^2 \alpha)/\alpha^2$, gives the diffraction pattern of a single slit; and the other, $\cos^2 \beta$, gives the interference pattern resulting from two slits. The intensity $I_\theta$ is zero when either of these functions is zero, and this occurs when $\alpha = \pi$, $2\pi$, $3\pi$, . . . , or when $\beta = \pi/2$, $3\pi/2$, $5\pi/2$, . . . . This results in two sets of minima, which are revealed in the plot of Eq. (13.6b) or Eq. (13.6C) and shown in Fig. 13.12,

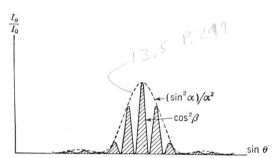

FIG. 13.12. Intensity variation in the Fraunhofer diffraction of a double slit.

drawn for the case $d = 3a$. The dotted curve we have already met in Fig. 13.5 as that of the diffraction pattern of a single slit but with the central maximum having an intensity four times that of a single slit. Superposed on this is the interference pattern of the two slits and indicated by the solid curve. The interference pattern, as it were, is modulated by the diffraction pattern. The entire pattern may be looked upon as resulting from the fact that the fringes are due to the interference between the light from both slits, the intensities of these fringes being governed by the diffraction occurring at the slits. Figure 13.13 shows a photograph of the diffraction pattern for two slits, showing the sharp interference fringes superposed on the diffraction bands.

Although the positions of the interference maxima are not given by any simple expression, they may be approximated by considering $(\sin^2 \alpha)/\alpha^2$ constant. Such an assumption is justified in the vicinity of the center of the pattern. The maxima then occur approximately at the positions given by $\beta = k\pi$ or $d \sin \theta = k\lambda$, $k = 0, 1, 2, \ldots$. The number of interference maxima that appear within the central diffraction maximum depends on the ratio $d/a$ (see Prob. 13.10), with the result that as this ratio increases the number of central interference maxima increases.

Fig. 13.13. Fraunhofer diffraction pattern of two slits. The slits are equal, and the ratio of opaque to open space is 3:1. (*By permission from "Light: Principles and Experiments,"* by *G. S. Monk. Copyright, 1937. McGraw-Hill Book Company, Inc.*)

The student should reread Sec. 12.5f on the stellar interferometer and see how that instrument operates in accordance with the principles here covered for double-slit diffraction.

**13.4. The Diffraction Grating.** In the last section we have seen that the use of two slits produces a pattern that exhibits sharp interference maxima in relation to the accompanying broad diffraction pattern of a single slit. By increasing the number of slits the sharpness of the maxima increases, and the intensity patterns can be worked out in a manner similar to the analysis for two slits. In Fig. 13.14 are shown a comparison of the photographs of the diffraction patterns from one to six equal and equidistant slits. For one slit there is shown the characteristic diffraction pattern only. For two slits, there is present a group of interference maxima in the central diffraction region. For three slits, observe that the central interference maxima are sharper and between each two there is a single weak secondary maximum. For four slits, the central interference maxima are still sharper, and there are now two secondary weaker maxima. For five slits, there are three secondary maxima between any two central interference maxima, which are now quite sharp. With a very large number of slits of equal width and equally spaced, the effect is to form a pattern that shows extremely sharp principal interference maxima with secondary maxima whose intensity is negligibly small. Such a device is known as a *diffraction grating* (which may be of the reflection type as well as of the transmission type) and is a very effective instrument for the study of spectra.   We shall now obtain the expression for the intensity in the Fraunhofer diffraction pattern of $N$ slits each of width $a$ and having a constant slit-to-slit separation $d$ as shown in Fig. 13.10, which is to be imagined as containing $N$ slits.   As for two slits,

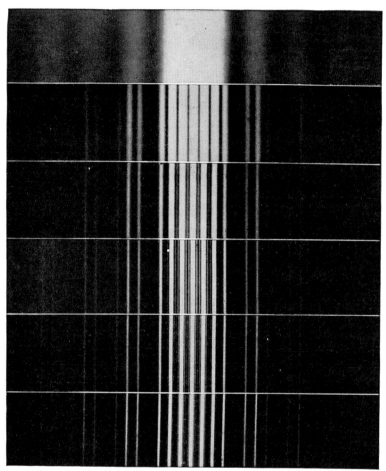

Fig. 13.14. Photographs of the Fraunhofer diffraction patterns from 1, 2, 3, 4, 5, 6 slits. Ratio of opaque to open space is 3:1.   (*By permission from "Light: Principles and Experiments," by G. S. Monk.   Copyright,* 1937.   *McGraw-Hill Book Company, Inc.*)

each opening contributes the same amplitude at some point in a direction $\theta$, and the problem here is to find the resultant of $N$ such amplitudes whose phases increase by a constant amount.   The noncalculus solution on the left and the calculus solution on the right of the two-column page follow.

Let $C$ be the amplitude from each of the $N$ slits, and let $2\beta$ be the constant phase difference so that

$$2\beta = \frac{2\pi d \sin \theta}{\lambda}$$

We then can construct a polygon of vector amplitudes, as in Fig. 13.2, with each vector of magnitude $C$ and common phase difference $2\beta$. As shown in Sec. 13.1, the resultant intensity is given by Eq. (13.1$d$), which here becomes

$$I_\theta \propto C^2 \frac{\sin^2 N\beta}{\sin^2 \beta}$$

Since $C^2$ is proportional to the intensity from a single slit, we have

$$I_\theta = I_0 \frac{\sin^2 \alpha}{\alpha^2} \frac{\sin^2 N\beta}{\sin^2 \beta} \quad (13.7a)$$

The integration for the double slit [Eq. (13.6$A$)] must now be extended to cover $N$ slits. Thus the disturbance is given by

$$u = K\left[ \int_{-a/2}^{a/2} \psi(z)\, dz \right.$$
$$+ \int_{d-(a/2)}^{d+(a/2)} \psi(z)\, dz$$
$$+ \int_{2d-(a/2)}^{2d+(a/2)} \psi(z)\, dz$$
$$+ \cdots + \left. \int_{(N-1)d-\frac{a}{2}}^{(N-1)d+\frac{a}{2}} \psi(z)\, dz \right]$$

where

$$\psi(z) = \sin 2\pi \left( \frac{t}{T} - \frac{r}{\lambda} + \frac{z \sin \theta}{\lambda} \right).$$

Integrating and simplifying,

$$u = Ka \frac{\sin \alpha}{\alpha}\left[ \sin 2\pi \left( \frac{t}{T} - \frac{r}{\lambda} \right) \right.$$
$$+ \sin 2\pi \left( \frac{t}{T} - \frac{r}{\lambda} + \frac{d \sin \theta}{\lambda} \right)$$
$$+ \sin 2\pi \left( \frac{t}{T} - \frac{r}{\lambda} + \frac{2d \sin \theta}{\lambda} \right)$$
$$+ \cdots + \sin 2\pi \left( \frac{t}{T} - \frac{r}{\lambda} \right.$$
$$\left. \left. + \frac{N-1}{\lambda} d \sin \theta \right) \right]$$

where $\quad \alpha = \dfrac{\pi a \sin \theta}{\lambda}$

Using the trigonometric relationship

$$\sum_{k=0}^{n} \sin (x + ky)$$
$$= \frac{\sin \left( x + \dfrac{ny}{2} \right) \sin \left( \dfrac{n+1}{2} y \right)}{\sin \dfrac{y}{2}}$$

we have

$$u = Ka \frac{\sin \alpha}{\alpha} \frac{\sin N\beta}{\sin \beta} \sin \left[ 2\pi \left( \frac{t}{T} - \frac{r}{\lambda} + \frac{N-1}{2\lambda} d \sin \theta \right) \right]$$

where $\qquad \beta = \dfrac{\pi d \sin \theta}{\lambda}$

The intensity in direction $\theta$ is therefore

$$I_\theta = I_0 \frac{\sin^2 \alpha}{\alpha^2} \frac{\sin^2 N\beta}{\sin^2 \beta} \qquad (13.7A)$$

Equation (13.7a) or Eq. (13.7A) is the required expression and the first factor, $(\sin^2 \alpha)/\alpha^2$, is simply the diffraction by a single slit which we have already discussed. The additional factor $(\sin^2 N\beta)/(\sin^2 \beta)$ must essentially account for the interference effects which we have observed in Fig. 13.14. The numerator of this quotient has the value zero when $N\beta = m\pi$, $m = 0, 1, 2, \ldots$ . The denominator has the value zero for $\beta = 0, \pi, 2\pi, 3\pi, \ldots$ . Since the quotient $0/0$ is indeterminate, $N\beta = m\pi$ is the condition for minima for all values of $m$ other than $m = 0$, $N, 2N, 3N, \ldots$ , where the value of $\theta$ for the minima is measured from the neighboring principal maximum. When the numerator and denominator are both zero, the ratio is finite and equal to $N^2$ (see Prob. 13.19). These represent the principal maxima, which are given by

$$d \sin \theta = k\lambda, \qquad k = 0, 1, 2, \ldots \qquad (13.8)$$

which is the familiar expression[1] that is employed in the determination of wavelengths by means of a grating and in which $k$ is the so-called "order." By comparison with the preceding section we see that, except for the influence of the factor $(\sin^2 \alpha)/\alpha^2$, the grating interference maxima coincide in position with the maxima for the double slit having the same slit width and slit separation. As a matter of fact, the double slit may be considered as a grating with two diffracting elements. Of course the grating maxima are much more intense on account of the factor $N^2$.

Since in the condition for a minimum $(\beta = m\pi/N)$ $m$ is an integer and for $m = 0$ and $m = N$ there occur principal maxima, we see that there are $N - 1$ minima or zero intensity points and $N - 2$ secondary maxima between any two neighboring principal maxima. These secondary maxima are very much weaker than the principal maxima and decrease

---

[1] When light is incident on the grating at an angle $i$, the more general grating equation is seen to be $d(\sin i + \sin \theta) = k\lambda$.

in intensity the more remote they are from the principal maximum. When $N$ becomes very large, as with a grating containing 15,000 apertures, the secondary maxima become very weak compared with the principal maxima. The intensity of the strongest secondary maximum, the one adjacent to a principal maximum, is about 4.5 per cent of the principal maximum. Thus with a slit source parallel to the grating slits, there is formed for each wavelength essentially a set of sharp lines with darkness between them. These sharp lines are images of the slit falling at the angles $\theta$ given by Eq. (13.8), the zero-order line corresponding to $k = 0$, the first-order line to $k = 1$, etc. The general features that we have so far presented are helpfully brought to light by plotting the interference function of Eq. (13.7$a$) or Eq. (13.7$A$) for some value of $N$, and the student is asked to do so in a problem. It must be remembered that such a plot takes into consideration only the interference part of the equation and that such a curve must be multiplied by the diffraction term $(\sin^2 \alpha)/\alpha^2$. This leads in general to an intensity pattern that has the features of Fig. 13.15.

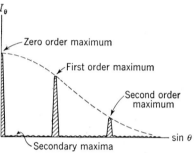

Fig. 13.15. Appearance of intensity pattern in Fraunhofer diffraction from a grating.

Gratings used for research and industrial purposes have something like 20,000 or more lines to the inch. These are ruled by a diamond point on a glass surface, thus forming a transmission grating in which the opaque sections correspond to the grooves that have been made by the ruling point. If the rulings are made on a polished surface such as a metal, the grating is of the reflection type which produces an interference-diffraction pattern like that of the transmission grating. Since the construction of a large number of fine equidistant parallel lines is not only an expensive but an extremely difficult task, *replica* gratings are most often employed. These are made by pouring a solution of collodion on an original grating, permitting the cast to harden, and then removing it. The impressions of the rulings so obtained are preserved by sandwiching the film between glass plates, thus forming a transmission grating, or the film may be mounted on a polished surface and used as a reflection grating.

If monochromatic light is incident on a diffraction grating of known grating space, its wavelength may be accurately determined by measuring the angles of diffraction in a known order and using Eq. (13.8). If the source is white light, there is produced in each order above the zero one a series of maxima corresponding to the different component wavelengths, with the result that a spectrum of the source is produced in each of these orders. The zero-order images all superimpose to form white light. Considerable overlapping usually occurs in the higher orders. For instance, suppose a range of wavelengths from 3600 to 7200 A is being observed with a grating. The second order of the violet 3600 A just falls on the first order of the red 7200 A. However, the red of the second order overlaps the violet of the third order. Because of the seriousness of overlapping in the higher orders, only the first few orders are ordinarily employed in diffraction gratings. Furthermore the diffraction factor $(\sin^2 \alpha)/\alpha^2$ causes the higher order maxima to have relatively low intensity.

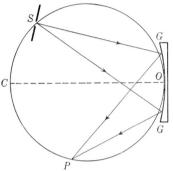

A very serious fault that a ruled grating could have is a periodic error in ruling, due to mechanical defects in the ruling machine. This introduces additional spectra corresponding to the erroneous periodicity, and such false spectra are termed *ghosts*. Ghosts in very finely ruled gratings, 50,000 lines and more to the inch, are in general more pronounced than in coarser gratings.

FIG. 13.16. The concave grating.

So far we have discussed the plane diffraction grating, which utilizes lenses for rendering the incident light parallel and for focusing the diffracted light. This suffers from the double disadvantage that lenses introduce chromatic aberration and ordinary glass does not transmit into the ultraviolet region of the spectrum. Rowland showed that if a grating is ruled on a concave mirror, it produces a spectrum that is sharply in focus without the use of lenses. The principle of the concave grating and the focusing circle are illustrated in Fig. 13.16. The grating $GOG$, whose rulings are normal to the plane of the figure, has its center of curvature at $C$. The circle shown has a diameter equal to the radius of curvature of the grating to which it is tangent at the grating mid-point $O$. If the slit source $S$ is situated on the circle, the spectra also lie on this circle, which is known as the *Rowland circle*. By curving the photographic plate $P$ so that it coincides with the circle, sharp images of the slit are thus brought into focus. There are various methods of mounting the concave grating, most of them utilizing this principle for focus. Concave reflection gratings are used almost exclusively in spectral analysis.

We shall see in the next chapter that the principal advantages of a grating over other instruments used for spectral work are that it possesses a large dispersion and a very large resolving power.

### PART II. FRESNEL DIFFRACTION  *Wednesday*  *Prob.*
*also*

**13.5. Fresnel Zones or Half-period Elements.** In the first part of this chapter we have considered the situation wherein the distance from the diffracting aperture to the source or observing screen is very large or wherein the size of the opening is relatively small. In such cases we were able to consider that the rays from all points on the aperture to the screen were parallel, leading to a description of the pattern, the Fraunhofer diffraction, in a given direction. The Fresnel class of diffraction, on the other hand, concerns itself with the pattern resulting when there are no lenses employed and the distances involved are small or the size of the

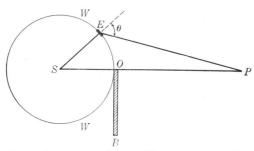

Fig. 13.17. Illustrating a spherical wave front incident on an obstacle in Fresnel diffraction.

aperture is relatively large. Clearly the Fresnel type of diffraction is the more general and gradually approaches the Fraunhofer class, for a given aperture, as the screen is removed from finite to infinite distance. Fresnel patterns are comparatively easy to obtain experimentally, but as we have already pointed out, they are more difficult to handle analytically. Instead of dealing with plane wave fronts in Fraunhofer diffraction, Fresnel diffraction must deal with spherical or cylindrical wave fronts. Thus in Fig. 13.17 is shown a point source $S$ and a spherical wave front $WW$ incident on an obstacle $OB$. The amplitude at point $P$ may be computed by considering each elemental area on $WW$, such as that indicated at $E$, as a secondary source of disturbance, and by superposition find the resultant effect at $P$. For a given wavelength, each element $E$ has a phase at $P$ that depends directly on its distance from $P$ and an amplitude at $P$ that is (1) directly proportional to the elemental area which determines the number of secondary wavelets, (2) inversely proportional to $SE$, which here is constant for all elements $E$, (3) inversely proportional to distance $EP$, (4) directly proportional to $\cos \theta + 1$. We have seen how the last factor, called the *obliquity factor*, eliminates the back wave in the original Huygens construction (see Sec. 10.7). The mathematical analysis embodying each of the variations enumerated is rather complicated, and we shall not go into it here. Instead we shall use an approximate method of computing the effect at $P$ after the simple and elegant method of Fresnel. This not only leads essentially to the correct results but lends itself easily to various individual applications.

For simplicity let us consider the Fresnel approximation for a plane wave (a spherical wave which has originated from a very distant point source) of wavelength $\lambda$. The plane wave front shown in Fig. 13.18 is

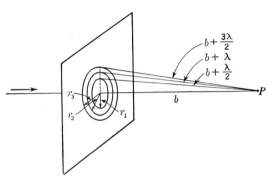

Fig. 13.18. Half-period zones on a plane wave front.

traveling in the direction of the arrow. To find the resultant effect at $P$ of all the secondary wavelets on the wave front, there is drawn a series of concentric circles whose radii $r_1$, $r_2$, $r_3$, . . . satisfy the condition

$$r_n^2 = \left(b + \frac{n\lambda}{2}\right)^2 - b^2 \tag{13.9}$$

where $r_n$ is the radius of the $n$th circle and $b$ is the perpendicular distance from $P$ to the center of the series of circles. Each circle is then a half wavelength farther from $P$ than its smaller neighboring circle. The wave front is thus divided into *zones*, which are known as *Fresnel*, or *half-period*, *zones*. From Eq. (13.9) the area of the first $n$ zones is

$$\pi r_n^2 = \pi\left(nb\lambda + \frac{n^2\lambda^2}{4}\right)$$

and the area of the $n - 1$ zones is

$$\pi r_{n-1}^2 = \pi\left[(n - 1)b\lambda + \frac{(n - 1)^2\lambda^2}{4}\right]$$

so that the area $S_n$ of the $n$th zone is

$$S_n = \pi b\lambda\left[1 + \frac{(2n - 1)\lambda}{4b}\right] \tag{13.10}$$

Since $\lambda$ is small compared with $b$, we may neglect the term in $\lambda/b$ and obtain

$$S_n = \pi b \lambda \qquad (13.11)$$

Therefore all the zones have approximately the same area, the values increasing very slowly with $n$.

The ratio of the area of the $n$th zone [Eq. (13.10)] to the mean distance of this zone from the point $P$ is

$$\frac{\pi b \lambda \left[ 1 + \dfrac{(2n - 1)\lambda}{4b} \right]}{b + \dfrac{(2n - 1)\lambda}{4}} = \pi \lambda$$

which is constant for all zones. We see then that the amplitudes of the successive zones depend on the obliquity factor $\cos \theta + 1$, which causes

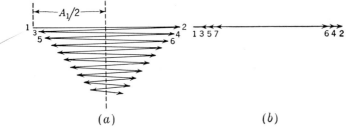

$(a)$ $(b)$

FIG. 13.19. Resultant amplitudes due to Fresnel half-period zones.

the amplitudes of the zones of increasing radii to decrease very slowly. Now, as to the phases of the waves reaching $P$ and coming from the zones, we can see that since each succeeding zone is, on an average, half a wavelength more distant from $P$, the waves from successive zones differ in phase by $\pi$. At $P$ then the resultant amplitude $A$ due to all the zones is given by a sum of terms that alternate in sign,

$$A = A_1 - A_2 + A_3 - A_4 + \cdots + (-1)^{n+1} A_n \qquad (13.12)$$

where $A_1$ is the amplitude of the first zone, $A_2$ that of the second zone, and in general $A_n$ that of the $n$th zone. To evaluate this sum, we keep in mind that we are finding the resultant of a series of $n$ vector amplitudes which diminish regularly and slowly, all the vectors acting along the same straight line, and each vector pointing opposite in direction to its preceding vector of slightly greater value. First let us look at a graphical representation. In Fig. 13.19$a$ the vector 12 represents the amplitude $A_1$ from the first zone, 23 the amplitude $A_2$ from the second zone, 34 that from the third zone, etc. These have been separated for clarity, but it must be remembered that they all lie along the same straight line as in (*b*). The resultant of the first two zones is the vector 13, that of the first three zones the vector 14, etc. Thus if the total number of zones is even, the resultant is represented by the vector drawn from 1 to the head of the $n$th vector pointing to the left, while if the total number of zones is odd, the resultant is drawn from 1 to the head of the $n$th vector pointing to the right. It is clear that as $n$ approaches a very large number, the resultant amplitude approaches the value $A_1/2$, or half the amplitude due to the first zone. This same result will now be obtained by evaluating the series given in Eq. (13.12).

Let us suppose that $n$ is odd. Then the series may be expressed in the following two alternative ways:

$$A = \frac{A_1}{2} + \left(\frac{A_1}{2} - A_2 + \frac{A_3}{2}\right) + \left(\frac{A_3}{2} - A_4 + \frac{A_5}{2}\right) + \cdots + \frac{A_n}{2}$$

or

$$A = A_1 - \frac{A_2}{2} - \left(\frac{A_2}{2} - A_3 + \frac{A_4}{2}\right) - \left(\frac{A_4}{2} - A_5 + \frac{A_6}{2}\right) - \cdots - \frac{A_{n-1}}{2} + A_n$$

Each of the parenthetical expressions is the difference between the arithmetic mean of the amplitudes due to two alternate zones and the amplitude due to the intermediate zone. Regardless of whether these are positive or negative, the sum $A$ lies between the limits $(A_1/2) + (A_n/2)$ and $A_1 - (A_2/2) - (A_{n-1}/2) + A_n$. In the last expression we may place $A_1 = A_2$ and $A_{n-1} = A_n$, since any one zone has an amplitude that is very nearly equal to that of the neighboring zone. We then obtain

$$A = \frac{A_1}{2} + \frac{A_n}{2}$$

The case where $n$ is even leads to the same result. Therefore we have found that the resultant amplitude at $P$ is equal to half the sum of the amplitudes due to the first and last zones. When $n$ is very large, corresponding to the whole spherical wave front, the amplitude due to the $n$th zone becomes negligibly small on account of the obliquity factor and we have the result that the resultant amplitude is given by half the amplitude of the first zone.

It is to be noted that the radii of the half-period zones depend on the wavelength and on the distance of $P$ from the wave surface, as can be seen from Eq. (13.9), which gives for the radii of the zones, neglecting the term in $\lambda^2$, $r_n^2 = nb\lambda$.

Our treatment of Fresnel zones has been concerned with the amplitudes $A_1$, $A_2$, $A_3$, . . . of Eq. (13.12), in which each of the amplitudes is the resultant due to each half-period element. Actually, each half-period zone may itself be considered divided into an infinite number of subzones between each of which there is a constant **phase** difference. This kind of subdivision leads to a vector amplitude curve that is very useful in the analysis of Fresnel diffraction problems. To illustrate its significance, let us consider that the first zone is divided into nine circular subzones which are constructed in a similar way to that employed for the half-period zones, *i.e.*, so that the distances to the point $P$ (Fig. 13.18) from the succeeding edges of the subzones differ by the same amount. The subzone areas will then be very nearly equal, and there will be a constant phase difference $\pi/9$ between the vibrations from any two neighboring subareas. The vector sum of the amplitudes due to

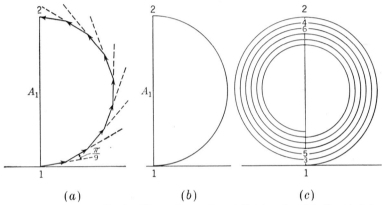

$(a)$ $(b)$ $(c)$

Fɪɢ. 13.20. Resultant amplitude of Fresnel zones by subdivision of each half-period element.

these nine subzones is shown as vector 12 or $A_1$ in Fig. 13.20$a$, where, in reality, each succeeding amplitude vector is slightly smaller than the preceding one owing to the obliquity factor, and where, it must be remembered, the phase difference between the first and ninth subzones is $\pi$. When the number of subzones is increased more and more, it is clear that the vector polygon forming the resultant approaches a half circle as shown in Fig. 13.20$b$, the resultant $A_1$ making an angle $\dfrac{1}{2}\dfrac{2\pi}{\lambda}\dfrac{\lambda}{2} = \dfrac{\pi}{2}$ with the horizontal (see also Fig. 13.3). Likewise the effect of the second half-period zone may be represented by the semicircle 23 (Fig. 13.20$c$), that of the third zone by the semicircle 34, etc., each of somewhat smaller radius due to the slow decrease in amplitudes. The semicircles therefore do not close, and the effect of all the Fresnel half-period zones is represented by a spiral that converges to a point midway between 1 and 2. Figure 13.20$c$ then graphically represents the summation of the series in Eq. (13.12), and again shows that the effect of the whole wave front is equal to half the effect of the first half-period zone. The numbers in Fig. 13.20 correspond to those in Fig. 13.19.

Although we have dealt with Fresnel zones on a plane wave front, the results obtained in this section are also true for the spherical wave front (see Prob. 13.31).

**13.6. Fresnel Diffraction by the Circular Aperture and Circular Obstacle.** We shall now see how, by the aid of Fresnel zones, we can obtain qualitative descriptions of two cases of Fresnel diffraction.

First let us consider the diffraction by a circular aperture. The arrangement of the monochromatic point source $S$, the screen containing the circular opening $C$, and the observing screen containing the axial point $P$ is shown in Fig. 13.21.

FIG. 13.21. Fresnel diffraction of light by a circular aperture.

If the radius of $C$ is equal to the radius of the first half-period zone, the amplitude at $P$ is given by $A_1$, which is twice the amplitude or four times the intensity when the wave front is entirely exposed. If next only the first two zones are uncovered, the amplitude at $P$ is $A_1 - A_2 \doteq 0$, or the intensity is approximately zero. This may be effected by enlarging $C$ or by moving the screen toward the opening, in which latter adjustment the radii of the zones have been

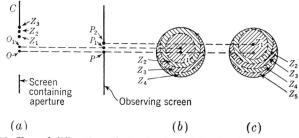

(a)                          (b)          (c)

FIG. 13.22. Fresnel diffraction effects at extra-axial points by a circular opening.

decreased. Therefore, if the distance between $C$ and $P$ is held fixed and the opening gradually enlarged, the intensity at $P$ will be a maximum or a minimum according as an odd or an even number of zones is exposed. If the circular opening is held fixed and the observing screen is moved toward $C$, maxima and minima of intensity occur along the axis. (The student should here recall that the Fraunhofer diffraction through a circular aperture always produces a maximum at $P$.) To consider the effect at a point which is a small distance off the axis is more complicated, but we can see what comes about by considering Fig. 13.22. The circular opening, on which plane monochromatic light is incident, is shown of a size to permit three unexposed zones $Z_1$, $Z_2$, and $Z_3$, producing a maximum at the axial point $P$. For the effect at the extra-axial point $P_1$ the Fresnel zones are constructed about $O_1$ as center, the point $O_1$ being the intersection point of the perpendicular from $P_1$ to the wave front. In (b) is shown the unsymmetrical appearance of the zones (dotted circles) with respect to the circular aperture, where it is seen that the first and second zones are fully exposed and about two-thirds of the third and about one-fifth of the fourth zones are uncovered. The first two zones approximately cancel, leaving some residual amount for the effect of the third and fourth zones. The intensity at $P_1$ is then less than at $P$. For the point $P_2$, (c) shows that in addition to the first zone being fully exposed the following approximate parts of succeeding zones are uncovered: two-thirds of the second zone, one-half of the third zone, one-third of the fourth zone, and a small fraction of the fifth zone. Thus as $P$ moves upward, successive zones become uncovered, the fraction of each exposed part of a zone depending on the location of $P$. The contributions from the exposed portions give rise to a pattern of dark and bright rings surrounding the central spot. When the center of the zone system or $P$ lies just above the edge of the geometrical shadow, the student can verify, by a similar diagram, that part of the first zone is exposed and

FIG. 13.23. Fresnel diffraction by a circular aperture.

varying parts of many more zones are uncovered, with the result that there is a small but definite amount of intensity inside the geometrical shadow. When the center of the zone system is far above the circular outline of the opening, then the first few zones are cut off. Some one zone is the first to become partly exposed; then some are uncovered to a larger extent, and the larger zones again become covered. The first and last terms of Eq. (13.12) are zero, and the contributions due to the partly exposed intervening zones cancel, giving an intensity that is zero well into the geometrical shadow. Figure 13.23 is a photograph of the Fresnel diffraction pattern from a small circular opening. A point source of monochromatic light was used distant ½ meter from the aperture, and 1½ meters beyond this was the photographic plate.

As a second illustration of the application of Fresnel zones, consider the Fresnel diffraction by a circular obstacle. The obstacle will obscure the first $l$ zones, and since the $l + 1$st zone is the first exposed zone, the rest of the wave front thereafter contributing, the resultant amplitude at the point $P$, lying on the axis passing perpendicularly through the center of the obstacle, is given by

$$A = \frac{A_{l+1}}{2}$$

The method of half-period elements then predicts that the center of the geometrical shadow is bright, and if $l$ is just a few zones, the intensity at $P$ is appreciable. Arago demonstrated the existence of this bright spot, which is clearly visible in Fig. 13.24, a photograph of the diffraction by a circular obstacle. The existence of this central bright spot provides a most powerful argument in favor of the wave theory of light. By considering the effect at points off the axis, as with the circular aperture, it is clear that fluctuations of intensity occur as $P$ is moved off the axis, so

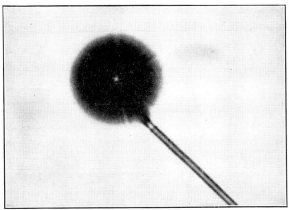

Fig. 13.24. Diffraction by a circular obstacle showing brightness at the center of the shadow. [*After Dr. Charlotte Z. LeMay, T. M. Cunningham, and Dr. Newton Gaines (T.C.U. Laboratories).*]

that the diffraction pattern of a small obstacle shows a bright central spot surrounded by dark and bright circular rings.

**13.7. The Zone Plate.** We have seen that the radii of the Fresnel zones are proportional to $\sqrt{n}$, where $n = 1, 2, 3, \ldots$. By drawing on white paper a set of concentric circles whose radii are proportional to $\sqrt{n}$, blackening out every other zone, say the even ones, and photographing the resulting set so that the negative shows a very much diminished image of the ring set, there is obtained what is called a *zone plate*, as shown in Fig. 13.25. By allowing plane monochromatic waves to fall on the zone plate and placing a screen on the emergent side at such a distance that the actual Fresnel zones coincide with the zones appearing on the zone plate, the light coming through the unblackened areas is all in phase, having a resultant amplitude $A = A_1 + A_3 + A_5 + \cdots$. Thus a maximum of very large intensity is produced on the axis of the zone plate at the screen position. The zone plate acts very much like a converging lens in gathering the light down to a point focus, and it is left as a problem for the student to show that the object and image distances bear the same lens-formula relationship to the zone plate's focal length, which here is given by $b = r_n^2/n\lambda$. Since $r_n = \sqrt{n}\, r_1$, $b = r_1^2/\lambda$.

This gives the most intense focus, and there are a series of foci of decreasing intensity as we go along the axis toward the zone plate. For instance, if the image distance is decreased so that the first zone of the zone plate contains three actual half-period elements, then there will again be produced at $P$ a maximum of intensity and the corresponding focal length is $(r_1/\sqrt{3})^2/\lambda = b/3$. In the same way there is a still less bright

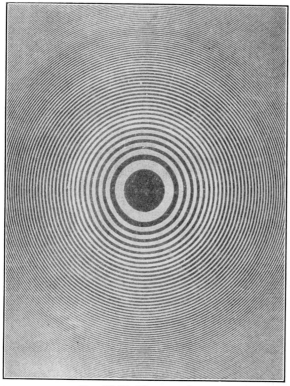

Fig. 13.25. The zone plate.

focus at $b/5$, corresponding to each zone of the zone plate containing five half-period elements, another still fainter at $b/7$, corresponding to each zone of the zone plate containing seven half-period elements, etc.

**13.8. Cylindrical Wave Fronts. The Cornu Spiral.** We have so far considered the wave front originating from a point source, *i.e.*, a spherical wave front, or its special case, a plane wave front having infinite radius of curvature. When a slit is used as a source of light, the wave front is cylindrical, having the slit as the cylindrical axis. We must now see how to deal with the Fresnel diffraction phenomena when a cylindrical wave front is incident on an obstacle, such as a straight edge, which is parallel to the cylindrical axis of the wave front, or when the wave front passes through a rectangular slit whose long edges are parallel to the wave-front axis.

Instead of using concentric rings to form the Fresnel zones, as we did for the spherical wave front, half-period zones in the form of strips parallel to the cylindrical axes are employed, and the method of such a division of the cylindrical wave front is illustrated by Fig. 13.26. The figure shows a slit source $S$, a circular section of the cylindrical wave front $CW$, the axis of the cylinder coinciding with the slit axis perpendicular to the plane of the figure through $S$, and the axial point $P$. The division of the wave front into half-period strips is made by choosing the point 1 in the upper

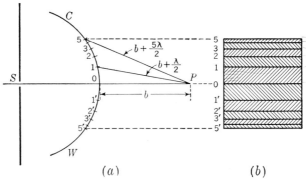

$$(a) \qquad\qquad (b)$$

Fɪɢ. 13.26. Formation of Fresnel half-period strips for a cylindrical wave front.

half of the wave front and the corresponding point 1' in the lower half of the wave front so that each is distant $\lambda/2$ farther from $P$ than the point 0 at the pole of the wave front. Points 2 and 2' are chosen so that each is distant farther from $P$ by another half wavelength. This procedure is followed to locate the points 3 and 3', 4 and 4', etc. Lines drawn through these points, parallel to the cylindrical axis, divide the wave front into half-period strips, which appear to an observer at $P$ as shown in Fig. 13.26b. A significant difference between the circular division of the wave front previously considered and the strip division for the cylindrical wave front is that in the former case the zone areas formed were practically constant, while in the latter case the areas formed are not equal. The half-period zones of Fig. 13.26b differ in area rapidly at first and then much more slowly as we proceed out along the wave front from 0. We can again form a diagram of vector amplitudes similar to that of Fig. 13.20a to illustrate a finite subdivision of half-period strips or more correctly like Fig. 13.20b for an infinite subdivision of half-period strips. This leads to the curve shown in Fig. 13.27. One half of the curve, that in the first quadrant, is the diagram of vector amplitudes corresponding to the upper half of the wave front, and the other half, in the third quadrant, is a diagram of the vector amplitudes corresponding to the lower half of the wave front. The entire curve is known as a *Cornu spiral*, whose characteristics and exact nature are best obtained by mathematical analysis. We give the mathematical derivation of the Cornu spiral in Appendix IE, and what we shall do here is examine its general features and usefulness.

The portion of the curve from $O$ to point 1 results from joining the vector amplitudes corresponding to the substrips of infinitesimal widths, obtained by subdividing the first half-period strip in the upper half of the wave front of Fig. 13.26. For the second half-period strip the vector amplitudes join to form the portion 12. For the third half-period strip there results the curve 23, and so on, each succeeding half-period strip being represented by another half convolution which becomes smaller and smaller and more nearly circular, the curve terminating in the asymptotic point $K$. The vector amplitudes for the lower half of the wave front join to form the curve from $O$ to $K'$, the points $1'$, $2'$, $3'$, . . . corresponding again, respectively, to the first, second, third, etc., half-period strips.

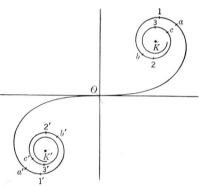

Fig. 13.27. The Cornu spiral.

The resultant amplitude at $P$ (Fig. 13.26), say for the upper half of the wave front, is, as before, represented by the vector joining the starting and terminating points of the curve, or $OK$. For the lower half of the wave front the amplitude is given by $K'O$, and if the whole wave front is exposed, the resultant amplitude is represented by $K'K$. If, on the other hand, only the first half-period strips in both halves of the wave front are exposed, the resultant amplitude is given by the vector drawn from point $1'$ to point 1.

As shown in Appendix IE, the Cornu spiral may be plotted in a universal fashion so that it can be applied to any case having given values of $S0$, $b$, and $\lambda$ in Fig. 13.26. There it is seen that distances measured along the spiral are proportional to the distances measured on the exposed portion of the wave front. The origin of coordinates in Fig. 13.27 is an inflection point, and the coordinates of $K$ and $K'$ are respectively $(\frac{1}{2}, \frac{1}{2})$ and $(-\frac{1}{2}, -\frac{1}{2})$. In the next section we illustrate the use of the Cornu spiral in the solution of the diffraction by a straight edge and by a narrow slit.

**13.9. Applications of the Cornu Spiral to Diffraction Problems.** Let us first consider the Fresnel diffraction by a straight edge. In Fig. 13.28 are shown a long, narrow slit source $S$, an opaque screen $MN$ having a straight edge at $M$, and an observing screen.   Figure 13.28$a$, $b$, $c$ shows different positions of the observation point $P$ on the screen.   Let us first consider that $P$ is far into the geometrical shadow as in ($a$).   A line from $P$ to $S$ divides the wave front at 0 into upper and lower halves, whose half-period strips are indicated by the numbers 1, 2, . . . and $1'$, $2'$, . . . .   With $P$ sufficiently far down, only the very distant zones in the upper half of the wave front are exposed, giving an amplitude or intensity that is practically zero.   Calling the resultant amplitude vector

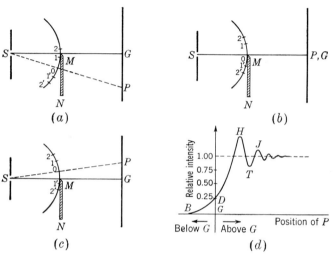

Fig. 13.28.  Illustrating the Fresnel diffraction of a cylindrical wave front by a straight edge.

on the Cornu spiral $A$, its value is zero, which means that its tail and head are located at the point $K$ in Fig. 13.27.   This is also represented as point $B$ on the relative-intensity plot in Fig. 13.28$d$.   As $P$ moves upward, the head of vector $A$ remains fixed at $K$, while its tail moves along the spiral, producing a vector $A$ that steadily increases, and the corresponding intensity rises as shown in ($d$).   When $P$ is at $G$, as in ($b$), the tail of $A$ is at $O$ in Fig. 13.27 and $A$ is equal to $OK$ and represented by $D$ in the intensity plot.   As $P$ moves above $G$, shown in ($c$), all of the upper half and more and more of the lower half of the wave front become exposed, the tail of vector $A$ now shifting over to the other half of the spiral.   The intensity rises rather rapidly, reaching a maximum at $H$ when the tail of $A$ is at $a'$ (Fig. 13.27) and $A$ has the value $a'K$.   For $P$ farther above $G$, the tail of $A$ follows the convolutions of the spiral, resulting in a decreasing intensity until point $b'$ (Fig. 13.27) is reached, when the intensity reaches a minimum at $T$.   Thereafter a series of decreasing maxima and minima occurs as shown in ($d$) until the tail of $A$ reaches $K'$, when the amplitude has the value $A = K'K = 2OK$.

The intensity maxima and minima fluctuate about and approach a value four times that at $D$ (Fig. 13.28$d$) (given the ordinate value 1.00 relative to which the intensities are plotted). This intensity value of 1.00, proportional to the square of the vector $A = 2OK$, is that due to the unobstructed wave front. The diffraction pattern due to a straight edge is therefore characterized by a series of bands as shown in the photograph of Fig. 13.29. The gradual decrease of intensity into the geometrical shadow of the straight edge, the region from $B$ to $D$ in Fig. 13.28$d$, is observable in the photograph.

The Fresnel diffraction from a slit can also be obtained by use of the Cornu spiral. A diffraction slit whose sides are parallel to the source slit

Fig. 13.29. Photograph of the Fresnel diffraction by a straight edge. $\lambda 4300$ A. (*By permission from* "*Fundamentals of Optics*," *by F. A. Jenkins and H. E. White.* Copyright, 1950, *Second Edition.* McGraw-Hill Book Company, Inc.)

is in effect two straight edges which serve to expose a small portion of the wave front. We have stated that distances measured along the exposed portion of the wave front are proportional to distances measured along the spiral. Therefore the exposed wave front, or the width of the slit, determines a certain length of spiral which is effective in determining the distribution of light on the screen. The chord length or amplitude of this constant length of Cornu spiral is determined by the position occupied by the piece of spiral, and this in turn is a function of the point $P$ on the screen. The amplitude variations are obtainable by sliding this constant length of spiral along the Cornu curve and measuring the length of chord between its ends. The intensities are proportional to the squares of these values. The character of the diffraction pattern is determined by the width of the slit. For instance, suppose the slit width is such that the first upper and lower half-period strips are uncovered. The amplitude at $P$, when it is equidistant from the slit edges, is given by the vector from 1' to 1 in Fig. 13.27. All other positions of $P$ give amplitude vectors smaller than this, so that the center of the diffraction pattern is a maximum. On the other hand, if the slit is widened to uncover the first two upper and first two lower half-period strips, the amplitude corresponding to $P$ at the central position is given by the vector from 2' to 2 (Fig. 13.27), while for the point $P$ somewhat above the symmetrical position, sliding the piece of spiral 2'2 slightly toward $K$ causes the chord between its ends to be greater than the chord 2'2. The intensity at the center of the diffraction pattern is in this case a minimum. When the slit is very narrow, so that the constant length of spiral is small, the pattern is very much like the Fraunhofer diffraction pattern for a single slit with maxima and minima (which here do not go down to zero) occurring in the region of the shadow only. When the slit is wide, there are fluctuations of intensity in the central part of the pattern, and as the slit is widened even more, the pattern takes on the appearance of two straight-edge patterns joined at their low-intensity regions.

Cornu's spiral may be used to treat other diffraction problems such as the diffraction by a cylindrical wire that covers a certain portion of the wave front. The student should realize that for such a problem two segments of the Cornu spiral must be dealt with. The end points of the constant length of spiral corresponding to the unexposed wave front are used to form two amplitude vectors, one by joining one end with $K'$, and another by joining the other end with $K$. The vector sum of these gives the resultant amplitude.

Quantitative treatments of diffraction problems may be made by employing the equations developed in Appendix IE in connection with the accurately drawn Cornu spiral given there. It must be noted that the Fresnel theory of diffraction, which we have employed in this chapter, holds within the limits of its simplifying assumptions and leads to useful results that agree in general with the experimental observations. A more mathematical treatment of diffraction by Kirchhoff, based on the solution of the wave equation and on assumptions which have been the focus of much criticism, also leads to results in general accord with experiment. Although Kirchhoff's theory[1] has some advantages over Fresnel's, making it possible, for instance, to compute absolute intensities of diffraction as well as relative ones, the Fresnel theory is a great deal simpler to apply. Neither theory gives an adequate account of diffraction when the wave employed has a length that is comparable with the dimensions of the diffracting aperture, as in the diffraction of microwaves of a few centimeters wavelength. In such cases Fresnel's and Kirchhoff's theories afford only useful approximations of the resulting diffraction patterns.

**13.10. Shadow Photographs.** Some striking diffraction effects may be obtained by using a brilliantly illuminated pinhole a few meters distant from a photographic plate and various kinds of obstacles placed between the source and the plate. In Fig. 13.30 are such shadow photographs, of a drill in (*a*), of a triangular opening in (*b*), of a screw in (*c*),

---

[1] G. Kirchhoff, *Berlin Ber.*, 1882, p. 641; *Ann. Physik u. Chem.* (2), **18**, 663, 1883.

For simplified treatments see P. Drude, "Theory of Optics," p. 169, Longmans, Green & Co., Inc., New York, 1933; and J. Valasek, "Introduction to Theoretical and Experimental Optics," pp. 173, 183, John Wiley & Sons, Inc., New York, 1949.

and of three joined washers in (*d*).  The obstacles were suspended mid-way between the point source and the film, which were separated by 4 m.  The photographs bring out the fact that the shadows are not sharp but consist of series of diffraction maxima and minima immediately outside the geometrical shadows.

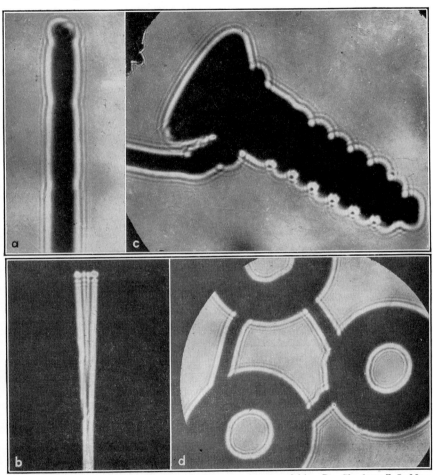

Fig. 13.30.  Shadow photographs of miscellaneous objects.  [*After Dr. Charlotte Z. LeMay, T. M. Cunningham, and Dr. Newton Gaines (T.C.U. Laboratories).*]

**13.11. X-ray Diffraction.**  No treatment in diffraction of light would be satisfactory without at least a brief discussion of the diffraction of X rays, a subject which has had a tremendously useful development since its discovery in 1912.

Roentgen discovered X rays in 1895.  They are generated when high-speed electrons, or cathode rays, are directed to be incident on matter acting as a target.  The X rays originate in the immediate vicinity that is struck by the electrons.  The high-speed electrons are obtained by establishing a high difference of potential between the cathode and the target.  When a material is irradiated with X rays, it emits secondary X rays.

Results of early experiments on the diffraction of X rays by narrow slits indicated that if X rays had wavelike properties, their wavelengths were of the order of $10^{-8}$ or $10^{-9}$ cm.  These results were not conclusive enough, however, to establish the true nature of X rays.  It was not

until 1912 that von Laue conceived of the idea that the ordered arrangement of the atoms in a crystal should provide a three-dimensional grating for the diffraction of X rays, just as a two-dimensional optical grating diffracts light.  The reasoning follows the fact that the spacing between the rulings on an optical grating are of the same order of magnitude as the wavelength of the light employed.  Since the spacings between the atoms of a crystal are of the order of $10^{-8}$ cm, von Laue

Fig. 13.31.  Laue photograph of NaCl crystal. *(By permission from G. L. Clark, "Applied X Rays," 3d Ed., McGraw-Hill Book Company, Inc.)*

suggested that a crystal would act as a space grating for X rays.  Friedrich and Knipping, following von Laue's suggestion, passed a collimated beam of X rays through a thin crystal of zinc blende (ZnS) and obtained a diffraction pattern on a photographic plate placed on the emergent side of the crystal. They found that, in addition to a strong central spot, the X rays diffracted in such a way as to produce intense, sharply defined spots which had a symmetrical arrangement about the central spot.  Such a pattern, known as a *Laue diffraction pattern*, is shown in Fig. 13.31 for the crystal NaCl.  The results successfully demonstrated that the X rays were interfering to produce regions of maximum and minimum intensity and established beyond doubt that the X ray possesses wavelike properties, just as light does.  Historically the experiment marks the birth of X-ray spectroscopy and crystallography.  It is now possible to produce interference and diffraction effects with X rays by means of narrow slits, crystals, ruled gratings, solids, liquids, and gases.  The X rays are electromagnetic waves characterized by wavelengths ranging from approximately 0.01 to 1000 A, so that the interference and diffraction elements must be much smaller than those employed in light.

To see more clearly what happens when a crystal diffracts X rays, we must first remember that each atom of the crystal may be considered as consisting of electrons surrounding a positively charged nucleus. When an X-ray beam penetrates the crystal, the periodic electric vibration of the electromagnetic wave sets the electrons into forced oscillation. According to the electromagnetic theory the accelerated electrons of the atoms become sources of electromagnetic waves. These secondary waves have the same frequency and wavelength as the primary X ray, and we say that the electrons *scatter* the X rays (see Secs. 15.3 and 15.5). Each of the atoms in a crystal therefore acts as a source of scattered X rays, and the total effect of these scattered waves constitutes the diffracted wave.

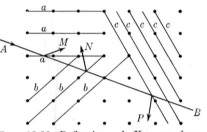

FIG. 13.32. Reflection of X rays from atomic planes.

A crystal is a three-dimensional array of atoms (or molecules) that is built up by some fundamental unit of structure, called the *unit cell*, which repeats regularly and indefinitely in the three dimensions. The problem of diffraction from such a lattice array of atoms may be treated formally. However, there is a simpler approach which was given by W. L. Bragg, who showed that the diffraction pattern could be interpreted as the reflection of the incident X-ray beam from the series of atomic planes within the crystal. Thus in Fig. 13.32 are shown the atomic scattering centers in a plane section of a cubic crystal, and three of the many possible sets of planes formed by the atoms of the crystal are shown. The series of planes *a* are richer in atoms than the series *b*, which in turn are richer than the planes *c*. This illustrates the fact that the density of population of atoms in any plane depends on the orientation of this plane in relation to the principal planes. For a beam of X rays incident on the crystal in the direction *AB* some of the energy is reflected from the planes *a* in the direction indicated by the arrow at *M*. Likewise there is reflection from the planes *b* in the direction indicated by the arrow at *N* and from the planes *c* in the direction indicated by the arrow at *P*. In all cases the angle of reflection is equal to the angle of incidence. The diffracted beams from each different set of planes give rise to a Laue spot, and those sets of planes which have the greater population of atoms give rise to the more intense spots.

The condition governing the reinforcement of the reflected X rays from a series of equidistant crystal planes is obtained with the aid of Fig. 13.33. X rays of wavelength $\lambda$ are incident at an angle $\theta$ with the crystal face, known as the *glancing angle* of incidence. The parallel atomic planes are a distance *d* apart. The figure shows a single ray incident on one atom in the top plane $A$.   Actually a large number of atomic scattering centers are bathed in the pencil of radiation, and the diffracted waves from all these atoms reinforce for all wavelengths and for any separation of atoms if the angle of diffraction (reflection) is equal to the angle of incidence.   Only a small fraction of the incident energy is reflected at the top layer, and the rays penetrate to the interior planes.   For the waves, reflected from successive planes, to interfere constructively the figure shows that the path difference $2d \sin \theta$ must be equal to an integral multiple of a wave-length, or

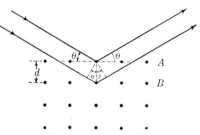

FIG. 13.33. Diagram used to derive Bragg's law.

$$2d \sin \theta = k\lambda \qquad (13.13)$$

where $k$ is the order of the diffraction.   Equation (13.13) is known as Bragg's law and expresses the condition under which the diffracted rays from a series of crystal planes reinforce to produce an intense spot. The Laue spots are explained by the fact that when an X-ray beam, containing a continuous range of wavelengths, is incident on a crystal, the glancing angle of incidence for the different sets of planes is different. For some of the sets of planes of spacing $d$ there is the appropriate wavelength $\lambda$ to satisfy Bragg's law, thus giving a diffracted beam in a direction $\theta$, forming a Laue spot.   It can be shown that the spots lie on sets of ellipses which contain the central spot.

Bragg's law is fundamental in the field of X-ray spectroscopy and in the analysis of the structure of crystalline materials by X-ray diffraction.   By using a crystal of known grating space $d$, wavelength determinations may be made by observing the angles of diffraction $\theta$.   For instance, the cubic crystal rock salt (NaCl), whose planes parallel to the cube surface are spaced 2.814 A apart, may be employed.   A more suitable crystal is the rhomboidal crystal calcite with a grating space of 3.029 A.   For very precise work the Bragg law must be corrected for the slight amount of refraction of the X rays as they enter the crystalline material.   The modified form of Bragg's law, corrected for refraction, is

$$2d \left( 1 - \frac{1 - n}{\sin^2 \theta} \right) \sin \theta = k\lambda \qquad (13.14)$$

where $n$ is the index of refraction of X rays in the crystal.   In general $1 - n$ is of the order of $10^{-6}$.

In the determination of the structure of a crystal an application of Bragg's law yields the interplanar spacings within the crystal.   In addition to Laue photographs, which are taken with a polychromatic beam of

X rays, *powder* X-ray diffraction patterns and *rotating-crystal* X-ray diffraction patterns may be obtained. In the powder method, a monochromatic X-ray beam is incident on a mass of tiny crystals having all possible orientations, produced by forming a cylindrical sample of powdered crystal. For every set of planes with the corresponding spacing $d$, there are crystals oriented in such a way that $\sin \theta = k\lambda/2d$ is satisfied.

FIG. 13.34. X-ray diffraction powder pattern of copper. Cylindrical camera radius 5.57 cm. Radiation $\lambda 1.54$ A.

The diffracted rays thus form cones about the incident X-ray beam. A photographic film placed to receive the diffracted rays will reveal a pattern like that shown in Fig. 13.34. Each X-ray diffraction ring surrounding the center of the pattern corresponds to one order of reflection from a set of planes with a given spacing. Since each crystalline substance yields a pattern with a characteristic series of spacings and intensities, the powder pattern of a crystalline material is a reliable "fingerprint" of the material. In the rotating-crystal method, a monochromatic beam of X rays is incident on a small, single crystal. The crystal is continuously rotated about an axis normal to the primary beam. In this way the Bragg law is satisfied for a large number of planes when $\sin \theta = k\lambda/2d$. The pattern, taken on a cylindrical film whose axis is the axis of rotation of the crystal, is composed of a large number of diffraction spots forming a series of horizontal lines called "layer lines." Such a photograph is shown in Fig. 13.35. In the rotating-crystal method, we

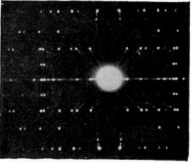

FIG. 13.35. Rotation diffraction pattern of $Na_3PO_412H_2O$. (*By permission from G. L. Clark, "Applied X Rays," 3d Ed., McGraw Hill Book Company, Inc.*)

have a procedure that is simple and powerful. By rotating the crystal about any one of its three principal crystallographic axes, a measurement of the resulting layer-line pattern readily yields the length of that axis. The measurement and analyses of such patterns make it possible to determine the complete structure of a crystal. Observations of the diffraction patterns yield not only the directions of the diffraction maxima but also their intensities. From the directions of the diffracted beams it is possible to determine the size and shape of the crystal unit cell, and from the intensities of the diffraction maxima it is possible to determine the distribution of the atoms in the unit cell. It will be recalled that the crystal is built up by a regular repetition of the unit cell in three dimensions. The student should realize that there are quantities in an optical diffraction grating that are analogously related to the directions and to the intensities of the diffraction maxima.

**13.12. X-ray Diffraction by Gases, Liquids, and Amorphous Solids.** In addition to the diffraction of X rays by a crystalline material, which,

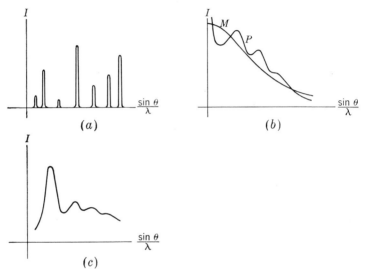

Fig. 13.36. X-ray diffraction intensity curves for (*a*) crystalline material, (*b*) monatomic and polyatomic gases, (*c*) liquids and amorphous solids.

as we have seen, is characterized by a regular array of atoms or scattering units, there is the application of the diffraction of X rays by gases, by liquids, and by solids. In each of these cases the resulting diffraction patterns are amenable to mathematical analysis and yield sometimes partial and sometimes fairly complete information regarding the structure and arrangement of the atoms and molecules in each of the three states. In general the diffraction patterns obtained yield an intensity curve that is a plot of the intensity of the diffracted X rays as a function of the angle of diffraction. A mathematical analysis of these curves leads to information regarding the atomic or molecular distribution.

The intensity curve derived from the powder X-ray diffraction pattern of a typically crystalline material is illustrated in Fig. 13.36*a*, where *I* is the intensity, $2\theta$ the angle that the diffracted ray makes with the original

beam direction, and λ the wavelength of the radiation. It is characterized by a series of sharp maxima, with spacings and relative intensities
characteristic of the crystalline material. In (*b*) are shown the intensity
curves resulting from the diffraction by gases, in which the atoms or
molecules have a random distribution and scatter independently. Curve
*M* illustrates what is obtained for a monatomic gas like helium or neon,
there being a high intensity in the forward direction and a gradual falling
off in intensity with increasing angle. Curve *P* is representative of
polyatomic gases like oxygen or nitrogen, the scattering at small angles
having a high intensity, and there are present a few maxima and minima.
Here there is a definite distance between the atoms of a molecule, giving
rise to interatomic interferences which result in the hump-and-valley
characteristic. From such a curve the arrangement and separations of
the atoms of a molecule may be deduced. In (*c*) is shown the intensity-
curve characteristic of a liquid such as water or liquid sodium or an
amorphous solid such as a glass like vitreous silica or fused quartz. The
diffraction pattern usually shows three or four broad, diffuse halos or
rings characteristic of amorphous substances. These substances show
diffraction patterns intermediate between those for a crystal and those for
a gas. The atoms in a liquid cannot approach closer than a distance
equal to the atomic diameter, and from the center of an atom there is to be
found a certain number of so-called "nearest neighbors" whose positions
are indefinite and continually changing. Beyond this distance there is
maintained, in a more indefinite fashion, a number of second neighbors,
and beyond this the structure gradually becomes "washed out." This
short-range type of structure permits interatomic interference effects
which are responsible for the broad, diffuse rings. In a glass there is no
unit of structure that repeats itself regularly in three dimensions, but
each atom has permanent neighboring atoms at definite distances, the
interatomic interferences giving rise to the broad, diffuse diffraction rings.
Glass is an undercooled liquid which has not passed through a sharp
transition in going from the liquid to the solid state. A crystal, on the
other hand, does have such a definite transition.

From the experimental intensity curve of a liquid or amorphous solid, a
straightforward, mathematical Fourier analysis leads to a radial-distribution curve which gives directly the number of neighbors that surround
any atom at any distance from it. This is illustrated by Figs. 13.37 to
13.39. In Fig. 13.37 are shown the X-ray diffraction patterns of water
for five different temperatures, obtained by the author.[1] The photographs were obtained with X radiation from a molybdenum target,
λ = 0.71 A. It can be seen that, with rising temperature, the second

[1] J. Morgan and B. E. Warren, *J. Chem. Phys.*, **6**, 666, 1938.

diffuse ring becomes less and less sharp, indicating the gradual disappearance of the sharper structure present in water at low temperatures. This is more easily seen in the corresponding intensity curves obtained from the photographs and shown in Fig. 13.38. The radial-distribution

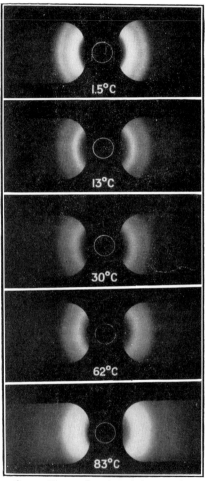

Fig. 13.37. X-ray diffraction patterns of water at temperatures 1.5°, 13°, 30°, 62°, and 83°C. Camera radius 5.57 cm. Radiation λ0.71 A.

curves obtained from the experimental intensity curves by the method of Fourier analysis[1] are shown in Fig. 13.39. The ordinate is the radial-distribution function $4\pi r^2\rho(r)$, where $r$, the abscissa, is the distance in angstroms measured out from the center of any oxygen atom (or $H_2O$ molecule) and $4\pi r^2\rho(r)\,dr$ gives the number of oxygen atoms (or $H_2O$

[1] Warren, Krutter, and Morningstar, *J. Am. Ceram. Soc.*, **19**, 202, 1936.

molecules) to be found between the distances $r$ and $r + dr$. The curves give the average distribution of neighboring molecules as a function of the distance from the center of any water molecule. The area under one of the curves between any two values of $r$ gives the number of water molecules in that range of distance. The area under the first peak yields the

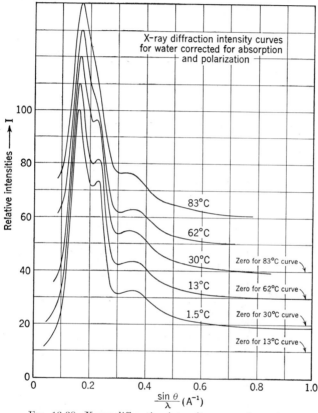

Fig. 13.38. X-ray diffraction intensity curves for water.

number of nearest neighboring molecules at an average distance corresponding to the position of the peak. The number of nearest neighbors is roughly 4. The peak position varies from about 2.90 to 3.05 A, showing that the intermolecular distance in water is somewhat greater than in the crystalline ice structure, and increases with temperature. The number of neighbors in the ice structure is shown by the solid vertical lines drawn upward from the abscissa. In ice the number of nearest neighbors is 4 at a distance of 2.76 A. The curves yield useful information regarding the heat of fusion and the density change from water to ice. Figure 13.39 shows that the first peak is not well resolved, whereas in a glass, such as vitreous silica, the first peak is completely resolved, the minimum after the first peak coming down near the abscissa.   This is interpreted to mean, a fact already mentioned, that in a liquid the neighbors of a

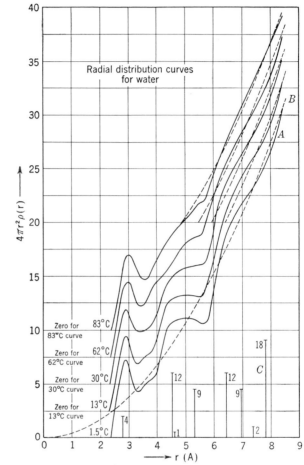

FIG. 13.39.  Radial distribution curves for water.   The vertical lines drawn upward from the abscissa give the number and position of the neighbors in ice.   The dotted curves represent the average density.

molecule are not permanent, whereas in a glass there is a definite number of neighbors at definite distances.

## PROBLEMS

**13.1.**  Prove the relationship given in Eq. (13.1c) for the trigonometric series $S_2$.

**13.2.**  Obtain Eq. (13.1g) directly from Fig. 13.3.   What is the significance of the ratio of the chord to the arc in the figure?

**13.3.** Plane waves of wavelength 5461 A are incident normally on a slit, on the emergent side of which is a focusing lens of 40.0 cm focal length placed close to the slit. If the slit has a width of 0.450 mm, what is the distance from the principal maximum to the first minimum of the diffraction pattern?

**13.4.** A single-slit Fraunhofer diffraction pattern is formed using white light. For what wavelength of light does the second minimum coincide with the third minimum for the wavelength 4000 A?

**13.5.** The intensities of the secondary maxima in the single-slit Fraunhofer diffraction pattern may be approximately calculated using Eq. (13.1$g$) by assuming that they occur at the halfway positions between minima. Find the values of the relative intensities for the first five secondary maxima.

**13.6.** Show that the intensity in Eq. (13.1$g$) is a maximum for those values of $\alpha$ satisfying Eq. (13.2). [HINT: Differentiate Eq. (13.1$g$) with respect to $\alpha$ and equate to zero.]

**13.7.** Find the values of $\alpha$ [Eq. (13.2)] and the corresponding values of $I_\theta/I_0$ in Eq. (13.1$g$) for the first five secondary maxima, and observe that the maxima do not lie midway between minima but have a displacement, toward the center of the pattern, that increases with decreasing order of maxima. Compare these intensity ratios with the approximate ones in Prob. 13.5.

**13.8.** Show that the value of the second integral in Eq. (13.5$C$) is zero.

**13.9.** The objective of a telescope has a diameter of 3.50 cm and a focal length of 25.0 cm. Find the radius of the first dark ring in the diffraction image of a star formed in the focal plane of the telescope. Take the effective wavelength of white light as 5500 A.

**13.10.** Show that the number of interference maxima under the central diffraction maximum of the double-slit diffraction pattern is given by $(2d/a) - 1$, where $a$ is the slit width and $d$ is the distance between slits.

**13.11.** Write a paragraph giving your interpretation of the distinction between interference and diffraction.

**13.12.** Describe the diffraction pattern resulting with the arrangement shown in Fig. 13.10 when ($a$) only the upper slit is blocked off, ($b$) only the lower slit is blocked off, ($c$) when both slits are open. Is the position of the pattern for ($a$) and ($b$) different?

**13.13.** What is the effect on the diffraction pattern from a double slit if ($a$) $d$ is kept unchanged and $a$ is varied and ($b$) $a$ is kept fixed and $d$ is varied?

**13.14.** In double-slit Fraunhofer diffraction, missing orders occur at those values of sin $\theta$ which satisfy at the same time the condition for interference maxima and the condition for diffraction minima. Show that this leads to the condition $d/a$ = integer. What orders are missing when $d/a = 2$; when $d/a = 3$? Use the approximate relation $d \sin \theta = k\lambda$ as the condition for interference maxima.

**13.15.** Show that

$$\sum_{k=0}^{N-1} \sin 2\pi \left( \frac{t}{T} - \frac{r}{\lambda} + \frac{kd \sin \theta}{\lambda} \right) = \frac{\sin \dfrac{\pi N d \sin \theta}{\lambda} \sin 2\pi \left( \dfrac{t}{T} - \dfrac{r}{\lambda} + \dfrac{N-1}{2\lambda} d \sin \theta \right)}{\sin \dfrac{\pi d \sin \theta}{\lambda}}$$

**13.16.** Find the angular separation in the first and second orders between the wavelengths 4000 and 7000 A when a plane transmission grating of 15,000 lines per inch is used.

**13.17.** A parallel beam of light, having the wavelength range 4500 to 6500 A, falls normally on a plane transmission grating whose grating space is 0.0150 cm. What focal-length lens placed just beyond the grating will cause the first-order spectrum to have a width of 0.5 cm in the focal plane of the lens?

**13.18.** Apply Eq. (13.7a) to find the intensity expression for the Fraunhofer diffraction from two equal-width slits.

**13.19.** Show that the value of $(\sin^2 N\beta)/(\sin^2 \beta)$, as both $N\beta$ and $\beta$ approach integral multiples of $\pi$, is $N^2$.

**13.20.** Plot the interference function $(\sin^2 N\beta)/(\sin^2 \beta)$ of Eq. (13.7a) as a function of $\beta$ between $\beta = 0$ and $\beta = 2\pi$ for $N = 6$. Do this by plotting separately and to the same scale $\sin^2 N\beta$ and $\sin^2 \beta$ against $\beta$. Then divide the ordinates of one by those of the other.

**13.21.** What is the reason why a grating is more suitable for the measurement of dispersed spectra than a prism? Prismatic spectra are known to be *irrational*, while grating spectra are called *rational*.

**13.22.** Using Fig. 13.16, show that, for any position $P$ on the Rowland circle, the rays diffracted from any point on the grating pass through $P$. Assume that the length of grating is small compared with its radius of curvature.

**13.23.** A Fresnel diffraction pattern through a circular aperture is produced with a point source of light of wavelength 6000 A. If the observing screen is distant 80 cm from the aperture, find what diameter opening will expose (*a*) the first Fresnel zone, (*b*) the first five Fresnel zones.

**13.24.** Plane monochromatic microwaves of 10.0 cm wavelength are incident on a circular aperture, and the diffraction pattern is detected at a distance of 1 m from the aperture. What radius aperture will expose only the central Fresnel zone?

**13.25.** Light of wavelength 5461 A from a point source passes through a circular hole 2.96 mm in diameter; and the Fresnel diffraction pattern is examined 100 cm beyond the opening. Is the center of the diffraction pattern bright or dark?

**13.26.** If the solution in Prob. 13.25 is dark (or bright), by how much must the screen be moved away from the opening to cause the center of the diffraction pattern to be bright (or dark)?

**13.27.** Describe the Fresnel diffraction effects when a plane monochromatic wave is incident on a rectangular aperture when the center of the system of zones (*a*) lies well within the aperture, (*b*) is near the edge of the aperture, (*c*) is well behind the aperture.

**13.28.** A dime is used as a circular obstacle to obtain the white spot at the center of the geometrical shadow using Fresnel diffraction. How far from the dime must the screen be mounted for the most favorable arrangement? Would the effect be observable? If not, what changes would you introduce to obtain the effect?

**13.29.** Consider a circular obstacle so large that it covers a great many half-period Fresnel zones. Discuss this case of Fresnel diffraction, pointing out the connection with the principle of the approximate rectilinear propagation of light.

**13.30.** In the accompanying figure $S$ is the light source of wavelength $\lambda$, $OB$ a zone plate, and $P$ the image point at which the rays from the exposed zones reinforce.

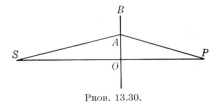

PROB. 13.30.

Show that the reciprocal of the object distance plus the reciprocal of the image distance is equal to the reciprocal of the equivalent focal length of the zone plate, or

$$\frac{1}{SO} + \frac{1}{OP} = \frac{n\lambda}{r_n^2}$$

[HINT: With $OA$ as the radius of the $n$th zone $r_n$, show that

$$(SA + AP) - (SO + OP) = \frac{r_n^2}{2}\left(\frac{1}{SO} + \frac{1}{OP}\right)$$

assuming $AO$ is small compared with $SA$ or $AP$. The result follows.]

**13.31.** Using Fresnel zones on a spherical wave front of radius $a$ and distant $b$ from a point directly ahead of the wave front, show that the area of the $n$th zone is given by

$$\frac{\pi ab\lambda}{a+b}\left[1 + \frac{(2n-1)r}{4b}\right]$$

Observe that this reduces to Eq. (13.10) for a plane wave front. [HINT: Using calculus, show that the area of the first $n$ zones is equal to $2\pi a^2(1 - \cos \alpha)$, where $\alpha$ is the angle between the normal to the wave front at the $n$th zone and the line drawn from $P$ to the $n$th zone.]

**13.32.** A zone plate has a central zone whose diameter is 0.150 cm. A point source of light of wavelength 5000 A is placed 4.00 m from the zone plate. (a) Find the focal length of the zone plate. (b) Where is the most intense image formed?

**13.33.** Using Table E.1, make a conveniently large scale plot of a Cornu spiral, and indicate the values of $v$ on the spiral.

**13.34.** Using the graph of the Cornu spiral in Prob. 13.33 or in Fig. E.2, obtain the diffraction pattern of a straight edge (Fig. 13.28), using $a = 100$ cm, $b = 200$ cm, $\lambda = 6000$ A. Employ Eq. (E.10), and observe, from Eq. (E.1), that the distance $l$ on the screen, measured vertically from point $P$, is $l = [(a + b)/a]q$. Plot the intensity relative to that due to the unobstructed wave front as a function of $l$. Do this by tabulating the measured distances from the asymptotic point $K$ to various points on the spiral, then dividing all these values by the measured distance $K'K$. The squares of the resulting values are the relative intensities. Note that the coordinates of the points may optionally be employed to yield the amplitude distances. The intensities so obtained will be relative to the value 2 for the unobstructed wave since the distance from $K'$ to $K$ is $\sqrt{(\frac{1}{2} + \frac{1}{2})^2 + (\frac{1}{2} + \frac{1}{2})^2} = \sqrt{2}$ and the square of this is 2.

**13.35.** For values of $a$, $b$, and $\lambda$ the same as those given in Prob. 13.34 plot the diffraction pattern for a single slit of width 0.02 cm, using the graph of Prob. 13.33. To do this, use Eq. (E.10) in the form $\Delta v = [2(a + b)/ab\lambda]\Delta q$, where $\Delta q$ is the slit width and $\Delta v$ is the constant length of the Cornu spiral. The value of $v$ which determines the position of this length of spiral is that for the central point of the arc whose chord gives the corresponding amplitude. Tabulate $v$, the chord length, and its square corresponding to different locations of the spiral section. Plot the intensity relative to that of the unexposed wave front as a function of $l$, as in Prob. 13.34.

**13.36.** Find the glancing angles on the cube face of a rock salt crystal ($d = 2.814$ A) corresponding to diffraction maxima in the first and second orders for X rays of wavelength 0.710 A.

**13.37.** If $1 - n = 1.85 \times 10^{-6}$ and $\theta = 10°$, what is the percentage error introduced in the value of $d$ when Eq. (13.13) is used instead of Eq. (13.14)?

# CHAPTER 14

## RESOLVING POWER

Although we have indicated the importance of the consideration of resolving power in our discussion of the microscope and telescope (Secs. 8.6 and 8.9), we have not in general considered diffraction effects in our study of optical instruments. We have seen that the wave nature of light gives rise to these effects and thereby introduces limitations in the use of optical instruments. For instance, whenever light passes through a lens, it has passed through a circular aperture forming a diffraction pattern characterized by a central maximum surrounded by circular fringes. Even in the absence of all aberrations, the lens does not produce a point image of a point object, and the limited portion of the wave front that it transmits forms the circular diffraction pattern. Two point objects, resulting in two corresponding diffraction patterns, are resolvable by an optical system if the diffraction patterns are sufficiently small or are far enough apart so that they are distinguishable as separate image patterns. Again, when an analyzing instrument, such as a spectroscope, is employed, we are concerned with the ability of the instrument to separate two images of the same slit source due to two closely neighboring wavelengths. In this chapter we shall examine the *resolving power*, or *limit of resolution*, of some of the more significant optical instruments that we have already encountered.

**14.1. The Rayleigh Criterion for Resolving Power.** According to Lord Rayleigh's criterion, two point sources are just resolvable by an optical system when their distance apart is such that the central maximum of the diffraction pattern of one source coincides in position with the first minimum of the diffraction pattern of the other source. To illustrate the meaning of this, consider Fig. 14.1a, which shows two single-slit diffraction patterns, of the type given in Fig. 13.5, corresponding to the two neighboring sources. For each pattern, $\theta_1$ is the angular distance from the central maximum to the first minimum, and $\Omega$ is the angular separation of the two central maxima. The figure is drawn for $\Omega = \theta_1$ as stipulated by the Rayleigh criterion. For this case, the resultant pattern is a double-humped curve with a minimum $M$ between the maxima as shown in (b). As the sources get farther apart, so that $\Omega$ becomes greater than $\theta_1$, the minimum $M$ moves downward until there is no overlapping of the central diffraction maxima, with the result that two distinct images become clearly recognizable. When the sources approach each other so that $\Omega < \theta_1$, the minimum point $M$ rises, making it impossible to distinguish two separate images. Although there is some arbitrariness in stating when the two images coalesce, this being a function of the acuteness of vision of the observer, it is generally agreed that the criterion for the resolution of two diffraction patterns is that stated by Rayleigh, namely, $\Omega = \theta_1$. This angle $\Omega = \theta_1$ is called the angle

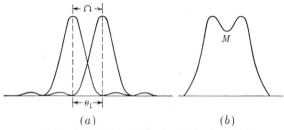

(a)                                          (b)

Fig. 14.1. Rayleigh criterion for limit of resolution.

corresponding to the limit of resolution, or the minimum angle of resolution, so that the resolving power is larger the smaller $\theta_1$. In a rather broad sense, the term resolving power is employed to signify the limit of an optical system's ability to exhibit detail in an object. Diffraction effects set a theoretical limit to the resolving power of any optical system.

**14.2. Limit of Resolution of a Single Slit and Double Slits.** For a single slit of width $a$ it was shown, in Sec. 13.1, that the first minimum of the diffraction pattern occurs when $\alpha = (\pi a \sin \theta_1)/\lambda = \pi$. Therefore, using $\sin \theta_1 \doteq \theta_1$, the minimum angle of resolution is

$$\theta_1 = \frac{\lambda}{a} \qquad (14.1)$$

which shows that as the aperture narrows, $\theta_1$ increases and the resolving power decreases.

For the double-slit diffraction pattern, application of the Rayleigh criterion gives $\beta = (\pi d \sin \theta_1)/\lambda = \pi/2$, or the minimum angle of resolution is

$$\theta_1 = \frac{\lambda}{2d} \qquad (14.2)$$

where $d$ is the slit separation, so that the resolving power increases with increase in $d$. In Eqs. (14.1) and (14.2) it is clear that the angle $\theta_1$ is also the angular separation of the two sources. From a comparison of both equations it follows that the resolving power of two rectangular openings, of separation $d = a$, is twice that for a single opening of width $a$. It is therefore possible to increase the resolving power of a telescope by placing a double slit over its objective. A loss in brightness is of course thereby incurred. The stellar interferometer, discussed in Sec. 12.5f, it will be recalled, has just such a double slit in front of the objective.

**14.3. Limit of Resolution of a Circular Aperture.** In accordance with Rayleigh's criterion, the diffraction images by a circular aperture of two objects are just resolved when the central maximum of one falls on the first dark ring of the other. Equation (13.5F) then yields for the minimum angle of resolution

$$\theta_1 = \frac{1.22\lambda}{a} = \frac{0.61\lambda}{a_0} \tag{14.3}$$

where $a$ and $a_0$ are, respectively, the diameter and radius of the aperture. Since the greater part of the light falls in the central bright disk, the presence of the outer parts of the diffraction patterns may be disregarded. It is to be noted again that the resolving power increases with increase in radius of the circular outline.

**14.4. Limit of Resolution of a Microscope.** In Fig. 14.2 the objective of a microscope is represented by a simple spherical converging lens which forms the images $P'_1$ and $P'_2$ of two self-luminous point objects $P_1$ and $P_2$, respectively. Let the objective subtend an angle $2u$ at the object plane, and let the refractive indices in the object and image planes be $n$ and $n'$, respectively. The image $P'_1$

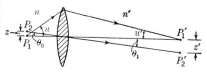

Fig. 14.2. Limit of resolution of a microscope.

of the object $P_1$ consists of a diffraction disk surrounded by rings since the light has passed through a circular aperture. For the neighboring object point $P_2$ there is formed another similar diffraction pattern with center at $P'_2$. If the object points $P_1$ and $P_2$ are just resolvable, the distance $z'$ between the central maxima of the two diffraction patterns is equal to the radius of either central diffraction disk. From Eq. (13.5F) the minimum angle of resolution is given by

$$\sin \theta_1 = \frac{0.61\lambda}{n'a_0} \tag{14.4}$$

where we have introduced the refractive index in the image space, so that $\lambda$ here is the wavelength in vacuum and the wavelength in the image space is $\lambda/n'$. The symbol $a_0$ stands for the radius of the objective. Using Snell's law $n \sin \theta_0 = n' \sin \theta_1$, the angle $\theta_0$ subtended at the lens by the object points is

$$\sin \theta_0 = \frac{0.61\lambda}{na_0} \tag{14.5}$$

From the figure, since $\theta_1$ is small, we may use $\sin \theta_1 = \tan \theta_1$, and since the image distance is large compared with $a_0$, we may use $\sin u' = \tan u'$.

Thus

$$\frac{z'}{\sin \theta_1} = \frac{a_0}{\sin u'}$$

and Eq. (14.4) yields

$$z' = \frac{0.61\lambda}{n' \sin u'} \tag{14.6}$$

which is an expression for the linear separation between the centers of the images. This can be converted into the linear separation between the object points by the sine law [Eq. (2.12)], $nz \sin u = n'z' \sin u'$. Thus

$$z = \frac{0.61\lambda}{n \sin u} \tag{14.7}$$

Equation (14.7) gives the smallest separation $z$ of two point objects that are resolvable in light of wavelength $\lambda$. We have already called attention to the fact that $n \sin u$ is the numerical aperture of the optical system (see Sec. 8.6), and we see that the resolving power increases with decrease in wavelength and increase in numerical aperture. It must be noted that Eq. (14.6) holds for self-luminous objects. When light from a substage condenser is used to illuminate the objects, the resolving power is given by $z = \lambda/(2n \sin u)$, as explained in Secs. 8.6 and 8.7. There it is also pointed out that by immersing the objects in oil the numerical aperture, and hence resolving power, may be increased. We have there also already discussed the interrelationship between magnifying power, resolving power, and light-gathering power. It was there seen that full advantage of the inherent resolving power of the instrument is taken if its exit pupil coincides in size and position with the entrance pupil of the eye. Then the magnifying power of the instrument is normal, and there is no sacrifice in light-gathering power. The ratio of the numerical aperture of the objective to that of the eye gives the normal magnifying power of the microscope.

We have seen that the resolving power of an optical microscope is limited by the wavelength of the light employed. Even with short-wavelength ultraviolet light and quartz optical systems it is not possible to resolve two objects that are closer than about $10^{-6}$ cm. Points closer than this can, however, be resolved by the more recent electron microscope. In Chap. 18 it is brought out that electrons behave very much like waves and have associated with them a wavelength which is given by

$$\lambda_e = \frac{h}{mv}$$

where $\lambda_e$ is the "De Broglie wavelength" associated with the electron, $h$ is Planck's constant, whose value is $6.62 \times 10^{-27}$ erg sec, and $mv$ is the momentum of the electron. The momentum of the electron, which alone determines the value of $\lambda_e$, depends on the voltage used to accelerate the electron. If $V$ is the accelerating potential and $e$ the electronic charge, then the velocity acquired by the electron is given by

$$\tfrac{1}{2}mv^2 = eV$$

or

$$v = \sqrt{\frac{2eV}{m}}$$

and we have

$$\lambda_e = \frac{h}{\sqrt{2meV}}$$

The increase in resolving power comes about in the relatively smaller values obtainable for the effective wavelength $\lambda_e$. Thus if $V = 100$ volts, then, using $m = 9.10 \times 10^{-28}$ gm, $e = 4.80 \times 10^{-10}$ esu,

$$\lambda_e = \frac{6.62 \times 10^{-27}}{\sqrt{2 \times 9.1 \times 10^{-28} \times 100\!\!\;/\!\!\;_{300} \times 4.8 \times 10^{-10}}} = 1.22 \times 10^{-8} \text{ cm}$$

which is of the order of 1 A as compared with a few thousand angstroms employed in the optical microscope. The accelerating voltage in an electron microscope can be as high as 100,000 volts, giving a wavelength about $\tfrac{1}{30}$ A and resulting in a high resolving power. An electron microscope employs "magnetic lenses" or "electric lenses" to control the paths of the electrons and bring them to a focus.

**14.5. Limit of Resolution of a Telescope.** For a telescope the same general principles considered for the microscope apply. With a telescope we are interested in the angular separation between two points rather than the linear separation between the points that can be resolved, since the telescopic system is designed for viewing objects at a considerable distance. Thus for a telescope whose objective is a spherical lens, the minimum angle of resolution is given by Eq. (14.3),

$$\theta_1 = \frac{1.22\lambda}{a}$$

where $a$ is the diameter of the objective. The smaller the angle $\theta_1$, the higher the resolving power, which, as we see, increases with the diameter of the objective. As for the microscope, and as discussed in Sec. 8.9, to realize the inherent resolving power of a telescope the magnifying power should be normal, so that the exit pupil coincides in size and position with the entrance pupil of the eye. As there explained, it is practical to employ a magnifying power somewhat larger than normal in order to increase the ease of observation at the expense of some loss in illumination and field of view.

**14.6. Resolving Power of a Prism.** When the term resolving power is applied to a spectrum-producing device, such as a prism or a grating (see Sec. 14.7), it is used to signify the ability of the instrument to form separate images of two neighboring wavelengths. It is expressed by the ratio $\lambda/\Delta\lambda$, where $\Delta\lambda$ is the smallest wavelength difference that can be resolved at the wavelength $\lambda$. In Fig. 14.3 is shown a prism spectroscope with slit source $S$, collimating lens $L_1$, prism, and focusing lens $L_2$. The image

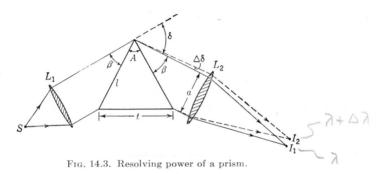

Fig. 14.3. Resolving power of a prism.

$I_1$ corresponds to the wavelength $\lambda$, and the image $I_2$ corresponds to the wavelength $\lambda + \Delta\lambda$. Since the wavelength difference $\Delta\lambda$ is small, it is assumed that the setting of the prism satisfies the condition of minimum deviation for both the solid and dotted paths. The refracting angle of the prism is $A$ and the length of its base $t$. The face of the prism limits the beam incident upon it to a rectangular section of width $a$, and the Rayleigh criterion is then to be applied to a rectangular aperture. This gives for the limiting angle of resolution $\Delta\delta$, between the dotted and solid lines,

$$\Delta\delta = \frac{\lambda}{a} \tag{14.8}$$

where $\delta$ is the angle of minimum deviation. From the figure we see that $\beta = [(\pi/2) - (A + \delta)/2]$ so that $\sin\beta = \cos[(A + \delta)/2]$, or

$$\cos\frac{A + \delta}{2} = \frac{a}{l} \tag{14.9}$$

where $l$ is the length of the prism legs. Also,

$$\sin\frac{A}{2} = \frac{t}{2l} \tag{14.10}$$

With the aid of Eqs. (14.8) to (14.10) we are now in a position to evaluate the expression for the resolving power of the prism. The treatment on the left of the double-column page is a simple approximate method, while that on the right makes use of the calculus.

From Eq. (1.16) we have

$$\sin \frac{A + \delta}{2} = n \sin \frac{A}{2} \quad (14.11a)$$

where $n$ is the refractive index of the prism at the wavelength $\lambda$. For the neighboring wavelength we have

$$\sin \frac{A + \delta + \Delta\delta}{2}$$

$$= (n + \Delta n) \sin \frac{A}{2} \quad (14.11b)$$

Subtracting Eqs. (14.11a) and (14.11b),

$$\sin \frac{A + \delta + \Delta\delta}{2} - \sin \frac{A + \delta}{2}$$

$$= \Delta n \sin \frac{A}{2}$$

and expanding the first term,

$$\sin \frac{A + \delta}{2} \cos \frac{\Delta\delta}{2}$$

$$+ \cos \frac{A + \delta}{2} \sin \frac{\Delta\delta}{2}$$

$$- \sin \frac{A + \delta}{2} = \Delta n \sin \frac{A}{2}$$

Since $\Delta\delta$ is small, we may set $\cos(\Delta\delta/2) = 1$ and

$$\sin \frac{\Delta\delta}{2} = \frac{\Delta\delta}{2}$$

Thus

$$\frac{\Delta\delta}{2} \cos \frac{A + \delta}{2} = \Delta n \sin \frac{A}{2}$$

Now, using Eqs. (14.8) to (14.10), we obtain

$$\lambda = t \, \Delta n$$

Dividing both sides of the equation by $\Delta\lambda$, we have

$$\frac{\lambda}{\Delta\lambda} = t \frac{\Delta n}{\Delta\lambda} \quad (14.11c)$$

From Eq. (1.16) we have

$$\sin \frac{A + \delta}{2} = n \sin \frac{A}{2} \quad (14.11A)$$

The quantities $\delta$ and $n$ are functions of $\lambda$. Differentiating Eq. (14.11A) with respect to $\lambda$ yields

$$\frac{1}{2} \cos \frac{A + \delta}{2} \frac{d\delta}{d\lambda} = \frac{dn}{d\lambda} \sin \frac{A}{2}$$
$$(14.11B)$$

Now substitute Eqs. (14.9) and (14.10) into Eq. (14.11B). This gives

$$a \frac{d\delta}{d\lambda} = t \frac{dn}{d\lambda}$$

For the quantity $d\delta$ we may substitute the finite quantity $\Delta\delta$ from Eq. (14.8) and, at the same time, replace $d\lambda$ by the finite difference $\Delta\lambda$. Using these approximations, we have

$$\frac{\lambda}{\Delta\lambda} = t \frac{dn}{d\lambda} \quad (14.11C)$$

where the second factor on the right side of the equation is the slope to the dispersion curve giving $n$ as a function of $\lambda$ (see Fig. 15.5, Sec. 15.7).

where the ratio $\Delta n/\Delta\lambda$ is to be interpreted as the value of the slope of the dispersion curve giving $n$ as a function of $\lambda$ (see Fig. 15.5, Sec. 15.7).

$$\frac{\lambda}{\Delta\lambda} = t\,\frac{dn}{d\lambda}$$

$P_{rism}$

The resolving power is thus seen to depend on the width of the prism base. The expression gives the resolving power only when the prism is employed at minimum deviation, and provided the prism acts as the aperture stop of the optical system. If this is not so, the value of the over-all resolving power will be different from that given by Eq. (14.11c). We have seen that the resolving power of a spectrum-producing instrument indicates the amount of detail that is visible. There is another quantity, dispersion, which has close connection with resolving power. The dispersion of a prism is taken up in Chap. 15.

**14.7. Resolving Power of a Grating.** It was shown in Sec. 13.4 that the maxima in the diffraction pattern of a grating occur [Eq. (13.8)] at angles given by $\sin\theta = k\lambda/d$, where $k$ is the order and $d$ is the spacing between grating elements. Also, the direction of the first minimum on either side of the $k$th-order principal maximum is given by

$$\sin\theta = \frac{k\lambda}{d} \pm \frac{\lambda}{Nd}$$

where $N$ is the number of grating elements. Applying the Rayleigh criterion, two neighboring wavelengths of separation $\Delta\lambda$ are just resolved if the principal maximum of the diffraction pattern of one coincides with the first minimum of the other. Thus if the wavelength $\lambda + \Delta\lambda$ has a principal maximum of order $k$ in the direction $\theta$, then

$$\sin\theta = \frac{k}{d}(\lambda + \Delta\lambda) \qquad (14.12)$$

To be in accord with the Rayleigh criterion, this wavelength must fall at the same value of $\theta$ at which the first minimum of wavelength $\lambda$ occurs in the same order. Thus

$$\sin\theta = \frac{k\lambda}{d} + \frac{\lambda}{Nd} \qquad (14.13)$$

Equating the right-hand members of Eqs. (14.12) and (14.13) leads to

$$\frac{\lambda}{\Delta\lambda} = kN \qquad (14.14)$$

which is the well-known expression for the resolving power of a grating. We see that the resolving power is proportional to the order $k$ and to the total number of lines being utilized in the grating.  It is independent of the spacing $d$ of the slits.  A grating ruled with say 16,000 lines to the inch for a length of 5 in. would have a resolving power in the second order of $2 \times 5 \times 16,000 = 160,000$.  Thus, in the wavelength region 6400 A, the smallest wavelength difference that can be resolved is $\Delta\lambda = 6400/160,000 = 0.04$ A.  A glass prism with a comparable resolving power would need to have an impracticably large base.

The dispersion of a grating is taken up in Chap. 15.

**14.8. Resolving Power of an Echelon Grating.**  From the expression for the resolving power of a grating it is seen that a high degree of resolution is obtainable either by using a large number of grating elements, as

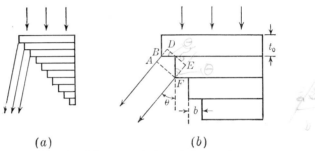

(a)                                   (b)

FIG. 14.4. The transmission echelon grating.

is accomplished by the ruled grating, or by increasing the order of the spectrum.  With the ruled grating it is not practicable to employ an order of spectrum greater than the third because of the loss of intensity in the higher orders.  In the *echelon* grating, devised by Michelson, the number of elements $N$ is relatively small, of the order of 30, and a very high resolving power is made possible by the very large value of the order employed.  As shown in Fig. 14.4, the echelon consists of a pile of plane-parallel plates.  These are arranged in a step formation which accounts for the name "echelon."  The figure illustrates the transmission-type echelon although the grating may also be employed as a reflection instrument.  The plates are all of constant thickness $t_0$, with each plate projecting a distance $b$ beyond the one below it.  Above the echelon there is a collimator lens (not shown) which permits parallel light to fall upon it.  Every point on the steps can be considered to act as a secondary source of disturbance sending out rays in all possible directions.  On the emergent side a telescope (not shown) collects the diffracted rays.

To obtain the working equation of the grating, consider the two parallel transmitted rays shown in (b) making an angle of diffraction $\theta$ with the incident light.  The path difference between these rays is

$$nt_0 - AB = nt_0 - (t_0 \cos\theta - b \sin\theta)$$

where $n$ is the refractive index of the glass plates. The grating equation giving the principal maxima is then

$$t_0(n - \cos \theta) + b \sin \theta = k\lambda$$

where $k$ is the order of spectrum. Since $\theta$ is small, we have

$$t_0(n - 1) + b\theta = k\lambda \tag{14.15}$$

which is the working equation for the echelon. The resolving power of the echelon grating is given approximately by the same expression as for the ruled grating. Thus

$$\frac{\lambda}{\Delta\lambda} = kN \tag{14.16}$$

where $N$ is the number of plates in the echelon.[1] The plates ordinarily have a thickness of about 1 or 2 cm and are put together so that $b$ is usually about 1 or 2 mm. Taking $\theta \doteq 0$, $n = 1.50$, $t = 2.00$ cm, and $\lambda = 5000$ A,

$$k = \frac{2 \times 0.5}{5000 \times 10^{-8}} = 20,000$$

If the number of plates is 30, the resolving power is

$$\frac{\lambda}{\Delta\lambda} = 20,000 \times 30 = 600,000$$

The disadvantage of an echelon grating is that it cannot be used to examine a great length of spectrum, in view of the fact that successive orders are very close together, resulting in a large amount of overlapping. However, the diffraction maxima corresponding to the passage of light through each step are very narrow, with the result that very bright images are produced in one or two high orders.

The echelon grating is used to advantage in the analysis of the hyperfine structure of an individual spectral line which is actually composed of several component lines very close together. To avoid overlapping, an auxiliary prism is used to isolate the spectrum line under examination.

When the echelon is employed as a reflection grating, the light is incident on the instrument from below (Fig. 14.4) and the offset section of each step is made highly reflecting. The grating equation is then given by $2t_0 - b\theta = k\lambda$ (see Prob. 14.10).

**14.9. Resolving Power of the Fabry-Perot Interferometer.** The theory of the Fabry-Perot interferometer was taken up in Sec. 12.3, and the reader is urged to reread that section at this point. At the center of the interference ring system $\phi = 0$, and we may rewrite Eq. (12.2) in the form

$$K\lambda = 2d \tag{14.17}$$

[1] The more correct expression is $\lambda/\Delta\lambda = kN - Nt_0(dn/d\lambda)$.

where $K$ represents the order of interference at the center and in general is not an integer. For a given ring of order $k$, $K$ exceeds $k$ by some fractional amount. It will be recalled that the order of the rings increases as we go toward the center of the pattern. The resolving power is now obtainable from Eq. (14.17). For the wavelength $\lambda + \Delta\lambda$ Eq. (14.17) gives

$$K + \Delta K = \frac{2d}{\lambda + \Delta\lambda} \tag{14.18}$$

Subtracting Eq. (14.17) from Eq. (14.18), we have

$$\frac{\Delta K}{K} = - \frac{\Delta\lambda}{\lambda + \Delta\lambda} = - \frac{\Delta\lambda}{\lambda\,[1 + (\Delta\lambda/\lambda)]}$$

and since $\Delta\lambda/\lambda \ll 1$, we have for the resolving power

$$\left| \frac{\lambda}{\Delta\lambda} = - \frac{K}{\Delta K} \right| \tag{14.19}$$

where again $K$ is the order of interference at the center of the ring system, and $\Delta K$ is the smallest change in order detectable. The negative sign indicates that a positive increase in $\lambda$ corresponds to a negative change in $K$.

We can find the value of $\Delta K$ by using Eq. (12.7),

$$I = \frac{I_{\max}}{1 + [4r^2/(1 - r^2)^2]\sin^2(\delta/2)}$$

giving the intensity of the fringes $I$ as a function of the phase difference $\delta$. A plot of this equation has the general form shown in Fig. 14.5, exhibiting

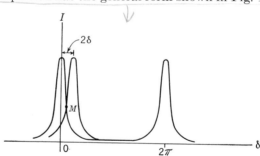

Fig. 14.5. General appearance of interference pattern in a Fabry-Perot interferometer; used to compute the resolving power.

sharp maxima at the positions $\delta = 0, 2\pi, 4\pi, \ldots,$ with broad minima between the maxima. Applying the Rayleigh criterion, which holds approximately here, we wish to find $\Delta K$ corresponding to the separation $2\delta$ of two adjacent interference fringes having wavelengths $\lambda$ and $\lambda + \Delta\lambda$. Diffraction theory shows (see Prob. 14.4) that the intersection point $M$, midway between two maxima that are just resolvable, corresponds, for either pattern, to the condition $I = 0.405I_{\text{max}}$. Applying this here, we have

$$\sin^2 \frac{\delta}{2} = \frac{(1 - 0.405)(1 - r^2)^2}{4 \times 0.405r^2}$$

or

$$\delta = 2 \sin^{-1} \left[ \frac{0.367(1 - r^2)^2}{r^2} \right]^{\frac{1}{2}}$$

Now a change of order of 1 corresponds to a change in $\delta$ of $2\pi$ so that the change in order $\Delta K$ is given by

$$\frac{1}{2\pi} = \frac{\Delta K}{2\delta}$$

$$\Delta K = \frac{\delta}{\pi} = \frac{2}{\pi} \sin^{-1} \left[ \frac{0.367(1 - r^2)^2}{r^2} \right]^{\frac{1}{2}}$$

Substituting this value for $\Delta K$ into Eq. (14.19) gives

$$\frac{\lambda}{\Delta\lambda} = \frac{-K\pi}{2 \sin^{-1} \left[ \dfrac{0.367(1 - r^2)^2}{r^2} \right]^{\frac{1}{2}}} \tag{14.20}$$

The resolving power may thus be increased by increasing the reflecting power or intensity reflection coefficient $r^2$, or by increasing the order of interference. The order of interference is increased by moving the Fabry-Perot plates farther apart. As an example of the order of magnitude of resolving power obtainable, suppose $d = 1.00$ cm and $\lambda = 5000$ A. Then from Eq. (14.17), $K = 40,000$. Equation (14.20) then gives for $r^2 = 0.5$ a resolving power of 141,700, and for $r^2 = 0.9$ the resolving power is 985,500, showing again the desirability of having a high reflecting power. For the visible region a metallic coating of silver applied by evaporation in a vacuum yields a high reflectance. If a lower resolving power can be tolerated, aluminum is the better metal to use in view of the fact that silver tarnishes. In addition silver is transparent in the ultraviolet.

## PROBLEMS

**14.1.** Consider that the diameter of the pupil of the eye is 2.00 mm, that the eyeball has a diameter of 2.50 cm, and that the index of refraction of the vitreous humor, in which the retinal image is formed, is 1.33. When viewing objects in air at the distance of distinct vision (25.0 cm), find (a) the numerical aperture of the eye, (b) the linear distance between two point objects that are just resolvable, (c) the linear distance between the centers of the diffraction disks appearing on the retina corresponding to the two resolvable object points, (d) the angular separation between the two objects that are just resolvable. Assume that $\lambda = 5500$ A.

**14.2.** The headlights of an automobile are 5.00 ft apart. (a) What is the angle subtended at the eye pupil by the diffraction centers on the retina when the two sources, considered as points, are just resolvable? (b) At what distance are the headlights when they are just resolvable? (c) What is the linear distance between the centers of the retinal images when the automobile is 2000 m away? Use a wavelength of 5500 A and a pupillary diameter of 2.00 mm. The refractive index in the image space is 1.33, and the diameter of the eyeball is 2.50 cm.

**14.3.** The two headlights of an automobile are 1.50 m apart and 20,000 m away. A telescope, equipped with an adjustable slit in front of the objective, is used, with the width of the slit running parallel to a line through the sources. If the effective wavelength is 5500 A, find (a) what width of slit will just make the source resolvable, (b) the distance of the automobile for the two sources to be just resolvable when the slit is removed. The diameter of the objective is 3.00 cm.

**14.4.** Find the intensity relative to the intensity maximum, for either pattern, of the point $M$ midway between the images (Fig. 14.1) when the Rayleigh condition for the limit of resolution is satisfied.

**14.5.** A microscope is used to resolve two self-luminous point objects separated by $4.00 \times 10^{-5}$ cm. (a) For use with light of wavelength 5461 A, what must be the numerical aperture of the objective? (b) Find the angle subtended at the eye when it views (unaided) the objects at a distance of 25.0 cm. (c) What must be the minimum over-all magnifying power of the microscope necessary to see the resolved images? Assume that the smallest angular separation resolvable by the eye is 1.50 min. The objects are in air.

**14.6.** A plane transmission grating is ruled with 14,000 lines to the inch for a length of 6 in. In the wavelength region 5000 A find (a) the resolving power of the grating in the first order and the smallest wavelength difference that can be resolved, (b) the base of a flint prism necessary to resolve this wavelength difference if the rate of change of refractive index with wavelength, at 5000 A, is 800 cm$^{-1}$.

**14.7.** The rulings on a grating having 110,000 lines to the inch are examined with an oil-immersion microscope in light of wavelength 4000 A. What numerical aperture is required to resolve the rulings?

**14.8.** The sodium $D$ line of wavelength 5893 A is a doublet whose components are 5896 and 5890 A. What is the least number of lines necessary for a grating to resolve this doublet in the first order?

**14.9.** What is the resolving power of a transmission echelon having 30 steps each 1 cm thick? Take the index of refraction as 1.50 and the wavelength as 4000 A. Assume $\theta \doteq 0$. The value of $dn/d\lambda = -1000$ cm$^{-1}$.

**14.10.** Show that the working equation for a reflection echelon grating is

$$2t_0 - b\theta = k\lambda$$

where $\theta$ is the angle that the reflected light makes with the incident light as shown in

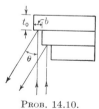

PROB. 14.10.

the figure. For $\theta \doteq 0$ and $n = 1.5$ what is the ratio of the order of the reflection to that of the transmission ehelon for a given $\lambda$, $t_0$, and $b$?

**14.11.** Using Eq. (14.20), plot the resolving power as a function of the reflecting power employing values of $r^2$ ranging from 0.10 to 0.90. Use $d = 1.00$ cm and $\lambda = 5000$ A.

**14.12.** The mirrors of a Fabry-Perot interferometer have a reflecting power of 80 per cent. What must be their separation to possess a resolving power equal to that of a 6-in. grating of 20,000 lines to the inch in the first order? Assume $\lambda = 5000$ A.

# CHAPTER 15

## ABSORPTION, SCATTERING, AND DISPERSION

When light traverses matter, be it solid, liquid, or gas, its intensity decreases with distance of penetration and its velocity is a function of the wavelength of the light. The decrease in the intensity of the light, we shall see, is due to the processes of absorption and scattering, each of which abstracts energy from the original beam. The effect of the medium on the velocity of the light wave we have encountered in Sec. 1.9, where we presented Newton's observation that different colors, when sent through a transparent material, are deviated by different amounts. Different colors are then characterized by different indices of refraction in a given medium, and this change in refractive index necessitates a change in the velocity of the wave, which in turn means a change in wavelength. We have also met this change in velocity with wavelength in our discussion of the group and wave velocities [Sec. 10.9, Eq. (10.19)], where it was shown that the group velocity is equal to the wave velocity only when there is no change in velocity with wavelength. This change in velocity with wavelength gives rise to the phenomenon of dispersion, and the rate of change of the refractive index with wavelength, for a given medium, is termed the *dispersion* of the medium. We shall examine what functional relationship there is between the refractive index and the wavelength, and we shall look into the physical reason for the corresponding change in velocity.

In discussing absorption, scattering, and dispersion it is not the intention to present an exhaustive treatment, which would take us far afield in the extensive subject of the interaction of light with material media. It is our purpose here to present enough of a treatment to introduce the student to the phenomena and theories involved.

**15.1. Absorption.** In Fig. 15.1 is shown a beam of light of a single color passing through an absorbing material. The intensity of the light at $x = 0$ is $I_0$, and as the wave passes through the material, its amplitude decreases. After passing through a length $x$ of material, its intensity has diminished to the value $I$. The expression showing the relationship between $I$, $I_0$, and $x$ is obtained by applying Bouguer's law of absorption, which states that each element of thickness of absorbing

Fig. 15.1. Absorption of light.

306

substance absorbs the same fraction of the light intensity that is incident upon it. In what follows we give the calculus treatment in the right side of the double-column page and an algebraic treatment on the left.

If we imagine the material to be divided into vertical layers of equal unit thicknesses, then the intensity entering the second layer to the right of $x = 0$, that is, after traversing unit thickness of absorber, is $t_c I_0$, where $t_c$ is a fraction known as the *transmission coefficient*. The intensities entering succeeding layers are $t_c^2 I_0$, $t_c^3 I_0$, $t_c^4 I_0$, . . . , etc. With the same fraction absorbed by each succeeding layer, the intensity $I$, after traversing a thickness $x$ of material, is

$$I = I_0 t_c^x \qquad (15.1a)$$

Set

$$t_c = e^{-\alpha}$$

Then

$$I = I_0 e^{-\alpha x} \qquad (15.1b)$$

where $\alpha$ is known as the *absorption coefficient* and $e$ is the base of natural logarithms.

Consider an infinitesimal thickness $dx$ of the absorbing material. The decrease in intensity $-dI$, after the light passes through the thickness $dx$, is proportional to the initial intensity $I$ entering the element and to $dx$. Thus

$$-dI \propto I\ dx$$

or

$$\frac{dI}{I} = -\alpha\ dx \qquad (15.1A)$$

where $\alpha$ is called the *absorption coefficient*. Integrating Eq. (15.1A),

$$\ln I = -\alpha x + \ln I_0$$

where $I_0$ is the value of $I$ at $x = 0$. Thus

$$I = I_0 e^{-\alpha x} \qquad (15.1B) \quad$$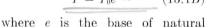

where $e$ is the base of natural logarithms.

The law expressed by Eq. (15.1b) or Eq. (15.1B) was first enunciated by Bouguer in 1729 but often goes by the name Lambert's law after its rediscoverer. The ratio of the intensity of the transmitted light to that of the incident light $I/I_0$ is called the *transparency*, or *transmissivity*, corresponding to any thickness $x$. Therefore, from Eq. (15.1a), we see that the transmission coefficient is the same as the transparency, or transmissivity, for unit thickness. Equation (15.1A) shows that the absorption coefficient signifies the fractional decrease in intensity per unit distance traversed by the light beam. We see that the absorption coefficient is equal to the negative of the natural logarithm of the transmission coefficient. The value of the absorption coefficient depends on the wavelength of the light.

For a solution, the absorption is in general proportional to the concentration of the absorbing molecules. If $c$ is the concentration and $\beta$ is the absorption coefficient per unit concentration, then Eq. (15.1B) becomes

$$I = I_0 e^{-\beta c x} \qquad (15.2)$$

which is known as Beer's law.    Beer's law does not hold when the absorption per unit concentration varies with the concentration.

Absorption may be of the type that is termed *general*, or it may be of the type that is termed *selective*.    If the absorption is general, it is very nearly the same for all or for a very wide range of wavelengths.    Substances exhibiting general absorption are exemplified by finely divided metal and lampblack.    These have porous surfaces so that the rays falling upon them are reflected in the interior spaces between the particles, a partial absorption occurring at each reflection.    After many reflections the intensity quickly falls to zero, the energy being transformed into heat by absorption.    Such surfaces therefore appear black.    When the absorption is termed selective, certain colors or spectral regions are strongly absorbed, while others are easily transmitted.    Most media that are colored exhibit a color which is accounted for by the phenomenon of selective absorption.    Thus a piece of red glass absorbs most of the colors in the spectrum except red and orange, and the transmitted light appears red to the eye.    On the other hand, uncolored glass transmits the visible spectrum but selectively absorbs the ultraviolet and infrared radiation.    Again the colors of pigments and naturally colored objects result from selective absorption.    The light, after penetrating some distance into the surface, undergoes internal reflections and refractions and then emerges divested of colors, which have been selectively absorbed.    For example, in a mixture of blue and yellow paints, the blue paint selectively absorbs the yellow and red-orange, and the yellow paint absorbs the blue and violet, so that the mixture selectively absorbs all the colors except green, which is the color sensation produced by the mixture.    This is different from the result obtained when blue and yellow light are mixed, producing white light.

There are also the situations in which bodies exhibit a surface color which is due to *selective reflection*.    The metallic luster of a gold surface gives the sensation of a yellow color because the surface selectively reflects this color.    That this color is not due to the absorption of the other colors is shown by examining the reflected and transmitted light when a thin gold foil is illuminated with white light.    The reflected light is yellow, and the transmitted light is blue-green, showing that the yellow has been absorbed.    In general selective reflection usually takes place at those wavelengths for which the medium is strongly absorbent.

**15.2. Absorption by Solids, Liquids, and Gases.**  Some substances, by selective absorption, are capable of transmitting a wide range of wavelengths.    All glasses absorb in the ultraviolet and infrared regions, the positions of the cutoff being a function of the composition of the glass.    The transparency of the crown and flint glasses ranges from the neighborhood of about 3500 to about 20,000 A, the crown glass transmitting a few hundred angstroms more than the flint in the ultraviolet, and the flint glass transmitting a few thousand angstroms more than crown in the infrared region. Special types of glass will transmit down to about 2500 A, and quartz will transmit somewhat below 2000 A and up to about 40,000 A. Although rock salt and quartz transmit about equally in the ultraviolet, the upper limit of transmission for rock salt is more than three times that for quartz. However, for obvious reasons, quartz glass is much superior to rock salt for use in spectrographs. To transmit further down into the ultraviolet, fluorite may be used, having a lower limit in the neighborhood of 1200 A and an upper limit about 100,000 A. However, to employ fluorite in an ultraviolet spectrograph necessitates removing the air, which itself is opaque to radiation below 1850 A. In the neighborhood of 1500 A and less, specially prepared photographic plates must be employed, since at these low wavelengths the gelatin supporting the particles of the emulsion becomes opaque. The liquid, water, in addition to being transparent to the visible region is very transparent in the ultraviolet and in the infrared. Liquid salt solutions can be made to have a variety of transmission and selective absorption characteristics. When we go into the still shorter wavelength regions, solids and liquids that have strong selective absorption in visible light become very transparent. This is the region of wavelengths called X rays. We discuss the absorption of X rays in Sec. 15.5.

In true absorption, the energy which has been taken away from the traversing beam of light goes into heating the absorbing material. There are some substances, certain solids, liquids, and gases, that absorb light of one wavelength group and reemit light of another wavelength group. This phenomenon is known as *fluorescence* and according to Stokes' law, to which there are exceptions, the wavelength of the fluorescent light is greater than that of the absorbed light. The atoms of the solid, liquid, or vapor become excited when the incident light passes through them and afterward emit the fluorescent radiation. For instance, the mineral fluorspar fluoresces in the blue region when irradiated with sunlight. Ultraviolet light causes the cornea and lens of the eye, the teeth, the hair, and skin to give off a bluish fluorescence. Artificial teeth, however, appear jet black. Some solids continue to emit light for a time (from a fraction of a second to several hours) after the exciting light is removed. This phenomenon is called *phosphorescence*. For some gases at low pressures the reemitted light has the same wavelength as the incident light. This is called *resonance radiation*, discovered by R. W. Wood, and so named for its analogy to the resonance vibration or excitation produced in a tuning fork by sound waves of a frequency equal to the natural frequency of the tuning fork. The resonance radiation of sodium vapor can be easily demonstrated.[1]

[1] R. W. Wood, "Physical Optics," 3d ed., p. 587, The Macmillan Company, New York, 1934.

**15.3. Scattering.** There are two distinct ways in which energy from a light beam may be removed when it traverses a medium. One of these, true atomic absorption, we have seen, has to do with the conversion of the abstracted energy into heating the substance. The other is by *scattering* the energy, which, as we shall see, is an absorption and reradiation of energy by the atomic or molecular constituents of the absorbing substance. The coefficient $\alpha$ in Eq. (15.1$b$) or Eq. (15.1$B$) refers to the total coefficient since it measures the fractional decrease in light intensity per unit distance. This coefficient is often written as the sum of two coefficients $\alpha = \alpha_a + \alpha_s$, where $\alpha_a$ is the true absorption coefficient and $\alpha_s$ is the scattering coefficient. The effect of scattering can be seen by passing a light beam through a gas chamber containing smoke particles or a suspension of small particles in water and observing the light scattered at right angles to the path of the light beam. The scattered light will appear blue.

An understanding of why this is so, and in general a clearer picture of the process of scattering, may be obtained by utilizing some of the principles of electromagnetic theory and electrodynamics. As discussed in Sec. 11.4, a light wave contains periodic electric and magnetic vibrations which are in planes perpendicular to the direction of the wave propagation. We have also seen that Wiener's experiment (Sec. 11.8) leads to the choice of the electric vector as the one responsible for optical effects. Now an atom contains electrically charged particles of both signs, so that when it is acted on by an external electric field, the positive charges move in the direction of the field and the negative charges move opposite to the direction of the field. There is thus produced a separation of equal and opposite charge forming what is known as an *electrical dipole*. With an aggregate of atoms or molecules, as in a gas or dielectric, there are formed in each element of volume, in the presence of an external electric field, dipoles which have been induced by the field. The charges are held together by what can be thought of as elastic forces, and when the electrical field is removed, the dipoles disappear. When the electric field is that due to an electromagnetic wave, the charges become displaced first in one direction and then in the opposite direction, and there result induced oscillating electric dipoles. An oscillating electric dipole, in accordance with classical electromagnetic theory, is itself a radiator of electromagnetic waves. These secondary waves due to the induced oscillating dipoles are the ones which form the scattered light. In Fig. 15.2 is shown an unpolarized light wave traveling in the downward $y$ direction incident on dielectric or gas molecules at $O$. As explained in Sec. 11.4, we may use the equivalent component electric-vector amplitudes $E_x$ and $E_z$ for all the $E$ vectors in the $xz$ plane. These are shown incident on molecules at $O$, causing induced oscillating dipoles with their

charges vibrating in the $x$ direction and in the $z$ direction.   Since the
reradiated light is transverse in character, it is observable in the $x$ direction, from which direction it appears linearly polarized with its vibration
parallel to the $z$ direction, or in the
$z$ direction, from which direction it
appears linearly polarized with its
vibration parallel to the $x$ direction.
We shall have more to say about the
state of polarization of the scattered
radiation in the next chapter.   We
here notice that if the incident light
is plane-polarized, the dipole will
oscillate parallel to the direction of
vibration of the electric vector, with
no scattered intensity in this direc-
tion and with maximum scattered intensity at right angles, the scattered
intensity being plane-polarized.

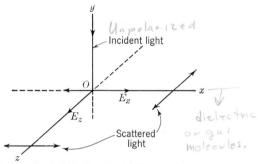

Fig. 15.2. Scattering of unpolarized light.

   The dependence of the scattering by small particles on the wavelength
of the incident radiation is obtained by setting up the classical differential
equation of motion of the oscillating dipole.   The equation is that for the
forced motion of a simple harmonic oscillator.   By assuming that the
dipole is small in dimensions compared with the wavelength of the incident light and solving the equation, an expression for the scattered intensity is arrived at.   We shall not carry this through but shall discuss the
result thus obtained and given in Eq. (15.3).   The scattering power is
the ratio

$$\text{Scattering power} = \frac{8\pi N e^4}{3m^2c^4} \frac{1}{[(\nu_0^2/\nu^2) - 1]^2} \qquad (15.3)$$

of the amount of light scattered per unit volume of material to the
intensity of the incident wave; $e$ is the electronic charge, $m$ is the electronic mass, $c$ is the velocity of light, $N$ is the number of dipoles per unit
volume, $\nu_0$ is the natural frequency of the oscillating dipole, and $\nu$ is the
frequency of the incident electromagnetic wave.   In arriving at Eq.
(15.3) it should be realized that the $N$ dipoles have been assumed to
scatter independently, as the molecules of a gas do.   There the molecules
have a completely random distribution, with the result that there is no
fixed phase relationship between the individual scattered waves of the
molecules.   Only in the forward direction of propagation is there a fixed
phase relation, all of the waves being in phase.   Therefore the scattered
intensity due to $N$ dipoles per unit volume is given by $N$ times the intensity of a single dipole.   Since the scattering is incoherent (see Sec. 10.5),
we may add intensities instead of amplitudes.

For a normal atom the natural frequency lies far into the ultraviolet so that $(\nu_0/\nu)^2 \gg 1$ in the visible region, and Eq. (15.3) becomes

$$\text{Scattering power} = \frac{8\pi N e^4}{3m^2\nu_0^4\lambda^4} \qquad (15.4a)$$

where $\lambda$ is the wavelength of the incident light. Equation (15.4a) is known as Rayleigh's scattering formula. We note that the scattering power varies inversely as the fourth power of the wavelength so that the blue light is scattered much more than the red light. The blue color of the sky is thus explained as due to the scattering of the light by the molecules of the atmosphere. The scattered light is blue, but the transmitted light, with the blue removed more effectively than the red, looks red, accounting for the red color of the sun at sunset. If the earth had no atmosphere, the sky would be perfectly black.

In the other extreme when $(\nu_0/\nu)^2 \ll 1$, Eq. (15.3) becomes

$$\text{Scattering power} = \frac{8\pi N e^4}{3m^2 c^4} \qquad (15.4b)$$

Equation (15.4b), known as Thomson's scattering formula for the scattering of X rays, is independent of the wavelength. We shall have occasion to refer to it later.

In the case where $\nu$ and $\nu_0$ become very nearly equal, the scattering can become very large. In this case the expression given in Eq. (15.3) should be replaced by one which includes a damping term; then the denominator does not vanish when $\nu = \nu_0$. The condition $\nu = \nu_0$ leads to the scattering known as *resonance scattering*, which we have met in Sec. 15.2.

The scattering from a liquid or a solid produces a comparatively weak intensity in directions that are different from the forward direction. This is so because liquids and especially solids are characterized by a more ordered distribution of molecules, so that the secondary waves experience interference effects. Only in the forward direction is there appreciable intensity, and in this direction the scattered light and the incident light combine to form the refracted wave.

The effect of the size of the particles on the scattering is strikingly brought out by using a solution made by adding some drops of dilute sulfuric acid to a dilute solution of photographic hypo (sodium thiosulfate). A precipitate of fine particles of sulfur is formed, and blue light is scattered laterally. The transmitted light is reddish as seen at sunset. After a while the sulfur particles increase in size, causing a larger proportion of the longer wavelengths to be scattered. When the particles are large enough, the solution, when viewed from any direction, appears white.

**15.4. The Raman Effect.** Raman in 1928 discovered that when an intense source of monochromatic light is used to irradiate a liquid, in addition to the appearance of the incident frequency $\nu$ in the scattered light there are present radiations whose frequencies are displaced above and below the frequency $\nu$. This appearance, in the scattered light, of frequencies other than those present in the incident light is known as the *Raman effect*, which was also discovered in the case of solids by Landsberg and Mandelstam. The effect was predicted by Smekal in 1923 on the basis of the quantum theory, which explains the effect. The classical electromagnetic theory is not adequate in giving a complete explanation of the phenomenon. As stated in Sec. 10.1, the quantum theory asserts that light is composed of small packets of energy, all of the same magnitude, called light quanta, or photons, the energy of each photon being represented by $h\nu$, where $h$ is Planck's constant and $\nu$ is the frequency of the radiation. When photons interact with matter the following processes may take place: (1) If the photon possesses the requisite amount of energy, it may be completely absorbed by an atom, in which case the atom gains the energy and is in an excited state. The atom may now lose its acquired energy by radiation, or by collision it may pass the energy on to another particle. (2) The photon may have enough energy to ionize the atom and thus eject an electron from it. The ion may then radiate energy, may transfer it to another particle, or may recapture an electron. (3) Part of the energy of the photon may go into ionizing the atom, with the result that a photon of lower energy, in addition to an electron, leaves the atom. This process is the well-known *Compton effect*, which is taken up in Sec. 15.6. (4) Part of the energy of the photon may go to excite the atom or molecule and the rest of it scattered as radiation with an increased wavelength, or the photon may receive a certain amount of energy from an excited molecule and thus emerge with a decreased wavelength. This last process is what takes place in Raman scattering. The photon, of course, may be scattered with no loss or gain in energy and give rise to the unmodified frequency in the Raman spectrum. When the photon gives up part of its energy to cause excitation of higher rotational and vibrational states of the molecule, the Raman scattered radiations of lower frequency are called *Stokes' lines* because of their analogy to the production of the longer wavelength radiation in fluorescence and given by Stokes' law. When some rotational or vibrational energy is transferred from the molecule to the photon, the shorter wavelength radiations scattered are called *anti-Stokes' lines*. Raman scattering is of rather weak intensity and is best observable under relatively prolonged photographic exposure.

**15.5. Absorption and Scattering of X Rays.** When X rays traverse matter, they are absorbed in accordance with the exponential law [Eq.

(15.1$b$) or (15.1$B$)], which we shall here restate as

$$I = I_0 e^{-\mu x} \tag{15.5}$$

where $\mu$ is the *linear absorption coefficient* since it represents the fraction of the energy removed per centimeter of path traversed by the X-ray beam. For a comparison of the absorption coefficients of different substances, Eq. (15.5) is ordinarily used in the form

$$I = I_0 e^{-\mu_m \rho x} \tag{15.6}$$

where $\rho$ is the density, $\rho x$ is the mass per square centimeter of absorbing material, and $\mu_m = \mu/\rho$ is called the *mass absorption coefficient* and refers to the energy removed from unit cross section of the X-ray beam by 1 gm of material. By multiplying $\mu_m$ by the mass of an atom of the absorber, which is the atomic weight divided by the Avogadro number $6.02 \times 10^{23}$, one obtains the *atomic absorption coefficient*, which refers to the energy removed, from a beam of X rays of unit cross section, by one atom.

The absorption coefficients above refer to the total loss of energy from an X-ray beam. There are essentially two main types of X-ray absorption processes corresponding to the two ways in which a material removes energy from the X-ray beam: by true or fluorescent absorption, and by scattering. The total mass absorption coefficient is then written as

$$\mu_m = \frac{\sigma}{\rho} + \frac{\tau}{\rho} \tag{15.7}$$

where $\sigma/\rho$ and $\tau/\rho$ are, respectively, the *mass scattering coefficient* and the *mass fluorescent transformation coefficient*. As we have seen, on the basis of the classical theory of scattering, the electrons in the scattering material are set into forced vibration by the oscillating electric field of the X radiation, and these oscillating electrons radiate the scattered, or secondary, X rays in all directions. In fluorescence, or what is termed true absorption of X rays, the atom absorbs the energy delivered by the X ray, and there results a process of transformation of X rays in the material. One of the electrons may become completely dislodged from the atom. The atom, in having electrons fall into the energy level vacated (see Sec. 17.5), thus regaining its normal state, then radiates X rays which are characteristic of the atom. The electrons leaving the atom when ionization takes place are ejected as high-speed photoelectrons (see Sec. 17.3). For an electron ejected from a position nearest the nucleus, a large amount of energy is liberated when an electron returns to the vacated position. In this case the frequency of the fluorescent radiation is large. The two most effective types of fluorescent X rays excitable in most atoms are the $K$ and $L$ characteristic radiations. These correspond, respectively,

$$\frac{1}{cm} \cdot \frac{cm^3}{g} = \frac{cm^2}{g}$$

to the ejection of an electron from the innermost, or most stable, energy level and from the next innermost position.    The $K$ radiation is more penetrating than the $L$ radiation for a given element.    The fluorescent X rays may also be produced by the bombardment of an element with high-speed electrons, so that characteristic X rays are also given off from the target of an X-ray tube.

The mass absorption coefficient is a function of the nature of the absorbing element and the wavelength of the X radiation.    For a given absorbing material the empirical functional relationship is

$$\mu_m = C\lambda^3 + \frac{\sigma}{\rho} \tag{15.8}$$

The mass scattering coefficient $\sigma/\rho$ has an approximately constant value of about $0.2/\text{gm}/\text{cm}^2$ over a wide range of wavelengths, and $C$ is approximately constant over certain ranges.

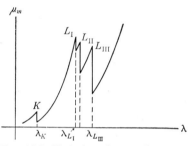

For different elements $C$ depends on the fourth power of the atomic number (equal to the number of extra-nuclear electrons in a neutral atom). The absorption due to the scattering process is small compared with that due to the photoelectric or fluorescent process except at very small wavelengths.    The manner in which the mass absorption coefficient varies with the wavelength is illustrated by Fig. 15.3.

Fig. 15.3. Variation of mass absorption coefficient with wavelength.

It is seen that the experimental curve contains discontinuities known as *absorption edges*.    An interpretation of these is readily obtained in terms of the quantum theory of radiation, according to which the energy of each X-ray photon is given by $E = h\nu = hc/\lambda$, where $\nu$ and $\lambda$ are the frequency and wavelength, respectively, $c$ is the velocity of light, and $h$ is Planck's constant.    We use the fact that electrons within the atom exist in well-defined energy levels.    Beginning at short wavelengths, the absorption increases according to Eq. (15.8), the X rays having sufficient energy to eject photoelectrons from the innermost, or $K$, energy level of the atom.    This increase occurs until the wavelength $\lambda_K$ is reached, at which point the absorption suddenly drops to a low value.    The reason for this is that an X-ray photon of wavelength greater than $\lambda_K$ does not have sufficient energy to eject a $K$ electron.    This discontinuity at $\lambda_K$ is the so-called "$K$ absorption edge."    For wavelengths larger than $\lambda_K$ the absorption curve increases again according to Eq. (15.8) until the wavelength $\lambda_{L_I}$ is reached, corresponding to one of the three $L$ energy levels of the atom.    For X rays with wavelengths greater than $\lambda_{L_I}$ the photons do not have sufficient energy to eject electrons from the $L_I$ level, giving rise to the $L_I$ absorption edge.   There are three $L$ absorption edges, five $M$ absorption edges, etc.   Equation (15.8) applies to the region between two absorption edges, and a plot of $\mu_m$ against $\lambda^3$ yields almost a straight line with a different value of $C$ for each region.   The existence of absorption edges make it possible to obtain filtered X radiation by selective absorption.

From Eq. (15.4$b$) we have for the mass scattering coefficient

$$\frac{\sigma}{\rho} = \frac{8\pi N e^4}{3m^2 c^4 \rho} \tag{15.9}$$

an equation which was deduced on the basis of the classical theory of scattering.   The equation indicates that the scattering is independent of the wavelength and the nature of the scatterer.   Actually, however, this is not the case, as we shall see below.   The expression was employed by Barkla (1911) to determine the number of scattering electrons per carbon atom.   Barkla, and later Hewlett, using a wavelength of 0.71 A, found for the mass scattering coefficient of carbon a value 0.2.   Thus the number of electrons per cubic centimeter is given by

$$N = 0.2 \frac{3m^2 c^4}{8\pi e^4} \rho$$

Since $\rho$ is the density of carbon, $N/\rho$ is the number of electrons per gram of carbon and the number of electrons per atom of carbon is $N/\rho$ multiplied by the atomic weight divided by the Avogadro number.   Thus

Number of carbon scattering electrons

$$= 0.2 \frac{3m^2 c^4}{8\pi e^4} \frac{12}{6.02 \times 10^{23}}$$

$$= \frac{0.2 \times 3(9.1 \times 10^{-28})^2 (3.0 \times 10^{10})^4 \times 12}{8 \times 3.14(4.80 \times 10^{-10})^4 (6.02 \times 10^{23})}$$

$$\doteq 6$$

The close agreement between experiment and Thomson's classical theory is due to the fact that the experimental determination of the mass scattering coefficient was done on a relatively light element as scatterer at a wavelength greater than 0.2 A.   Equation (15.9) is found to be in accord with experiment for the very light elements, and provided the wavelength employed is greater than about 0.2 A.   If the wavelength is smaller than this, the mass scattering coefficient is smaller than that computed from Eq. (15.9).   For the heavier elements and for wavelengths greater than 0.2 A, the mass scattering coefficient increases with the wavelength and with the atomic number of the scatterer.   The classical theory also predicts values for the intensity of the scattered X rays that are much smaller than those obtained experimentally for wavelengths greater than 0.2 A, while for wavelengths smaller than 0.2 A the observed intensity is less than that predicted for all angles of scattering. The classical theory of scattering is unable to account for these experimental facts, which find their explanation in the modern quantum theory.

**15.6. The Compton Effect.** We have seen that, on the basis of the classical theory of scattering, the wavelength of the scattered X radiation should be the same as that of the incident radiation for all angles of scattering. The scattered X rays, however, are found to contain not only radiation of the same wavelength as that of the primary rays but also X radiation having a wavelength measurably longer than that of the incident radiation. The radiation of the same wavelength as the incident radiation is called "unmodified," and the radiation of greater wavelength is called "modified." To explain the observed X-ray scattering phenomena given at the end of the last section and the effect giving rise to the modified radiation, A. H. Compton advanced the quantum theory of scattering. The modified radiation also goes by the name "Compton scattering," and the quantum mechanism explaining the effect is known as the *Compton effect*.

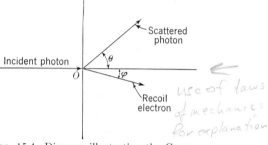

FIG. 15.4. Diagram illustrating the Compton effect.

Compton applied the quantum properties of radiant energy, according to which a beam of X rays is considered to consist of discrete bundles of energy $h\nu$, where $h$ is Planck's constant and $\nu$ is the frequency of the radiation. These quanta travel with the speed of light $c$ and possess momentum given by $h\nu/c$. The laws of the conservation of energy and the conservation of momentum are applied to the collision between an X-ray quantum and an electron in the scattering material. A diagram illustrating the interaction between the X-ray quantum or photon, and a free electron of mass $m$, assumed to be at rest at $O$ before collision, is shown in Fig. 15.4. As a result of the collision the electron recoils with a velocity $v$ in the direction making an angle $\varphi$ with the direction of the incident photon, and a photon with reduced energy is scattered in a direction making an angle $\theta$ with the direction of the original photon. The energy and momentum of the incident photon are, respectively, $h\nu$ and $h\nu/c$. The energy and momentum of the scattered photon are, respectively, $h\nu'$ and $h\nu'/c$, where $\nu'$ is the frequency of the scattered radiation. To obtain the energy and momentum of the recoil electron, it is necessary to make use of Einstein's principle of the equivalence of mass and energy. Einstein has shown, in his theory of relativity, that a mass $m$ is equivalent to an amount of energy $E$, the relation being

$$E = mc^2 \qquad (15.10)$$

where $c$ is the velocity of light. He has also shown that the inertial property of a particle varies with its velocity in accordance with the relation

$$m = \frac{m_0}{\sqrt{1 - (v/c)^2}} \qquad (15.11)$$

where $m_0$ is the mass of the particle at rest and $m$ its mass when it is moving with the velocity $v$. The total energy of the recoil electron is then a sum of its kinetic energy $E_k$ plus its rest mass energy. Hence

$$mc^2 = m_0c^2 + E_k$$

or, using Eq. (15.11), the kinetic energy of the recoil electron is

$$E_k = m_0c^2 \left[ \frac{1}{\sqrt{1 - (v/c)^2}} - 1 \right] \qquad (15.12)$$

and its momentum is

$$mv = \frac{m_0v}{\sqrt{1 - (v/c)^2}}$$

We may now apply the laws of mechanics to the problem. The equations for the conservation of momentum along the horizontal and vertical axes are

$$\frac{h\nu}{c} = \frac{h\nu'}{c} \cos \theta + m_0 v\beta \cos \varphi \qquad (15.13)$$

$$0 = \frac{h\nu'}{c} \sin \theta - m_0 v\beta \sin \varphi \qquad (15.14)$$

where we have set $\beta = (1 - v^2/c^2)^{-\frac{1}{2}}$. The equation for the conservation of energy is

$$h\nu = h\nu' + m_0c^2(\beta - 1) \qquad (15.15)$$

Eliminating $\varphi$ from Eqs. (15.13) and (15.14), we have

$$m_0^2 v^2 \beta^2 = \left(\frac{h\nu}{c}\right)^2 + \left(\frac{h\nu'}{c}\right)^2 - \frac{2h^2\nu\nu'}{c^2} \cos \theta$$

and dividing by $m_0^2 c^2$,

$$\frac{v^2\beta^2}{c^2} = \left(\frac{h\nu}{m_0c^2}\right)^2 + \left(\frac{h\nu'}{m_0c^2}\right)^2 - \frac{2h^2\nu\nu'}{m_0^2c^4} \cos \theta$$

From the value for $\beta$, we see that $v^2\beta^2/c^2 = \beta^2 - 1$, so that

$$\beta^2 - 1 = \left(\frac{h\nu}{m_0c^2}\right)^2 + \left(\frac{h\nu'}{m_0c^2}\right)^2 - \frac{2h^2\nu\nu'}{m_0^2c^4} \cos \theta \qquad (15.16)$$

Substituting the value of $\beta$ from Eq. (15.15) into Eq. (15.16) and simplifying leads to

$$\frac{1}{\nu'} - \frac{1}{\nu} = \frac{h}{m_0 c^2}(1 - \cos\theta) \qquad (15.17)$$

Equation (15.17) shows that, for $\theta = 0$, the incident and scattered photons have the same frequency. For all other angles of scattering the right-hand member of the equation is positive, and $\nu' < \nu$. The corresponding energy difference is taken up by the recoil electron. The longer wavelength shift is obtained by substituting the relations $\nu' = c/\lambda'$ and $\nu = c/\lambda$, giving

$$\lambda' - \lambda = \frac{h}{m_0 c}(1 - \cos\theta) \qquad (15.18)$$

The change in wavelength expressed by Eq. (15.18) is known as the *Compton shift,* and we see it is independent of the incident wavelength and depends on the angle of scattering. Using the values

$$h = 6.62 \times 10^{-27} \text{ erg sec}$$
$$m_0 = 9.10 \times 10^{-28} \text{ gm, and } c = 3.00 \times 10^{10} \text{ cm/sec}$$

$\lambda' - \lambda = 0.0242 \times 10^{-8}(1 - \cos\theta)$, which gives a maximum shift of 0.0485 A at $\theta = 180°$ and a shift of 0.0242 A at $\theta = 90°$. The shift at 90° was detected by Compton[1] in 1922 by scattering the characteristic $K$ molybdenum radiation from a carbon block. The equation for the Compton shift has also been derived by Schrödinger[2] using the modern wave mechanics.

The above analysis assumes that the electron is at rest. It has been extended[3] to take into account the fact that the electrons within the atoms move with various speeds in different directions. A correction term containing the precollision velocity of the electron shows there is actually a different wavelength shift for each collision. However, in observing the effect of a multitude of collisions the wavelength shift is on the side of increasing wavelength. When the electron is held firmly to the atom, so that it cannot be dislodged, the mass that enters in the Compton equation is that of the atom, which is the recoiling particle. For such impacts the shift is negligibly small, and the corresponding scattered radiation is the unmodified component.

The accurate agreement of Eq. (15.18) with experiment shows that the process of X-ray scattering is one in which there is a collision between

[1] A. H. Compton, *Bull. Natl. Research Council* 20, p. 16, 1922; *Phys. Rev.*, **21**, 715, 1923, **22**, 409, 1923.

[2] E. Schrödinger, Ann. Physik, **82**, 257, 1927.

[3] G. E. M. Jauncey, "Modern Physics," 3d ed., p. 328, D. Van Nostrand Company, Inc., 1948.

a photon and an electron of the type described. The Compton effect offers one of the most convincing forms of evidence that radiation has a corpuscular as well as a wavelike character.

It is only the unmodified radiation that is coherently scattered, the modified radiation being incoherently scattered. In our discussion of the use of X-ray diffraction in the determination of the structure of matter it is the coherent, or unmodified, radiation that is significant, and the modified, or Compton, scattered radiation must in general be sub-tracted from the total scattered radiation in the analysis of the experi-mental data. A more precise equation than the classical Thomson expression for the intensity of X rays scattered from free electrons has been derived by Klein and Nishina[1] using the modern methods of quan-tum mechanics. This expression holds down to X-ray wavelengths, where the scattering is almost entirely incoherent, and is thus used for calculating the numbers of quanta scattered and of recoil electrons.

We have seen that the process of absorption gives rise to an ejected photoelectron, and the process of scattering is accompanied by a recoil electron. Therefore the ratio of the observed number of photoelectrons to the observed recoil electrons should equal the ratio of the fluorescent coefficient to the scattering coefficient. Experiments have shown that this is true.

**15.7. Dispersion.** Another phenomenon that involves the interaction of a light wave with the electrons in an atom is dispersion. Dispersion of light manifests itself by a variation of refractive index with wavelength, or, as we have already indicated previously, by the quantity $dn/d\lambda$. By using a spectrometer like that shown in Fig. 8.19 and determining the angles of minimum deviation for different wavelengths the variation of the refractive index with wavelength may be obtained. A plot of $n$ against $\lambda$ yields for the prism material a dispersion curve which has the general form shown in Fig. 15.5. The curve illustrates what is designated as *normal dispersion* and shows an increase in refractive index with decreas-ing wavelength. The slope to the curve at any point, yielding the dispersion $dn/d\lambda$ at that point, is negative, and for different substances the slope for a given wavelength is generally greater in absolute value the larger the value of $n$. For the usual optical materials the visible range of wavelengths falls in a region somewhat as indicated in the figure. An empirical equation between $n$ and $\lambda$ that fits the curve very well in the visible region is the Cauchy dispersion formula

$$n = A + \frac{B}{\lambda^2} + \frac{C}{\lambda^4} \tag{15.19}$$

where $A$, $B$, and $C$ are constants for any one substance. In practice the

[1] O. Klein, and Y. Nishina, *Z. Physik*, **52**, 853, 1929.

constants may be evaluated from the dispersion curve by setting up three equations each containing a different pair of values for $n$ and $\lambda$.   A solution of these equations yields values of the constants.   Often it is sufficient to use the Cauchy formula with only two constants, the term in $\lambda^4$ being neglected.   Thus

$$n = A + \frac{B}{\lambda^2} \qquad (15.20)$$

*In Lab.*

which is a simpler expression to use for practical purposes.   Another empirical expression that gives an accurate representation, if the range of wavelengths is not too large, is that due to Hartmann,

$$n = n_0 + \frac{b}{\lambda - \lambda_0} \qquad (15.21)$$

where $n_0$, $\lambda_0$, and $b$ are constants to be determined from the observations.

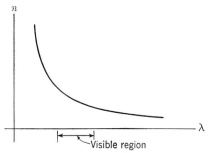

FIG. 15.5. Illustrating the form of the normal dispersion curve.

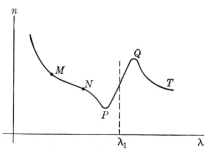

FIG. 15.6. Form of dispersion curve in the neighborhood of an absorption band. Anomalous dispersion.

When the refracting material shows selective absorption in the range of wavelengths, so that there are one or more absorption bands, the dispersion curve has an appearance like that shown in Fig. 15.6.   The region between $M$ and $N$ is normal in form, being approximately represented by one of the above empirical dispersion equations.   As an absorption band in the neighborhood of the absorption wavelength $\lambda_1$ is approached, the index of refraction decreases more rapidly in the region $NP$ than the Cauchy or Hartmann formulas can account for. Through the absorption band the change in refractive index follows the section $PQ$.   On the long-wavelength side of the absorption band the refractive index is high, decreasing rapidly, and then, beyond $T$, the curve takes on a form which is again represented approximately by a Cauchy or Hartmann formula with a new set of constants.   Within the absorption band it is extremely difficult to obtain the experimental portion $PQ$, although it has been measured, and in general the experimental data show a branch from $M$ to $P$ and then the branch from $Q$ to

*Separating light into its components colors*

*T*. On one side of the absorption band, *QT*, the dispersion is normal although it has abnormally high values for the refractive index, and on the other side, *NP*, the dispersion with respect to the normal branch is termed "anomalous" and has abnormally low values for the refractive index. In view of the fact that the refractive index is greater for the longer wavelengths in the neighborhood of an absorption band, this phenomenon is called *anomalous dispersion*. A prism made of iodine vapor has an absorption band in the visible region so that the red rays are here bent more than the violet. When there are present several absorption bands, the dispersion curve exhibits an anomalous curve in the neighborhood of each absorption band, with a normal dispersion curve lying between two absorption bands. All substances show selective absorption in some wavelength regions if the index of refraction is measured over a long spectral range.

An expression that represents the variation of the refractive index as an absorption band is approached from the short- and long-wavelength sides was first given by Sellmeier in 1871 and has the form

$$n^2 = 1 + \sum_j \frac{A_j \lambda^2}{\lambda^2 - \lambda_j^2} \tag{15.22}$$

This equation was derived by Sellmeier on the basis of the elastic-solid theory of light in which he supposed that the particles of the medium were subject to elastic forces and possessed natural frequencies of vibration. The effect of the light wave traveling through the medium was to impress a periodic oscillatory force so that the particles took up the motion characteristic of a forced vibration. In Eq. (15.22) $\lambda$ is the wavelength corresponding to the frequency of the incident light wave and the $A_j$'s are constants corresponding to the various natural frequencies or absorption wavelengths $\lambda_j$. The summation gives a series of similar terms to take care of the several absorption bands that the dispersing medium may have. Each term has its $\lambda_j$ and also $A_j$, which depends on the number of particles per unit volume having the natural frequency or wavelength $\lambda_j$. A plot of Eq. (15.22) for the simple case of two oscillators, $j = 1, 2$, is shown in Fig. 15.7. For this case Sellmeier's equation is

$$n^2 = 1 + \frac{A_1 \lambda^2}{\lambda^2 - \lambda_1^2} + \frac{A_2 \lambda^2}{\lambda^2 - \lambda_2^2}$$

For $\lambda = 0$, the curve starts at the value $n = 1$. As $\lambda$ increases, the curve falls, approaching a value $n = -\infty$ at resonance when $\lambda = \lambda_1$. On the long-wavelength side of $\lambda_1$ or $\lambda_2$ the refractive index has an abnormally large value, being infinite at the resonant wavelength. Between $\lambda_1$ and $\lambda_2$ the curve has an inflection point and again approaches large values toward $-\infty$ as $\lambda$ approaches the second natural frequency $\lambda_2$. On the long-wavelength side of $\lambda_2$ the curve decreases from a large positive value to the value $n = 1 + A_1 + A_2$ for large values of $\lambda$. Sellmeier's equation is thus successful in explaining the anomalous variation of a higher index of refraction for a longer wavelength than for some shorter wavelengths in the neighborhood of an absorption frequency. However since $n$ becomes $-\infty$ or $+\infty$ according as $\lambda$ approaches $\lambda_j$ from the short- or long-wavelength sides, Eq. (15.22) cannot represent the dispersion very close to an absorption band. For other regions Sellmeier's equation fits the experimental dispersion curve very well. In fact, the Cauchy equation is simply an approximation to Sellmeier's equation, and the student is asked to show this in the problems.

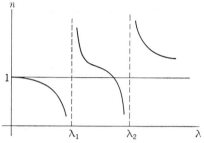

Fig. 15.7. Variation of refractive index with wavelength according to Sellmeier's dispersion formula for two natural frequencies.

**15.8. Theories of Dispersion.** We have seen that a theory like that of Sellmeier, although successful in explaining dispersion in regions not too close to an absorption band, fails to represent the experimental curve in the region $PQ$ of Fig. 15.6. This failure is due principally to the fact that Sellmeier's development does not consider that the oscillators as they vibrate experience a frictional resistance the effect of which increases as the frequency of the wave approaches the natural frequency of an oscillator, thus taking account of the absorption of energy of the wave. A theory based on the electromagnetic theory and on the electron theory of Lorentz and Drude yields an expression that is essentially representative of the variation of refractive index with wavelength. The development considers that the electrons of a dispersing medium are held to positions of equilibrium by linear restoring forces and are subject to resistances that are proportional to their velocities. A solution of the differential equation of the forced vibration motion of the electrons due to the interaction of the light wave with the oscillating electrons, and containing a damping term, leads to the equation

$$(n - i\kappa)^2 = 1 + 4\pi \sum_j \frac{N_j(e^2/m)}{\omega_j^2 - \omega^2 + i\omega g_j} \qquad (15.23)$$

where $e$ and $m$ are the electronic charge and mass, respectively, $N_j$ is the number of electrons or oscillators of the $j$th kind per unit volume having the natural angular velocities $\omega_j$ and the damping constants $g_j$ which determine the magnitude of the frictional forces acting, and $\omega$ is the angular velocity of the light wave. The symbol $i$ stands for the imaginary quantity $\sqrt{-1}$. The right-hand member of Eq. (15.23) necessitates introducing a complex quantity $n - i\kappa$, where $n$ is the index of refraction and $\kappa$ is called the *extinction coefficient*. Using $\omega_j = 2\pi c/\lambda_j$ and $\omega = 2\pi c/\lambda$, where $c$ is the velocity of light, Eq. (15.23) takes the form

$$(n - i\kappa)^2 = 1 + \sum_j \frac{A_j \lambda^2}{\lambda^2 - \lambda_j^2 + iG_j\lambda} \tag{15.24}$$

where we have placed $A_j = N_j e^2 \lambda_j^2 / \pi m c^2$ and $G_j = \lambda_j^2 g_j / 2\pi c$. Multiplying the numerator and denominator in the summation by the conjugate of the denominator and separating the real and imaginary parts leads to the two equations

$$n^2 - \kappa^2 = 1 + \sum_j \frac{A_j \lambda^2 (\lambda^2 - \lambda_j^2)}{(\lambda^2 - \lambda_j^2)^2 + G_j^2 \lambda^2} \tag{15.25}$$

and

$$2n\kappa = \sum_j \frac{A_j G_j \lambda^3}{(\lambda^2 - \lambda_j^2)^2 + G_j^2 \lambda^2} \tag{15.26}$$

The indicated summations make the equations applicable to as many absorption bands as the material may have. The extinction coefficient is related to the coefficient of absorption $\alpha$ in Eq. (15.1B) by the relation

$$\kappa = \frac{\lambda}{4\pi} \alpha \tag{15.27}$$

and signifies the fact that the ratio of the emergent to the incident intensity, when the light beam traverses a distance $x$ of material, is $e^{-4\pi\kappa x/\lambda}$. Graphs of Eqs. (15.25) and (15.26) for $n$ and $\kappa$ as a function of $\lambda$, for one natural frequency $\lambda_j = \lambda_1$, have the forms shown in Fig. 15.8. It is seen that the absorption curve has a maximum at $\lambda = \lambda_1$ and falls off rapidly on either side of $\lambda_1$, exhibiting the property of resonance. The index of refraction now represents the dispersion in the anomalous as well as in the normal regions. In the regions of high absorption $G_j$ is important, and $n$ does not go to infinity when $\lambda = \lambda_j$ as can be seen from the equations. When $\lambda$ is not near an absorption wavelength, both $\kappa$ and $G_j$ are negligible and the equations reduce to

$$n^2 = 1 + \sum_j \frac{A_j \lambda^2}{\lambda^2 - \lambda_j^2}$$

which is Sellmeier's equation holding well for regions of normal dispersion. Equation (15.23) applies strictly to the dispersion in gases, where it is assumed that the influence of neighboring molecules on a given molecule is negligible.   However, in the case of dispersion in solids and liquids, an added force acting on the electron, due to the charge separations in the neighboring molecules, must be included.   When this is done, an equation of precisely the same form as Eq. (15.23) is obtained, with the difference that in place of $\omega_j^2$ there appears the quantity $\omega_j^2 - (4\pi/3)N_j(e^2/m)$, amounting to an alteration in the natural frequencies.

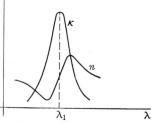

The phenomenon of scattering leads to a physical interpretation of dispersion.   The light scattered by the individual atoms of a substance interferes in the forward direction with the primary wave to produce a phase change in the primary wave.   This change in phase manifests itself as a change in the phase or wave velocity.   Since the phase of the scattered waves varies with the

FIG. 15.8. Variation of indices of refraction and absorption with wavelength.

frequency of the incident radiation, there results a change in velocity with frequency as the light wave enters a refracting medium.

The theory of dispersion thus far discussed is based on the classical concepts of the behavior of oscillating electrons.   According to the quantum theory the atoms and molecules of a material possess energy levels in which the electrons may exist, and the phenomenon of the emission and absorption of radiant energy is not associated with the oscillating frequencies but is accounted for by transitions between the energy levels.   The frequency $\nu$ associated with a transition from an energy level $E_2$ to an energy level $E_1$ is given by $(E_2 - E_1)/h$, where $h$ is Planck's constant.   We shall not develop the quantum-mechanical theory of dispersion, which is beyond the scope of this text, but when this is done, it proves to be true that the net result is essentially equivalent to that of the classical development.   However, there is a difference in the interpretation of the quantities appearing in the quantum dispersion formula, the frequencies appearing there being associated with the transitions between the energy states.

**15.9. Dispersion of a Prism.**   We have seen that the index of refraction varies with wavelength so that different wavelengths refracting through a prism are deviated by different amounts.   In Sec. 1.9 we saw that the angular dispersion for any two wavelengths represents the difference between the deviations for those wavelengths.   We are now in a position to define more rigorously the *angular dispersion* as the rate of change of the angle of deviation with wavelength.   If we consider the curve drawn for the angle of deviation $\delta$ as a function of the wavelength, the slope to this curve at any point gives the angular dispersion at that point and is represented by $d\delta/d\lambda$. For a prism this ratio is obtainable by multiplying the quantities $d\delta/dn$ and $dn/d\lambda$, giving

$$\frac{d\delta}{d\lambda} = \frac{d\delta}{dn}\frac{dn}{d\lambda} \qquad (15.28)$$

where $n$ is the index of refraction, $d\delta/dn$ is the rate of change of the angle of deviation with $n$, and $dn/d\lambda$ is the rate of change of $n$ with $\lambda$, or the dispersion of the prism. Expressions for the two quantities on the right of Eq. (15.28) may be obtained to yield an expression for the angular dispersion of a prism. The treatment on the left of the following double-column page is algebraic and geometric, while that on the right contains the calculus.

The quantity $dn/d\lambda$ may be obtained from Cauchy's or Hartmann's dispersion formulas, which, as we have seen, are satisfactory for ordinary transparent materials like glass or quartz. Thus using Cauchy's equation (15.20) and expressing the change in the refractive index $\Delta n$ corresponding to a change in wavelength $\Delta\lambda$, we have

$$n + \Delta n = A + \frac{B}{(\lambda + \Delta\lambda)^2}$$

Taking the difference between this equation and Eq. (15.20), we have

$$\Delta n = B\left[\frac{1}{(\lambda + \Delta\lambda)^2} - \frac{1}{\lambda^2}\right]$$

or

$$\frac{\Delta n}{\Delta\lambda} = \frac{-B(2\lambda + \Delta\lambda)}{\lambda^2(\lambda + \Delta\lambda)^2}$$

The quantity $\Delta n/\Delta\lambda$ gives the average change in $n$ in the region $\Delta\lambda$. What we want is the value of this ratio in the limit when $\Delta\lambda$ approaches zero. Of course, as $\Delta\lambda \to 0$, $\Delta n \to 0$; but the ratio of $\Delta n/\Delta\lambda$ remains finite, becoming $dn/d\lambda$, or the slope to the curve of $n$ plotted as a function of $\lambda$.

Using Cauchy's dispersion formula to evaluate $dn/d\lambda$ we have, differentiating Eq. (15.20) with respect to $\lambda$,

$$\frac{dn}{d\lambda} = \frac{-2B}{\lambda^3} \qquad (15.29A)$$

the negative sign indicating that $n$ decreases as $\lambda$ increases. To evaluate $d\delta/dn$, we make use of Eq. (1.15) relating the angle of deviation $\delta$ with $n$. Thus

$$\delta = \phi_1 + \sin^{-1}[(n^2 - \sin^2\phi_1)^{1/2} \sin A - \sin\phi_1\cos A] - A$$

The refracting angle of the prism is $A$, and the angle of incidence is $\phi_1$. Differentiating this equation with respect to $n$, keeping $\phi_1$ constant, gives

$$\frac{d\delta}{dn} = \frac{n(n^2 - \sin^2\phi)^{-1/2}\sin A}{\sqrt{1 - \sin^2\phi_2}}$$

which reduces to

$$\frac{d\delta}{dn} = \frac{\sin A}{\cos\phi_2\cos\phi_1'} \qquad (15.29B)$$

where $\phi_1'$ is the angle of refraction at the incident side of the prism and $\phi_2$ is the angle of emergence

Hence, setting $\Delta\lambda = 0$ in the last expression, we obtain

$$\frac{dn}{d\lambda} = \frac{-2B}{\lambda^3} \qquad (15.29a)$$

the minus sign indicating that $n$ decreases as $\lambda$ increases. The quantity $d\delta/dn$ is obtainable in a similar manner by utilizing Eq. (1.15) giving the angle of deviation $\delta$ as a function of $n$ and remembering that the angle of incidence $\phi_1$ is kept constant. We shall not carry this through, but the result is

$$\frac{d\delta}{dn} = \frac{\sin A}{\cos \phi_2 \cos \phi_1'} \qquad (15.29b)$$

where $A$ is the refracting angle of the prism, $\phi_1'$ is the angle of refraction at the incident side of the prism, and $\phi_2$ is the angle of emergence (see Fig. 1.10). The angular dispersion of the prism is therefore

$$\frac{d\delta}{d\lambda} = \frac{-2B \sin A}{\lambda^3 \cos \phi_2 \cos \phi_1'} \qquad (15.29c)$$

(see Fig. 1.10). Substituting Eqs. (15.29A) and (15.29B) into Eq. (15.28) yields for the angular dispersion of the prism

$$\frac{d\delta}{dn} = \frac{-2B \sin A}{\lambda^3 \cos \phi_2 \cos \phi_1'} \qquad (15.29C)$$

*rate of change of Δof deviation with n*

From Eq. (15.29c) or Eq. (15.29C) we observe that the dispersion of a prism of given refracting angle depends on the constant $B$, which in turn is characteristic of the glass, varies inversely as the cube of the wavelength, and is a function of the angle $\phi_1'$. The angle $\phi_2$ itself depends on $\phi_1$, $\phi_1'$, $A$, and $B$. For minimum deviation we have seen that $\phi_2 = \phi_1$ and $\phi_1' = A/2$. Then we have

$$\frac{d\delta}{d\lambda} = \frac{-2B \sin 2\phi_1'}{\lambda^3 \cos \phi_1 \cos \phi_1'} \qquad \sin 2\phi_1' = 2\sin \phi_1' \cos \phi_1'$$

or

$$\frac{d\delta}{d\lambda} = \frac{-4B \sin (A/2)}{\lambda^3 \cos \phi_1} \qquad (15.30)$$

which is the expression for the angular dispersion of a prism set for minimum deviation. The units of dispersion are radians (or degrees) per millimeter, centimeter, or angstrom. Often, instead of the angular dispersion of an instrument, one uses the *linear dispersion*, which has the units of millimeters or centimeters per angstrom and involves the focal length of the objective lens used to focus the emergent spectrum onto the photographic or observing surface. The reciprocal of linear dispersion, expressed as so many angstroms per millimeter, is also employed. For instance, if the dispersion is 5 A/mm in a certain region of the spectrum, this means that two spectrum lines whose wavelengths differ by 5 A have a separation on the photographic plate of 1 mm. In view of the fact that the dispersion of a prism varies inversely as the cube of the wavelength, the spectrum produced by a prism is very much extended or spread out on a larger scale for the violet end than it is for the red end. For this reason a prism does not produce a *normal* spectrum. We shall see in the next section that the spectrum produced by a grating is normal. Furthermore, as the equations show, a prism of one type of glass will produce spectral lines whose relative spacing is not in agreement with the relative spacing of the spectral lines produced by a prism of another type of glass. For this reason prismatic spectra are said to be *irrational*, and this is a consequence of the fact that the dispersion curve shown in Fig. 15.5 has a different shape for different substances.

**15.10. Dispersion of a Grating.** The angular dispersion of a ruled transmission grating is obtained by evaluating $d\theta/d\lambda$, using the grating equation $d \sin \theta = k\lambda$, where the angle of deviation here is the angle of diffraction. The student should have no difficulty in showing, either by differentiating the equation with respect to $\lambda$ or by using the method of the increments $\Delta\theta$ and $\Delta\lambda$, that the angular dispersion is given by

$$\frac{d\theta}{d\lambda} = \frac{k}{d \cos \theta} \qquad (15.31)$$

If the method of increments is used, it must be remembered that the limiting value of $\sin x/x$ as $x$ approaches zero has the value unity. We see that the angular dispersion depends on the order of the spectrum $k$, on the grating spacing $d$, and on $\theta$. For a given spectral order, the angular dispersion increases slowly with increasing angle $\theta$. In practice, the range of $\theta$ is small so that $\cos \theta$ remains approximately constant over a reasonable angular interval. Therefore the angular dispersion is very nearly proportional to the order of the spectrum, so that the $k$th-order spectrum is $k$ times as wide as the first-order spectrum. In a given order the angular dispersion is essentially constant, and the separation of two spectral lines is very nearly proportional to their wavelength difference. The spectrum produced by a grating is therefore normal, which, as we have seen, is not the case for a prismatic spectrum. Other advantages of a grating have been considered in Chap. 14.

## PROBLEMS

**15.1.** In Eq. (15.1*b*), $I$ can experimentally be obtained as a function of $x$. Describe what quantities are determinable by plotting the logarithm of $I$ as a function of $x$.

$mu$, $mu_m$, $mu_a$ – atomic absorption coeff
— mass absorption coefficient in x-rays
└ linear absorption coefficient in x-rays

ABSORPTION, SCATTERING, AND DISPERSION 329

**15.2.** Explain the mechanism of resonance radiation in accordance with the electromagnetic theory.

**15.3.** A piece of glass 0.200 cm thick transmits 0.040 per cent of the light incident upon it. What are the absorption and transmission coefficients?

**15.4.** The mass absorption coefficient of X rays at 0.710 A for nickel is 48.1/gm/cm². The density of nickel is 8.75 gm/cm³. For what thickness nickel will the intensity of the X-ray beam be reduced to one-third its initial value?

**15.5.** Remembering that the mass absorption coefficient is the absorption per gram per square centimeter, find the mass absorption coefficient of $Al_2O_3$ for X rays of wavelength 0.710 A. At this wavelength the mass absorption coefficients of aluminum and oxygen are, respectively, 5.22/gm/cm² and 1.22/gm/cm². The atomic weight of aluminum is 27.0, and that of oxygen is 16.0. (HINT: The mass absorption coefficient of an element is the same whether the element is in combination with other elements or not. Find how many grams of Al and O there are in 1 gm of $Al_2O_3$.)

**15.6.** The mass absorption coefficient for X rays at a wavelength of 0.710 A is 0.605/gm/cm² for carbon. Using Eq. (15.8), find the mass absorption coefficient for a wavelength of 0.631 A.

**15.7.** The atomic weight of aluminum is 27, and its atomic number is 13. (a) Find the number of scattering electrons in 1 gm of aluminum. (b) Using Thomson's classical formula [Eq. (15.9)], calculate the mass scattering coefficient. For what wavelengths would this value hold?

**15.8.** (a) From the equations for the Compton wavelength shift show that

$$\cot (\theta/2) = [1 + (h\nu/m_0c^2)] \tan \varphi$$

(b) Show also that the kinetic energy of the recoiling electron is given by

$$E_k = h\nu \frac{2\alpha \cos^2 \varphi}{(1 + \alpha)^2 - \alpha^2 \cos^2 \varphi}$$

where $\alpha = h\nu/m_0c^2$.

**15.9.** Calculate the shift in wavelength given by Compton's equation for the angles 0°, 30°, 45°, 90°.

**15.10.** Plot a polar graph of Eq. (15.18) showing $\Delta\lambda = \lambda' - \lambda$ as a function of $\theta$.

**15.11.** The index of refraction as a function of the wavelength for fused quartz is given in the accompanying table. Plot a dispersion curve. Using three pairs of

| $\lambda$, A | 3034 | 3404 | 3968 | 4358 | 4800 | 5461 | 5893 | 6563 | 7065 |
|---|---|---|---|---|---|---|---|---|---|
| $n$ | 1.486 | 1.479 | 1.471 | 1.467 | 1.463 | 1.460 | 1.458 | 1.456 | 1.455 |

values $n$, $\lambda$, obtain three simultaneous equations by using Cauchy's equation (15.19); the three pairs should be chosen at the beginning, at the middle, and at the end of the range. From this evaluate the constants $A$, $B$, and $C$. Plot the resulting Cauchy equation with the determined constants from 3000 to 7000 A on the same graph. Determine the constants in Eq. (15.20), and plot the resulting equation on the same graph. Determine the constants in Eq. (15.21), and plot the resulting equation on the same graph. The final graph should show an experimental curve, a three-constant Cauchy curve, a two-constant Cauchy curve, and a Hartmann curve. Which of the curves more nearly represents the data?

**15.12.** What is the angular dispersion of a prism of refracting angle 60° and set for minimum deviation? The radiation of wavelength 5000 A is incident at an angle of

50°.  Use Eq. (15.30), in which $B = 1.50 \times 10^6$ A.  Express the result in radians per angstrom and radians per centimeter.

**15.13.**  Show that Sellmeier's equation $n^2 = 1 + [A_1\lambda^2/(\lambda^2 - \lambda_1^2)]$ leads to Cauchy's equation when $\lambda \gg \lambda_1$.

**15.14.**  Show that the angular dispersion of a prism is given by $d\delta/d\lambda = -2Bt/a\lambda^3$, where $a$ is the width of the rectangular section of the beam formed by the prism and $t$ is the width of the prism base (see Fig. 14.3).  Assume that the dispersion is given by Cauchy's equation (15.20).

**15.15.**  Show that the angular dispersion of an echelon grating for small angles of deviation is given by $d\theta/d\lambda = [(n - 1) - \lambda \, dn/d\lambda] \, t_0/b\lambda$, where $t_0$ and $b$ are as shown in Fig. 14.4$b$.

# CHAPTER 16

## POLARIZATION

One of the most significant facts concerning the nature of a wave is that it is transverse in character. Maxwell's electromagnetic theory requires that the light vibrations be transverse, the electric and magnetic variations comprising the electromagnetic disturbance being in mutually perpendicular planes which are transverse to the direction of propagation of the wave. The experimental proof that light is transverse is afforded by a study of the polarization of light, as we shall see in this chapter. It will be recalled (Sec. 11.4) that *unpolarized* light possesses symmetry around the direction of propagation and that when the light is made to take on some form of asymmetrical character, as when all directions of vibration except one are quenched, the light is then polarized. We shall see that in addition to such linear or plane polarization there can be produced circular and elliptical polarization.

We first take up the various methods of producing polarized light, and we shall see that these entail the phenomena of reflection, refraction, scattering, double refraction, and absorption. We then consider the phenomenon of the interference of polarized light. Last, we shall study some of the principles of *optical activity*, a property possessed by certain substances which have the ability to rotate the plane of polarization of polarized light that passes through them. It must be realized at the outset that some of these branches of study are vast in scope and application. Our primary aim here is to present enough of the material to equip the student with a fundamental knowledge of the phenomena, of the principles involved, and of some of the applications of polarized light in the fields of optics and optical engineering.

**16.1. The Fresnel Equations.** In Sec. 11.4 we stated the Fresnel equations [Eqs. (11.14) to (11.17)] for reflection and refraction and used them to show that there occurs a phase change of 180° when a light wave reflects from an optically denser medium. We shall here derive the equations in accordance with electromagnetic theory and then employ them to indicate the character of polarization of the reflected and refracted beams. For this purpose Fig. 11.12a,b is repeated as Fig. 16.1a,b. At this point the student should reread Sec. 11.4, where it was explained that a beam of ordinary unpolarized light may be considered as composed of two electric vibrations in two mutually perpendicular planes which are both transverse to the direction of beam travel.   In accordance with the plan outlined in Sec. 11.4, Fig. 16.1a shows the incident light as plane-polarized with the electric vector in the plane of incidence (the plane of the figure), and Fig. 16.1b considers the incident light plane-polarized with the electric vector perpendicular to the plane of incidence and indicated by the symbol $(\cdot)$.   The angle of incidence (and reflection) is $\phi$ in medium $n_1$, and the angle of refraction is $\phi'$ in medium $n_2$.   The electric amplitudes of the incident  reflected  and refracted (transmitted)

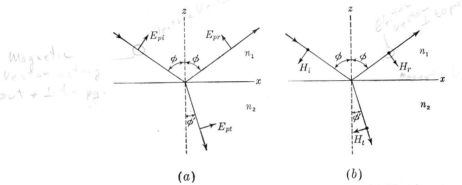

**(a)**                                    **(b)**

FIG. 16.1.  Reflection and refraction of a plane-polarized wave.   (a) Electric vector parallel to the plane of incidence.   (b) Electric vector perpendicular to the plane of incidence.

light vibrating parallel to the plane of incidence are represented, respectively, by $E_{pi}$, $E_{pr}$, and $E_{pt}$.   The magnetic vectors accompanying each of these, shown in Fig. 16.1a, are acting out and normal to the plane of the figure.   The electric amplitudes of the incident, reflected, and refracted (transmitted) light vibrating normal to the plane of incidence are represented, respectively, by $E_{Ni}$, $E_{Nr}$, and $E_{Nt}$, which are acting normal and out of the plane of Fig. 16.1b, which also shows the corresponding magnetic vectors.

Maxwell's electromagnetic theory is embodied in four differential equations which we need not state here; these contain the vectors $E$, $H$, $D$, and $B$.   The electric-intensity vector $E$ and the magnetic-intensity vector $H$ are the ones with which we have been dealing.   The electric-displacement vector $D$ is defined by $D = \epsilon E$, where $\epsilon$ is the dielectric constant of the medium, and the magnetic-induction vector $B$ is given by $B = \mu H$, where $\mu$ is the magnetic permeability of the medium.   The equations reveal that the velocity $v$ of an electromagnetic wave, in a medium whose constants are $\epsilon$ and $\mu$, is given by $v = c/\sqrt{\epsilon\mu}$, where $c$ is the velocity of light in free space.   Hence the refractive index is given by $n = \sqrt{\epsilon\mu}$.   Now at the interface separating the medium of refractive index $n_1$ from that of refractive index $n_2$ the refractive index has a sudden change, and certain *boundary conditions* must be fulfilled in order that the change in the electric and magnetic forces across the boundary be continuous and not abrupt. By applying Maxwell's equations to small regions containing the interface the following boundary conditions obtain at a surface of discontinuity of the type we are considering, *i.e.*, for a transparent dielectric: *The normal components of D and B on one side of the boundary are equal, respectively, to those on the other side of the boundary, and the tangential components of E and H on one side of the boundary are equal, respectively, to those on the other side of the boundary.* An application of these boundary conditions to the cases given in Fig. 16.1 yields the Fresnel equations.

First consider Fig. 16.1a. Applying the condition of continuity of the normal components of $D$, we have, remembering that for a transparent dielectric $\mu \doteq 1$ and $D = \epsilon E = n^2 H$,

$$n_1^2 E_{pi} \sin \phi + n_1^2 E_{pr} \sin \phi = n_2^2 E_{pt} \sin \phi'$$ boundary conditions

or

$$E_{pi} \sin \phi + E_{pr} \sin \phi = {}_1 n_2^2 E_{pt} \sin \phi' \qquad (16.1)$$

where ${}_1 n_2 = n_2/n_1$ is the relative index of refraction. There are no normal components of $B$. The continuity of the tangential components of $E$ yields

$$E_{pi} \cos \phi - E_{pr} \cos \phi = E_{pt} \cos \phi' \qquad (16.2)$$

The tangential components of $H$, using the fact, obtainable from Maxwell's equations, that $H = nE$, gives

$$n_1 E_{pi} + n_1 E_{pr} = n_2 E_{pt}$$ conditions for tang. of H

or

$$E_{pi} + E_{pr} = {}_1 n_2 E_{pt} \qquad (16.3)$$

Observe that when Snell's law $\sin \phi = {}_1 n_2 \sin \phi'$ is substituted in Eq. (16.1), there results Eq. (16.3). We now have

$$E_{pi} - E_{pr} = \frac{E_{pt} \cos \phi'}{\cos \phi} \quad \text{and} \quad E_{pi} + E_{pr} = {}_1 n_2 E_{pt}$$ 16.13

Adding these equations, we have

$$\frac{E_{pt}}{E_{pi}} = \frac{2 \cos \phi \sin \phi'}{\cos \phi' \sin \phi' + \cos \phi \sin \phi}$$

or

$$\frac{E_{pt}}{E_{pi}} = \frac{2 \cos \phi \sin \phi'}{\sin (\phi + \phi') \cos (\phi - \phi')} \qquad (16.4)$$ juggling tug. Math

Substitution into the second of the paired equations obtains

$$E_{pi} + E_{pr} = \frac{2 \sin \phi \cos \phi}{\sin (\phi + \phi') \cos (\phi - \phi')} E_{pi}$$

which reduces to

$$\frac{E_{pr}}{E_{pi}} = \frac{\tan (\phi - \phi')}{\tan (\phi + \phi')} \tag{16.5}$$

Equation (16.4) gives the fraction of the original amplitude refracted, and Eq. (16.5) gives the fraction of the original amplitude reflected when the electric vector of the incident wave is parallel to the plane of incidence.

Now consider Fig. 16.1*b*.   There are no normal components of $D$ here. From the continuity of the normal components of $B$ we have, remembering that $B = H = nE$ for a transparent dielectric,

$$-n_1 E_{Ni} \sin \phi - n_1 E_{Nr} \sin \phi = n_2 E_{Nt} \sin \phi'$$

or

$$E_{Ni} \sin \phi + E_{Nr} \sin \phi = {}_1 n_2 E_{Nt} \sin \phi' \tag{16.6}$$

From the continuity of the tangential components of $E$,

$$E_{Ni} + E_{Nr} = E_{Nt} \tag{16.7}$$

and for the tangential components of $H$ to be continuous

$$-n_1 E_{Ni} \cos \phi + n_1 E_{Nr} \cos \phi = -n_2 E_{Nt} \cos \phi'$$

or

$$-E_{Ni} \cos \phi + E_{Nr} \cos \phi = -{}_1 n_2 E_{Nt} \cos \phi' \tag{16.8}$$

Again we see that substitution of $\sin \phi = {}_1 n_2 \sin \phi'$ into Eq. (16.6) leads to Eq. (16.7).   We now have

$$E_{Ni} + E_{Nr} = E_{Nt}$$
$$E_{Ni} - E_{Nr} = \frac{{}_1 n_2 E_{Nt} \cos \phi'}{\cos \phi}$$

Adding these equations leads to

$$\frac{E_{Nt}}{E_{Ni}} = \frac{2 \sin \phi' \cos \phi}{\sin (\phi + \phi')} \tag{16.9}$$

and using the first of the paired equations gives

$$\frac{E_{Nr}}{E_{Ni}} = \frac{-\sin (\phi - \phi')}{\sin (\phi + \phi')} \tag{16.10}$$

Equation (16.9) gives the fraction of the original amplitude refracted, and Eq. (16.10) gives the fraction of the original amplitude reflected when the electric vector of the incident wave is normal to the plane of incidence.   Equations (16.4), (16.5), (16.9), and (16.10) are the Fresnel formulas.   By squaring Eqs. (16.5) and (16.10) we obtain the ratios of the reflected intensity to the original intensity for each case, thus,

$$\frac{I_{pr}}{I_{pi}} = \frac{\tan^2 (\phi - \phi')}{\tan^2 (\phi + \phi')} \tag{16.11}$$

and

$$\frac{I_{Nr}}{I_{Ni}} = \frac{\sin^2 (\phi - \phi')}{\sin^2 (\phi + \phi')} \tag{16.12}$$

where $I_{pr}$ and $I_{pi}$ represent the intensity of the reflected and incident beams, respectively, when the electric vector is parallel to the plane of incidence and $I_{Nr}$ and $I_{Ni}$ represent the intensity of the reflected and incident beams, respectively, when the electric vector is perpendicular to the plane of incidence. These ratios represent the reflecting powers in each case. From the conservation of energy we have

$$I_{pr} + I_{pt} = I_{pi}$$

which we can use to obtain the expression for $I_{pt}$, the intensity of the refracted beam. Thus

$$\frac{I_{pt}}{I_{pi}} = 1 - \frac{I_{pr}}{I_{pt}} = 1 - \frac{E_{pr}^2}{E_{pi}^2}$$
$$= \frac{(E_{pi} - E_{pr})(E_{pi} + E_{pr})}{E_{pi}^2}$$

and using the appropriate paired equations above,

$$\frac{I_{pt}}{I_{pi}} = {}_1n_2 \frac{E_{pt}^2 \cos \phi'}{E_{pi}^2 \cos \phi} \tag{16.13}$$

In the same way

$$\frac{I_{Nt}}{I_{Ni}} = {}_1n_2 \frac{E_{Nt}^2 \cos \phi'}{E_{Ni}^2 \cos \phi} \tag{16.14}$$

Therefore the intensity ratios of the refracted beam in each case depends not only on the ratios of the corresponding squares of the amplitudes but also on the relative index of refraction and on the ratio $\cos \phi'/\cos \phi$, which factor takes care of the change in cross-sectional area of the refracted beam.

It is clear that if the incident light is linearly or plane-polarized with the electric vector vibrating in a direction making an angle with the plane of incidence, then the electric vector may be considered as having a $p$ component parallel to the plane of incidence and an $N$ component normal to the plane of incidence. Equations (16.11) and (16.12) then give the amount of each component reflected.

**16.2. Polarization by Reflection and Refraction.** Since unpolarized light may be considered as being made up of two mutually perpendicular linearly polarized beams having a $p$ and an $N$ component, we may apply the Fresnel equations to ascertain the state of polarization of the reflected and refracted beams when light is incident on a transparent dielectric. Equations (16.11) and (16.12) show that, for normal incidence $\phi = 0°$, $I_{pr} = I_{pi}$ and $I_{Nr} = I_{Ni}$, so that the $p$ and $N$ components are equal, remembering that for unpolarized light $E_{pi} = E_{Ni}$. In this case we have seen [Eqs. (11.18) and (11.19)] that the reflecting power is given by $[(_1n_2 - 1)/(_1n_2 + 1)]^2$, which for $_1n_2 = 1.5$ has the value $\frac{1}{25}$, or 4 per cent. For $\phi = 90°$, Eqs. (16.4) and (16.9) show that there is no refracted beam and both components are entirely reflected. There is one angle of incidence $\phi = \bar{\phi}$ for which there is no reflected $p$ component. By setting Eq. (16.11) equal to zero, we see that at this angle $\bar{\phi} + \phi' = 90°$ and the reflected component is plane-polarized with the electric vector vibrating perpendicular to the plane of incidence. The angle $\bar{\phi}$ is known as the *polarizing angle*, or *principal angle* of incidence. Since, at the polarizing angle, the incident and refracted rays are at right angles to each other, there results from Snell's law

$$\sin \bar{\phi} = {}_1n_2 \sin (90 - \bar{\phi}) = {}_1n_2 \cos \bar{\phi}$$

or

$$\tan \bar{\phi} = {}_1n_2 \tag{16.15}$$

a relationship that expresses the polarizing angle in terms of the relative index of refraction and is known as Brewster's law. Thus the polarizing angle for a given material varies with the wavelength, although in the visible region this variation for the usual glass is not much. For $_1n_2 = 1.54$, Eq. (16.15) gives for the polarizing angle 57°. At this angle Eq. (16.12) yields

$$\frac{I_{Nr}}{I_{Ni}} = \sin^2 (2\bar{\phi} - 90) = \cos^2 2\bar{\phi} = \left(\frac{1 - {}_1n_2^2}{1 + {}_1n_2^2}\right)^2 = 0.165$$

or about 16.5 per cent of the component normal to the plane of incidence is reflected, the remaining 83.5 per cent being refracted. For all angles of incidence other than 90° Eqs. (16.4) and (16.9) show that the refracted beam contains both components in unequal amounts so that it is partially polarized. For a partially polarized beam the degree of polarization is expressed by the equation

$$\% \text{ polarization} = \frac{I_p - I_N}{I_p + I_N} 100 \tag{16.16}$$

where $I_p$ and $I_N$ are the intensities corresponding, respectively, to the components vibrating parallel and perpendicular to the plane of incidence. For instance, at the polarizing angle we have, for the refracted beam,

$$\% \text{ polarization} = \frac{100 - 83.5}{100 + 83.5} 100 = 8.8\%$$

The facts so far obtained may be illustrated by the diagrams in Fig. 16.2, showing an unpolarized beam incident at the air-glass interface (a) at an angle $\phi \neq \bar{\phi}$ and (b) at an angle $\phi = \bar{\phi}$. The vibrations in the incident unpolarized light are represented by the symbol ($\updownarrow$) indicating the component parallel to the plane of incidence and by the symbol (·) indicating the component perpendicular to the plane of incidence.

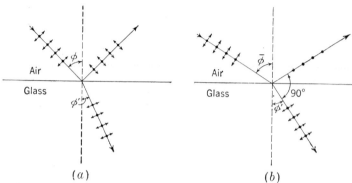

Air

Glass

90°

(a)                              (b)

FIG. 16.2. Reflection and refraction of unpolarized light for an angle of incidence (a) not equal to and (b) equal to the polarizing angle.

The amplitudes of these components, $E_{pi}$ and $E_{Ni}$, are equal for the unpolarized light. In (a) both the reflected and refracted rays are partially plane-polarized. In (b) the angle of incidence is the polarizing angle so that the reflected ray is plane-polarized with the electric vector vibrating perpendicular to the plane of incidence and the refracted ray is partially plane-polarized, the percentage polarization for $\bar{\phi} = 57°$ being 8.8 per cent. Here the transverse character of a light wave is clearly revealed. When the refracted ray is perpendicular to the reflected ray, none of the component vibrating parallel to the plane of incidence in the refracted ray can exist in the reflected

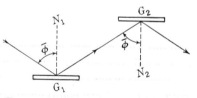

FIG. 16.3. Polarization by reflection from two glass reflectors.

ray, since then a longitudinal disturbance should appear in the reflected ray which is contrary to experimental observation.

By permitting the reflected ray in Fig. 16.2b to reflect off another surface, the presence of the polarization may be convincingly demonstrated. The demonstration makes use of the components illustrated in Fig. 16.3, The two glass plates $G_1$ and $G_2$, shown in cross section, are so positioned that the unpolarized light beam is incident on $G_1$ at the polarizing angle $\bar{\phi}$ and the reflected beam from $G_1$ is incident at the angle $\bar{\phi}$ on $G_2$. As the glass plate $G_2$ is rotated about the line $G_1G_2$ as axis, starting when the normals $N_1$ and $N_2$ are parallel, it is found that the light intensity reflected from $G_2$ decreases from a maximum down to zero for a rotation of $90°$, then increases to the same maximum with further rotation at $180°$, then decreases to zero at $270°$, and increases to the maximum at $360°$. The reason for this is clear when we remember that the plane of incidence in any case is defined by the plane in which lie the incident ray, the reflected ray, and the normal to the reflecting surface. When the normals to $G_1$ and $G_2$ are parallel, both planes of incidence are parallel and the vibrations perpendicular to the plane of incidence of $G_1$ appear in the reflected beam from $G_2$. When $G_2$ is rotated, keeping $\bar{\phi}$ fixed, the normal $N_2$ makes various angles with the plane of incidence of $G_1$, and when the rotation is $90°$ or $270°$, $N_2$ lies in a plane perpendicular to the plane of incidence of $G_2$. Hence the vibrations in the reflected beam of $G_1$ are parallel to the plane of incidence of $G_2$, which reflects zero intensity. For intermediate angles of rotation of $G_2$, only a component of the vibration is in a direction perpendicular to its plane of incidence.

In referring to a linearly or plane-polarized beam it is important to specify the *plane of vibration,* or the plane in which the electric vector of the polarized beam is vibrating. The student, however, should be acquainted with the fact that older texts and treatises on polarization refer to the *plane of polarization.* The plane of polarization was originally defined as that particular plane of incidence in which polarized light is reflected by the maximum amount. This designation was made before the true nature of the light vibrations was known. What is called the plane of polarization is actually at right angles to the plane of vibration. We shall avoid using the older term and continue to make designations in terms of the plane in which the electric vector vibrates.

**16.3. Polarization by a Pile of Plates.** We have seen that when light is incident on a glass surface at the polarizing angle, the reflected beam removes about 16.5 per cent of the light vibrating perpendicular to the plane of incidence and the refracted beam is partially plane-polarized, containing all the light vibrating parallel to the plane of incidence. If a beam of light is incident at the polarizing angle on a pile of thin parallel-faced plates laid one on top of the other, then at each reflection more of the component vibrating perpendicular to the plane of incidence is removed, with the result that the reflected beams form light that is plane-polarized with the electric vector vibrating perpendicular to the plane of incidence and the transmitted beam is almost plane-polarized with the electric vector vibrating parallel to the plane of incidence. For a pile of 10 plates of refractive index 1.54 the percentage polarization of the transmitted beam is about 67 per cent, for 20 plates it is about 80 per cent, and for 45 plates it is about 90 per cent. Since a pile of plates effectively separates the light into its two linearly polarized beams and thus produces plane-polarized light, it is called a *polarizer*. If two such piles are mounted in tandem, as shown in Fig. 16.4, the first pile receiving the light acts as a polarizer transmitting vibrations parallel to the plane of incidence. The second pile of plates, placed as shown, will also transmit this parallel component, but if it is rotated about the direction of the beam passing through it as an axis, the transmitted intensity gradually diminishes until it is practically extinguished after a 90° rotation. Then its plane of incidence is perpendicular to the vibration plane of the polarized beam incident upon it, and practically all the light is reflected. In a 360° rotation there will be two positions of maximum and two positions of minimum transmission. When used in this fashion, the

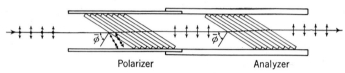

Polarizer          Analyzer

Fig. 16.4. Two piles of plates acting as polarizer and analyzer.

second pile of plates is called an *analyzer*. The analyzer not only indicates that the light falling upon it is linearly polarized but also is able to reveal its vibration plane.

The transmitted intensity is a function of the angle of rotation of the analyzer or the angle that the electric vector of the linearly polarized light makes with the transmission plane of the analyzer. We have met a similar situation in the case of Fig. 16.3, where $G_2$ acts as an analyzer on the linearly polarized beam reflected from $G_1$. In any case, when the analyzer is so oriented that the electric vector of the polarized beam of amplitude $E_0$ makes an angle $\theta$ with the transmission plane of the analyzer, then the component $E_0 \sin \theta$, perpendicular to the transmission plane, is not transmitted, while the component $E_0 \cos \theta$ gets through the analyzer. Therefore the intensity $I$ transmitted through the analyzer is given by $E_0^2 \cos^2 \theta$, or

$$I = I_0 \cos^2 \theta \qquad (16.17)$$

where $I_0$ is the intensity of the linearly polarized light incident on the analyzer. The variation of the intensity with the square of the angle was experimentally discovered by Malus in 1809, and Eq. (16.17) is known as the *law of Malus*. The law, of course, holds strictly when the light falling on the analyzer is entirely linearly polarized, which is true in Fig. 16.3 and very nearly so for the pile of plates. The equation does not take into account losses due to absorption, which would alter the value of $I_0$. When the angle between the transmission directions of polarizer and analyzer is 0°, Eq. (16.17) shows that the transmitted light has a maximum intensity. When this angle $\theta = 90°$, the transmitted light is zero and in this case the polarizer and analyzer are said to be *crossed*.

**16.4. Polarization by Scattering.** In Sec. 15.3, Fig. 15.2, it was shown that the scattering process may be considered as due to the vibrations of the induced dipoles, resulting in light which is linearly polarized when observed in a direction at right angles to the direction of the incident unpolarized light. In other directions the light is only partially polarized. We have seen that the blue light from the sky is accounted for by the Rayleigh scattering formula [Eq. (15.4a)], and this blue light, in accordance with the mechanism of scattering, is polarized, as can be tested with an analyzer. The polarization, however, is not complete owing to the occurrence of multiple scattering by the molecules of the atmosphere.

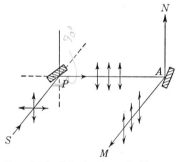

FIG. 16.5. Polarization of X rays using a polarizer *P* (scatterer) and analyzer *A* (scatterer).

The experiments performed by Barkla[1] in 1906 on the polarization of X rays proved that they were transverse waves. The experiment, which was repeated with improved apparatus in 1924 by Compton and Hagenow,[2] was made with an arrangement like that illustrated in Fig. 16.5. Unpolarized X rays, collimated in the direction *SP*, were incident on a scatterer at *P*, which here acts as a polarizer. In a direction *PA*, at 90° from *SP*, the electromagnetic theory predicts that the light is linearly polarized with the vibration plane as shown. To show that this is so, another scatterer at *A*, acting as analyzer, was used. The rescattered X rays, examined in the direction *AN*, showed zero intensity and in the direction *AM* showed a maximum intensity, thus establishing the transverse character of X rays.

**16.5. Polarization by Double Refraction.** Up to this point we have been concerned with optical media which are homogeneous and *isotropic*, *i.e.*, the velocity of light through them is independent of the direction of light travel and of the polarization of the light wave. There are other transparent media, on the other hand, such as the crystals calcite, tourmaline, and quartz which are homogeneous but *anisotropic*, *i.e.*, they exhibit different optical properties in different directions of light travel through them. For instance they are *birefracting*, causing a beam incident upon them, under the proper conditions, to refract into two separated beams. The doubly refracting crystals may be classified as *uniaxial* or *biaxial*.

[1] C. G. Barkla, *Proc. Roy. Soc.* (*London*), **A77**, 247, 1906.

[2] A. H. Compton and C. F. Hagenow, *J. Optical Soc. Am.* and *Rev. Sci. Instruments*, **8**, 487, 1924.

*Uniaxial*

In the former there is one preferred direction, called the *optic axis*, along which the two sets of refracted waves travel with the same velocity, and in the latter there are two such preferred directions along which the velocities are the same. *Biaxial* Our treatment will be concerned only with the uniaxial type, which are exemplified by calcite, tourmaline, and quartz. The crystals topaz and aragonite are examples of the biaxial type.

The uniaxial doubly refracting crystal calcite ($CaCO_3$), or *Iceland spar*, which has the rhombohedral crystalline form, is illustrated in Fig. 16.6. At the two opposite corners $A$ and $B$ the angles formed by the three faces are the same and equal to $101°55'$. At the other corners there are formed two angles of magnitude $78°5'$ and one angle of $101°55'$. The optic axis of the crystal is a direction parallel to the line drawn through corner $B$, making equal angles with the three edges that meet there. A plane that contains the optic axis and is perpendicular to

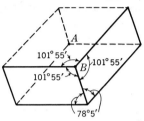

FIG. 16.6. The calcite crystal.

two opposite faces of the rhomb is called a *principal section*. Since there are an infinite number of lines parallel to the direction defined by the optic axis, there are an infinite number of principal sections. A principal section cuts the rhomb surfaces in a parallelogram whose angles are $71°$ and $109°$. At this point the student should study an actual calcite crystal or, better still, make a model from a piece of soap or modeling clay which can be pierced by a toothpick to obtain the optic-axis direction and cut to form a principal section.

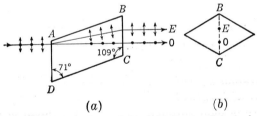

(a)                                    (b)

FIG. 16.7. Double refraction through a calcite crystal. (a) Principal section of crystal. (b) End view looking toward $BC$ from the right.

Let us now consider what happens when an unpolarized light beam is incident normally on the surface of a calcite crystal. In Fig. 16.7a, $ABCD$ is a principal section, and a beam of light is shown incident on a face of the crystal. Inside the crystal the beam breaks up into two beams, one of which, $O$, passes through the crystal undeviated and the other, $E$, is refracted as shown and emerges parallel to the $O$ beam. The $O$ ray, called the *ordinary ray*, obeys Snell's law of refraction for all angles of incidence of the light beam. The $E$ ray, refracting for normal incidence, is called the *extraordinary ray* and does not obey Snell's law, the ratio of the sine of the angle of incidence to the sine of the angle of refraction varying with the angle of incidence.  Since Snell's law physically represents the ratio of the velocity of light in vacuum to that in the medium, it is clear that the velocity of the *O* ray in the crystal is the same in all directions, whereas the velocity of the *E* ray in the crystal is different in different directions.  For a uniaxial crystal the one direction along which the velocity of the *E* ray is equal to that of the *O* ray is that which is parallel to the optic axis.  The *O* ray in the medium is always in the plane of incidence.  In general this is not true for the *E* ray.  When the plane of incidence is a principal section, as in Fig. 16.7*a*, the *E* ray is to be found also in the plane of incidence.  In addition to the principal section there are also designated the *principal planes*, one for the *O* ray, containing this ray and the optic axis, and the other for the *E* ray, containing this ray and the optic axis.  In the case illustrated in Fig. 16.7*a*, the plane of incidence is a principal section so that the principal planes of the *O* and *E* rays are also in the principal section.  This, however, is not in general the case, and the principal planes of the *O* and *E* rays are not in general coincident, since the principal planes vary with the direction of the light, while the principal section is fixed by the orientation of the crystal surface in relation to the optic axis.

If we consider that the face *AD* is placed down on a piece of paper on which a dot has been made, we should see the two images *O* and *E* on looking at the top face *BC*.  The line joining the images is in a principal section, and either lies along the shorter diagonal, as shown in Fig. 16.7*b*, or is parallel to this direction *BC*.  Thus when the crystal is rotated about a vertical axis passing through the dot, the image *O* remains fixed in position but the image *E* rotates in a circle around the *O* image, keeping the line through the images parallel to *BC* in Fig. 16.7*b*.

When the *O* and *E* rays of Fig. 16.7*b* are examined by an analyzer, it is found that the *O* ray is plane-polarized with the vibration plane perpendicular to the principal section and the *E* ray is plane-polarized with its vibration plane in the principal section as shown in Fig. 16.7*a*.  The effect of the crystal then is to break the light up into two linearly polarized component rays whose vibration planes are perpendicular to each other, so that when the analyzer shows a maximum intensity for the *E* ray it also shows the *O* ray to be absent.  A rotation of the analyzer by 90° shows the *O* ray to have maximum intensity and the *E* ray to be absent. The law of Malus holds for all angles of rotation of the analyzer.

The phenomenon of double refraction, or *birefringence*, for calcite has made it possible to produce a very convenient polarizer and hence analyzer.  Since the *O* and *E* rays are each linearly polarized, it is necessary only to remove one of these rays, thus leaving a linearly polarized

beam.   The problem was solved by William Nicol in 1828, and his device
goes by the name *nicol prism*.   Its method of construction and operation
are illustrated by Fig. 16.8.   The prism is made of a rhombohedron of
calcite about three times as long as it is wide.   In the principal section
$ABCD$ the two end faces $AD$ and $BC$ are cut down, as shown, reducing
the angles at $D$ and $B$ to $68°$ instead of $71°$.   The resulting crystal
$A'BC'D$, with optic axis $OA$ as shown, is then cut into two parts along
the plane $A'C'$, polished to optical flatness, and then cemented together
with Canada balsam, a transparent substance, so that the crystal is just
as transparent as it was previous to its having been sliced.   Now the
indices of refraction of Canada balsam $n_B$, of the $O$ ray $n_O$, and of the

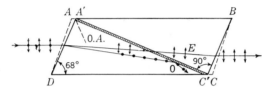

FIG. 16.8. Operation of the Nicol prism.

$E$ ray $n_E$ are, respectively, $n_B = 1.55$, $n_O = 1.658$, $n_E = 1.486$ (see Sec.
16.7) at the mean wavelength $\lambda = 5893$ A.   Since $n_O > n_B$ and $n_E < n_B$,
the $E$ ray is refracted and transmitted through the Canada balsam, while
the $O$ ray is totally reflected for angles of incidence on the balsam greater
than the critical angle $\sin^{-1} (1.55/1.658) \doteq 69°$.   By blackening the sides
of the prism the ordinary ray is effectively absorbed, and there is produced at the emergent end linearly polarized light vibrating in the principal section.   By looking at the nicol prism end on, the plane of vibration
of the transmitted light is observed to be parallel to the diagonal direction $BC$ in Fig. 16.7$b$.   Two nicol prisms arranged in tandem serve as
polarizer and analyzer, the combination forming what is known as a
*polariscope*.   When the nicols are in the parallel position, so that their
principal sections are parallel, the $E$ ray is transmitted through the analyzer.   When the nicols are crossed, so their principal sections are perpendicular, then the $E$ ray from the first polarizer nicol acts as an $O$ ray for
the analyzer nicol and is lost by total reflection in the analyzer.   For
intermediate angles between the principal sections of polarizer and analyzer, the intensity of the beam transmitted by the analyzer follows
Malus' law.

    Although nicol prisms are excellent polarizers throughout the entire
visible spectrum, they possess several disadvantages.   In the first place
nicol prisms are very costly since they require large pieces of clear calcite,
which are expensive, and the process of polishing adds to the cost.   Then,
too, the effective field of view is limited since the original beam entering

the prism cannot be too convergent or divergent; otherwise, on the one hand, the $O$ ray will be incident on the balsam surface at an angle less than the critical angle resulting in its transmission, and, on the other hand, the $E$ ray will be totally reflected at the balsam surface. Total reflection of the $E$ ray is possible since, as we shall see later, the refractive index for the extraordinary ray varies from 1.486 to 1.658 depending upon its direction of passage through calcite, and for some angles of incidence of the original light the balsam is optically less dense than what corresponds to $n_E$. Thus, to avoid the transmission of the $O$ ray and total reflection of the $E$ ray, the angle between the extreme rays of the incoming beam is limited to about 28°.

The nicol prism is also made with end faces that are cut perpendicular to the rhomb sides. With such an arrangement the field of view is increased but requires larger crystals of calcite. In another type, known as the Foucault prism, the balsam film is replaced by an air film. Even though $n_O$ and $n_E$ are each greater than the refractive index of air, their critical angles are sufficiently different so as to effect again the removal of the $O$ ray by total reflection and permit the transmission of the $E$ ray. It is here necessary to reduce the ratio of the length to the width of the crystal, which is an advantage. The Foucault prism is suitable for use in the region of the ultraviolet, which is absorbed by Canada balsam. The prism, however, suffers from a very small effective field of view and gives rise to troublesome multiple reflections in the air film.

**16.6. Observations with Two Calcite Crystals.** The use of two calcite crystals, as demonstrated by Huygens, convincingly reveals the polarization of light. If another similar calcite crystal is placed on top of the one used in the previous section to view a dot on paper and the principal planes of both crystals are parallel, the ordinary and extraordinary images transmitted through the second crystal and represented by $O'$ and $E'$ are separated twice as much as with one crystal. This indicates that the amount of displacement is proportional to the thickness of the crystal. Figure 16.9a shows this; the end face $a'b'c'd'$ of the top crystal is superposed on the end face $abcd$ of the bottom crystal. The vibration in the $O$ ray is parallel to $a'c'$, and that in the $E$ ray is parallel to $b'd'$. Now consider rotating the top crystal with respect to the bottom one about a vertical axis. In (b) the crystal has been rotated through some small angle $\theta$. There are now four images, $O'$, $E'$, $O_1'$, $E_1'$. The images $O'$ and $E'$ are less intense than in Fig. 16.9a, and the images $O_1'$ and $E_1'$ are rather faint. To explain this, it must be remembered that the principal sections of the crystals make a small angle with each other and that each of the rays $O$ and $E$, emerging from the bottom crystal and incident on the lower face of the top crystal, is refracted into two components. Thus the $O$ ray, entering the top crystal with an amplitude $A_0$, is broken up into two components $O'$ with an amplitude $A_0 \cos \theta$ and $E_1'$ with an amplitude $A_0 \sin \theta$. The $E$ ray, entering the top crystal with an amplitude $A_E$, is broken up into the component $E'$ with an amplitude $A_E \cos \theta$ and the component $O_1'$ with an amplitude $A_E \sin \theta$. The extraordinary components $E'$ and $E_1'$ are vibrating parallel to the direction $b'd'$, or in the principal section of the top crystal, and the ordinary components are vibrating perpendicular to the principal section of the top crystal, or parallel to the direction $a'c'$. The four image points form a parallelogram

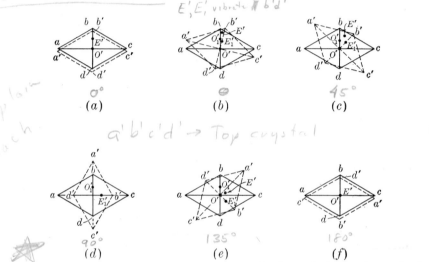

FIG. 16.9. Double refraction through two calcite crystals whose principal sections make the angles (a) 0°, (b) θ, (c) 45°, (d) 90°, (e) 135°, (f) 180°.

whose sides $O'E_1'$ and $O_1'E'$ are parallel to the principal section of the top crystal and sides $O'O_1'$ and $E_1'E'$ are parallel to the principal section of the bottom crystal. In Fig. 16.9c the angle $\theta$ is 45°, and the four images are equally bright since $\sin 45° = \cos 45°$. In Fig. 16.9d $\theta = 90°$, so that the $O'$ and $E'$ components are zero and there appear only two images as shown. The component $E_1'$ is vibrating along the direction $b'd'$, and the $O_1'$ component is vibrating perpendicular to the direction $b'd'$. After passing through 90°, the components $O'$ and $E'$ reappear, first faintly and then increasing in intensity with increasing angle (the $O_1'$ and $E_1'$ components correspondingly decrease in intensity). At $\theta = 135°$ (Fig. 16.9e), four images are again of equal intensity. At $\theta = 180°$ (Fig. 16.9f), the two principal sections are oriented in such a way that the $O'$ and $E'$ beams coalesce as they emerge from the top crystal, forming a single image point which has vibrations both parallel and perpendicular to the principal section of the top crystal. The $O$ and $E$ rays in the bottom crystal proceed as $O$ and $E$ rays, respectively, through the top crystal.

**16.7. Huygens' Construction for Double Refraction.** Huygens extended his principle of secondary wavelets to explain the phenomenon of double refraction in uniaxial crystals. Accordingly, a point source of monochromatic light in a doubly refracting medium is the origin of two wave fronts or wave surfaces. The ordinary wave has the same velocity in all directions so that the corresponding wavelets are spherical. On the other hand, the velocity of the extraordinary ray varies with direction, and Huygens considered the corresponding wavelets to be ellipsoids of revolution, which assumption has been borne out by experiment. By applying Maxwell's electromagnetic equations to an anisotropic medium it can be shown that the Huygens wavelets for the extraordinary wave, in a crystal like calcite or quartz, are ellipsoids of revolution. In view of the fact that the velocities of the $O$ and $E$ rays are the same along the direction of the optic axis, the $O$ and $E$ wavelets come in contact at the points where the optic axis intersects them. The two wave fronts surrounding a point source $S$ of light in a calcite crystal are shown in Fig.

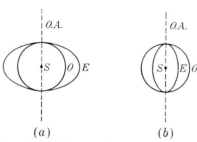

FIG. 16.10. Wave surfaces for $O$ and $E$ rays for (*a*) negative uniaxial crystal, (*b*) positive uniaxial crystal.

16.10*a*. The figure is to be considered as rotated about the optic axis, forming a sphere as the wave surface for the $O$ ray and an ellipsoid as the wave surface for the $E$ ray. The velocity of the $E$ ray varies as the radius vector of the ellipsoid, being a maximum at right angles to the direction of the optic axis, and being least along the direction of the optic axis and equal to the velocity of the $O$ ray, which is constant in all directions. The ordinary wave surface lies within the extraordinary wave surface, a fact that exemplifies the *negative uniaxial* crystal in which $n_E < n_O$ as in calcite. On the other hand, there is also the *positive uniaxial* crystal, like quartz. Here $n_E > n_O$, and the extraordinary wave surface lies within the ordinary wave surface, so that the velocity of the extraordinary ray is least in a direction perpendicular to and greatest in a direction along the optic axis. We shall now apply Huygens' construction to several very significant cases. In doing so we must remember that in accordance with the Huygens theory, the wave surfaces in uniaxial crystals are a sphere and a spheroid which touch each other at two points, and the direction of the line joining these points of contact is the optic axis of the crystal.

For the first consideration we shall take the case of a plane wave incident obliquely on a calcite crystal cut so that the optic axis is in the plane of incidence and has an arbitrary direction in this plane, as shown in Fig. 16.11. The point $A$ of the plane wave front $AB$ is the center of the ordinary spherical secondary wavelet $O$ and the extraordinary ellipsoidal secondary wavelet $E$. In the time it takes the incident wave to travel from $B$ to $C$, the ordinary wavelet and the greater velocity extraordinary wavelet have assumed the positions shown. Following the same method of construction as used for an isotropic medium (see Sec. 10.7), the tangent planes from $C$ to the spherical wavelet at $D$ and to the ellipsoidal wavelet at $F$ are drawn. The line from $A$ drawn through $D$ gives the direction of the $O$ ray and from $A$ to $F$ gives the direction of the

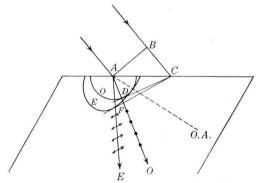

FIG. 16.11. Huygens' construction for a plane wave incident obliquely on a calcite crystal cut with the O.A. in the plane of incidence.

$E$ ray. The directions of the vibrations of the $O$ and $E$ rays are in accordance with the rule that the vibrations for the $O$ ray are along the direction which is perpendicular to the principal plane of the $O$ ray and tangent to the spherical surface, while the vibrations for the $E$ ray are along the direction which is in the principal plane of the $E$ ray and tangent to the ellipsoidal surface. In Fig. 16.11 the principal planes of the $O$ and $E$ rays and the O.A. (optic axis) are in the plane of incidence. If the O.A. is not in the plane of incidence, the point $F$ will be above or below the plane of the figure and the $E$ ray will not be in the plane of incidence. The planes $CD$ and $CF$ are now the ordinary and extraordinary refracted wave fronts, respectively. It will be noticed that in general the refracted $E$ ray is not perpendicular to the extraordinary refracted wave front $CF$.

Now consider Fig. 16.12, in which the plane wave front is incident normally on the crystal cut as in Fig. 16.11. The wave front originally parallel to the surface remains so after refraction. The refracted wave fronts are given by the tangent plane $CD$ to the spherical wavelets for the $O$ vibrations and by the tangent plane $FG$ to the ellipsoidal wavelets for the $E$ vibrations. The $O$ and $E$ rays in the crystal have the directions shown and correspond to Fig. 16.7$a$. The ordinary and extraordinary wave fronts are parallel and the *O* and *E* rays are separated, since the *E* ray is not perpendicular to its wave front.

In Fig. 16.13 is shown the case of a plane wave front incident normally on the crystal, which is now cut with its optic axis in the plane of incidence and parallel to the crystal surface. Here the ordinary and extra-

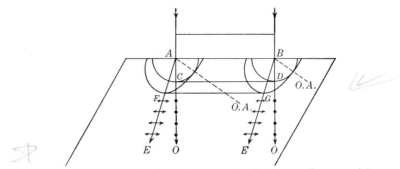

Fig. 16.12. Huygens' construction for a plane wave incident normally on a calcite crystal cut with the O.A. in the plane of incidence.

ordinary wave fronts *CD* and *FG*, respectively, are parallel, and the *O* and *E* rays are perpendicular to them. The *O* and *E* rays are not separated, but the *E* wave, traveling faster, is ahead of the *O* wave. We shall see later that this is a very significant case. The case of the incident wave

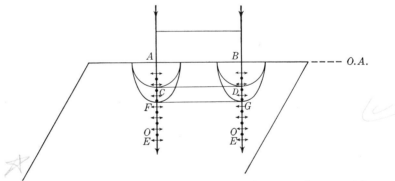

Fig. 16.13. Huygens' construction for a plane wave incident normally on a calcite crystal cut with the O.A. in the plane of incidence and parallel to the surface.

falling obliquely on the crystal in Fig. 16.13 results in the separation of the *O* and *E* rays, and its construction is left as an exercise in the problems.

In Fig. 16.14 is shown the case of a plane wave incident normally on a calcite crystal cut with the optic axis also normal to the surface. Here there is no separation of the *O* and *E* rays, which travel with the same velocity along the optic axis. The ordinary and extraordinary wave fronts coincide, and the refractive index for the *E* ray has its least value and is equal to that for the $O$ ray. If the incident wave falls obliquely on the crystal in Fig. 16.14, there results double refraction with a separation of the $O$ and $E$ rays. This case is left as an exercise in the problems.

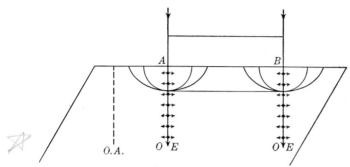

FIG. 16.14. Huygens' construction for a plane wave incident normally on a calcite crystal cut with the O.A. normal to the surface.

As a final important illustration consider the Huygens construction for a plane wave incident obliquely on the surface of a calcite crystal cut with the optic axis perpendicular to the plane of incidence. In Fig. 16.15, the O.A. is normal to the plane of the paper. Since the spherical and ellipsoidal wavelets are figures of revolution about the optic axis, it is clear that the sections for the $O$ and $E$ wavelets in the incident plane are both circular as shown. The construction then leads to a separation of the $O$ and $E$ rays, and in this plane the velocity of the $E$ ray is the same in all directions. Snell's law then holds for both rays when in this plane, and the light travels at all times perpendicular to the direction of the optic axis. By referring to Fig. 16.10a it is seen that the velocity of the $E$ ray, traveling perpendicular to the optic axis, is a maximum. The index of refraction of the $E$ ray is defined for this case and is called the

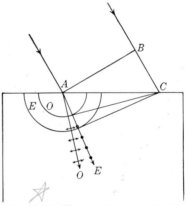

FIG. 16.15. Huygens' construction for a plane wave incident obliquely on the surface of a calcite crystal cut with the O.A. normal to the plane of incidence.

*principal index of refraction,* which is the ratio of the sine of the angle of incidence to the sine of the angle of refraction when the refracted ray travels perpendicular to the optic axis. This is physically the ratio of the velocity in vacuum to the maximum velocity of the $E$ ray. These definitions hold for the negative uniaxial crystals. For the positive uniaxial crystals the principal index (see Fig. 16.10b) is given by the ratio of the velocity in vacuum to the minimum velocity of the $E$ ray.   The indices of refraction of the $O$ ray and the principal indices of refraction for the $E$ ray for some uniaxial crystal substances are as follows: for the negative crystal calcite $n_O = 1.658$, $n_E = 1.486$; for the negative crystal tourmaline $n_O = 1.64$, $n_E = 1.62$; for the positive crystal quartz $n_O = 1.544$, $n_E = 1.553$; for the positive crystal ice $n_O = 1.306$, $n_E = 1.307$. The index of refraction for the $O$ ray and the principal index of refraction for the $E$ ray are readily determined experimentally by cutting, say a calcite crystal, in the form of a refracting prism with the optic axis parallel to the refracting edge and placing the prism on a spectrometer table.   For a given wavelength an $O$ and an $E$ ray appear separated on the emergent side of the prism, the $O$ ray vibrating parallel to the plane of incidence and the $E$ ray vibrating perpendicular to the plane of incidence.   Setting the prism for minimum deviation for each of the rays and using Eq. (1.16) determines $n_O$ and $n_E$.   When the wave is incident normally on the crystal in Fig. 16.15, the $O$ and $E$ rays are not separated but the corresponding wave fronts are.   The student is asked to make this construction in the problems.

There are seven crystal systems, known as triclinic, monoclinic, orthorhombic, tetragonal, hexagonal, rhombohedral (which is often classed under hexagonal), and cubic.   To explain these is beyond the scope of this text, but it is worth pointing out that crystals belonging to the tetragonal, hexagonal, and rhombohedral systems are uniaxial, while crystals belonging to the triclinic, monoclinic, and orthorhombic systems are biaxial.   On the other hand, the crystals of the cubic system are isotropic and do not exhibit double refraction.   As pointed out before, it is not our purpose to study the refraction in biaxial crystals, and the student is referred to other sources for such a treatment.[1]

An adequate presentation of the theory of double refraction entails an application of Maxwell's electromagnetic equations to crystalline media. For anisotropic media the value of the dielectric constant (see Sec. 16.1) depends on the direction of the optic axis in relation to the electric field, which, as we have seen, produces electric dipoles in the medium.   For a transparent solid the electric field at an atom is made up of the electric field of the waves and the fields resulting from the dipoles in neighboring atoms.   For a given crystal the atoms are of a given type arranged in some particular way so that they are more easily influenced by the electric field vibrating in one plane than in another.   From the view of electron theory the electrons in anisotropic crystals possess binding forces and

[1] R. W. Wood, "Physical Optics," 3d ed., The Macmillan Company, New York, 1934.

F. A. Jenkins, and H. E. White, "Fundamentals of Optics," 2d ed., McGraw-Hill Book Company, Inc., New York, 1950.

natural frequencies that are different in different directions. A variation of the dielectric constant with direction in anistropic media means a corresponding variation of refractive index with direction, and these facts when combined with Maxwell's electromagnetic equations lead to the phenomenon of double refraction. For a detailed treatment the student is referred to other sources.[1]

**16.8. Double-image Polarizing Prisms.** We have seen that a nicol prism cannot be used in the ultraviolet on account of Canada balsam, which absorbs these rays. Furthermore it is sometimes desirable to have $O$ and $E$ components present and more widely separated on the emergent

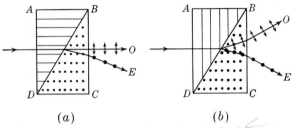

(a)                    (b)

Fig. 16.16. Double-image polarizing prisms of quartz. (a) Rochon type. (b) Wollaston type.

side of the prism. Two schemes for accomplishing this are shown in Fig. 16.16, each of which is made of two wedge-shaped prisms of calcite or quartz and cemented together with glycerin or castor oil.

In the Rochon prism (Fig. 16.16a), the prism $ABD$ is cut with the optic axis parallel to the incident light and in the plane of incidence, while the prism $DBC$ has the optic axis perpendicular to the plane of incidence. A ray incident normally on the face $AD$ proceeds in accordance with Fig. 16.14 until the oblique surface $DB$ is reached. The rays entering $DBC$ now travel perpendicular to the optic axis. The $O$ ray is transmitted undeviated and is achromatic, but the $E$ ray refracts as shown and is chromatic.

In the Wollaston prism (Fig. 16.16b), the prisms $ABD$ and $DBC$ are cut with the optic axes as shown. A ray incident normally on the face $AD$ proceeds in accordance with Fig. 16.13, the $O$ and $E$ disturbances traveling at different speeds. The vibrations in the $O$ ray are perpendicular to the plane of the figure, and after passing $BD$ these vibrations

[1] P. Drude, "Theory of Optics," Chap. III, Longmans, Green & Co., Inc., New York, 1933.

N. H. Frank, "Introduction to Electricity and Optics," 1st ed., pp. 318–320, McGraw Hill Book Company, Inc., New York, 1940.

G. Joos, "Theoretical Physics," Chap. XIX, G. E. Stechert & Company, New York, 1932.

Jenkins and White, *op. cit.*, pp. 520–523.

are parallel to the principal plane of prism *BCD*. Thus the *O* ray in *ABD* is transmitted as an *E* ray in *BCD*. Also, the *E* ray in *ABD* is transmitted as an *O* ray in *BCD*. The rays interchange velocities, one ray bending toward the normal while the other bends away from the normal to the refracting surface *BD*. For instance, the effective index of refraction for the *O* ray at the face *BD* is $n_E/n_O$, and that for the *E* ray is $n_O/n_E$. In quartz, $n_E > n_O$ so that the *O* ray, in passing *BD*, is refracted toward the normal as an *E* ray, and the *E* ray is refracted away from the normal as an *O* ray, as shown in Fig. 16.16*b*. Additional refraction at the emergent face *BC* causes the rays to diverge more. Both the *O* and the *E* beams are chromatic, or colored. The cut *BD* can be made at such an angle that the two emergent beams are equally inclined to the face *BC*. The prism is useful in determining the percentage of polarization in a partially polarized beam providing, for examination, two images with vibrations in two perpendicular directions.

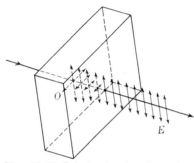

FIG. 16.17. Polarization by absorption in tourmaline.

**16.9. Polarization by Absorption.** There is a class of doubly refracting substances that absorb the *O* and *E* rays unequally, thereby producing linearly polarized light. The name given to this phenomenon is *dichroism*, and crystals or minerals exhibiting this property are said to be *dichroic*. A crystal showing dichroism to a marked degree is tourmaline, whose action is illustrated in Fig. 16.17. When unpolarized light is incident on a thin slab of tourmaline cut with its face parallel to the optic axis, the emergent beam is plane-polarized as shown. The *O* beam is completely absorbed in a small thickness of crystal (less than 1 mm), while the *E* beam, only slightly absorbed, emerges. The use of tourmaline as polarizer and analyzer is limited because of the fact that the absorption of the *E* beam varies with the wavelength and the emergent light is chromatic.

In 1852 the English physician, W. B. Herapath, discovered the synthetic crystalline material iodosulfate of quinine (called herapathite after its discoverer) in the form of small crystals which have a very marked dichroism, transmitting linearly polarized light for all colors in the visible spectrum. Herapathite crystals are mechanically unstable, pulverizing easily under relatively slight stress. In 1932 E. H. Land was successful in inventing a process whereby the herapathite crystals are embedded in a transparent matrix, which prevents the crystals from shattering and serves to keep the small crystals aligned with their optic axes all parallel.

This process is the basis of the commercial substance known as *polaroid.* In this way there are available polarizing sheets with an area many times that obtainable from a nicol prism and at relatively small cost. In one form of polaroid the small, elongated dichroic crystals are embedded with their optic axes parallel in a film of cellulose acetate. In another type a sheet of polyvinyl alcohol is stretched, thus orienting the molecules parallel to the direction of stress. The material thus becomes birefracting and when impregnated with iodine becomes dichroic. To protect the polaroid sheeting, it is placed between plates of glass, forming polaroid glass. When two polaroid disks are crossed so that their transmission directions are at right angles, there is almost perfect extinction of the light. Actually some transmission at both ends of the visible spectrum takes place.

Polaroid filters and films find wide applications. The student is familiar with polarizing sunglasses, which are employed to minimize the amount of glare present in bright weather. Annoying glare is due to the reflections of sunlight from horizontal surfaces such as wet pavements and automobile hoods. This specularly reflected light is partially polarized with horizontal vibrations, while the useful diffusely reflected light is unpolarized. The useful- to glare-light ratio is much improved by viewing the surfaces through polarizing glasses whose direction of transmission is vertical. This same principle is employed in polarized desk lamps, which contain a suitably oriented polarizing filter in front of the lamp to eliminate the vibrations that would cause glare by reflection from glossy horizontal surfaces. Polaroid film is being used to produce three-dimensional moving pictures, to project stereoscopic pictures, to eliminate the headlight glare in motorcar night driving, to improve the color contrasts in old oil paintings, as glass windows in trains and airplanes in which there is a fixed outer and a rotatable inner polaroid disk for controlling the amount of light coming in from the outside, in photography, and for innumerable other purposes in industry, at home, and at play.

**16.10. Circularly and Elliptically Polarized Light.** For plane or linearly polarized light, the light vector varies simple harmonically along a straight line. The resultant light vector can also be made to rotate without changing its magnitude, in which case the light is said to be *circularly polarized*, or it may be made to rotate and also change its magnitude, in which case the light is said to be *elliptically polarized*. Let us now see under what conditions circular and elliptical motions can be effected. In Fig. 16.18a is shown a linearly polarized beam incident normally on a calcite crystal cut with its optic axis as in Fig. 16.13 but oriented so that the vibration direction of the incident beam makes an angle $\theta$ with the optic-axis direction as indicated in Fig. 16.18b. The crystal breaks the light of amplitude A into two components, A cos θ along the optic axis forming the E ray, and A sin θ perpendicular to the optic axis forming the O ray.   These, as we have seen, traverse the crystal unseparated but at different speeds, the speed of the E ray being larger for calcite.   As a consequence, there is a difference in phase between the O and E vibrations, and this difference in phase, for a given wavelength, depends on the relative velocities of both rays and on the thickness of the crystal traversed by them.   Suppose the thickness of the crystal is such as to introduce a phase difference δ between the O and E beams after

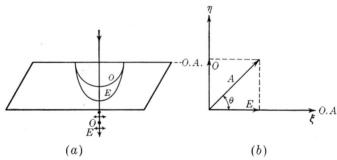

(a)                         (b)

Fig. 16.18. (a) Linearly polarized light incident normally on a calcite crystal cut with the O.A. in the plane of incidence and parallel to the surface. (b) Top view showing the vibration direction of incident light making an angle θ with the O.A.

they have passed through the crystal.   We thus have the familiar case of the superposition of two mutually orthogonal simple harmonic vibrations of the same frequency with arbitrary amplitude and phase difference.   This, as we have seen in Sec. 10.4, Eq. (10.15), yields a motion which is in general elliptic.   If we use the symbols ξ and η to represent the coordinate axes of Fig. 16.18b, then Eq. (10.15) gives

$$\frac{\xi^2}{a^2} - \frac{2\xi\eta}{ab} \cos \delta + \frac{\eta^2}{b^2} = \sin^2\delta \tag{16.18}$$

where a and b are the amplitudes A cos θ and A sin θ of the E and O vibrations, respectively.   The equation represents an ellipse with center at the origin for all values of δ other than 0, π, 2π, 3π, . . . .   For δ = π/2, 3π/2, 5π/2, . . . the axes of the ellipse are parallel and perpendicular, respectively, to the principal section of the crystal.   For all values of δ other than an integral multiple of π the ellipse is rotated with respect to the ξ and η axes.   Both cases represent elliptically polarized light, the resultant vibration vector sweeping out an ellipse.   When δ = 0, 2π, 4π, . . . , Eq. (16.18) yields a straight line with positive slope, which means that the emergent light is plane-polarized with the vibration direction the same as the original linearly polarized beam.   When δ = π, 3π, 5π, . . . , Eq. (16.18) yields a straight line with an equal negative slope, which means that the emergent light is linearly polarized with the vibration direction making an angle $2 \tan^{-1} (b/a) = 2\theta$ with that of the incident beam. In the special case where $\theta = 45°$, we have $a = A \cos 45 = b = A \sin 45$ and $\delta = \pi/2,\ 3\pi/2,\ 5\pi/2,\ \ldots$ , Eq. (16.18) yields a circle, and the emergent beam is circularly polarized. Figure 16.19 shows the sequence of polarization forms that take place as the beams traverse the crystal, thus steadily increasing the phase difference. The figures correspond to $\theta \neq 45°$. When $\theta = 45°$, the

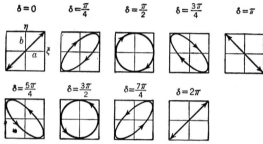

FIG. 16.19. Linearly and elliptically polarized-light vibration figures.

vibrations for $\delta = \pi/2$ and $\delta = 3\pi/2$ are circular. For other angles $\theta$, the eccentricities of the ellipses can be varied at will. Notice the change from clockwise to counterclockwise sense of polarization. All the figures are enclosed in the rectangle of sides $2a$ and $2b$.

**16.11. Retardation Plates.** A crystal plate used to introduce a given phase difference between the $O$ and $E$ beams, as outlined in the previous section, is called a retardation plate. If the thickness of the plate is $d$, the path difference introduced is $(n_E - n_o)d$ and the phase difference is

$$\delta = \frac{2\pi}{\lambda} (n_E - n_o)d \qquad (16.19)$$

an equation that is employed to compute the thickness of plate necessary to introduce a given phase difference.

When the plate's thickness is such as to introduce a phase difference of $\pi$, it is called a *half-wave plate* and its thickness is given by $d = \lambda/2(n_E - n_o)$. As we have seen, the effect of a half-wave plate is to alter the vibration direction of the incident polarized light by the angle $2\theta$. More generally, since $a = A \cos \theta$ and $b = A \sin \theta$ and $\theta$ can be varied by rotation of the half-wave plate, it may be used to rotate the vibration direction of the incident light through any angle.

When the thickness of the plate is such that the phase difference introduced is $\pi/2$, the plate is called a *quarter-wave plate* and its thickness is given by $d = \lambda/4(n_E - n_o)$. The quarter-wave plate can be used to produce elliptically polarized light of any desired eccentricity. For the special case of $\theta = 45°$ the quarter-wave plate produces circularly polarized light.

A quarter-wave plate in conjunction with a polarizing analyzer, such as a nicol prism or polaroid filter, is used to determine the kind of polarization present in a beam of light. First, the light is passed through the analyzer, and the analyzer is rotated about the direction of the beam as axis. If the light can be extinguished, then it is linearly polarized with a vibration direction perpendicular to the principal section of the analyzer. If there is no change in intensity of the light transmitted through the analyzer, which has been rotated, then the light is either unpolarized or it is circularly polarized. The conclusion that it may be circularly polarized follows from the fact that a circular vibration is equivalent to two equal amplitude linear vibrations differing in phase by $\pi/2$ and mutually orthogonal. Thus consider circularly polarized light passing through an analyzer whose plane of transmission makes an angle $\theta$ with one of the orthogonal vibrations of the circularly polarized light of amplitude $a$ as shown in Fig. 16.20. The other orthogonal vibration makes an angle $90° - \theta$ with the transmission plane of the analyzer. Hence along the transmission direction there are superposed two vector amplitudes $a \cos \theta$ and $a \sin \theta$ differing in phase by $\pi/2$ and giving for the resultant amplitude $\sqrt{(a \cos \theta)^2 + (a \sin \theta)^2} = a$. The intensity of the transmitted beam is therefore not altered when the analyzer is rotated. We must now test whether the light is unpolarized or circularly polarized. This is accomplished by inserting a quarter-wave plate in front of the analyzer. If the light is unpolarized, it is unaffected by the quarter-wave plate and a rotation of the analyzer shows no changes in intensity. On the other hand, if the light is circularly polarized, it contains two orthogonal vibrations differing in phase by $\pi/2$ and, after passing through the quarter-wave plate, an additional phase change of $\pi/2$ has been introduced so that the total phase difference is either 0 or $\pi$. In either case the light entering the analyzer is now linearly polarized, and a rotation of the analyzer will cause extinction when its principal section is perpendicular to the direction of vibration of the linearly polarized light. To complete the analysis, we must consider one more possibility. When the original beam is sent through the analyzer, the intensity of the transmitted beam may neither remain constant nor be extinguished upon rotation of the analyzer. There may be changes in intensity with maxima and minima. In this case the light is either partially plane-polarized or elliptically

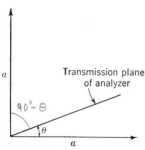

FIG. 16.20. Vibration vectors for circularly polarized light incident on an analyzer.

Transmission plane of analyzer

$90° - \theta$

$\theta$

polarized. These can be distinguished by again inserting a quarter-wave plate in front of the analyzer. The elliptical vibration is composed of two linear vibrations parallel to the major and minor axes of the ellipse and differing in phase by $\pi/2$. The quarter-wave plate can then be oriented in two positions, so that its fast axis (the direction of the $E$ vibrations in calcite) of transmission is parallel to the major or minor diameter of the elliptic motion. The light is then converted into plane-polarized light for these two positions due to the additional phase of $\pi/2$ by the quarter-wave plate, and a rotation of the analyzer will produce extinction in two positions 90° apart. Partially polarized light, on the other hand, is not rendered plane-polarized by the quarter-wave plate.

The required thickness of a retardation plate is a function of the wavelength, and in practice the principal indices $n_E$ and $n_O$ are employed for the sodium $D$ line 5893 A. Retardation plates are made of quartz or more usually of mica. Quartz is positive uniaxial, and mica, which has the advantage of having natural cleavage planes, is negative biaxial. Although there are two optic axes in mica, there are some forms of mica for which the angle between the two axes is small enough to make it useful as a retardation plate.

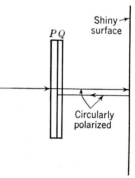

FIG. 16.21. The polaroid filter for eliminating specular reflection.

There is obtainable commercially a polarization filter that embodies the above principles, using circularly polarized light to eliminate light that is specularly reflected from a shiny surface. As illustrated in Fig. 16.21, the circular polarizing sheet is composed of two adjacent layers, a linear polarizer $P$ followed by a quarter-wave plate $Q$ oriented at 45° to the direction of vibration of the linearly polarized light. Light incident on $P$ as shown is transmitted through the composite sheet as circularly polarized light which proceeds to the shiny surface. After reflection the circularly polarized light, on the return trip, shown by the displaced line for clearness, is first incident on the quarter-wave plate, which introduces an additional phase retardation of $\pi/2$, producing linearly polarized light whose direction of vibration is perpendicular to the transmission direction of the polarizer. The specularly reflected light is therefore "trapped," so to speak. When the right-hand face of the polarizing sheet is placed in lighttight contact with the shiny surface, the specularly reflected light is effectively eliminated.

**16.12. The Babinet Compensator.** In working with polarized light it is advantageous to be able to effect a variable phase difference between the two mutually perpendicular vibrations discussed in the preceding section.   The Babinet compensator shown in Fig. 16.22 makes it possible to accomplish this.   It consists of two quartz wedges of equal angle arranged so that one can be moved past the other by means of a micrometer screw.   The wedge on the left is cut with the optic axis perpendicular to the refracting edge, and that on the right has its optic axis parallel to the refracting edge.   As with the Wollaston prism (Fig. 16.16*b*), the *O* and *E* rays in the first prism are transmitted as *E* and *O* rays, respectively, in the second prism, the rays interchanging velocities.   Therefore at a point where the distance traversed by the rays in one wedge is equal to that in the other wedge, the acceleration produced by one wedge annuls the retardation produced by the other, and the phase difference is zero.   The phase difference increases linearly with the distance measured on each side of the point of zero phase difference.   By sliding one wedge over the other any desired phase difference can be obtained.

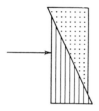

Fig. 16.22. The Babinet compensator.

The Babinet compensator has been modified by Soleil and contains two wedges like those shown in Fig. 16.22 but both cut with the optic axis perpendicular to the refracting edge of either prism, and attached to the right-hand wedge is a rectangular parallel plate of quartz cut with its optic axis parallel to the refracting edges of the prisms.   This modification makes it possible to produce a thickness change which is uniform over a large field.   A given plate thickness in the Babinet compensator is limited to a very small region.   The Soleil compensator is well adapted for used with parallel light.

The Babinet and Soleil compensators are very useful in producing and analyzing polarized light.

**16.13. Interference of Polarized Light.**   Let us return for a moment to Fig. 16.18 and consider the vibrations in the emergent beam.   We have seen that the *O* beam of amplitude $A \sin \theta$ and the *E* beam of amplitude $A \cos \theta$ originate from the same linearly polarized monochromatic wave of amplitude *A* whose direction of vibration makes an angle $\theta$ with the optic axis of the birefracting crystal.   The beams have the same frequency and a constant phase difference between them.   They satisfy all conditions of interference stated in Sec. 11.2 except condition (5).   Since the *O* and *E* beams vibrate at right angles to each other, they cannot be made to interfere.   Condition (5) can be satisfied and the beams made to interfere if the emergent light in Fig. 16.18 is passed through an analyzer such as a nicol prism, for then a component of each vibration is transmitted in the principal section of the prism with the result that both vibrations are brought into the same plane.   The state of affairs can be represented by Fig. 16.23.   The direction *BP* represents the direction of vibration transmitted by the polarizer of amplitude $A$ and making an angle $\theta$ with the optic axis of the birefracting crystal. The crystal transmits an $E$ vibration parallel to the direction $BE$ and of amplitude $A \cos \theta$ and an $O$ vibration parallel to $BO$ and of amplitude $A \sin \theta$. These vibrations are now incident on the nicol prism, which of course acts as an analyzer whose transmission plane is in the direction $BN$ making an angle $\beta$ with the direction $BE$. The analyzer therefore transmits the components $A \cos \theta \cos \beta$ and $A \sin \theta \sin \beta$. These two component vibrations have a phase difference $\delta$ and, by Eq. (10.10), compound to give the resultant amplitude $A_r$ transmitted by the analyzer as

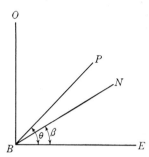

Fig. 16.23. Illustrating components of linearly polarized light transmitted by a doubly refracting crystal and an analyzer.

$$A_r^2 = A^2 \left(\cos^2 \theta \cos^2 \beta + \sin^2 \theta \sin^2 \beta + 2 \cos \theta \cos \beta \sin \theta \sin \beta \cos \delta\right)$$

Substituting $1 - 2 \sin^2 (\delta/2)$ for $\cos \delta$, the expression reduces to

$$A_r^2 = A^2 \left[ \cos^2 (\theta - \beta) - \sin 2\theta \sin 2\beta \sin^2 \frac{\delta}{2} \right] \qquad (16.20)$$

Equation (16.20) shows how the intensity of the emergent light varies with $\theta$, $\beta$, and $\delta$ when a doubly refracting crystal, cut parallel with its optic axis, is inserted between a polarizer and an analyzer. We have seen that $\delta$ depends on the thickness of the crystal and the wavelength. Let us now see what the result is in several significant arrangements.

When the analyzer is parallel to the polarizer, $\beta = \theta$ and

$$A_r^2 = A^2 \left(1 - \sin^2 2\theta \sin^2 \frac{\delta}{2}\right) \qquad (16.21)$$

For a given $\delta$, if the crystal is now rotated, then in one revolution, for $\theta = 0$, $\pi/2$, $\pi$, and $3\pi/2$, $A_r^2 = A^2$ and the transmitted intensity is equal to the original intensity, neglecting reflection and absorption losses. These four positions occur when the $E$- and $O$-transmission directions in the crystal coincide with the vibration directions of polarizer and analyzer. The beam either passes through as an $E$ beam or as an $O$ beam.

When the polarizer and analyzer are crossed, $\theta - \beta = 90°$ and Eq. (16.20) becomes

$$A_r^2 = A^2 \sin^2 2\theta \sin^2 \frac{\delta}{2} \qquad (16.22)$$

Thus for any value of $\delta$ other than $2\pi$, $4\pi$, $6\pi$, . . . , the intensity transmitted is given by Eq. (16.22) even though the polarizer and analyzer are crossed. For the positions $\theta = 0$, $\pi/2$, $\pi$, $3\pi/2$ there is darkness. If the crystal has a variable thickness, say in the form of a wedge, $\delta$ changes along the wedge for a given wavelength and dark interference bands, running parallel to the edge of the wedge, appear at those positions where the thickness of the wedge corresponds to $\delta = 2\pi$, $4\pi$, $6\pi$, . . . . If white light is used, the interference bands are colored, since when $\delta = 2\pi$ for one wavelength, the neighboring wavelengths are not interfering destructively, and at this position the white light is minus this wavelength or is colored. In white light the interference band of zero order, where the birefringence is zero for all wavelengths, is black for the crossed and white for the parallel arrangement of polarizer and analyzer. If the crystal is of constant thickness, it will in general appear colored with white light owing to the fact that certain regions of the spectrum meet with destructive interference in the analyzer.

Instead of using a parallel beam of light and effecting a continuous change in phase between the $O$ and $E$ rays by means of a variable-thickness crystal, interference patterns may be obtained in convergent or divergent polarized light. The interference patterns so obtained for uniaxial crystals take the form of concentric rings and radial brushes or fringes having hyperbolic loci depending on the cut of the crystal. For biaxial crystals the *isochromatic lines*, or interference-fringe loci of all points at which the phase difference is constant, are families of the mathematical lemniscates crossed by brushes. For a more detailed treatment of such interference patterns the student is referred to other sources.[1]

**16.14. Temporary Double Refraction.** We have seen that when a polarizer and an analyzer are arranged in the crossed position no light is transmitted through the analyzer. However, when a doubly refracting crystal is placed between polarizer and analyzer, light is transmitted through the analyzer and an interference pattern may in general be produced. Some isotropic substances like strain-free glass, celluloid, and bakelite become temporarily doubly refracting when subjected to strain or stress, and in general the birefringence disappears when the strains are removed. When such an isotropic substance is inserted between crossed nicols and stressed, the accompanying birefringence results in light being transmitted through the analyzer. The resulting interference pattern makes visible the regions of stress in the material. This is the basis of a highly developed optical method of stress analysis called *photoelasticity*, which makes possible a quantitative stress analysis in structural

---

[1] Drude, *op. cit.*, pp 349–357.
Jenkins and White, *op. cit.*, pp. 537–540.

engineering that exceeds all other methods. In practice a model of a mechanical construction is formed out of a transparent isotropic material such as a plastic. This model is placed between crossed polarizer and analyzer and subjected to various loading conditions. The resulting deformations change the isotropic character of the material, and an entering ray of light travels faster along one principal plane than along the other, the material behaving like a doubly refracting crystal. An analysis of the resulting polarization pattern leads to a knowledge of the magnitudes of the stresses set up in the model under test. Figure 16.24 shows two optical stress patterns. In (*a*) the pattern is for a beam subjected to bending, and in (*b*) the pattern is for a square block subjected to a diagonal load as shown by the arrows. The interference bands are loci of points of equal phase difference, and a fringe in the stress pattern corresponds to a phase difference of one wavelength, or an integral number of wavelengths. In white light the bands are colored. The theory and application of optical stress analysis are thoroughly covered in the two-volume work of M. M. Frocht.[1]

There is another class of transparent materials, solids and liquids, and to a small extent gases, that are isotropic but exhibit double refraction when subjected to a strong electric field. This effect was discovered by Kerr in 1875 and is known as the *Kerr electro-optic effect*. Kerr experiments are performed with liquids like nitrobenzene or carbon disulfide which are usually placed in a cell the sides of which are transparent. When the cell is inserted in a polariscope with crossed polarizer and analyzer and an electric field is established across the cell, light is transmitted. The double refraction of the liquid, similar to a uniaxial crystal with optic axis in the direction of the electric field, is temporary, disappearing when the electric field is removed. The phase difference between the *O* and *E* components, transmitted through the polariscope, is proportional to the length of path traversed in the liquid by the light and to the square of the applied electric field strength. The Kerr effect depends on the difference in the dipole moments produced by the electric field along different axes of the molecule, and such measurements give information about the molecular structure of the liquid. When Kerr cells are used in a polariscope with a rapidly oscillating electric field, they act as an electro-optical shutter. The student should review the Kerr cell method of the measurement of the velocity of light described in Sec. 10.8 in connection with Fig. 10.16.

The magnetic analogue of the Kerr electro-optic effect is the *Cotton-Mouton effect*. Cotton and Mouton, in 1907, demonstrated that when a liquid like nitrobenzene or carbon disulfide is placed in a transverse mag-

[1] M. M. Frocht, "Photoelasticity," John Wiley & Sons, Inc., New York, Vol. I, 1941, Vol. II, 1950.

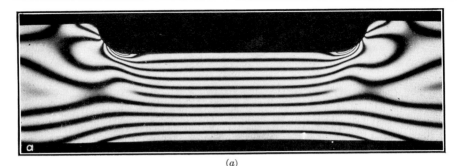

(a)

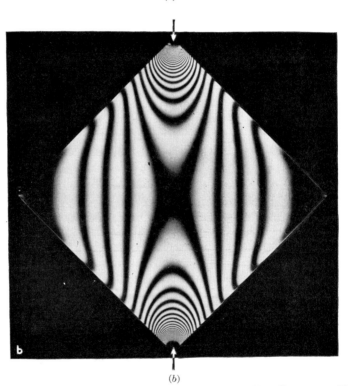

(b)

Fig. 16.24. Optical stress patterns for (a) a beam in pure bending, (b) a square block subjected to diagonal loads as shown. (*Reproduced by permission from "Photoelasticity," Volume* I *by M. M. Frocht, published by John Wiley & Sons, Inc., 1941.*)

netic field the liquid becomes doubly refractive. The phase difference produced by this effect is proportional to the square of the field strength. The double refraction is due to an orientation of the molecules in the magnetic field resulting in optical anisotropy. Both the Cotton-Mouton effect and the Kerr electro-optic effect are dependent on the temperature.

**16.15. Optical Activity.** We have seen that if a polarizer and analyzer are crossed, no light is transmitted through the analyzer. If a piece of calcite, cut with its optic axis as in Fig. 16.14, is inserted so that the light from the polarizer is incident normally on the face of the crystal, there is no double refraction, the light emerges from the calcite with its plane of vibration unchanged, and no light is transmitted through the analyzer. On the other hand, if a section of a quartz crystal is similarly cut and inserted so that the light from the polarizer is directed along the optic axis of quartz, light is transmitted by the analyzer. Furthermore, if the analyzer is then rotated to a new position, so that it is no more crossed with the polarizer, the light is again extinguished. These observations show that the light is still linearly polarized after passing through the quartz and that the vibration plane has been rotated through an angle equal to the angle through which the analyzer was turned to reextinguish the light. This property that certain crystals and other substances have of rotating the plane of vibration of polarized light is called *optical activity*. Some crystalline forms and substances rotate the plane of vibration in one sense, and others rotate it in the opposite sense. From the viewpoint of an observer looking at the light traveling toward him, after passage through the optically active substance, the rotation is clockwise, or positive, and is called *right-handed*, or *dextrorotatory*, and if counterclockwise, or negative, is designated *left-handed*, or *levorotatory*. In addition to certain crystals, substances that exhibit optical activity include liquids such as turpentine and solutions of an optically active substance in an inactive solvent, such as a sugar solution.

In the case of quartz or optically active liquids the angle through which the plane of vibration is rotated for a given wavelength is proportional to the length of path traversed in the substance. In solutions the rotation angle, for a given wavelength and length of light path, is proportional to the concentration.

The fact that the rotation produced by a solution depends on the concentration has afforded a means of rapidly determining the amount of optically active substance in solution. Commercially this method is used to determine the amount of cane sugar in a sample of sugar solution. The instrument used for such an analysis contains essentially a polarizer and analyzer and is known as a *saccharimeter*. Comparisons are made in terms of the *specific rotation* $[\alpha]$, which is defined for a given wavelength and temperature, as the rotation produced by a liquid 10 cm in length and containing 1 gm of optically active material per cubic centimeter of solution. Thus if $C$ represents the concentration in grams of active substance per cubic centimeter and $l$ is the length in centimeters of the liquid path traversed by the light, we have for the rotation of the plane of polarization $\theta$

$$\theta = \frac{[\alpha]lC}{10} \qquad (16.23)$$

Since crystals are much more optically active than liquids, the specific rotation for a crystal is defined for a 1-mm thickness of crystal. Our previous statement that the rotation produced by a solution is proportional to the concentration holds only if the concentration is not too large or if the range of concentrations is not too wide. Empirically the specific rotation is represented by a complete polynomial of the second degree in the concentration of the active material in solution.

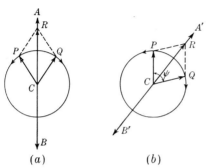

FIG. 16.25. (a) Combination of two circularly polarized vibrations to form a linearly polarized vibration. (b) Rotation of the plane of vibration of linearly polarized light.

The specific rotation for crystals, liquids, and solutions is usually stated as being very nearly inversely proportional to the wavelength. This gives rise to the phenomenon of *rotatory dispersion* and results in the various colors being rotated by different amounts. The dependence of specific rotation on wavelength is similar to that of refractive index, and the Cauchy two-constant formula [Eq. (15.20)] may be used in the form

$$[\alpha] = g + \frac{h}{\lambda^2} \qquad (16.24)$$

where the constants $g$ and $h$ are determinable from experiment.

**16.16. Fresnel's Theory of Optical Activity.** In Sec. 16.10 we have seen that linearly polarized light may be considered as the resultant of two mutually perpendicular linearly polarized vibrations having a phase difference equal to zero or an integral multiple of $\pi$. A linearly polarized vibration may also be considered as the resultant of two circularly polarized vibrations rotating in opposite directions with the same angular velocity. This is illustrated in Fig. 16.25a, which represents a circularly polarized wave vector $CP$ rotating counterclockwise and one $CQ$ rotating clockwise, both with the same angular velocity. The waves may be thought of as advancing toward the reader with equal speed. As is evident, the vectors $CP$ and $CQ$ combine to form a resultant $CR$ which obtains its maximum values $CA$ and $CB$. The horizontal components of $CP$ and $CQ$ cancel, leaving a linearly polarized vibration with an amplitude $CA = CB$. Fresnel assumed that when linearly polarized light enters the crystal along the optic axis it is resolved into two beams circularly polarized in opposite senses. Along the optic axis of a crystal like calcite the circularly polarized vibrations have the same velocity, and the resultant linearly polarized light is along $AB$ as in Fig. 16.25a. On the other hand, along the optic axis of a crystal like quartz the circularly polarized components advance (toward the reader) with different velocities, the clockwise rotation advancing faster for right-handed optically active crystal types while for the left-handed type the counterclockwise rotation travels faster. Consequently, when the light emerges from the crystal, one of the circularly polarized components has rotated through a greater angle $\psi$ than the other, as shown in Fig. 16.25b, where we have assumed that the clockwise rotation advances with the greater velocity. The resultant of the two circularly polarized components lies along the direction $A'B'$ which makes an angle $\psi/2$ with the vibration plane of the incident wave, the amplitude and frequency of the vibration along $A'B'$ being the same as those of the incident wave $AB$ in Fig. 16.25a. Therefore in passing through the crystal the plane of vibration has been rotated by an angle that is proportional to the thickness of the path in the crystal. The phase difference between the two circularly polarized components, in traversing a crystal thickness $d$, is given by Eq. 16.19, which here has the form

$$\frac{\delta}{2} = \frac{\pi}{\lambda} (n_P - n_Q)d \qquad (16.25)$$

where $n_P$ and $n_Q$ are the refractive indices of the $P$ and $Q$ circularly polarized components and $\delta/2$ represents the angle in radians through which the vibration plane has been rotated. The equation is generally employed to compute the difference $n_P - n_Q$ from the observed rotation. The two wave surfaces shown touching along the optic axis in Fig. 16.10 do not quite touch in quartz, and this causes the two circularly polarized components to advance with slightly different velocities, resulting in optical activity. Fresnel was able to demonstrate experimentally the existence of such a double refraction in the form of two oppositely directed circularly polarized rays. He put together a composite prism made of negative and positive optically active quartz prisms. By passing linearly polarized light through the prism, he obtained two oppositely directed circularly polarized emerging beams.

Basically the cause of the phenomenon of optical activity is an asymmetry in the structure of the crystalline material or molecules of the liquid. The crystal quartz ($SiO_2$) has a structure which shows that the silicon and oxygen atoms form a spiral arrangement along the optic axis. In one form of quartz the spiraling is right-handed, and in another form it is left-handed. In optically active liquids or solutions the asymmetry is with respect to the carbon atoms that are usually present. For an explanation of optical activity on the basis of the electromagnetic theory the student is referred to other sources.[1]

[1] E. U. Condon, *Rev. Modern Phys.*, **9**, 432–457, 1937.

**16.17. Temporary Optical Activity.** Michael Faraday, in 1845, discovered that when an isotropic medium is placed in a strong magnetic field it acquires the property of optical activity, rotating the plane of vibration of the light traveling parallel to the magnetic field. The *Faraday effect*, as it is known, is shown by such substances as glass, carbon disulfide, water, and gases. The angle of rotation $\theta$, for a given substance, temperature, and wavelength, is proportional to the field strength $H$ and the length of path $l$ traversed in the medium by the light, or

$$\theta = VHl \qquad (16.26)$$

where $V$, called the *Verdet constant*, is characteristic of the given medium. For instance, for sodium light the Verdet constant of water at 20°C is 0.0131 min of arc per oersted per centimeter. The sense of the rotation is dependent on whether the light is traveling in the direction of the magnetic field or opposite to this direction; if it is clockwise in one case, it is counterclockwise in the other. Thus the plane of vibration is rotated through an angle $\theta$ when the light passes through the medium while under the influence of the magnetic field and is again rotated through the same angle when the light reflects back through the medium, the total rotation angle being $2\theta$. On the other hand, when a reflection occurs in an optically active substance like quartz, the rotations in the forward and backward traversal of the beam cancel. Since the sense of rotation is reversed when the direction of the magnetic field is reversed, the positive rotation corresponds to the rotation of a right-handed screw when it advances in the direction of the magnetic field. An explanation of the Faraday effect follows the principles taken up in reference to the Zeeman effect discussed in Sec. 17.9.

**16.18. The Cornu-Jellet Polarimeter.** We have seen that the concentration of an optically active substance, in the presence of an optically inactive one, is determinable by measuring the angle of rotatory polarization. This is done by using a polariscope whose analyzer is equipped with a circular scale and which is then called a *polarimeter*. The saccharimeter mentioned in Sec. 16.15 is a polarimeter specially designed to test sugar solutions.

In the simple form of polarimeter the polarizer and analyzer nicols are in a crossed position, the optically active substance is inserted, and the analyzer is reset to produce extinction again. Angles of rotation obtained with this simple type of polarimeter have rather low precision in view of the fact that it is difficult to locate the position of the analyzer for extinction with any high degree of certainty. In 1860 Jellet overcame this difficulty by utilizing the photometric principle of matching two adjacent illuminated fields. The prism he devised for this purpose was modified by Cornu; its method of construction and operation is illustrated in Fig. 16.26, and it is known as the Cornu-Jellet prism. It consists of a nicol prism with a removed wedge-shaped section running the full length of the nicol and shown by the dotted lines in the end view (a). The two parts are then cemented together as shown in (b), with the result that the vibration planes of the two parts make a small angle with each other. When this prism is used as polarizer in the polarimeter, there is no position of the analyzer that causes simultaneous extinction of the beams transmitted by both parts of the prism. However, there is a position of the analyzer for which the transmitted beams are of equal intensity, and each half of the field looks equally bright. Such a setting can be made with greater precision since the eye is able to detect very small differences of intensity.

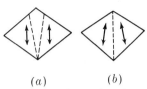

(a)        (b)

FIG. 16.26. Principle of the Cornu-Jellet prism.

The angle made by the vibration planes of the two parts of the Cornu-Jellet prism is called the *half-shadow angle*. There are other polarimeters that utilize some "half-shade" scheme that produces a sharply divided field of view, the vibration plane of one half making a small angle with that of the other half. For a treatment of the various kinds of polarimeters the student is referred to other sources.[1]

### PROBLEMS

**16.1.** On the same graph plot the reflecting power [Eqs. (16.11) and (16.12)], in per cent as a function of the angle of incidence $\phi$ from $0°$ to $90°$. Plot also the curve obtained by adding one-half of Eq. (16.11) to one-half of Eq. (16.12). Discuss the significance of the curves. Use $_1n_2 = 1.50$.

**16.2.** An unpolarized beam in air is incident at an angle of $30°$ on a glass medium of refractive index 1.50. Calculate the percentages of the light refracted, using Eqs. (16.13) and (16.14).

**16.3.** What is the polarizing angle for glass whose index of refraction for the light used is 1.682?

**16.4.** A source is placed in front of a polariscope which is first set at $30°$ and then set at $45°$. What is the intensity ratio of the transmitted light for both settings?

**16.5.** The intensities of two sources are compared by a polariscope as follows: The transmitted intensity is noted when one source is used and the principal sections of polarizer and analyzer make an angle of $30°$ with each other. Then the second source is used and the analyzer adjusted to give the same amount of transmitted intensity for which the principal sections make an angle of $60°$. Find the intensity ratio of the two sources.

**16.6.** The polarizer and analyzer of a polariscope are in parallel relationship, and a birefracting crystal is inserted between them with its principal section oriented at $60°$

[1] Sir Richard Glazebrook, "A Dictionary of Applied Physics," pp. 474–490, Macmillan & Co., Ltd., London, 1923.

with that of the polarizer.   Find the amplitude ratio of the vibration components transmitted through the crystal and through the analyzer.

**16.7.** Draw a ray diagram showing the passage of the $O$ and $E$ beams passing through the principal sections illustrating the case shown in Fig. 16.9*f*.

**16.8.** Make a Huygens construction for the case of a plane wave incident obliquely on the crystal of Fig. 16.13.

**16.9.** Make a Huygens construction for the case of a plane wave incident obliquely on the crystal of Fig. 16.14.

**16.10.** Make a Huygens construction for the case of a plane wave incident normally on the crystal of Fig. 16.15.

**16.11.** White light is incident on each of the calcite prisms shown in the figure.   In (*a*) the optic axis is parallel to the refracting edge of the prism as shown by the dots. In (*b*) the optic axis is perpendicular to the refracting edge as shown by the horizontal lines.   For each case indicate what is obtained on the emergent side of the prism.

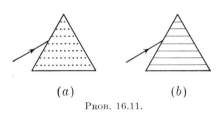

(*a*)                    (*b*)

Prob. 16.11.

**16.12.** Could the Rochon prism be used with light incident on face *BC* of Fig. 16.16*a*?   Explain.

**16.13.** The principal indices of refraction for calcite are measured by a spectrometer with a 60° calcite refracting prism cut with the optic axis parallel to the refracting edge.   For sodium light the angles of minimum deviation for the $O$ and $E$ rays are found to be 52° and 36°, respectively.   Compute the indices of refraction.

**16.14.** A beam of linearly polarized light, of wavelength 5461 A, falls normally on a calcite crystal slab cut with the optic axis in the plane of incidence and parallel to the surface.   (*a*) For what minimum thickness of crystal are the emergent $O$ and $E$ beams $\pi/3$ out of phase?   (*b*) What is the thickness if quartz is used?   Principal indices of refraction are for calcite $n_O = 1.662$, $n_E = 1.488$; for quartz $n_O = 1.546$, $n_E = 1.555$.

**16.15.** Compute the minimum thickness of quarter- and half-wave plates of calcite and quartz for the wavelength 5461 A.   The indices of refraction are given in Prob. 16.14.

**16.16.** Show that the phase difference of the rays emerging from a Babinet compensator is given by $(2\pi/\lambda)(d_1 - d_2)(n_E - n_O)$, where $d_1$ is the thickness traversed by the rays in one wedge and $d_2$ is the thickness traversed in the other wedge of Fig. 16.22. What is the significance of the condition $d_1 = d_2$?

**16.17.** A Babinet compensator is inserted between two crossed nicols and oriented at 45° with the polarizer.   Describe the appearance of the pattern emerging from the analyzer for (*a*) monochromatic light, (*b*) white light.

**16.18.** Plot Eq. (16.21) as a function of $\delta$ for $\theta = 45°$ and $A = 1$.   Interpret the graph.

**16.19.** Plot Eq. (16.22) as a function of $\delta$ for $\theta = 45°$ and $A = 1$.   Interpret the graph.

**16.20.** The specific rotation of quartz for 5893 A is 21.72°/mm. What thickness of quartz, cut perpendicular to its optic axis and inserted in a polariscope with parallel nicols, will cause no light to be transmitted?

**16.21.** The specific rotation of sucrose at 5893 A and 20°C is 66.5°/dm/gm/cm³. (a) What rotation is produced for sodium light by a 20.0-cm solution containing 25.0 gm of sucrose per 100 cm³ of solution at 20°C? (b) How much is the circular birefringence? (c) The expression for the specific rotation of sucrose is $66.5 + 0.87C - 2.4C^2$, where $C$ is the concentration in grams per cubic centimeter of solution. By what percentage does the result change in (a) if this expression is employed?

**16.22.** The specific rotation for quartz is 25.54°/mm at 5461 A and 48.95°/mm at 4047 A. Determine the constants in Eq. (16.24) in this range of wavelengths.

**16.23.** A glass plate 3.00 cm thick is placed in a magnetic field of 20,000 oersteds. Through what angle is linearly polarized sodium light rotated when directed through the glass and in the direction of the field? The Verdet constant of the glass is 16.2 $\times$ $10^{-3}$ min of arc per oersted per centimeter.

**16.24.** Sodium light is linearly polarized by a nicol prism and then passes through a 1.00-cm path of $CS_2$ placed in a magnetic field. If the light is made to reflect back through the solution, for what field strength is the rotation of the vibration plane such that no light returns through the polarizer? The light is directed parallel to the magnetic field. The Verdet constant of $CS_2$ at 5893 A is 42.3 $\times$ $10^{-3}$ min of arc per oersted per centimeter.

# CHAPTER 17

## SPECTRA

In this chapter we shall be concerned with the emission of light by various light sources and with the physical mechanism of the emission and absorption of radiation by atoms. The subject is part of the large field known as *spectroscopy*, whose experimental and theoretical researches have led not only to a satisfactory understanding of atomic structure but also to such revolutionary developments as the quantum theory and wave mechanics. We shall see how the vast amount of experimental data that had been accumulated over the past 67 years (really since 1666, when Newton discovered that different colors when passing through a prism were refracted by different amounts, thus marking the beginning of spectroscopy) necessitated for their explanation a radical departure from the classical concepts.

In devoting one chapter to the subject of spectra it will not be possible to offer an adequate treatment. In presenting an outline of some of the experimental facts and an indication of how they have been brought into harmony with modern mathematical theory, we hope that the student will have been stimulated sufficiently to pursue the subject further.

**17.1. Kinds of Spectra.** Spectra are classified as either *emission spectra* or *absorption spectra*. To obtain an emission spectrum, the light from a luminous source is sent through a spectroscope. For an absorption spectrum the light from a luminous source, giving off a continuous range of wavelengths, is first sent through the absorbing substance and then through the spectroscope. Emission and absorption spectra are further classified according to their appearance as *line, continuous*, and *band* spectra.

When the light emitted from a given source is concentrated on the slit of a prism or grating spectroscope, there is produced a spectrum of the different colors or wavelengths present in the light. If the source is a low-pressure atomic or ionic gas, made luminous by passing an electrical discharge through it or a flame containing a salt or by producing an incandescent gas between the terminals of an electrical arc or spark, the spectrum is discontinuous, showing a series of parallel, differently colored lines. Each line is an image of the slit formed by light of a wavelength corresponding to the particular color of the slit image. The entire series of images is called a *line emission spectrum*, and the linear shape of the

370

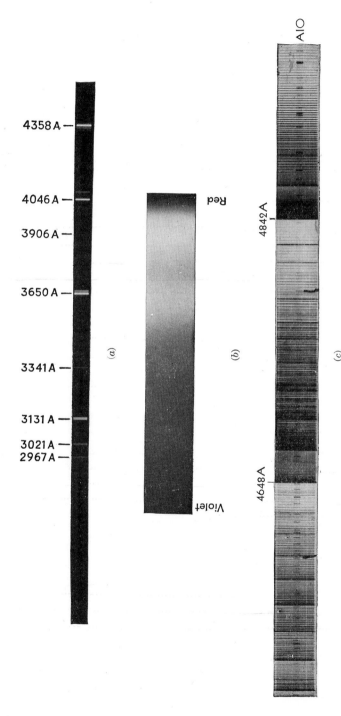

FIG. 17.1. Examples of (a) a line spectrum of mercury, (b) a continuous spectrum of an incandescent tungsten source, (c) a band spectrum of a diatomic aluminum oxide molecule. [*Photograph (c) by permission from "Physics—Principles and Applications" by H. Margenau, W. W. Watson, and C. G. Montgomery. Copyright, 1949. McGraw-Hill Book Company, Inc.*]

images is due to the use of a slit as a secondary source of light. The use of a narrow slit has advantages over an opening of other shapes such a circular opening, *viz.*, the narrow slit images in neighboring wavelengths are more easily discernible; a low-intensity image is much easier to observe when it is long and straight; a good adjustable slit can more easily be made than a small adjustable circular opening. A typical line spectrum is illustrated by the photograph of the spectrum of a gas in Fig. 17.1*a*. The particular set of wavelengths obtained from such a photograph together with the relative intensities of the lines are uniquely characteristic of the light-emitting element. The student should note especially that the line spectrum represents the emission of a discrete set of colors or wavelengths. In order to explain the line spectrum, it is necessary to employ the quantum theory.

When the emitting source is an incandescent solid or liquid, or an incandescent gas at high pressure, the spectrum is continuous, containing light of all wavelengths as shown in Fig. 17.1*b*. In a liquid, solid, or high-pressure gas the atoms are much closer together than in a low-pressure gas with the result that any atom is under the influence of its neighbors. The definite discrete frequencies emitted by the atoms of a low-pressure gas are thus modified in the more closely packed states to the extent that a continuous spread of frequencies results. The quantum theory is again successful in explaining this phenomenon.

In Fig. 17.1*c* is shown a photograph of a band spectrum. Such a spectrum contains a series of bands each of which is characterized by what is called a *head* or sharp edge on one side, and from there the band gradually shades off. On closer examination under high dispersion and resolving power it is found that each band is composed of many individual lines. In other words, the individual spectral lines are so close together with a nonuniform distribution in frequency and intensity that they form what appears to be a band. Whereas line spectra are due to the emission from the atoms or ions of a gas, band spectra arise as a result of the radiation from gas molecules. For example, gases such as oxygen ($O_2$) and nitrogen ($N_2$) are diatomic, containing two atoms per molecule. If the excitation is insufficient to dissociate the molecule into atoms, there is produced a band spectrum. The quantum theory is again necessary to give an adequate explanation of band spectra.

The corresponding absorption spectra are obtained when the absorbing substance, gas, solid, or liquid, is interposed between a source emitting a continuous range of wavelengths and the slit of the spectroscope. In such cases certain wavelengths are absorbed, and the spectrum appears dark on a bright background. For instance, a line absorption spectrum is formed when the absorbing substance is a monotomic gas at low pressure and lower temperature than that of the light source. A familiar example of such a spectrum is the solar spectrum, which is continuous with the exception of the *Fraunhofer lines*, which are easily observed in a slit spectroscope directed toward the sky. The most prominent Fraunhofer lines are designated by letters, and some of these are shown in Table 17.1 together with the corresponding wavelengths and absorbing elements. The explanation of the dark Fraunhofer lines in the solar

TABLE 17.1. THE MOST PROMINENT FRAUNHOFER LINES

| Line | Wave length, A | Absorbing element | Line | Wave length, A | Absorbing element |
|------|----------------|-------------------|------|----------------|-------------------|
| $A$ | 7594–7621 | $O_2$ | $G'$ | 4340.47 | H |
| $B$ | 6867–6884 | $O_2$ | $G$ | 4307.91 | Fe |
| | | | | 4307.75 | Ca |
| $C$ | 6562.82 | H | $g$ | 4226.73 | Ca |
| $D_1$ | 5895.92 | Na | $h$ | 4101.74 | H |
| $D_2$ | 5889.95 | Na | $H$ | 3968.47 | Ca |
| $D_3$ | 5875.62 | He | $K$ | 3933.67 | Ca |
| $E_2$ | 5269.55 | Fe | $L$ | 3820.44 | Fe |
| $b_1$ | 5183.62 | Mg | $M$ | 3727.64 | Fe |
| $b_2$ | 5172.70 | Mg | $N$ | 3581.21 | Fe |
| $F$ | 4861.33 | H | $O$ | 3441.02 | Fe |

spectrum was first given by Kirchhoff. He concluded that the sun is surrounded by an atmosphere of cooler gases which absorb the bright lines emitted from the hot interior. Kirchhoff also enunciated the law that bears his name and states that *the ratio between the powers of emission and the powers of absorption of rays for the same wavelength and temperature is a constant for all bodies.* According to this law the gas absorbs those wavelengths which it emits when it is an incandescent source. In the laboratory this can be demonstrated by passing white light from an arc through sodium vapor and observing that there appear in the continuous spectrum two black lines at the exact wavelength positions of the two sodium yellow emission lines $D_1$ and $D_2$. The Fraunhofer lines given in Table 17.1 are then due to absorption in the upper layers of the sun's atmosphere and in the earth's atmosphere. The $A$ and $B$ Fraunhofer lines are bands due to the absorption by molecular oxygen in the earth's atmosphere.

The appearance of a dark line due to absorption, where normally there would be a bright spectral line, is termed *reversal.* The Fraunhofer lines are reversed emission lines. When an atom absorbs certain lines which it itself emits, the phenomenon is termed *self-reversal.* In such cases there appears a sharp absorption line at the center of a broader emission line. For instance, the copper lines 3247 A and 3274 A from a copper spark are broader than usual, and the copper atoms of the cooler vapor of the outer portion of the spark absorb the center of the broad copper emission line, forming a central sharp absorption line against the background of a bright emission line.

**17.2. Spectral Series.** The relative positions of the lines of a typical spectral series is illustrated in Fig. 17.2. Such a simple line spectrum is obtained from the hydrogen atom and shows the characteristics of a gradual decrease in interline spacings and intensities with decrease in

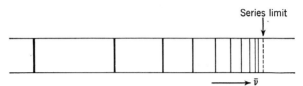

FIG. 17.2. Appearance of a spectral series.

wavelength and of an approach to a limiting wavelength. The symbol $\bar{\nu}$ shown in the figure, is the *wave number* defined by the relation

$$\bar{\nu} = \frac{1}{\lambda} \tag{17.1}$$

which represents the number of waves per centimeter of light path in vacuum and measured in reciprocal centimeters. The frequency of spectrum lines is usually expressed in wave numbers for convenience and given by $\bar{\nu} = \nu/c$, where $\nu$ is the frequency and $c$ is the velocity of light. In the spectra of the elements, lines may be found that appear to form a series having the characteristics illustrated in Fig. 17.2.

That there was a definite order in a spectral series was first shown, in 1885, by Balmer, who discovered the law of the visible hydrogen-line series. He showed that the wavelengths of the lines were represented by an empirical simple formula which, in accordance with the modern notation, has the form

$$\bar{\nu} = \frac{1}{\lambda} = 109{,}678 \left( \frac{1}{2^2} - \frac{1}{n^2} \right) \tag{17.2}$$

The formula gives the wave number in cm$^{-1}$ of the first line of the series when $n = 3$, of the second line when $n = 4$, of the third when $n = 5$, etc. As $n$ approaches infinity, the lines crowd together and approach the series limit whose value is 27,419.5 cm$^{-1}$ or 3647 A. Following Balmer's work, there were discovered other spectral series for hydrogen, named after their discoverers Lyman, Paschen, Brackett, and Pfund. Below are listed the formulas representing these series including the Balmer series. **The successive indicated values**

$$\nu = R Z^2 \left( \frac{1}{n_2} - \frac{1}{n_1} \right) \quad \text{Rydberg Constant}$$

$R$

$$\bar{\nu} = 109{,}678 \left( \frac{1}{1^2} - \frac{1}{n^2} \right) \qquad n = 2, 3, 4, \ldots \text{ ultraviolet}$$
$$\text{(Lyman series)}$$

$$\bar{\nu} = 109{,}678 \left( \frac{1}{2^2} - \frac{1}{n^2} \right) \qquad n = 3, 4, 5, \ldots$$
$$\text{(Balmer series)}$$

$$\bar{\nu} = 109{,}678 \left( \frac{1}{3^2} - \frac{1}{n^2} \right) \qquad n = 4, 5, 6, \ldots$$
$$\text{(Paschen series)} \qquad (17.3)$$

$$\bar{\nu} = 109{,}678 \left( \frac{1}{4^2} - \frac{1}{n^2} \right) \qquad n = 5, 6, 7, \ldots \text{ infrared}$$
$$\text{(Brackett series)}$$

$$\bar{\nu} = 109{,}678 \left( \frac{1}{5^2} - \frac{1}{n^2} \right) \qquad n = 6, 7, 8, \ldots$$
$$\text{(Pfund series)}$$

for $n$ yield the lines of the particular series. All the series are emitted by atomic hydrogen in a glow discharge in which the $H_2$ molecules dissociate into H atoms. The Lyman series lie in the ultraviolet, and the Paschen, Brackett, and Pfund series lie in the infrared.

The vast amount of work that has been done on the analysis of spectra since the time of Balmer has shown that for elements other than hydrogen the spectral lines can in general be grouped into series. The spectra are much more complex, and there occurs for a given element in general several different series. For instance, in the spectra of the alkali atoms, lithium, sodium, potassium, rubidium, and cesium, the lines of each element can be fitted into four series. Three of the series were originally named the *principal, sharp,* and *diffuse* series, since the appearance of the lines in the series was respectively very strong, sharp, and diffuse. The fourth series, in the infrared region and of weak intensity, is called the Bergmann series after its founder. In addition each of the series of the higher atomic weight elements consists of doublets, triplets, quartets, or higher multiplet groups of lines. We shall have more to say about complex spectral series later in the chapter, after we have seen that the spectrum of a hydrogenlike atom is explainable by Bohr's quantum theory.

**17.3. Quantum Theory of Radiation.** In 1900 Planck introduced the basic concept of the quantum theory in his explanation of the radiation emitted from a black body. A black body is one which is capable of absorbing all the radiation of every wavelength incident upon it. There is no known surface that absorbs all the radiant energy incident on it although some substances absorb up to 99 per cent. Nevertheless, a black body may be approximated to a high degree by an enclosure containing an extremely small opening. Radiant energy entering the opening is almost entirely "trapped" owing to the repeated reflection and absorption in the interior of the enclosure, thus giving the opening the characteristics of a black body. A hot black body emits radiation of all wavelengths having a spectral-energy distribution that exhibits a maximum at a wavelength that depends on the temperature of the black body. On either side of the maximum the energy falls, more rapidly on the short-wavelength side than on the long-wavelength side. All attempts to explain this distribution of energy among the continuous range of wavelengths, on the basis of the classical theory of light, had failed. In his explanation Planck assumed that the radiating body was composed of a large number of oscillators having all possible frequencies of vibration. To obtain agreement with experiment, he made the revolutionary assumption that these oscillators, which give rise to the radiant energy, cannot assume any arbitrary value of energy but that the energy $E$ of a resonator is proportional to an integral multiple of its frequency $\nu$. His postulate of so-called *quantized* energy values is embodied in the equation

$$E = h\nu \tag{17.4}$$

where $h$ is the proportionality constant known as Planck's constant and $h\nu$ is a *quantum* of energy of frequency $\nu$. The radiation of frequency $\nu$ is thus emitted or absorbed in discrete bundles of energy or quanta, the energy of each quantum being given by Eq. (17.4). Each oscillator can contain an integral number of such quanta, and when it loses one quantum of energy, radiation of energy $h\nu$ is emitted. The universal constant $h$ has the value $6.62 \times 10^{-27}$ erg sec.

In Planck's assertions the view was held that the resonators could take on only those energies which were in accord with the quantum condition expressed by Eq. (17.4), but the energy that was radiated by the oscillators Planck considered to be propagated through space in accordance with the classical electromagnetic theory. Several years later, in 1905, Einstein extended the quantum condition to the radiation itself and expressed the idea of light quanta, or *photons* as he called the discrete packets of energy. Accordingly radiation is not continuous in energy but is composed of packages of energy, or photons, whose value is given by Eq. (17.4). A light source does not then radiate a spherical wave with energy uniformly distributed over the wave front, but there occurs instead a statistical emission of photons in all directions. That light does possess this corpuscular aspect has undoubtedly been confirmed by various phenomena involving the interaction between radiation and matter. Two such phenomena are outstanding for the evidence they furnish in favor of the corpuscular nature of photons. One of these is the Compton effect, which we have discussed in Sec. 15.6. The other is the *photoelectric effect*, which cannot be explained by the electromagnetic theory of light and awaited the application of quantum theory by Einstein for its complete understanding. When light of a suitable wavelength falls on a metal plate, such as ultraviolet light on zinc, electrons are liberated, or emitted, from the metal surface and this phenomenon is known as the photoelectric effect. The essential features of the experimental results are as follows:

1. When the intensity of the incident monochromatic light is varied, the maximum velocity of the electrons emitted from the surface is independent of the light intensity. On the basis of classical electromagnetic theory the emission of the electrons is due to the forces exerted on them by the electric and magnetic fields of the light wave. The penetration of the light wave somewhat into the interior of the metal gives rise to photoelectrons at different depths below the surface, and those electrons which originate in the deeper layers lose more energy in emerging from the metal than do the electrons originating near the surface. The photoelectrons having the maximum kinetic energy are then those originating on the metal surface. However, increasing the intensity of the light means increasing the electromagnetic field, and, classically, we should expect an increase in the maximum velocity of the photoelectrons. On the contrary, experiment shows that light-intensity variation has no effect on the velocities of the expelled electrons but proportionally increases the rate of expulsion of the electrons.

2. When the intensity of the incident light is held constant and the wavelength is varied, experiment shows that the maximum velocity of the expelled photoelectrons increases as the frequency of the incident radiation increases. According to the electromagnetic theory a change of frequency, say from the infrared to the ultraviolet, should have little if any effect on the velocities of the expelled electrons. Furthermore, experiment shows that the photoelectric effect ceases when the frequency gets down to a value known as the *threshold* frequency below which no electrons are emitted.

The quantum theory, as applied by Einstein, was immediately successful in explaining the experimental facts of the photoelectric effect. According to Einstein, when light of frequency $\nu$ is employed, photons of energy $h\nu$ fall onto the metal and the energy of each photon that contributes to the photoelectric effect is transferred to a single electron. An amount $w$ of this energy is required to liberate the electron from the metal surface, and the remainder appears as kinetic energy of the electron. Thus the maximum kinetic energy $E_k$ with which the electron leaves the surface is given by

$$E_k = h\nu - w \qquad (17.5)$$

which is the well-known Einstein photoelectric equation, in which the quantity $w$ is called the *work function* of the surface. An electron that originates at some depth below the surface may expend an energy greater than $w$ in emerging and so possesses a kinetic energy less than the maximum. Millikan, in 1915, made an accurate test of Einstein's equation and found it in harmony with the experimental results. The equation shows that the maximum velocity of the photoelectrons increases with increase in frequency; the greater the energy of a photon, the greater the energy transferred to the electron and the greater its kinetic energy. When $h\nu < w$ for a given surface, no electrons can be photoelectrically emitted so that the threshold frequency is given by $\nu = w/h$ or the corresponding wavelength is $ch/w$. When the intensity of the light is increased and the wavelength is kept constant, the energy of each incident photon remains the same but there are more of them striking unit area of the surface per unit time. Therefore more photoelectrons are expelled per unit area of the surface per unit time, their maximum kinetic energy remaining the same.

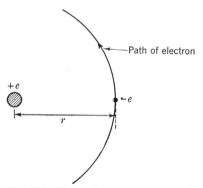

Fig. 17.3. The nucleus (charge $+e$) and the electron (charge $-e$) of the hydrogen atom.

Einstein's extension of the Planck quantum concept to radiation itself, and the consequent explanation of the photoelectric effect, is a significant example of the manifestation of the corpuscular aspect of radiation when it interacts with matter. In 1913 Niels Bohr extended the quantum theory to the atom and not only was successful in explaining the spectral series of hydrogen but thus laid the basis of our modern views of atomic structure. We turn to this development in the next section.

**17.4. Bohr's Theory of the Hydrogen Atom.** Bohr's derivation of a quantitative relationship for a spectral series, on the basis of an atomic model, started with his adopting Rutherford's nuclear model of the atom. Rutherford's researches had led him to hypothesize that an atom consists of a small core or nucleus possessing a positive charge and comprising almost the entire mass of the atom. It was further proposed that the nucleus is surrounded, at distances far removed from it, by a distribution of negatively charged electrons so that under normal conditions the atom is electrically neutral with as much negative charge balancing the positive charge of the nucleus. To prevent the electrons from being drawn to the nucleus by the existing attractive forces, Rutherford postulated that the electrons revolved about the nucleus in closed orbits, the Coulomb force of attraction between nucleus and electron supplying the requisite centripetal force. The simplest case at hand is the hydrogen atom containing a nucleus of charge $+e$, and a single planetary electron of charge $-e$ at a distance $r$ from the nucleus, as shown in Fig. 17.3. Bohr first considered the electron to revolve in a circular orbit with the relatively massive nucleus at rest at the center of the orbit. The electrostatic force of attraction between the charges, and given by Coulomb's law, is equal to the centripetal force, or

$$\frac{mv^2}{r} = \frac{e^2}{r^2}$$

which yields

$$mv^2 = \frac{e^2}{r} \tag{17.6}$$

where $m$ is the mass of the electron and $v$ its linear speed along the circular path. The kinetic energy of the electron is $\frac{1}{2} mv^2$. The potential at a distance $r$ from the nucleus is $e/r$ so that the potential energy of the electron at this distance is $(e/r)(-e) = -e^2/r$. This potential energy represents the fact that we must do an amount of work $e^2/r$ on the system in order to remove the electron to infinity from a point distant $r$ from the nucleus, the zero level of potential energy being considered at infinity. The total energy $E$ is given by

$$E = \frac{1}{2} mv^2 - \frac{e^2}{r} \tag{17.7}$$

Substituting the value for $mv^2$ from Eq. (17.6), we have

$$E = -\frac{e^2}{2r} \tag{17.8}$$

Since the nucleus has been considered stationary, Eq. (17.8) represents the total energy of the atom and this energy decreases as $r$ decreases. The energy is negative as a consequence of having chosen the zero level of potential energy at infinity.

In accordance with the classical picture thus far presented, Eq. (17.8) states that the atom should radiate energy continuously in view of the fact that classical electromagnetic theory requires that energy be radiated as a result of acceleration of electric charge and a particle rotating in a circle is continuously accelerated toward the center of curvature. The total energy of the atom would then have to decrease, which means that $r$ would gradually decrease and approach a zero value spiraling into the nucleus. Equation (17.8) states also that the atom could have any possible energy value whatsoever, since $r$ could have any value consistent with the corresponding value $v$. These facts add up to the conclusion that the hydrogen spectrum should be continuous with all frequencies present. As we have seen, such a conclusion contradicts the experimental fact that hydrogen atoms emit a sharp line spectrum with sharply defined frequencies. It was this failure of the classical theories to account for line spectra that led to the development of the quantum theory of spectra by Bohr and others.

To explain the then existing discrepancy, Bohr introduced the following famous two postulates:

1. *Not all electron orbits dictated by the classical theory are permitted, only those orbits being allowable for which the angular momentum of the electron is an integral multiple of $h/2\pi$, where $h$ is Planck's constant and has the value $6.62 \times 10^{-27}$ erg sec. Also, while an electron is in one of these orbits, known as a "stationary" state, the atom does not radiate any energy even though the electron has an acceleration $v^2/r$.*

2. *Energy is emitted or absorbed by an atom in whole quanta of amount $h\nu$, and then only when an electron passes over, or jumps, from one orbit of one allowable radius to another orbit of another permissible radius. If the electron changes from an initial orbit of energy $E_i$ to a final orbit of energy $E_f$, then the energy radiated or absorbed is $E_i - E_f$ and the frequency $\nu$ of the radiation is*

$$\nu = \frac{E_i - E_f}{h} \tag{17.9}$$

*If $E_i$ is associated with an outer orbit and $E_f$ with an inner orbit, then $E_i > E_f$ and the energy is radiated. If $E_i$ is associated with an inner orbit and $E_f$ with an outer orbit, then the energy is absorbed.*

Since the angular momentum, or moment of momentum, of the electron is $mvr$, the quantum principle expressed in the first postulate takes the form

$$mvr = \frac{nh}{2\pi}, \qquad n = 1, 2, 3, \ldots \tag{17.10}$$

Substituting the value for $v$ from Eq. (17.10) into Eq. (17.6) and solving for the permissible radii $r_n$, corresponding to the orbit number or quantum number $n$, gives

$$r_n = \frac{n^2 h^2}{4\pi^2 m e^2} \tag{17.11}$$

Utilizing Eq. (17.8), the corresponding expression for the energy $E_n$ is

$$E_n = -\frac{2\pi^2 m e^4}{h^2 n^2} \tag{17.12}$$

Making use of the second postulate [Eq. (17.9)] and representing the initial and final energy states by $E_{n_i}$ and $E_{n_f}$ corresponding to the quantum numbers $n_i$ and $n_f$, we have for the wave numbers the expression

$$\bar{\nu} = \frac{2\pi^2 m e^4}{ch^3} \left( \frac{1}{n_f^2} - \frac{1}{n_i^2} \right) \tag{17.13}$$

Equation (17.13) is more often written in the form

$$\bar{\nu} = R \left( \frac{1}{n_f^2} - \frac{1}{n_i^2} \right) \tag{17.14}$$

where

$$R = \frac{2\pi^2 m e^4}{ch^3} \qquad \text{not quite right} \tag{17.15}$$

is called the *Rydberg constant.*

The theory shows that there is a definite set of stable orbits whose radii are calculable from Eq. (17.11) and whose energies are obtainable from Eq. (17.12), both depending on the value of the integral quantum number $n$. The wave numbers and hence the frequencies of the light waves emitted, when there is an electron transition from an orbit of higher quantum number $n_i$ to one of lower quantum number $n_f$, are calculable from Eq. (17.14). Equation (17.14) is of the same form as Eqs. (17.3), and to complete the identity, it is necessary to establish that the value of $R$ in Eq. (17.14) is the same as the empirical constant in Eqs. (17.3). Each quantity in Eq. (17.15) is determinable by means not dependent on the Bohr theory. The mass and charge of the electron are obtained from experiments with electrons, and $h$ can be obtained from the photoelectric effect. The quantity $c$ is the velocity of light. Substituting the values $m = 9.1055 \times 10^{-28}$ gm, $e = 4.8024 \times 10^{-10}$ esu,

$$h = 6.6234 \times 10^{-27} \text{ erg sec,}$$

$c = 2.9978 \times 10^{10}$ cm/sec yields

$$R = \frac{2\pi^2 m e^4}{ch^3} = 1.0976 \times 10^5 \text{ cm}^{-1} \tag{17.16}$$

which agrees with the empirically determined constant in Eqs. (17.3) to within 0.1 per cent. We have used the best modern values of the constants to calculate $R$, and when Bohr used the values known to him at the time, he concluded that the agreement was within the experimental errors involved in the determination of these constants. This constituted another great achievement of the quantum theory and represented a very significant advance in our understanding of atomic radiation. The Lyman series are then a result of the electrons in the different atoms falling from the second, third, fourth, etc., Bohr orbits to the first orbit, corresponding to $n_f = 1$ and $n_i$ taking on the values 2, 3, 4, etc. The Balmer series is produced when $n_f = 2$ and $n_i$ takes on the series of values 3, 4, 5, etc. Any one atom of course emits one photon of frequency $\nu$ at any instant, but while a group of atoms has electron transitions from, say, the third orbit to the second, there is a group having electron transitions from the fifth orbit to the second, and other groups having other possible electron transitions. With millions of atoms in a sample of incandescent hydrogen all the possible transitions are occurring, forming the observed series of lines. The relative intensity of a line depends on the relative number of atoms which are experiencing that particular electron transition.

It will be recalled that some simplifying assumptions have been introduced in the derivation of Eq. (17.14). In the first place, a fixed nucleus was considered, which means a nucleus of infinite mass. Actually the nucleus and electron rotate about their common center of mass, the electron revolving in a large circular orbit and the nucleus in a much smaller one. Taking $m_e$ as the mass of the electron which is distant $r_e$ from the center of mass and $m_N$ and $r_N$ as the corresponding quantities for the nucleus, we have

$$m_e r_e = m_N r_N \qquad (17.17)$$

The angular velocity of rotation $\omega$ is the same for electron and nucleus, so that the total angular momentum about the center of mass is

$$m_e r_e^2 \omega + m_N r_N^2 \omega = m_e r_e r \omega = \frac{m_e m_N}{m_e + m_N} r^2 \omega$$

where $r = r_e + r_N$ is the distance of the electron from the nucleus. Quantizing the total angular momentum according to Bohr's first postulate gives

$$\mu r^2 \omega = \frac{nh}{2\pi} \qquad (17.18)$$

where

$$\mu = \frac{m_e m_N}{m_e + m_N} \qquad (17.19)$$

is the so-called "reduced mass." The dynamical equation corresponding to Eq. (17.6) here takes the form

$$m_e r_e \omega^2 = \frac{e^2}{r^2}$$

and since $r_e = m_N r / (m_e + m_N)$, we have

$$\mu r \omega^2 = \frac{e^2}{r^2} \qquad (17.20)$$

The total kinetic energy is

$$\frac{1}{2} m_e r_e^2 \omega^2 + \frac{1}{2} m_N r_N^2 \omega^2 = \frac{1}{2} \mu r^2 \omega^2 = \frac{e^2}{r} \qquad (17.21)$$

and since the potential energy is as before $-e^2/r$, the energy of the atom is again given by

$$E = -\frac{e^2}{2r}$$

From Eqs. (17.18) and (17.20) we have, for the permissible values of the electron-nuclear distance $r_n$,

$$r_n = \frac{n^2 h^2}{4\pi^2 \mu e^2} \tag{17.22}$$

and for the total energy

$$E_n = -\frac{2\pi^2 \mu e^4}{h^2 n^2} \tag{17.23}$$

Comparing Eqs. (17.18) to (17.23) with the corresponding equations for the case of the fixed nucleus shows that the introduction of the motion of the nucleus has the effect of replacing the electronic mass by the reduced mass. The wave numbers corresponding to Eq. (17.14) are now more correctly given by

$$\bar{\nu} = R\left(\frac{1}{n_f^2} - \frac{1}{n_i^2}\right) \tag{17.24}$$

where the Rydberg constant is given by

Correct
Equation

$\mu$ introduced

$$R = \frac{2\pi^2 \mu e^4}{ch^3} = \frac{2\pi^2 m_e e^4}{ch^3}\frac{1}{1 + (m_e/m_N)} \tag{17.25}$$

Thus the nuclear motion causes the permissible orbital radii, the allowed energies, the wave numbers, and the Rydberg constant to vary slightly with $m_N$ or with the atomic weight. When $m_N$ is infinite, Eq. (17.25) shows that $R$ has its greatest value. This is designated as $R_\infty$ with the value

$$R_\infty = \frac{2\pi^2 m_e e^4}{ch^3} \tag{17.26}$$

which, as we now see, is the value we calculated in Eq. (17.16). The Rydberg constant for hydrogen is

$$R_H = \frac{R_\infty}{1 + (m_e/M_H)} \tag{17.27}$$

An experimental value for $R_\infty$ is obtained by using the spectroscopic value for $R_H$ and the ratio $m_e/m_H$. The very precise spectroscopic determination of $R$ is 109,737.30 cm$^{-1}$, and the value 1.0976 $\times$ 10$^{-5}$ cm$^{-1}$, computed from the constants in Eq. (17.26), differs from the experimental value by about 0.02 per cent.

So far we have considered a single electron in motion around an atomic nucleus. In Rutherford's atomic theory, the charge on the nucleus of the atom is $+Ze$, and the number of surrounding extranuclear electrons, or the atomic number, is $Z$. Equation (17.24) holds for an atom containing one electron and may be adjusted to hold for ions which have a hydrogenlike structure by tracing through the derivation and observing that this introduces the additional factor $Z^2$, so that Eq. (17.24) is replaced by

$$\bar{\nu} = Z^2 R \left( \frac{1}{n_f^2} - \frac{1}{n_i^2} \right)$$
(17.28)

where $R$ has the value given in Eq. (17.25). For the neutral hydrogen atom, $Z = 1$, and the Rydberg constant is designated as in Eq. (17.27). The empirical value of $R_H$ is the constant appearing in Eqs. (17.3). Equation (17.28) also holds for helium atoms ($Z = 2$) which have lost one electron or singly ionized helium atoms, for lithium atoms ($Z = 3$) which have lost two electrons or doubly ionized lithium atoms, for triply ionized beryllium ($Z = 4$), etc. For instance, for helium the wave numbers of the spectra are represented by

$$\bar{\nu} = 4R_{He} \left( \frac{1}{n_f^2} - \frac{1}{n_i^2} \right)$$
(17.29)

with

$$R_{He} = \frac{R_\infty}{1 + (m_e/m_{He})}$$
(17.30)

Helium series, which have been found experimentally, are the first Lyman series with $n_f = 1$ and $n_i = 2, 3, 4, \ldots$, the second Lyman series with $n_f = 2$ and $n_i = 3, 4, 5, \ldots$, the Fowler series with $n_f = 3$ and $n_i = 4, 5, 6, \ldots$, the Pickering series with $n_f = 4$ and $n_i = 5, 6, 7, \ldots$. Knowing the Rydberg constants for hydrogen and ionized helium, it is possible to obtain a value for the ratio of the mass of the proton to that of the electron. Such a determination, given in a problem at the end of the chapter, is in excellent agreement with the values obtained by other methods. Equation (17.28) shows that, for the same value of $Z$, nuclei of different masses should give rise to spectroscopic lines of somewhat different wave numbers. This has led to the discovery of the heavy isotope of hydrogen of mass value 2 and called deuterium.

Subsequent workers, principally Sommerfeld, developed the Bohr theory more generally. Successive refinements included the treatment of elliptic orbits, the effect of the relativistic variation of mass with velocity, and later the consideration of the effects of electron spin in connection with the observed fine structure of the spectral lines. We shall not go into a discussion of these since their treatment is beyond the scope of this text. For their study the student is referred to other works.[1]

[1] A. Sommerfeld, "Atomic Structure and Spectral Lines," Methuen & Co., Ltd., London, 1929.

H. E. White, "Introduction to Atomic Spectra," McGraw-Hill Book Company, Inc., New York, 1934.

**17.5. Energy-level Diagram for Hydrogen.** From Eq. (17.22) we see that the radii of the orbits increase as the square of the quantum number $n$, from Eq. (17.23) we see that the energies of these orbits vary inversely as the square of the quantum number $n$, and from Eq. (17.24) the wave numbers of a spectral series of lines are given by the difference between two terms, *viz.*, a fixed term $R/n_f^2$, representing the energy of

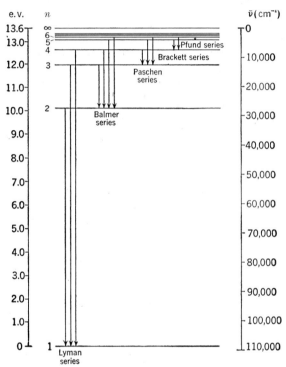

Fig. 17.4. Energy-level diagram for hydrogen.

the final state, and a variable or running term $R/n_i^2$, representing the energies of the initial states of the atom. For instance, in the Balmer series the fixed term is $R/2^2$, and the variable term is $R/n^2$ with $n$ taking on the series of integers 3, 4, 5, etc. The representation of a spectral line as a difference between two terms makes it possible to present the spectrum of an atom in graphical form by means of an energy-level diagram. The energy levels are drawn as horizontal lines to some convenient scale, as shown for the hydrogen atom in Fig. 17.4. The scale is usually either in wave-number units cm$^{-1}$ or in *electron volts*. An *electron volt* (ev) is a unit of energy expressing the energy acquired by an electron in passing through a potential increase of 1 volt. The wave number $\bar{\nu}$ is related to the energy $E$ by $\bar{\nu} = E/hc$ so that $1$ cm$^{-1}$ $= 19.856 \times 10^{-17}$ erg. Since 1 esu of potential is equal to 300 volts, it is seen that

$$1 \text{ electron volt} = 1.6008 \times 10^{-12} \text{ erg}$$

The wave-number scale is usually used to refer to the energy level or term value, and the electron volt is employed to represent the excitation energy associated with that energy level. Each horizontal line represents a term value

$$T_n = \frac{R}{n^2} \quad \text{cm}^{-1}, \qquad n = 1, 2, 3, \ldots \qquad (17.31)$$

where $R$ is the Rydberg constant and $n$ is the quantum number. The energy level for $n = 1$ corresponds to the term $T_1 = R$, and the term value corresponding to $n = \infty$ is $T_\infty = 0$. Energy levels corresponding to all other integral values of $n$ are represented by horizontal lines spaced in accordance with Eq. (17.31). Thus for $n = 2$, the term value is $T_2 = (R/4)$ cm$^{-1}$ and situated one-fourth of the way down from the $T_\infty$ level. The energy levels crowd together and decrease in absolute value as $n$ increases in going from the bottom to the top limiting value corresponding to $T_\infty$, which is indicative of the convergence of a spectral series to the series limit. This indicates that they are all negative term values in accordance with the negative energy stated in Eq. (17.23). Thus the energy level corresponding to $T_\infty$ represents the state of the atom when the electron has been completely removed, and the atom has its maximum energy equal to zero. The lowest energy corresponds to the value $n = 1$ and is designated the *normal*, or *ground*, state of the atom with its energy calculable from Eq. (17.23) as

$$E_1 = -\frac{2\pi^2 \mu e^4}{h^2} = -2178 \times 10^{-14} \text{ erg} = -13.61 \text{ electron volts}$$

It therefore takes 13.61 electron volts to remove an electron from a hydrogen atom to infinity, and this amount of excitation energy is called the *ionization potential* of the atom.

The atom may be raised to a higher energy state above its ground state by some form of excitation, as by collision with another atom in a gas at high temperature or by impact with a high-speed electron. The atom, in returning to a lower energy state, emits a quantum of radiation given by the energy difference between the corresponding upper and lower energy levels. Thus the first member of the Lyman series is produced by the transition from the energy level corresponding to $n = 2$ to the ground state, and this is indicated by an arrow drawn as shown. The corresponding wave number is given by

$$\bar{\nu} = -\left(\frac{R}{2^2}\right) - \left(\frac{-R}{1^2}\right) = R\left[\left(\frac{1}{1^2}\right) - \left(\frac{1}{2^2}\right)\right]$$

The other members of the Lyman series correspond to transitions from the higher energy levels to the ground state. The Balmer series are produced by transitions from energy levels corresponding to $n = 2, 3, 4, \ldots$ to that corresponding to $n = 1$. The other series are explained in like fashion. Above the series-limit term $T_\infty$ is a continuum of positive energies for the free electrons which are outside of the hydrogen orbits and are not subject to quantum conditions.

The length of each arrow representing a transition from one energy level to another is proportional to the wave number of the resulting spectral line. By computing the difference in wave number between two arrows having the same upper state there is obtained the difference between the two lower energy levels involved. For example, the difference between the arrows representing the second member of the Balmer series and the first member of the Paschen series yields the difference in term values corresponding to the levels for $n = 3$ and $n = 2$, giving the wave number of the first member of the Balmer series. Likewise the difference between the first and second arrows of the Balmer series yields the difference in term values for the levels $n = 4$ and $n = 3$. This we see represents the wave number of the first member of the Paschen series. These are illustrations of the *Ritz combination principle*, which states that if $\bar{\nu}_a$ and $\bar{\nu}_b$ are the wave numbers of two spectral lines of an atom, then in general there are spectral lines at the wave numbers $\bar{\nu}_a + \bar{\nu}_b$ and $\bar{\nu}_a - \bar{\nu}_b$. The principle has been borne out by experiment although there are observed wave-number combinations which predict spectral lines that do not actually occur. Nevertheless, an application of the Ritz combination principle affords a powerful method for the analysis of spectra. It has led to the discovery of many new spectral lines.

It is clear that an energy-level diagram yields all the possible wave numbers or frequencies that an atom can emit. In the absorption of light the atom is raised to some higher energy level, and the wave number or frequency of the light absorbed is the same as that of the radiation emitted when a transition takes place in the reverse direction.

Bohr's concept of stationary states, the term values of spectral lines, and the existence of excitation and ionization energies have been thoroughly verified by experiments on electron bombardment. The existence of energy levels was proved by collision experiments between electrons of known energy and atoms. If $E_1$ is the energy of the atom before collision and $E_2$ is the energy of an upper state of the atom, then when the bombarding electron's energy is less than $E_2 - E_1$ there results an elastic collision, the electron losing no energy and the atom taking on no energy.

However, if the electron's energy is equal to or greater than $E_2 - E_1$, it raises the atom to the upper energy state $E_2$. The atom in returning to the more stable energy state radiates this amount of energy $E_2 - E_1$.

**17.6. More Complicated Spectra.** At the end of Sec. 17.2 we mentioned the occurrence of the principal, sharp, diffuse, and Bergmann series which appear as superimposed series in the alkali and other elements. In 1889 Rydberg showed that the spectral series known at that time could be represented by

$$\bar{\nu} = \bar{\nu}_\infty - \frac{R}{(n_0 + \mu)^2} \qquad (17.32)$$

where $R$ is Rydberg's constant, $n_0$ is an integer, and $\mu$ is a constant less than unity and characteristic of a given series. The wave number $\bar{\nu}_\infty$ is the series limit approached by $\bar{\nu}$ for $n_0 = \infty$. To take care of ionized atoms, the second term on the right-hand side of the equation is multiplied by the square of the atomic number $Z$, which takes the value $Z = 2$ for singly ionized atoms, $Z = 3$ for doubly ionized atoms, etc. Rydberg's formula, representing a series by a fixed term $\bar{\nu}_\infty$ and a variable term that depends on the value of $n_0$, is similar to the frequency condition stated in Eq. (17.9), which takes the form $\bar{\nu} = (E_i/hc) - (E_f/hc)$. Using the customary letters $P$ for principal, $S$ for sharp, $D$ for diffuse, and $F$ for fundamental, which was the original name assigned to the Bergmann series because it was then considered significant that the terms of this series differed very little from those of hydrogen, we have the following Rydberg expressions for the four series representative of the alkalies Li, Na, K, Rb, and Cs:

$$
\begin{aligned}
\bar{\nu}_P &= \bar{\nu}_{\infty P} - \frac{R}{(n_0 + \mu_P)^2}, & n_0 &= 2, 3, 4, \ldots \\
\bar{\nu}_S &= \bar{\nu}_{\infty S} - \frac{R}{(n_0 + \mu_S)^2}, & n_0 &= 2, 3, 4, \ldots \\
\bar{\nu}_D &= \bar{\nu}_{\infty D} - \frac{R}{(n_0 + \mu_D)^2}, & n_0 &= 3, 4, 5, \ldots \\
\bar{\nu}_F &= \bar{\nu}_{\infty F} - \frac{R}{(n_0 + \mu_F)^2}, & n_0 &= 4, 5, 6, \ldots
\end{aligned}
\qquad (17.33)
$$

Empirically the following rules have been found to hold: When $n_0$ is placed equal to unity in the sharp-series expression, the value of the variable term is the limit of the principal series, or $\bar{\nu}_{\infty P} = R/(1 + \mu_S)^2$; when $n_0 = 2$ in the principal-series expression, the value of the variable term is the limit of the sharp series, or $\bar{\nu}_{\infty S} = R/(2 + \mu_P)^2$; the limit of the sharp series is equal to the limit of the diffuse series, or $\bar{\nu}_{\infty S} = \bar{\nu}_{\infty D}$; when $n_0 = 3$ in the diffuse-series expression the value of the variable term is the limit of the fundamental series, or $\bar{\nu}_{\infty F} = R/(3 + \mu_D)^2$.

Equations (17.33) can then be written

$$\bar{\nu}_P = \frac{R}{(1 + \mu_S)^2} - \frac{R}{(n_0 + \mu_P)^2}, \qquad n_0 = 2, 3, 4, \ldots$$

$$\bar{\nu}_S = \frac{R}{(2 + \mu_P)^2} - \frac{R}{(n_0 + \mu_S)^2}, \qquad n_0 = 2, 3, 4, \ldots$$

$$\bar{\nu}_D = \frac{R}{(2 + \mu_P)^2} - \frac{R}{(n_0 + \mu_D)^2}, \qquad n_0 = 3, 4, 5, \ldots \qquad (17.34)$$

$$\bar{\nu}_F = \frac{R}{(3 + \mu_D)^2} - \frac{R}{(n_0 + \mu_F)^2}, \qquad n_0 = 4, 5, 6, \ldots$$

and we see that the limiting wave number of each one of the four series is expressed in terms of the constants of one of the other series. The atoms of the alkali group contain one or more closed shells of electrons and a single external electron that can be easily excited and detached, forming the corresponding ion. For instance, in lithium, with 3 electrons surrounding the nucleus, 2 electrons form a closed configuration known as the "*K* shell," and the third electron is at a greater distance from the nucleus. The nucleus of positive charge 3 and the 2 innermost electrons form a core of approximately unit positive charge, and the outermost electron, called the emitting, active, or valence electron, may be thought of as revolving about the core. For sodium the atom core is composed of the nucleus of positive charge 11, a closed inner *K* shell of 2 electrons, and a closed more distant *L* shell of 8 electrons. The emitting electron is in the *M* shell, which can contain a maximum of 18 electrons. The other alkalies have similar electronic structures which are very much like the H atom with the difference, however, that the emitting electron in the alkalies does not move in a simple Coulomb field of the nucleus as does the electron in the hydrogen atom. There is thus present the effect of the disturbance of the valence electron by the core, giving rise to the four series and to the presence of the constant $\mu$ in Eqs. (17.34). Setting $\mu_P = \mu_S = \mu_D = \mu_F = 0$ in Eq. (17.34), we see that the principal series reduces to the hydrogen Lyman series, the sharp and diffuse series reduce to the hydrogen Balmer series, and the fundamental series becomes the Paschen series. There is a shorthand notation that is employed to represent the series in Eqs. (17.34). Thus

$$\bar{\nu}_P = 1S - n_0P, \qquad n_0 = 2, 3, 4, \ldots$$
$$\bar{\nu}_S = 2P - n_0S, \qquad n_0 = 2, 3, 4, \ldots$$
$$\bar{\nu}_D = 2P - n_0D, \qquad n_0 = 3, 4, 5, \ldots \qquad (17.35)$$
$$\bar{\nu}_F = 3D - n_0F, \qquad n_0 = 4, 5, 6, \ldots$$

in which $1S$ is written for the fixed term and $n_0P$ for the variable term in the principal series, $2P$ for the fixed and $n_0S$ for the variable term in the sharp series, and corresponding notations for the diffuse and fundamental series.

Energy-level diagrams analogous to that for hydrogen can be constructed for the alkali atoms as well as for the other elements based on the fact that the wave number of a spectrum line is given by the difference between two terms and that a series of lines is given by the difference between a fixed term and a series of variable or running terms.

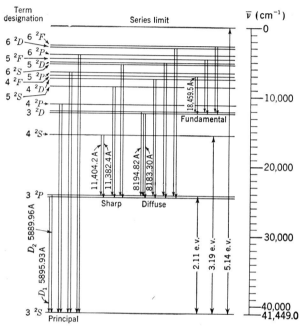

Fig. 17.5. Energy-level diagram of neutral sodium atoms.

Representative of the alkali group is the energy-level diagram of the neutral sodium atom shown in Fig. 17.5. The lowest level is an $S$ level having a value of 41,449.0 cm$^{-1}$. As we go up in the diagram, there is a $P$ level, then an $S$ level followed by a $D$ level, then a $P$ level, and so on as shown. The diagram is made up of a series of principal, sharp, diffuse, and fundamental energy levels approaching a common limit. As in the case of hydrogen, the energy levels represent the allowable energy states of the emitting electron, and the spectrum lines are a result of transitions between the energy states. To understand the term designation shown vertically to the left of the diagram, it must be realized that when the spectral lines of sodium are examined under high resolution, it is found that many of the lines show a doublet structure, *i.e.*, two spectral lines very close together. The student is familiar with this *fine structure* in the case of the sodium yellow line, which consists of two lines separated by about 0.6 A.  The first doublet of the principal series are the sodium $D_1$ and $D_2$ lines.  This fine structure is explainable in terms of the effect of the spin of the electron and causes the $P$, $D$, and $F$ energy levels of sodium to have a doublet structure, *i.e.*, two energy levels close together, while the $S$ state remains singlet.  The doublet character of the energy levels is indicated by the superscript placed at the upper left of the letter, such as $3^2P$, which is read "three doublet $P$."  Only the double levels for the lowest $P$ and lowest $D$ levels have been drawn on the figure for illustration, and the other $P$, $D$, $F$ levels have been drawn as single to simplify the appearance of the diagram, the separation of the components of a level being too small to represent on the wave-number scale shown. The integers 3, 4, 5, etc., preceding each letter designation, represent the total quantum number $n$ rather than the Rydberg integer $n_0$ in Eqs. (17.35).  This comes about in the following way: We have seen that the $n$th level of a hydrogen atom is given by the term values $-R/n^2$ [Eq. (17.24)], where $n$ is the quantum number.  For an atom having a valence electron outside a core made up of a nucleus and one or more closed shells of electrons, like the alkali group, one may introduce an *effective quantum number* $n_e$, so that the energy levels are given by the term values $-R/n_e^2$. The difference $n - n_e = \mu$ is called the *quantum defect* and is a measure of the departure of the energy level of the atom from the hydrogenic energy level having the same quantum number, *i.e.*, the departure of the actual electrical field from the pure Coulomb field.  The energy levels are then representable by the terms $-R/(n - \mu)^2$ instead of the Rydberg expression $-R/(n_0 + \mu)^2$.  The values of $\mu$ are not the same in both expressions, but we have retained the same symbol since $\mu$ has the significance of a correction value in each of them.  The integer $n_0$ in Rydberg's expression serves merely as a convenient identification of the spectral term in a sequence, while the quantum number $n$ is identifiable with modern theoretical calculations, with the manner in which the elements are built up in the periodic table, and with the modern atom models used in the analysis of spectra.  The various electrons of an atom are classified according to the particular *shell* they occupy, and all electrons in the same shell have the same quantum number $n$.  The first, or $K$, shell has the value $n = 1$ and is filled when it contains 2 electrons.  The second, or $L$, shell has the value $n = 2$ and is filled when it contains 8 electrons.  The third, or $M$, shell has the value $n = 3$ and is completed when it contains 18 electrons.  Thus the emitting electron for neutral sodium has the quantum number $n = 3$, and the lowest energy state is then a $3^2S$ state.  Since all the other states are doublets, the $S$ state is also designated a doublet $S$ state.  Using the abbreviation scheme of representation in Eqs. (17.35) but employing the total quantum number $n$, the four series of sodium, corresponding to the energy-level diagram in Fig. 17.5, are given by

$$\begin{aligned}
\bar{\nu}_P &= 3S - nP, & n &= 3, 4, 5, \ldots \\
\bar{\nu}_S &= 3P - nS, & n &= 4, 5, 6, \ldots \\
\bar{\nu}_D &= 3P - nD, & n &= 3, 4, 5, \ldots \\
\bar{\nu}_F &= 3D - nF, & n &= 4, 5, 6, \ldots
\end{aligned} \tag{17.36}$$

The lines of the principal series are due to transitions from a $P$ state to the lowest $S$ state. All these spectral lines, originating from each of the doublet $P$ levels and terminating on the single $S$ level, are doublets as shown in the figure, the first of these in the visible region being the

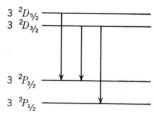

FIG. 17.6. Transitions forming a spectral multiplet of the diffuse series of sodium.

sodium $D$ lines whose wavelengths are indicated, and the other doublets of the principal series being in the ultraviolet region. The sharp series are due to transitions from the upper $S$ states to the $3^2P$ state. Again this series is composed of spectral doublets, the wavelengths of the components of the first doublet being indicated in the figure. Transitions from the $^2D$ levels to the $3^2P$ levels give rise to the diffuse series, and those from the $^2F$ levels to the $3^2D$ levels result in the fundamental series. For these, transitions from each of the two upper levels of a doublet term to each of the two lower levels of a doublet term give rise to a spectral multiplet. For instance, the origin of the first spectral multiplet of the diffuse series is more clearly indicated in Fig. 17.6. Each of the components of a doublet term is labeled with a subscript which signifies the total angular momentum $J$ of that state. The two $3^2P$ levels are indicated as $3^2P_{1/2}$ and $3^2P_{3/2}$, and those for the $3^2D$ levels are $3^2D_{3/2}$ and $3^2D_{5/2}$. These $J$ values are obtained from the theoretical developments which specify that only those transitions are allowed for which the change in $J$ is $\Delta J = \pm 1$, or 0. Spectral lines are thus permitted ordinarily only in accordance with this *selection rule*, and any other jump is forbidden. The resultant multiplet is then a triplet as shown in Fig. 17.6, the transition $3^2P_{1/2} - 3^2D_{5/2}$ being forbidden. The two most intense spectral lines of the triplet correspond to the transitions $3^2P_{3/2}$—$3^2D_{5/2}$ and $3^2P_{1/2}$—$3^2P_{3/2}$. The spectral line corresponding to the transition $3^2P_{3/2}$—$3^2D_{3/2}$ is very faint, appearing as a companion, or *satellite*, of the longer wavelength component $3^2P_{3/2}$—$3^2D_{5/2}$ with which the satellite fuses in the higher members of the spectral series. Only the doublet structure of the other spectral members of the diffuse and fundamental series are shown, the arrows being drawn from the mean value of the two upper doublet energy levels. It is to be noticed that no transitions are allowed between two $S$, between two $P$, between two $D$, or between two $F$ levels or in general between $S$ and $D$, $P$ and $F$, or $S$ and $F$ states. This again follows from the selection rule which stipulates that transitions can take place between $S$ and $P$ states, $P$ and $D$ states, and $D$ and $F$ states. More often the energy-level diagram is drawn by grouping the $S$, $P$, $D$, and $F$ energy levels in adjacent vertical columns. Then the transitions are indicated by lines from a level in one column to the allowed level in an adjacent column. Such diagrams are more suitable for spectral-analysis work.

The alkaline earth elements Be, Mg, Ca, Sr, Ba, Ra and the elements Zn, Cd, and Hg contain two active electrons outside the core. These elements emit spectra which may again be grouped into sharp, principal, diffuse, and fundamental classes. The energy levels for these are both singlet and triplet, giving rise to more complicated spectra and corresponding energy-level diagrams. As a general rule the complexity of the spectrum increases with the number of valence electrons: a one-valence electron system has associated with it doublet energy levels; for a two-valence electron system the energy levels are singlets and triplets; for a three-valence electron system the energy levels are doublets and quartets; for a four-valence electron system the energy levels are singlets, triplets, and quintets, etc. Thus spectral terms from successive elements in the periodic table alternate between even and odd multiplicities.

The older quantum theory of Bohr, frequently labeled as semiclassical, is successful only in its application to hydrogenlike and some of the simpler atoms. Even in hydrogen, the theory does not explain the hydrogen doublet fine structure. The theory is not as satisfactory when applied to atoms having many electrons. Furthermore Bohr's theory arbitrarily quantizes the angular momentum, arriving at a result that gives the frequency or wave number corresponding to a transition, but it does not set up a method for obtaining the relative intensities of the spectral lines. A consistent theory that affords a theoretical interpretation of spectra emitted by atoms or molecules containing more than one electron, as well as the hydrogenic atom, furnishing valid expressions for wave numbers, relative intensities, polarization of spectral lines, fine structure, and hyperfine structure (pattern of lines due to the presence of different isotopes or a multiplicity due to nuclear spin), is the wave-mechanical or quantum-mechanical theory of the atoms. Although the concept of electrons rotating in orbits no longer retains the significance originally attached to it, in the newer theory it is found that the existence of discrete energy states is valid and the wave number of a spectral line is proportional to the difference in the energies corresponding to the upper and lower energy states of the transition. In the next chapter we shall introduce some of the concepts of this new quantum theory, which has been developed principally by Schrödinger, Heisenberg, and Dirac. The very complex structure of band spectra, containing rotational and vibrational as well as electronic energy levels of the excited molecules, finds explanation in terms of the new quantum theory.

**17.7. X-ray Spectra.** Section 15.5, dealing with absorption and scattering of X rays, also indicated the mechanism by which X-ray spectra are produced. Let us now look into this somewhat more closely and especially in terms of the atomic energy levels.

In the preceding sections we have been concerned with the *optical spectra* of the atoms, and we have seen that these spectra arise from electron transitions in the outermost part of the atom. X rays, on the other hand, being high-frequency or low-wavelength radiation, arise as a result of the removal from the atom of an inner electron followed by electron transitions between the inner electron shells of the atom. It is very convenient to employ the concept of shells in describing the origin of X-ray spectral series. We have seen that the electrons of an atom appear to be arranged around the nucleus in shells, each shell being able to hold a maximum number of electrons. These shells are designated $K, L, M, N$, etc., and the respective maximum numbers of electrons that each shell can accommodate are 2, 8, 18, 32, etc. For example, of the 29 electrons of Cu, 2 are in the $K$ shell, 8 are in the $L$ shell, 18 are in the $M$ shell, and one is in the $N$ shell. The $N$ electron of Cu is the emitting electron responsible for the optical spectrum, and the unoccupied energy states into which the electron may be excited are the optical levels. The amount of energy required to excite the $N$ electron is relatively small in comparison with the energy necessary to excite a $K$ electron.

When high-speed electrons, ordinarily obtained by accelerating thermionically emitted electrons, are directed onto a target material, X-ray spectral-line series are emitted by the target. These series are best interpreted in terms of energy levels. The high-speed electrons, if they have sufficient energy, may eject a $K$ electron from the atom of the target and either ionize the atom or raise the $K$ electron to one of the unoccupied optical levels. The vacant place in the $K$ shell is then filled by a transition of an electron from the $L$, $M$, or $N$ shell, thus giving rise to the $K$-series spectra. The transitions from $L$ to $K$, from $M$ to $K$, and from $N$ to $K$ give rise, respectively, to the X-ray $K_\alpha$, $K_\beta$, and $K_\gamma$ characteristic lines. If the energy associated with the $K$ shell or level is $E_K$ and that associated with the $L$ shell or level is $E_L$, then the frequency of the $K_\alpha$ line is given by $\nu_{K\alpha} = (E_K - E_L)/h$ in accordance with the quantum frequency condition. The other lines of the $K$ series are given by corresponding expressions. The $L$ series of X-ray lines are given by transitions of electrons from the $M$ and $N$ shells to the $L$ shell. The $L$ series, which is a softer radiation (lower energy and longer wavelength) may accompany the appearance of the $K$ series or may occur without the appearance of the $K$ series. The emission of the $K_\alpha$ line creates a vacancy in the $L$ series which is filled by an electron from the $M$ or $N$ shell. On the other hand, if the bombarding electrons have sufficient energy to eject $L$ but not $K$ electrons, then the $L$ series is emitted without the presence of the $K$ series. In like manner the $M$ and $N$ series result when electrons from upper energy states fill electron vacancies created, respectively, in the $M$ and $N$ shells.

Moseley, in 1913, had made a systematic study of the characteristic X-ray line spectra emitted by various targets and found that, unlike optical spectra, the X-ray spectra of the elements were similar, their frequencies shifting linearly with increasing atomic number. Plotting the square root of the frequency of a given spectral line as a function of the atomic number of the target element, he obtained a straight line expressed by the equation

$$\nu = CR(Z - \sigma)^2 \tag{17.37}$$

where $\nu$ is the frequency, $C$ and $\sigma$ are constants, $Z$ is the atomic number, and $R$ is the Rydberg constant appearing in the Balmer formula for hydrogen. For the $K_\alpha$ line of the $K$ series of the elements Moseley found $C = \frac{3}{4}$ and $\sigma = 1$, giving

$$\nu_{K\alpha} = \frac{3}{4} R(Z - 1)^2 = R(Z - 1)^2 \left(\frac{1}{1^2} - \frac{1}{2^2}\right) \tag{17.38}$$

Equation (17.38), interpretable in terms of Bohr's theory, says that the $K_\alpha$ line is emitted when an electron jumps from the orbit of quantum number $n = 2$ ($L$ level) to the orbit of quantum number $n = 1$ ($K$ level). The appearance of the factor $Z - 1$ instead of $Z$ is explained by the fact that when one of the two $K$ electrons is removed from an atom, the remaining $K$ electron "screens" the nucleus so that the effective nuclear charge is very nearly $Z - 1$. Equation (17.37) also holds for the X-ray $L$-series spectra and approximately for the $M$ series. The significance of Moseley's work is fundamental in the arrangement of the elements in the periodic table according to their atomic number.

In the above simplified treatment of the origin of the X-ray spectral series we have ignored the fine structure of X-ray spectral lines. For instance, for most of the higher atomic number elements the $K_\alpha$ and $K_\beta$ lines are resolvable into two components $K_{\alpha_1}$, $K_{\alpha_2}$ and $K_{\beta_1}$, $K_{\beta_2}$. This fine structure is due to the multiplicity of some of the energy levels and is explainable on the basis of the newer quantum theory. The multiplicity of the energy levels is determinable from a study of the X-ray absorption spectra. In Sec. 15.5 we saw that the X-ray absorption curve contains absorption edges or absorption limits. It was there stated that there are three absorption limits $L_I$, $L_{II}$, and $L_{III}$ very close together. These occur in the $L$-series range of wavelengths and indicate that the $L$ shell consists of three energy levels.  The five absorption limits corresponding to the $M$-series region indicates that the $M$ shell has a multiplicity of five energy levels.  The $N$ shell is composed of seven energy levels.  It is seen that the absorption limits provide a direct means of determining the energy levels of an atom.  The frequency of an X-ray line is given by the difference between the frequencies of two absorption limits.  For instance, when a $K_\alpha$ line is emitted, the $h\nu$ value of this line is given by $h\nu_{K\alpha} = h\nu_K - h\nu_L$, where $\nu_K$ and $\nu_L$ are the frequencies of the $K$ and $L$ absorption limits, respectively.  For the $K_{\alpha_1}$ line the transition is from the level $L_{\text{III}}$ to the $K$ level.

In addition to the characteristic line spectrum emitted by an X-ray target there is also present a background of *continuous radiation* on which the line spectrum is superposed.  The curve of intensity as a function of the wavelength for the continuous spectrum exhibits the following characteristics: For some given voltage and target material the curve starts at zero intensity, corresponding to a short-wavelength limit, rises rapidly to a maximum, and then drops gradually, extending indefinitely toward the long-wavelength end.  The wavelength at which the maximum occurs depends on the voltage applied to the X-ray tube; for higher voltages the position of the maximum shifts to shorter wavelengths.  The position of the short-wavelength limit is independent of the material of the target but is smaller the higher the voltage.  The continuous spectrum is emitted by the impinging electrons when they are decelerated on striking the target.  The observed short-wavelength limit requires the quantum theory for its satisfactory explanation.  An electron, in its encounter with an atom of the target, may lose part of its energy, the lost energy being radiated as an X-ray photon of amount $h\nu$.  The electron may then experience many more collisions with atoms before coming to rest, with a consequent emission of smaller and smaller amounts of energy.  On the other hand, the electron may lose all its energy in a single encounter with an attendant emission of the maximum amount of energy $h\nu_{\text{max}}$.  There is thus emitted a continuous range of wavelengths down to a short-wavelength limit corresponding to $\nu_{\text{max}}$.  If $V$ is the potential difference through which the electron falls and $e$ is the electronic charge, then the equation for the maximum frequency of the emitted X rays is

$$eV = h\nu_{\text{max}} \qquad (17.39)$$

The peak, or maximum, intensity in the continuous spectrum is explainable on the basis of there being a most probable type of collision or encounter of the bombarding electron with the target atom.  Equation (17.39) is recognizable as the Einstein photoelectric equation [Eq. (17.5)], in which the work function is neglected, since the X-ray photons have such large energy. In fact, the phenomenon expressed by Eq. (17.39), in which $eV$ is the kinetic energy of the impinging electron, is looked upon as the *inverse photoelectric effect*. It will be recalled that in the photoelectric effect light of frequency $\nu$ causes the ejection of an electron, while in the inverse process an electron striking an atom results in the emission of a photon of frequency $\nu$.

**17.8. The Broadening of Spectral Lines.** As discussed in Secs. 10.6 and 10.9, a light wave is never perfectly monochromatic but must be considered as composed of a range of frequencies, and no spectral line is perfectly sharp in view of the fact that the radiation consists of individual wave trains of finite length. In accordance with classical electromagnetic theory, the emission from an oscillating charge is a damped wave, and a Fourier analysis of such a wave gives for the intensity as a function of the frequency a bell-shaped curve, appearing most intense in the center and fading out symmetrically on the low- and high-frequency sides of the maximum. A spectral line then contains a band of frequencies, and the *width* of the line is taken to mean the width of the bell-shaped curve at half its maximum intensity, or "half width." According to quantum-mechanical theory, the energy levels associated with an atom are not sharp but possess a finite width. This follows from the Heisenberg uncertainty principle (see Sec. 18.3), which shows that the width of an energy level is larger the smaller the mean life of that energy state. Transitions between levels of finite width therefore do not give rise to perfectly sharp spectral lines. From both the classical and quantum viewpoints, then, a spectral line possesses a *natural width* which does not depend on the resolving power of the observing spectroscope.

As contrasted with the natural width, which is due to an inherent property of the atom, there are other additional spectral-line-broadening effects. One of these is the so-called *Doppler broadening*, which has to do with the well-known Doppler principle as applied to the observed frequency of a radiated line. The student is no doubt familiar with the Doppler effect in sound, resulting in an apparent change in the observed pitch or frequency of a sound wave when there is relative motion between the sound source and the observer or receiver. In a stationary medium, with the observer at rest and the source of radiation in motion, the frequency observed has an apparent increase or decrease according as the source is approaching or receding from the observer. To see why this is so, consider that the source is approaching the observer with a velocity $v_s$, that the velocity of the radiation emitted by the source is $c$, and that the frequency of this radiation is $\nu$. In a time $t$ the number of waves emitted by the source is crowded into the length $ct - v_s t$, so that the wavelength in the line of observation is shortened to the amount $(c - v_s)/\nu$ and the apparent frequency $\nu'$, or the number of waves passing the observer per second, is given by

$$\nu' = \frac{c}{(c - v_s)/\nu}$$

or

$$\nu' = \frac{\nu c}{c - v_s} \tag{17.40a}$$

When the source is receding with the velocity $v_s$, then the apparent frequency is

$$\nu' = \frac{\nu c}{c + v_s} \tag{17.40b}$$

When the source is stationary and the observer or receiver is moving toward the source with a velocity $v_r$, the number of waves passing the observer in time $t$ is $\nu t + v_r t/\lambda$, where $\lambda$ is the wavelength of the radiation. The apparent frequency is now

$$\nu' = \frac{\nu t + (v_r t/\lambda)}{t}$$

and since $\lambda = c/\nu$,

$$\nu' = \frac{\nu(c + v_r)}{c} \tag{17.40c}$$

When the observer is receding from the stationary source,

$$\nu' = \frac{\nu(c - v_r)}{c} \tag{17.40d}$$

When the Doppler effect is considered for stellar spectra, the velocities of the stars are so large that there is an observable shift of the spectrum lines, the shift being toward the red if the star is receding from the earth and toward the violet if the star is approaching the earth, in accordance with Eqs. (17.40b) and (17.40a). Similar effects exist in the case of a luminous gas in which the atoms emitting the light move with high velocities that depend on the temperature. For those atoms which have a component of motion toward the observer there is a shift to higher frequency, while for those atoms which have a component of motion away from the observer there is an apparent decrease in frequency. Since the motions of the atoms of such a gas are random, the net result is a symmetrical broadening of the spectral line. The magnitude of this broadening is many times the natural width.

A second cause of spectral-line broadening is the phenomenon of *collision broadening*. If an atom, while emitting radiation, collides with another atom, the phase and amplitude of the radiation may change.

The collision has the effect of shortening the emitted wave trains, which is equivalent to broadening the spectral range of frequencies. Both the Doppler broadening and collision broadening depend on the pressure of the gas. At low pressures the Doppler broadening is larger, while at high pressures collision broadening is the larger effect.

Another cause of line broadening is due to the Stark effect (see Sec. 17.10). In the spectra of discharge tubes there are strong electric fields which, although not sufficient to produce an observable Stark effect splitting of a spectral line, cause an unresolved hyperfine structure which is observed as a broadening of the line.

**17.9. The Zeeman Effect.** In 1896 Zeeman discovered the effect of a magnetic field on the light emitted by a source when placed in the field. The effect was earlier investigated by Faraday in 1862 but without success because of the crudity of his apparatus. The phenomenon has to do with the splitting of a spectral line into several components when the source is placed in a strong magnetic field and is known as the *Zeeman effect*. The splitting of absorption lines into components when the absorbing medium is in the magnetic field is called the *inverse Zeeman effect*.

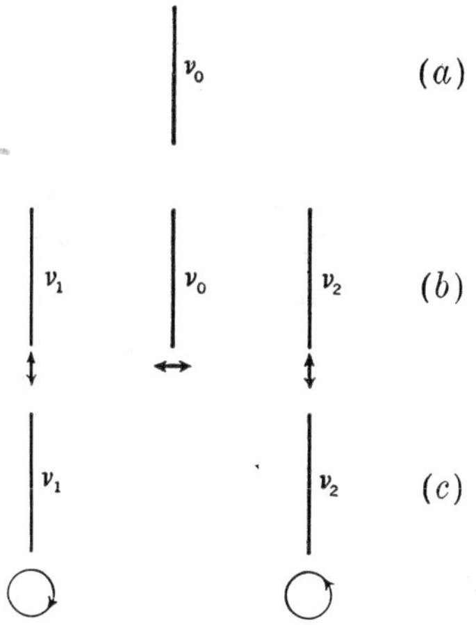

With the emitting source placed between the poles of a strong magnet, one of whose pieces is equipped with a hole running parallel to the magnetic field direction, a spectral line may be examined with a spectroscope from a direction at right angles to, as well as in a direction parallel to, the direction of the magnetic field. In the *normal* Zeeman effect, instead of a single spectral line observable in the absence of the magnetic field, there appears the following in the presence of the magnetic field: When the light is viewed at right angles to the magnetic field direction, three spectral line components are seen as shown in (b) of Fig. 17.7. The central component is in the same position and hence has the same frequency $\nu_0$ as the original line shown in (a). The outer components of frequencies $\nu_1$ and $\nu_2$ are displaced by equal amounts from the central component. The central component is linearly polarized with the electric vector vibrating parallel to the magnetic field direction, while the two outer components are linearly polarized with vibrations at right angles to that of the central component. The state of polarization is

FIG. 17.7. The normal Zeeman effect. (a) No magnetic field. (b) Viewed perpendicular to magnetic field which is directed from left to right. (c) Viewed parallel to magnetic field which is directed perpendicular to the plane of the figure and toward the reader.

indicated by the arrows below the spectral lines. When the light is viewed along a direction parallel to the magnetic field direction, only the two outer components are present and there is no central component as shown in (c). These components are circularly polarized in opposite senses as indicated below the lines. In the *anomalous* Zeeman effect, so-called because it cannot be accounted for on the basis of classical theory, a spectral line is separated into many more components.

Although the quantum-mechanical theory is necessary to establish an explanation of the entire Zeeman effects, classical electromagnetic theory affords an explanation of the normal Zeeman effect. This explanation was given by Lorentz in accordance with his electron theory which yields the correct expression for the frequency shift and state of polarization of the components. It will be recalled that according to the classical electron theory the vibrations of the electrons give rise to the emitted frequencies. In the presence of an external magnetic field the motions of the charged particles become modified. Thus suppose we have an electron vibrating with periodic linear harmonic motion in any assumed direction. This motion may be resolved into the equivalent of two component vibratory motions, one component parallel to the magnetic field direction and the other component in a plane perpendicular to the magnetic field direction. Furthermore, as we have seen in Sec. 16.16, a linear vibration may be considered as the resultant of two equal and oppositely directed circular motions. The electron vibrating in some arbitrary direction may then be considered as the equivalent of a vibration parallel to the magnetic field direction together with a clockwise and counterclockwise motion in a plane normal to the magnetic field direction. In the presence of a magnetic field the frequency of the component vibrating parallel to the direction of the field is unaltered, since no force is exerted by the field on the electron motion in this direction. However, the originally equal frequencies of the two circular motions in a plane perpendicular to the magnetic field direction are changed, owing to the force acting on the charge in a direction at right angles to the field and at right angles to the direction of motion of the charge.

To calculate the alteration in the frequency of the circular components, consider an electron of mass $m$ and charge $e$ rotating, in a circle of radius $r$, with a linear velocity $v_0$ and corresponding angular velocity $\omega_0$, as shown in Fig. 17.8. In the absence of a magnetic field the electron is held in its circular path by the centripetal force, or

$$\frac{mv_0^2}{r} = m\omega_0^2 r$$

which may be thought of as being supplied by an elastic force proportional to the displacement $r$. Now consider that a magnetic field $H$ is applied perpendicular to the plane of the figure. This has a twofold effect. First, while the field is being established, there is an electric force produced on the electron in a direction which is tangent to its orbit and arises from the resulting induced emf due to the changing magnetic flux. Depending on the direction of the magnetic field, this either increases or decreases the linear orbital velocity of the electron to the value $v$. Second, there is the additional force acting on the electron due to the magnetic field. The magnitude of this force is $Hev$, and its direction is either radially toward or radially away from the center depending on the sense of rotation of the electron. For a steady circular motion with radius $r$, the new centripetal force $mv^2/r$ is supplied in part by the elastic force $m\omega_0^2 r$ and in part by the force due to the field, or

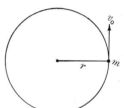

$$\frac{mv^2}{r} = m\omega_0^2 r \pm Hev \qquad (17.41)$$

Fig. 17.8. Illustrating the effect of a magnetic field on the circular motion of an electron.

in which $H$ and $e$ are in electromagnetic units. To use $e$ in electrostatic units the term in which it appears is to be divided by the velocity of light $c$. Placing $v = \omega r$, where $\omega$ is the new angular velocity, yields

$$\omega^2 - \omega_0^2 = \pm \frac{He\omega}{m} \qquad (17.42)$$

Since the change in frequency is small, we can set $\omega + \omega_0 = 2\omega$ and obtain for the change in frequency, using $\omega = 2\pi\nu$ and $\omega_0 = 2\pi\nu_0$,

$$\nu - \nu_0 = \pm \frac{He}{4\pi m} \qquad (17.43)$$

Calling the two frequencies $\nu_1$ and $\nu_2$, we have

$$\nu_1 = \nu_0 - \frac{He}{4\pi m} \qquad (17.44)$$

and

$$\nu_2 = \nu_0 + \frac{He}{4\pi m} \qquad (17.45)$$

For an electron rotating counterclockwise as in Fig. 17.8 with the magnetic field directed toward the reader, the force due to the field is directed radially toward the center so that this corresponds to the longer frequency $\nu_2$. The clockwise rotation of the electron corresponds to the lower frequency $\nu_1$. These frequencies $\nu_1$ and $\nu_2$ are the frequencies of the observed component lines in Fig. 17.7. Thus, when the light source is viewed parallel to the direction of the field so that the magnetic field is directed toward the observer as in Fig. 17.7c, the two line components have frequencies $\nu_1$ and $\nu_2$, each being shifted from the frequency $\nu_0$ by the amount $He/4\pi m$, and each being circularly polarized in opposite senses as indicated in the figure. The component of vibration along the magnetic lines of force with the unchanged frequency $\nu_0$ does not emit radiation in this direction in accordance with the principles of the transverse character of light. Hence in the longitudinal direction there are seen only the lines of frequencies $\nu_1$ and $\nu_2$, constituting what is called the *longitudinal effect* of the *normal Zeeman triplet*. When the light source is viewed perpendicular to the direction of the magnetic field, as in Fig. 17.7b, the circular vibrations, occurring in a plane at right angles to the magnetic field direction, appear like linear vibrations resulting in displaced lines of frequencies $\nu_1$ and $\nu_2$, each plane-polarized with the electric vector vibrating perpendicular to the magnetic field direction. The component of vibration parallel to the magnetic field direction gives rise to the unchanged frequency $\nu_0$, also plane-polarized with the electric vector vibrating parallel to the magnetic field direction. These three lines constitute what is called the *transverse effect* of the *normal Zeeman triplet*. The intensities of the two circularly polarized components in the longitudinal pattern are equal, while in the transverse pattern half the total intensity is shared equally by the two outer components and the other half intensity goes into the central component.

Most of the Zeeman patterns of spectral lines are anomalous rather than normal triplets, and there appear many more components. For instance, the longer wavelength component of the sodium principal spectral doublet splits up into four component lines, while the shorter wavelength component splits up into six spectral components. When the magnetic fields approach sufficiently strong values, anomalous Zeeman patterns become normal triplets, this being known as the *Paschen-Back effect*. The classical theory is successful in explaining only the Zeeman normal triplet. As we have already indicated, the more complex patterns are interpretable by quantum-mechanical theory, which also predicts for the normal triplet the same results as arrived at by the classical theory. The new theory deals with the changes in the energy levels brought about by the magnetic field as a result of the atom possessing a magnetic moment and the electron possessing a spin. For an extended treatment, the student is referred to other sources.[1]

**17.10. The Stark Effect.** Another effect that cannot be explained by classical theory is the *Stark effect*, discovered by Stark in 1913. The effect has to do with the splitting of a spectral line when the radiating source is in a strong electric field. In the transverse Stark effect for hydrogen some of the spectral components are linearly polarized with

[1] *Ibid.*, p. 384.

the electric vector vibrating parallel to the electric field and some are linearly polarized with the vibration perpendicular to the field, while in the longitudinal Stark effect only the latter components are observed in an unpolarized state. The ability of the early Bohr quantum theory, as extended by Epstein and others, in explaining the Stark effect in hydrogen constituted probably the most significant success of the theory. The Stark effect is now completely explained by the new quantum mechanics.

## PROBLEMS

**17.1.** Using Eqs. (17.3), calculate the wavelengths of the first three members of the Lyman, Balmer, and Paschen series and the wavelengths of the limit of each of these series.

**17.2.** A photoelectric surface has a work function of 1.80 electron volts. (*a*) For what threshold frequency and corresponding wavelength can photoelectrons be ejected from the surface? (*b*) For light of wavelength 2500 A incident on the surface, what is the maximum velocity of the emitted electrons?

**17.3.** Light of wavelength 2000 A falls on a surface which emits a maximum electron current of 2.00 microamperes. Find the number of photons per second striking the surface, assuming that 1 per cent of the incident photons is effective in ejecting a photoelectron. Find also the energy per second in the incident light. Take 1 coulomb as equivalent to $6.25 \times 10^{18}$ electrons.

**17.4.** Employing Eq. (17.27) for the H and He atoms, find the ratio of the mass of the proton $m_H$ to the mass of the electron $m_e$. Use as knowns only the values $R_H = 109,677.6$ cm$^{-1}$, $R_{He} = 109,722.4$ cm$^{-1}$, and assume $m_{He} = 4m_H$. [HINT: Show that $\dfrac{m_H}{m_e} = \dfrac{R_H}{R_{He} - R_H} \left( 1 - \dfrac{m_H}{m_{He}} \dfrac{R_{He}}{R_H} \right)$.]

**17.5.** Compute the wavelength separation of the two spectroscopic lines of the first member of the Balmer series corresponding to the chief isotope $H^1$ and the heavy isotope $H^2$ (deuterium) of hydrogen. Use $R_\infty = 109,737.3$, and take $m_{H^1}/m_e = 1837$ and $m_{H^2}/m_e = 3674$.

**17.6.** Calculate the radii of the first 10 Bohr circular orbits for hydrogen, and draw them to scale about a common center. On this diagram indicate, by means of vector lines, the transitions corresponding to the Lyman, Balmer, Paschen, Brackett, Pfund series. Use $9.10 \times 10^{-28}$ gm for $\mu$ in Eq. (17.22).

**17.7.** The Rydberg constants $R$ and nuclear masses $m_N$ of the hydrogenlike configurations of some elements are given in the accompanying table. Plot $R$ against $1/(1 + m_e/m_N)$, and thus determine the value $R_\infty$. Take the value of $m_H = 1837m_e$.

| Element | $R$, cm$^{-1}$ | $m_N$ | Element | $R$, cm$^{-1}$ | $m_N$ |
|---------|------------|-------|---------|------------|-------|
| H$^1$ | 109,678 | 1 | Be | 109,731 | 9 |
| H$^2$ | 109,707 | 2 | O | 109,734 | 16 |
| He | 109,722 | 4 | Sc | 109,736 | 45 |
| Li | 109,729 | 7 | | | |

**17.8.** (*a*) Show that the classical frequency of rotation of the electron in a circular Bohr orbit is $\nu = 2cR/n^3$, where $c$, $R$, and $n$ are the velocity of light, the Rydberg constant, and the quantum number, respectively. (*b*) Show that the frequency of the radiation emitted by electronic transitions between two orbital states approaches the classical value in (*a*) when the quantum numbers are large and the change in the quantum number is unity. This illustrates Bohr's *correspondence* principle, which states that, in the limit of high quantum numbers, the classical and quantum frequencies become equal.

**17.9.** To the accuracy with which you can read the term values in Fig. 17.5, find the wave numbers and wavelengths of the following transitions: $3^2S-4^2P$, $3^2S-5^2P$, $4^2S-4^2P$, $4^2P-6^2D$, $4^2D-6^2F$.

**17.10.** Draw the energy-level diagram shown in Fig. 17.5 by grouping the $S$, $P$, $D$, and $F$ energy levels in adjacent vertical columns. Indicate the transitions by lines from a level in one column to the allowed level in an adjacent column.

**17.11.** The values for the $3S$, $5P$, and $4D$ terms of sodium are, respectively, 41,449 cm$^{-1}$, 6408.9 cm$^{-1}$, and 6897.5 cm$^{-1}$. Find the corresponding quantum defects. Take $R = 109,734$ cm$^{-1}$.

**17.12.** The target of an X-ray tube is bombarded by 50-kilovolt electrons. If the short-wavelength limit of the continuous spectrum is 0.249 A, what is Planck's constant?

**17.13.** The $K$ absorption limit of copper is 1.38 A. What is the minimum voltage necessary across a copper-target X-ray tube to cause the appearance of the $K$-series X-ray lines?

**17.14.** With reference to Doppler broadening and collision broadening, explain their increase with increasing temperature and their decrease with increasing atomic weight.

**17.15.** A spectral line is found to show the normal Zeeman triplet pattern in a magnetic field of 30,000 oersteds. Find the wave-number difference between the undisplaced and shifted components.

## CHAPTER 18

# WAVE-PARTICLE ASPECTS OF LIGHT AND MATTER

We have seen, on the one hand, how the wave theory was triumphant in explaining such phenomena as interference and diffraction and, on the other hand, how it failed to explain such phenomena as the photoelectric effect, the Raman effect, the Compton effect, spectral-energy distribution of a black body, the emission and absorption of radiation, the short-wavelength limit of the continuous X-ray spectrum, the anomalous Zeeman effect, the Stark effect, and other phenomena entailing the interaction of light with matter. In dealing with the latter class of phenomena we have seen that it was necessary to invoke a quantum or corpuscular theory of radiation. After Planck's introduction of the quantum theory and its relatively rapid successes, it became recognized, as we have indicated, that radiant energy possesses a dual nature and that light behaves at times like waves and at other times like corpuscular quanta. We shall see in this chapter that, following Bohr's work, there was introduced by de Broglie in 1924 the theoretical conception that a similar dual character holds true for matter itself and that particles, such as electrons, possess wavelike as well as particlelike characteristics. It was this idea, developed into a precise mathematical theory, that gave rise to the modern quantum mechanics which provides a description of all atomic, as well as large-scale, processes.

We shall not attempt to give any detailed mathematical development of the quantum mechanics, which is beyond the scope of this text. In this concluding chapter we wish merely to present a brief introduction to certain of its methods and a description of some of its salient features. For a complete presentation of mathematical details of quantum mechanics the reader is referred to the references at the end of the chapter.

**18.1. De Broglie Waves and the Rise of Quantum Mechanics.** In what is termed the old quantum theory of Planck, Einstein, and Bohr, we have seen that for a photon the energy $E$ is

$$E = h\nu = \frac{hc}{\lambda} = mc^2 \tag{18.1}$$

where $\nu$ is the frequency, $\lambda$ the wavelength, and $h$ Planck's constant. The photons travel with the speed of light $c$. The momentum $p$ of the photon is $mc$, where $m$ is the mass equivalent of the energy $E$ as given by the Einstein energy-mass relationship [Eq. (15.10)].   Thus

$$p = \frac{E}{c^2} c = \frac{h\nu}{c} = \frac{h}{\lambda} \tag{18.2}$$

In Chaps. 16 and 17 some of the failures and limitations of the older theory were pointed out, and it became recognizable that the theory was inadequate in providing a complete description of atomic phenomena. We have already called attention to the fact that the older theory was unable to give a quantitative account of the intensities of spectral lines. It also failed to explain other phenomena such as the dispersion of light and experimental results in molecular spectra, as well as the phenomena enumerated in this chapter's introduction.

The rise of the new quantum mechanics as the theory fundamental to all atomic processes had its start with de Broglie[1] and Schrödinger[2] on the one hand and with Heisenberg[3] on the other.   Schrödinger built up his theory on the basis of the de Broglie hypothesis, which we take up below, and thus developed the theory known as *wave mechanics*.   Heisenberg, working independently, used a different approach and developed a scheme that was equally fruitful in describing atomic phenomena. Heisenberg does not make use of any physical quantities that are not experimentally determinable, for instance, the radii of electron orbits, which are not measurable.   On the other hand we do measure the wavelengths and intensities of spectral lines.   Using experimentally determinable quantities, he develops his theory of atomic systems by employing the highly specialized field of matrix mechanics, which is beyond the scope of this text.

Although both theories have different mathematical formulations, they were shown by Schrödinger to be equivalent.   The single theory into which they have both become fused is now known as the quantum mechanics.   Schrödinger's theory lends itself more easily to a brief discussion.   We shall here describe the de Broglie hypothesis and, in the next section, give some idea of the methods of quantum mechanics.

In accordance with the dualistic nature of radiation, the momentum $p$ and energy $E$ of a photon are related by Eqs. (18.1) and (18.2).   The corpuscular photons have associated with them waves which may be thought of as accounting for observed interference and diffraction effects. In analogy with the wave-particle dualism of radiation, de Broglie introduced the hypothesis that all material particles possess a wave character, so that matter also possesses a particle-wave dualism.   Accord-

---

[1] L. de Broglie, *Nature*, **112**, 540, 1923; thesis, University of Paris, 1924; *Ann. phys.* (10), **3**, 22, 1925.

[2] Schrödinger, *Ann. Physik.*, **79**, 361, 489, 1926.

[3] Heisenberg, *Z. Physik*, **33**, 879, 1925.

ingly, particles such as electrons, protons, neutrons, atoms, and molecules have associated with them wavelike characteristics. For a material particle of mass $m$ traveling with a velocity $v$ the wavelength $\lambda$ associated with the particle is, by analogy with Eq. (18.2),

$$\lambda = \frac{h}{p} = \frac{h}{mv} \qquad (18.3)$$

The velocity of propagation of these waves, called the phase velocity $u$, is related to the particle velocity $v$ through the expression $u = \lambda\nu$, where $\nu$ is the frequency. Thus,

$$u = \frac{h\nu}{p} = \frac{E}{mv} = \frac{c^2}{v} \qquad (18.4)$$

where we have used $E = h\nu = mc^2$. The associated waves are known as *de Broglie waves*, and the wavelengths given by Eq. (18.3) are called *de Broglie wavelengths*. For a material particle, $v$ is always less than $c$, so that $u$ is always greater than the speed of light. This is in keeping with the relativity theory since the energy or signal is transmitted not with the phase velocity but with the group velocity (see Sec. 10.9). The de Broglie wave concept for material particles holds also for photons. Thus setting $v = c$ in Eq. (18.4) gives $p = h\nu/c$. In this connection it is of interest to find an expression for the rest mass $m_0$ of a particle. Using the Einstein relationship for the mass as a function of velocity [Eq. (15.11)], we have

$$p = \frac{m_0 v}{\sqrt{1 - (v/c)^2}} \qquad (18.5)$$

Since $p = h/\lambda$ and $v = c^2 p/h\nu = c^2/\lambda\nu$ from Eqs. (18.3) and (18.4), the rest mass is given by

$$m_0 = \frac{h}{c} \sqrt{\frac{v^2}{c^2} - \frac{1}{\lambda^2}} \qquad (18.6)$$

For photons, $c = \nu\lambda$, and Eq. (18.6) yields $m_0 = 0$. A photon then has a rest mass equal to zero, which means that photons do not exist unless they are traveling with the speed of light. Material particles have a tendency to persist, whereas photons do not. Photons are easily absorbed or emitted, with an attendant disappearance or appearance of an amount of energy.

The de Broglie wave theory of matter was convincingly demonstrated experimentally by Davisson and Germer and G. P. Thomson, who showed that electrons are scattered from crystals as if they were waves rather than particles. By directing beams of electrons onto crystals there are produced diffraction patterns which show the characteristic X-ray diffraction ring patterns. Knowing the crystal structure of the diffracting material, the wavelength associated with the beam of electrons is determinable from the electron diffraction pattern. The results showed that the wavelength of these waves is related to the mass and velocity of the electrons by the de Broglie relationship given in Eq. (18.3). Since then, diffraction experiments with other particles have been successfully performed and have established definite evidence for the wave nature of matter.

In accordance with the concepts of de Broglie and Schrödinger, the quantized or stationary states of an atom correspond to the possible standing or stationary de Broglie wave patterns, each stationary state corresponding to a normal mode of vibration. The de Broglie waves produce sets of standing waves, as it were, analogous to the standing waves of a vibrating string. Thus corresponding to a simple circular Bohr orbit, there is a stationary wave with the circumference $2\pi r$ of the orbit containing an integral number $n$ of the de Broglie wavelengths, or $2\pi r = n\lambda$. Using the expression for the de Broglie wavelength,

$$2\pi r m v = n h$$

or

$$m v r = n \frac{h}{2\pi}$$

which is identical with Bohr's arbitrary postulate that the angular momentum of the electron is an integral multiple of $h/2\pi$.

**18.2. The Method of Quantum Mechanics.** To investigate the normal modes of oscillation in a vibrating system, such as a vibrating string or stretched membrane, one employs a differential equation of the wave motion and seeks a solution subject to certain boundary conditions, such as the fixed ends of the string or the fastened rim of the membrane. For instance, in the string there are nodes at fixed ends, and a standing-wave pattern is possible if the string length is an integral multiple of half wavelength. So also, in quantum mechanics, the problem is to seek solutions of the Schrödinger wave equation subject to appropriate boundary conditions. The Schrödinger wave equation is a second-order partial differential equation for the matter waves and expresses the change with coordinates of a quantity $\psi$ that represents the wave amplitude. The equation contains the total energy $E$, the potential energy $V$, the mass $m$ of the particle, and Planck's constant $h$. One seeks solutions for $\psi$ in accordance with the restrictive conditions that the solutions must be continuous, single-valued, and finite everywhere. In general such conditions can be satisfied only for certain discrete values of the total energy $E$. The values of $\psi$ corresponding to the allowed values of $E$ are known as the *wave functions*. The energy values for $E$ that lead to acceptable solutions of Schrödinger's equation are the stationary or quantum states or energy levels that we have met in our study of spectra. Thus by finding the solutions of the wave equation, there are determined the permissible energy levels which, as we have seen, are fundamental in the treatment of the emission of spectral lines. A discrete set of energy states, introduced in an arbitrary manner in the older quantum theory, appear here as solutions of Schrödinger's equation. For example, in the case of an electron at a given distance from a positive nucleus, as in the hydrogen atom, the solutions satisfying the restrictive conditions lead to an expression for the total energy which is identical with the Bohr expression for the energy of a stationary state [Eq. (17.12)]. Here the quantum number appears as an integer as a result of the solution of the wave equation without the injection of any other assumptions. The observed frequencies of spectral lines are due to transitions between the energy levels, and again given by the difference in the energies of two states divided by Planck's constant $h$. By computing the probability of transitions from one energy state to another, the relative intensities of spectral lines may be determined. Applications of the Schrödinger equation to various atomic problems are found in the references given at the end of the chapter.

The square of the absolute value of the wave amplitude, $|\psi|^2$, is interpreted to give the probability of finding the particle (electron) in a volume element surrounding any point. This probability has a small value everywhere except in the region where the matter waves are more nearly in phase. The places where there is maximum probability of finding the electron in the hydrogen atom, for example, are at distances from the nucleus equal to the Bohr orbit radii. In the theory of light photons, the electromagnetic field or light waves determine the probability that a photon shall take a certain path, and in the new particle dynamics it is the wave function that governs the motion of the electrons in the same way. The behavior of an atom containing a single electron may accordingly be thought of as being spread out over three-dimensional space in such a way that $|\psi|^2$ represents the electric charge density at any point. In like fashion, for an atom containing many extranuclear electrons, the charges may be thought of as distributed in a "charge cloud" whose density distribution is given by $|\psi|^2$. Such consideration, a smeared-out-electronic-cloud concept, although artificial is very useful and does lead to results that are in agreement with experiment.

The conditions that the wave amplitude be finite, continuous, and single-valued take the place of the arbitrary quantum conditions of the older theory. The results obtained for the hydrogen atom, using quantum mechanics, agree with some of the results of the older theory, and one can go much further with the new theory, especially with many electron atoms, than is possible with the old quantum theory. In the older theory, it was postulated that an atom does not radiate while in a stationary state, in disagreement with the laws of classical electrodynamics. But it can be shown that the charge-density distribution does not vary with time so that quantum mechanically no radiation results from a stationary atomic state. It is as though there is complete destructive interference between the radiations from the various volume elements of the charge distribution.

The Schrödinger equation for matter waves is applicable to large-scale mechanics as well as to the mechanics of particles belonging to the atomic realm. However, when the de Broglie relation [Eq. (18.3)] is applied to a moving mass of macroscopic dimensions, the associated wavelength is much too small to be detected, while in the realm of micromechanics, such as in the motion of an electron, the wavelength is of an observable magnitude. For large-scale masses, the deviations introduced by the use of Newtonian mechanics are entirely negligible.

**18.3. Heisenberg's Uncertainty Principle.** A revolutionarily significant consequence of the fact that radiation and matter exhibit particle and wave aspects is that there is a fundamental limitation on the accuracy of simultaneous observations of what are known as canonically conjugate pairs of dynamical variables associated with the particle, such as its position and momentum. The existence of such a limit was discovered by Heisenberg in 1927 and is known as the *uncertainty principle*, or *principle of indeterminacy*. In the classical dynamics of particles we are interested in determining the position and momentum of the particle at some given instant of time, so that we can then predict its position and momentum at any future time. Heisenberg's principle asserts that we can measure either the position or the momentum of the particle exactly but that it is by nature impossible to determine both the position and momentum simultaneously with unlimited accuracy. When an experiment is designed to measure simultaneously the position $q$ and corresponding momentum $p$ of a particle, Heisenberg's indeterminacy principle states that we are to expect an uncertainty $\Delta q$ and an uncertainty $\Delta p$ satisfying the relationship

$$\Delta q \, \Delta p \gtrsim \frac{h}{2\pi} \tag{18.7}$$

which reads that the product of the uncertainties is of the order of or greater than Planck's constant $h$ divided by $2\pi$. The uncertainties $\Delta q$ and $\Delta p$ are not a result of experimental errors of measurement but are inherent limitations and a consequence of the wave properties of the particle. The uncertainty relation above also states that it is not possible to specify precisely, say the $x$ component of the position of a particle, without realizing complete uncertainty about the $x$ component of momentum, and if the $x$ component of momentum is to be specified precisely, it will entail complete uncertainty as to its $x$ component of position. Another important pair of canonically conjugate variables for which the uncertainty principle may be stated are the energy $E$ of a particle and the time $t$ at which the particle is observed.   The uncertainty principle holds for photons and all material large-scale as well as small-scale particles.   However, in view of the fact that $h$ is relatively so small a magnitude, we are not aware of the inappreciable uncertainties $\Delta q$ and $\Delta p$ for masses dealt with in ordinary mechanics.   For such bodies of ordinary size, the mass is so great as to make the uncertainty in the velocity negligibly small in comparison with the ordinary inaccuracies of measurement.   Newtonian mechanics, which is a limiting form of quantum mechanics, entails no measurable discrepancy by not encountering these effects and thus gives an adequate representation of the facts of ordinary mechanics.   The uncertainty principle, on the other hand, becomes of importance only in particles of atomic dimensions, and the effect is quite perceptible for the moving electron.   As we shall see, the way in which the uncertainty comes into being is through the act of observation, which interferes with the motion of the particle by an amount that is not determinable.

The fact that it is impossible to specify precisely and simultaneously the position and momentum of an electron means that it is not possible to predict with certainty the future state of the electron.   In general the behavior of an individual particle cannot be predicted, but the average behavior of a large number of particles follows statistical laws.   This is implied in the wave amplitude function $\psi$ for the associated waves of the electron.   The statistical interpretation given to the square of the absolute value of $\psi$ is that it determines the probability with which the electron is to be found in a volume element.   The electron is likely to be in a region where the wave amplitude is large and is not likely to be in a region where the wave amplitude is small.

In the case of monchromatic light of a precisely measured wavelength $\lambda$, we know precisely the energy and momentum of each photon from the relations $E = h\nu$ and $p = h/\lambda$.   The assumption of monochomatic light means that we are considering a wave train of infinite extent so that we have no knowledge as to the position of the photon.   If we decrease the length of the wave train to a finite short amount, so as to obtain accurate knowledge of the position of the photon, we are unable to determine precisely the momentum of the photon, since a measurement of the wavelength of the finite wave train reveals that the monochromaticity has been destroyed.   The Fourier analysis of a finite wave train reveals the presence of a range of wavelengths.   Thus decreasing the uncertainty in position of the photon increases the uncertainty in its momentum.

The significance of the uncertainty principle may be emphasized by analyzing some experiments designed to measure the position and momentum of a particle. This we do in the next section.

**18.4. The Diffraction Slit, the $\gamma$-ray Microscope, and the Shutter.** As a first illustration of the uncertainty principle consider the diffraction of light by a single slit as shown in Fig. 18.1. The light emerging from the slit on the right produces a diffraction pattern whose first diffraction minimum is given, assuming Fraunhofer diffraction conditions, by Eq. (13.3), or

$$\sin \theta = \frac{\lambda}{a}$$

Light of course appears at angles greater than $\theta$, but most of the light is within this angle, which contains most of the photons. By decreasing

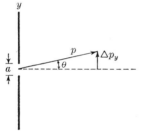

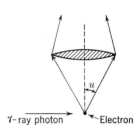

FIG. 18.1. Uncertainty principle illustrated by the diffraction of light through a slit.

FIG. 18.2. Illustrating the uncertainty principle with the $\gamma$-ray microscope.

the slit width $a$, the $y$ coordinate of the position of a photon becomes more defined, with an uncertainty $\Delta y = a$. But now the diffraction pattern spreads so that $\theta$ increases, resulting in a corresponding uncertainty in the $y$ component of momentum $\Delta p_y$ given by

$$\Delta p_y = p \sin \theta$$

where $p$ is the momentum of the photon. Thus

$$\Delta p_y = \frac{p\lambda}{\Delta y}$$

and using the de Broglie relation $p = h/\lambda$,

$$\Delta y \, \Delta p_y = h$$

which is in agreement with the uncertainty principle.

As a second example we take up the imaginary experiment of Heisenberg designed to measure simultaneously the $x$ components of position and momentum of an electron, using an idealized microscope. In Fig. 18.2 photons incident on the electron are scattered into the microscope objective, whose half angle subtended at the electron is $u$. The resolving power (Chap. 14) is of the order of $\lambda/\sin u$, which represents the order of the uncertainty in the $x$ component of a position determination of the electron, or

$$\Delta x \sim \frac{\lambda}{\sin u}$$

where $\lambda$ is the wavelength of the light used to illuminate the electron. To determine the position as precisely as possible, $\lambda$ must be as small as possible, and it is imagined that $\gamma$ rays may be employed. The least amount of light incident on the electron, one photon, is scattered into the objective, but its direction is uncertain through the range $2u$. The momentum of the scattered photon is, by de Broglie's relation, $h/\lambda$, and its $x$ component of momentum is of the order of $(h \sin u)/\lambda$, or

$$\Delta p_x \sim \frac{h \sin u}{\lambda}$$

As described by the Compton effect, the electron recoils, and the $x$ component of the momentum of the recoiling electron has an uncertainty equal to that for the photon. Therefore the product of the uncertainties in the $x$ components of position and momentum for the electron is

$$\Delta x \, \Delta p_x \sim h$$

a result which is again in agreement with the uncertainty relation. When the position of the electron is more accurately determined by reducing $\lambda$ sufficiently, there is introduced a large uncertainty in the momentum of the electron. The experiment emphasizes the fact that the uncertainty enters into the picture through the act of observation or interaction, which interferes with the motion of the electron by an amount that is not exactly determinable.

Canonically conjugate variables for which the uncertainty principle may be stated have the product dimensions gm cm$^2$ sec$^{-1}$, such as momentum times distance or energy times time. For instance, suppose we attempt to measure with exactness the time at which the photons, in a monochromatic wave, pass through a rapidly operating shutter. With the shutter open for a short time interval $\Delta t$ there is transmitted a short train of waves, or *wave packet*, which by a Fourier analysis is seen to contain a frequency range of waves of spread $\Delta\nu$. The shorter the wave-train length, the smaller the uncertainty in the time determination of the passage of a photon, but the greater the range $\Delta\nu$. From the intensity-vs. frequency-distribution curve it can be shown that the half-width value of the frequency spread is equal to the reciprocal of $\Delta t$. Thus $\Delta\nu \gtrsim 1/\Delta t$, and using the relation $\Delta E = h \, \Delta\nu$, there follows

$$\Delta E \, \Delta t \gtrsim h$$

showing that there is an increase in the uncertainty of determination of the energy when the uncertainty in the time is reduced. This form of the uncertainty principle is of importance in considering the quantum energy states or levels of an atom. In our treatment of the broadening effects of spectral lines we have seen that when all external broadening causes are absent, a spectral line still has a natural finite width. The energy levels then have a natural finite breadth. The smaller the average life $\Delta t$ of an energy state, the greater the uncertainty in the energy of the state $\Delta E$, and consequently the greater the breadth of the energy level. A spectral line due to a transition from this state has a corresponding natural width.

**18.5. Concluding Remarks.** We have seen that the particle and wave concepts of light, as well as matter, are intimately related. This follows from the de Broglie relation, in which $\lambda$ is fundamentally a characteristic of a wave, while $p$ is basically associated with a particle in motion. In any experiment, either the wave or the particle property is revealed depending on the kind of experiment. For light the wave character is apparent in phenomena of interference and diffraction, while the corpuscular photon behavior manifests itself in such phenomena as the Compton and photoelectric effects. Both the wave and particle concepts are valid, and both are necessary for a complete description of a physical system. According to Bohr's complementarity principle (1928) the wave and particle ways of describing a system complement each other, but, in view of the uncertainty principle, both cannot be revealed simultaneously.

Because of the small value of Planck's constant $h$, radiation of relatively low frequency, such as visible light, behaves more usually like waves, while radiation of relatively high frequency, such as $\gamma$ rays, behaves in most respects like photons. For small frequencies the value of each quantum is small, and a light beam of moderate intensity contains many photons. The wave theory then provides an accurate description of the average behavior of the photons. As the frequency increases to large values, the radiation takes on a more corpuscular character. For processes having to do with the interchange of energy by single photons, quantum mechanics is necessary to provide accurate descriptions. So also in dealing with matter of large masses, which are composed of numerous particles, classical Newtonian mechanics affords an accurate representation of the facts, but in treating a single particle of atomic size it is necessary to employ the quantum mechanics.

In the study of diffraction we have seen that, for obstacles or openings that are large compared with the wavelength, wave theory leads to the principles of geometrical optics. If Planck's constant $h$ were infinitesimally small, wave optics would be identical with geometrical optics since, from $E = h\nu = hc/\lambda$, the wavelength would be infinitesimal for all values of $E$. Quantum mechanics would then also become identical with classical mechanics. In the classical realm one neglects all effects that result from the finite value of Planck's constant $h$, which is undoubtedly the most significant, universal, and fundamental constant of nature.

## REFERENCES

Born, M., and P. Jordan: "Elementare Quantenmechanik," Verlag Julius Springer, Berlin, 1930.

Condon, E. U., and P. M. Morse: "Quantum Mechanics," McGraw-Hill Book Company, Inc., New York, 1929.

Dirac, P. A. M.: "The Fundamental Principles of Quantum Mechanics," 3d ed., Oxford University Press, New York, 1947.

Finkelnburg, W.: "Atomic Physics," McGraw-Hill Book Company, Inc., New York, 1950.

Heisenberg, W.: "Die Physikalischen Prinzipien der Quanten Mechanik," 2d ed., S. Hirzel, Leipzig, 1943.

Kemble, E. C.: "The Fundamental Principles of Quantum Mechanics," McGraw-Hill Book Company, Inc., New York, 1937.

Pauling, L., and E. B. Wilson, Jr.: "Introduction to Quantum Mechanics," McGraw-Hill Book Company, Inc., New York, 1935.

Richtmyer, F. K., and E. H. Kennard: "Introduction to Modern Physics," McGraw-Hill Book Company, Inc., New York, 1947.

Rojansky, V. B.: "Introductory Quantum Mechanics," Prentice-Hall, Inc., New York, 1938.

Schiff, L. I.: "Quantum Mechanics," McGraw-Hill Book Company, Inc., New York, 1949.

Schrödinger, E.: "Collected Papers on Wave Mechanics," Blackie & Son, Ltd., Glasgow, 1928.

Sommerfeld, A.: "Atombau und Spektrallinien," 4th ed., Vol. II, Friedrich Vieweg & Sohn, Brunswick, 1949.

## PROBLEMS

**18.1.** Find the de Broglie wavelength of (a) an electron whose kinetic energy is 100 electron volts, (b) a 1-gm mass whose kinetic energy is 0.500 erg. The rest mass of the electron is $9.106 \times 10^{-28}$ gm, and $h = 6.623 \times 10^{-27}$ erg sec.

**18.2.** Calculate the momentum and energy of a photon of light whose wavelength is 2000 A.

**18.3.** Show that the phase velocity of the de Broglie waves is given by

$$u = c \sqrt{1 + (m_0^2 c^2 \lambda^2 / h^2)}$$

where the symbols have the meanings in Eq. (18.6).

**18.4.** Using the expression $2\pi r = n\lambda$ for the circular path of a Bohr orbit of radius $r$, show that $2mnE\lambda^2 + 4\pi me^2\lambda - h^2 n = 0$. From this show that the energy levels are given by $E_n = -2\pi^2 me^4/h^2 n^2$. [HINT: Use $p = \sqrt{2m(E - V)}$ and $V = -e^2/r$, where $V$ is the potential energy and $E$ the total energy of the electron.]

**18.5.** A microscope is used to view a small particle which is illuminated by light of wavelength 4000 A. If the objective subtends an angle of 60° at the particle, find the order of the uncertainties $\Delta x$ and $\Delta p_x$ in position and momentum, respectively, of the particle.

**18.6.** Explain why it is experimentally impossible to localize a quantum in a monochromatic wave train.

**18.7.** Show that the product of the uncertainties in the $x$ components of position and momentum of the photon in the shutter experiment is of the order of $h$. Consider the $x$ component of momentum of the order of the momentum of the photon.

# APPENDIX I

**A. The Caustic by Refraction at a Plane for Rays from a Point Source.** **Derivation Eq. (1.7).** In Fig. A.1, $P$ is the light source at position $(0, -d)$, $P_1'$ is an image point formed by intersection of the refracted rays at $Q$ and $N$, and $P_2'$ is the image point formed by the refracted rays at $N$ and $M$. In this way, every refracted ray cuts the one next to it. The locus of their points of intersection is the required caustic by

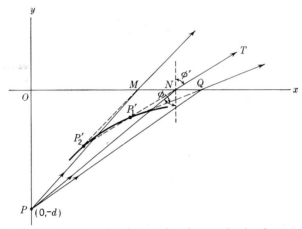

FIG. A.1. Caustic by refraction at a plane surface for rays issuing from a point source.

refraction, or diacaustic. Consider the refracted ray $NT$ as representative of all refracted rays. Its equation is

$$y = (x - d \tan \phi) \cot \phi' \tag{A.1}$$

The angle of incidence $\phi$ and angle of refraction $\phi'$ are related by $\sin \phi' = n \sin \phi$, so that

$$yn - \frac{x \sqrt{1 - n^2 \sin^2 \phi}}{\sin \phi} + \frac{d \sqrt{1 - n^2 \sin^2 \phi}}{n \cos \phi} = 0 \tag{A.2}$$

The required diacaustic is the envelope to this family of lines. This envelope may be obtained by differentiating Eq. (A.2) partially with respect to the parameter $\phi$, then eliminating $\phi$ between this resulting equation and Eq. (A.2). Differentiating Eq. (A.2) partially with respect to $\phi$ we obtain

$$\frac{-x \cos \phi}{\sin^2 \phi} - \frac{d(1 - n^2) \sin \phi}{\cos^2 \phi} = 0$$

which yields

$$\tan^3 \phi = \frac{x}{d(n^2 - 1)} \tag{A.3}$$

417

Now substituting the value for $\phi$ from Eq. (A.3) into Eq. (A.2) gives

$$n^{2/3}y^{2/3} + (n^2 - 1)^{1/3}x^{2/3} = d^{2/3} \tag{A.4}$$

which is the equation of the diacaustic.   This equation represents the evolute to the

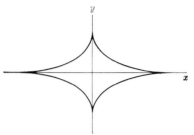

Fig. A.2. Plot of Eq. (A.4).

ellipse $x^2/n^2 + y^2/(n^2 - 1) = 1$ and is a four-cusped locus as shown in Fig. A.2 with the cusps on the $x$ axis given by $\pm d/\sqrt{n^2 - 1}$ and on the $y$ axis by $\pm d/n$.

**B. Properties of the Aplanatic Surface by Refraction.   The Cartesian Ovals.**   See Sec. 1.6.   In Fig. B.1a, $P$ is a point object at the origin in a medium of index $n_a$, its

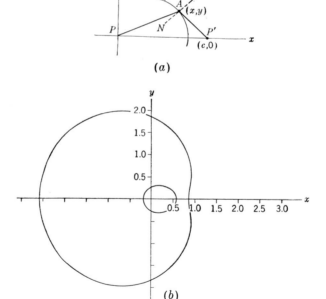

Fig. B.1. The Cartesian ovals.

image after refraction through the surface is at $P'$, coordinates $(c,0)$, in medium $n_b$, and $A$, coordinates $(x,y)$, is any point on the refracting surface.   The optical-path equation is

$$PA + {}_a n_b AP' = k, \qquad k = a \text{ constant}$$

From this equation, with a little algebraic manipulation, there results

$$[(x^2 + y^2)(1 - {_an_b^2}) + 2{_an_b^2}cx + k^2 - {_an_b^2}c^2]^2 = 4k^2(x^2 + y^2) \tag{B.1}$$

Expression (B.1) is the equation for the Cartesian ovals, which are plotted in Fig. B.1$b$. The surface must be convex toward the less refracting medium, that is, $n_a > n_b$ or ${_an_b} < 1$. By setting $y = 0$ in Eq. (B.1), the points at which the oval intersects the $x$ axis are found to be given by

$$\frac{k + {_an_b}c}{1 + {_an_b}}, \qquad \frac{k - {_an_b}c}{1 - {_an_b}}, \qquad \frac{{_an_b}c - k}{1 + {_an_b}}, \qquad -\frac{k + {_an_b}c}{1 - {_an_b}} \tag{B.2}$$

From expressions (B.2) it can be seen that when $k < c$, the ovals cut the $x$ axis to the right of the origin between $P$ and $P'$, and Fig. B.1$b$ is drawn for the values $k = 0.8$, $c = 1$, ${_an_b} = 0.5$.

In order that $P'$ be the image point of $P$ for all positions of $A$, the sine of the angle that $PA$ makes with the normal to the curve at $A$ must be related to the sine of the angle that $AP'$ makes with this normal by Snell's law. That the Cartesian oval satisfies this condition is shown as follows:

Referring to Fig. B.1$a$ and calling the angle that $PA$ makes with the normal $\phi$ and the angle that $AP'$ makes with the normal $\phi'$, then we must show that, for all positions of $P$, $\sin \phi = {_an_b} \sin \phi'$. Differentiating Eq. (B.1),

$$\frac{dy}{dx} = \frac{x[2k^2 - D(1 - {_an_b^2})] - {_an_b^2}cD}{y[D(1 - {_an_b^2}) - 2k^2]} \tag{B.3}$$

where $D = (x^2 + y^2)(1 - {_an_b^2}) + 2{_an_b^2}cx + k^2 - {_an_b^2}c^2 = 2k \sqrt{x^2 + y^2}$.
If we let

$$M_{PA} = \text{slope of } PA = \frac{y}{x}$$

$$M_{AP'} = \text{slope of } AP' = \frac{y}{x - c}$$

$$M_N = \text{slope of the normal } N$$

$$= \frac{y[D(1 - {_an_b^2}) - 2k^2]}{x[D(1 - {_an_b^2}) - 2k^2] + {_an_b^2}cD}$$

then

$$\tan \phi = \frac{M_N - M_{PA}}{1 + M_{PA}M_N} \qquad \text{and} \qquad \tan \phi' = \frac{M_{AP'} - M_N}{1 + M_N M_{AP'}}$$

Thus

$$\frac{\sin \phi'}{\sin \phi} = \frac{M_{AP'} - M_N}{M_N - M_{PA}} \sqrt{\frac{1 + M_{PA}^2}{1 + M_{AP'}^2}}$$

$$= \frac{D - 2k^2}{-{_an_b^2}D} \sqrt{\frac{x^2 + y^2}{(x - c)^2 + y^2}}$$

$$= \frac{\sqrt{x^2 + y^2} - k}{-n^2 \sqrt{(x - c)^2 + y^2}} \tag{B.4}$$

Using $k = PA + {_an_b}AP' = \sqrt{x^2 + y^2} + {_an_b} \sqrt{(x - c)^2 + y^2}$, we obtain

$$\sin \phi = {_an_b} \sin \phi'$$

which is the required relationship.

**C. The Caustic by Reflection of Parallel Rays Incident on a Circle. Derivation of Eq. (3.6).** In Fig. C.1 is shown the reflected paths of two parallel rays incident on a concave reflecting mirror of large aperture. The reflected rays intersect in a point whose coordinates are $(x, y)$ with respect to the center of the circle $C$ as origin. The equation of the reflected ray $NP''$, making an angle $2\phi$ with the axis, is

$$y = \tan 2\phi \left[ x - \frac{R \sec \phi}{2} \right] \tag{C.1}$$

where $R$ is the radius of the mirror. This equation contains the angle of incidence $\phi$ as a parameter and therefore represents the family of reflected rays. The envelope

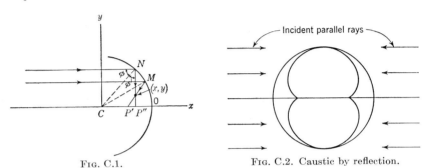

<table>
<tr><td>Fɪɢ. C.1.</td><td>Fɪɢ. C.2. Caustic by reflection.</td></tr>
</table>

to this family of lines is the required caustic and is obtained by expressing Eq. (C.1) in the form

$$y \cot 2\phi - x + \frac{R}{2} \sec \phi = 0 \tag{C.2}$$

and differentiating this equation partially with respect to the parameter $\phi$. This yields the expression

$$y = R \sin^3 \phi = \frac{R}{4} (3 \sin \phi - \sin 3\phi) \tag{C.3}$$

By means of Eq. (C.3), $y$ may be eliminated from Eq. (C.2) and a solution for $x$ obtained, thus:

$$x = \frac{R}{4} (3 \cos \phi - \cos 3\phi) \tag{C.4}$$

Equations (C.3) and (C.4) are the parametric equations for the catacaustic. The functional relationship between $x$ and $y$ may be obtained by eliminating $\phi$ between Eqs. (C.3) and (C.4). This gives

$$x^2 + y^2 - \frac{R^2}{4} = \frac{3}{4} R^2 \sin^2 \phi = \frac{3}{4} R^{4/3} y^{2/3}$$

or

$$[4(x^2 + y^2) - R^2]^3 = 27 R^4 y^2 \tag{C.5}$$

which is the required equation and represents a two-cusped epicycloid as shown in Fig. C.2. Other interesting caustics may be obtained in a similar way. For instance, if the incident rays diverge from a point that is on the circumference of the reflecting circle, the caustic curve can be shown to be a cardioid.

### D. The Tangential and Sagittal Foci for a Single Refracting Surface. Derivations of Eqs. (7.49) and (7.50).

Figure 7.14 is repeated as Fig. D.1. First consider the ray $QO$ incident on the refracting surface whose radius of curvature is $R$ with center at $C$. Let the position of the object point $Q$, measured along the ray $QO$, be $s$ and

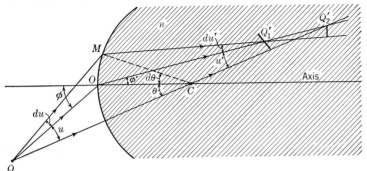

FIG. D.1. Astigmatic foci of a refracting surface.

the image position $Q_2'$, measured along $OQ_2'$, be $s_2'$. Equating the sum of the areas of triangles $QOC$ and $OCQ_2'$ to the area of triangle $QOQ_2'$ gives

$$\tfrac{1}{2}R|s|\sin\phi + \tfrac{1}{2}Rs_2'\sin\phi' = \tfrac{1}{2}|s|s_2'\sin(\phi - \phi') \tag{D.1}$$

Expanding the right-hand member and using $\sin\phi = n\sin\phi'$ leads to

$$nR|s| + Rs_2' = |s|s_2'(n\cos\phi' - \cos\phi)$$

Dividing by $R|s|s_2'$ yields

$$\frac{n}{s_2'} + \frac{1}{|s|} = \frac{n\cos\phi' - \cos\phi}{R}$$

In accordance with the sign conventions developed in the text, $s = -|s|$, so that

$$\frac{n}{s_2'} - \frac{1}{s} = \frac{n\cos\phi' - \cos\phi}{R} \tag{D.2}$$

which is Eq. (7.50) and is the required expression for the sagittal, or secondary, astigmatic focus, since all the rays emitted from $Q$ with the same angle $u$ will intersect at the point $Q_2'$.

Now consider the meridional beam whose rays all lie in the plane $QOC$. The ray $QM$ is very close to $QO$, intersecting at the primary focus $Q_1'$. The increments in angle corresponding to $u$, $\theta$, and $u'$ are indicated by $du$, $d\theta$, and $du'$. Since these incremental angles are small, we have

$$du = OM\frac{\cos\phi}{|s|}, \qquad |d\theta| = \frac{OM}{R}, \qquad |du'| = OM\frac{\cos\phi'}{s_1'} \tag{D.3}$$

where we have used the absolute values of $d\theta$ and $du'$ since, by our sign convention for angles, $u'$ and $\theta$ are negative. Now differentiating $\sin\phi = n\sin\phi'$,

$$\cos\phi\,d\phi = n\cos\phi'\,d\phi' \tag{D.4}$$

Since $\phi = u + |\theta|$ and $\phi' = |\theta| - |u'|$, Eq. (D.4) becomes

$$(du + |d\theta|)\cos\phi = n(|d\theta| - |du'|)\cos\phi'$$

and substituting the values from (D.3) leads to

$$OM \left( \frac{\cos \phi}{|s|} + \frac{1}{R} \right) \cos \phi = n \, OM \left( \frac{1}{R} - \frac{\cos \phi'}{s_1'} \right) \cos \phi'$$

which reduces to

$$\frac{n \cos^2 \phi'}{s_1'} + \frac{\cos^2 \phi}{|s|} = \frac{n \cos \phi' - \cos \phi}{R}$$

Using $s = -|s|$, we have

$$\frac{n \cos^2 \phi}{s_1'} - \frac{\cos^2 \phi}{s} = \frac{n \cos \phi' - \cos \phi}{R} \qquad (D.5)$$

which is Eq. (7.49), the required expression for the tangential, or primary, focus at $Q_1'$.

**E. Fresnel Integrals and the Cornu Spiral.** See Sec. 13.8. Figure E.1 shows a cylindrical wave front $CW$ diverging from the slit source $S$, which is perpendicular to the plane of the figure. To find the effect of this wave front on a line through $P$ parallel to $S$, we need consider only the section shown. A disturbance originating at the secondary wavelet of arc length $dq$ at $Q$ produces a displacement $du$ at $P$ proportional to $dq$, inversely proportional to the distance $\rho$ from $Q$ to $P$, and given by [see Eq. (13.1A)]

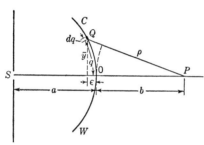

Fig. E.1. Diagram for deriving the resultant effect at $P$ of a cylindrical wave front.

$$du = \frac{A \, dq}{\rho} \sin 2\pi \left( \frac{t}{T} - \frac{\rho}{\lambda} \right) \qquad (E.1)$$

where $A$ is an arbitrary amplitude of the vibrations $A \sin (2\pi t/T)$ of all points in the cylindrical wave front and the other quantities have the usual meanings in the text. Now $\rho = b + \Delta$, where $\Delta$ is the path difference between $QP$ and $OP$. Hence Eq. (E.1) becomes

$$du = \frac{A \, dq}{\rho} \sin 2\pi \left( \frac{t}{T} - \frac{b}{\lambda} - \frac{\Delta}{\lambda} \right) \qquad (E.2)$$

The path difference is evidently a function of $q$, and we can find this function by dropping a perpendicular from $Q$ onto $SP$, forming the distances $\bar{y}$ and $\epsilon$ as shown. We now have, confining our attention to points $Q$ not far removed from 0,

$$\bar{y}^2 = a^2 - (a - \epsilon)^2 \qquad \text{or} \qquad \epsilon = \frac{\bar{y}^2}{2a}$$

Also

$$\bar{y}^2 = \rho^2 - (b + \epsilon)^2 = \frac{(\rho^2 - b^2)a}{a + b}$$

and

$$\bar{y}^2 + \epsilon^2 = q^2 = \frac{(\rho^2 - b^2)a}{a + b} + \frac{(\rho^2 - b^2)^2}{4(a + b)^2}$$

Since

$$\rho^2 - b^2 = (b + \Delta)^2 - b^2 = 2b\Delta$$

then

$$\frac{2ab\Delta}{a+b} = q^2$$

or

$$\Delta = q^2 \frac{a+b}{2ab} \qquad (\text{E.3})$$

In obtaining the function in Eq. (E.3) we have neglected the squares of the relatively small quantities. The disturbance at $P$, due to as many elements $dq$ on the wave front as we wish to consider, is given by integrating Eq. (E.2),

$$u = \frac{A}{\rho} \int \sin 2\pi \left( \frac{t}{T} - \frac{b}{\lambda} - \frac{\Delta}{\lambda} \right) dq \qquad (\text{E.4})$$

wherein we have taken $\rho$ out of the integral sign since it is essentially constant for points $Q$ in the vicinity of 0. The limits of the integral are to be taken for as much of the wave front as is being considered. Equation (E.4) can be expressed as

$$u = \frac{A}{\rho} \sin 2\pi \left( \frac{t}{T} - \frac{b}{\lambda} \right) \int \cos \frac{2\pi\Delta}{\lambda} dq - \frac{A}{\rho} \cos 2\pi \left( \frac{t}{T} - \frac{b}{\lambda} \right) \int \sin \frac{2\pi\Delta}{\lambda} dq \quad (\text{E.5})$$

If we write

$$R \cos \theta = \frac{A}{\rho} \int \cos \frac{2\pi\Delta}{\lambda} dq \qquad (\text{E.6})$$

and

$$R \sin \theta = \frac{A}{\rho} \int \sin \frac{2\pi\Delta}{\lambda} dq \qquad (\text{E.7})$$

then Eq. (E.5) is expressible as

$$u = R \sin \left[ 2\pi \left( \frac{t}{T} - \frac{b}{\lambda} \right) - \theta \right] \qquad (\text{E.8})$$

Equation (E.8) gives the disturbance at the point $P$ having an amplitude $R$ whose square provides the intensity. This is obtained by squaring Eqs. (E.6) and (E.7) and adding. Thus

$$R^2 = \frac{A^2}{\rho^2} \left[ \left( \int \cos \frac{2\pi\Delta}{\lambda} dq \right)^2 + \left( \int \sin \frac{2\pi\Delta}{\lambda} dq \right)^2 \right] \qquad (\text{E.9})$$

It is much more convenient to obtain integrals that are independent of the particular values $\lambda$, $a$, and $b$. This can be done by making a change of variable. Hence introducing the new variable $v$ defined by the equation

$$\frac{2\pi\Delta}{\lambda} = \frac{\pi v^2}{2}$$

and using Eq. (E.3), we have

$$q^2 = \frac{ab\lambda}{2(a+b)} v^2 \qquad (\text{E.10})$$

Substitution in Eq. (E.9) leads to

$$R^2 = \frac{A^2 ab\lambda}{2\rho^2(a+b)} \left[ \left( \int_{v_1}^{v_2} \cos \frac{\pi v^2}{2} dv \right)^2 + \left( \int_{v_1}^{v_2} \sin \frac{\pi v^2}{2} dv \right)^2 \right] \qquad (\text{E.11})$$

and the intensity at $P$ is given by

$$I_P = k \left[ \left( \int_{v_1}^{v_2} \cos \frac{\pi v^2}{2} \, dv \right)^2 + \left( \int_{v_1}^{v_2} \sin \frac{\pi v^2}{2} \, dv \right)^2 \right] \tag{E.12}$$

where $k$ is a constant for a given wavelength and geometrical arrangement.

The integrals in Eq. (E.12) are known as the *Fresnel integrals*. When these are integrated between specified values of $v$, they yield the resultant disturbance from the corresponding portion of the wave front, as obtainable from Eq. (E.10). They are evaluated by means of the *Cornu spiral*, which is a graph of one of the integrals taken as ordinate and the other taken as abscissa, the lower limit being zero. The Cornu spiral is thus a graph of

$$x = \int_0^v \cos \frac{\pi v^2}{2} \, dv \tag{E.13}$$

$$y = \int_0^v \sin \frac{\pi v^2}{2} \, dv \tag{E.14}$$

where $x$ is the abscissa and $y$ is the ordinate. The integrals of Eqs. (E.13) and (E.14) may be evaluated for different $v$ values from the series formed after integration. The resulting numerical values are given in Table E.1. The corresponding plot is shown

TABLE E.1.  TABLE OF FRESNEL INTEGRALS

| $v$ | $x$ | $y$ | $v$ | $x$ | $y$ | $v$ | $x$ | $y$ |
|---|---|---|---|---|---|---|---|---|
| 0.00 | 0.0000 | 0.0000 | 1.60 | 0.3655 | 0.6388 | 3.30 | 0.4058 | 0.5193 |
| 0.10 | 0.1000 | 0.0005 | 1.70 | 0.3238 | 0.5492 | 3.40 | 0.4385 | 0.4296 |
| 0.20 | 0.1999 | 0.0042 | 1.80 | 0.3336 | 0.4508 | 3.50 | 0.5326 | 0.4153 |
| 0.30 | 0.2994 | 0.0141 | 1.90 | 0.3945 | 0.3734 | 3.60 | 0.5880 | 0.4923 |
| 0.40 | 0.3975 | 0.0334 | 2.00 | 0.4883 | 0.3434 | 3.70 | 0.5419 | 0.5750 |
| 0.50 | 0.4923 | 0.0647 | 2.10 | 0.5815 | 0.3743 | 3.80 | 0.4481 | 0.5656 |
| 0.60 | 0.5811 | 0.1105 | 2.20 | 0.6362 | 0.4556 | 3.90 | 0.4223 | 0.4752 |
| 0.70 | 0.6597 | 0.1721 | 2.30 | 0.6267 | 0.5530 | 4.00 | 0.4984 | 0.4205 |
| 0.80 | 0.7230 | 0.2493 | 2.40 | 0.5550 | 0.6197 | 4.10 | 0.5737 | 0.4758 |
| 0.90 | 0.7648 | 0.3398 | 2.50 | 0.4574 | 0.6192 | 4.20 | 0.5418 | 0.5632 |
| 1.00 | 0.7799 | 0.4383 | 2.60 | 0.3890 | 0.5500 | 4.30 | 0.4494 | 0.5540 |
| 1.10 | 0.7638 | 0.5365 | 2.70 | 0.3925 | 0.4529 | 4.40 | 0.4383 | 0.4623 |
| 1.20 | 0.7154 | 0.6234 | 2.80 | 0.4675 | 0.3915 | 4.50 | 0.5260 | 0.4342 |
| 1.30 | 0.6386 | 0.6863 | 2.90 | 0.5625 | 0.4102 | 4.60 | 0.5672 | 0.5162 |
| 1.40 | 0.5431 | 0.7135 | 3.00 | 0.6058 | 0.4963 | 4.70 | 0.4914 | 0.5671 |
| 1.50 | 0.4453 | 0.6975 | 3.10 | 0.5616 | 0.5818 | 4.80 | 0.4338 | 0.4968 |
|  |  |  | 3.20 | 0.4664 | 0.5933 | 4.90 | 0.5002 | 0.4350 |
|  |  |  |  |  |  | 5.00 | 0.5636 | 0.4992 |

in Fig. E.2. The coordinates of the asymptotic point $K$ are obtained from the relations

$$\int_0^\infty \cos (p)^2 \, dp = \int_0^\infty \sin (p)^2 \, dp = \frac{1}{2} \sqrt{\frac{\pi}{2}}$$

which here give

$$\int_0^\infty \cos \frac{\pi v^2}{2} \, dv = \int_0^\infty \sin \frac{\pi v^2}{2} = \frac{1}{2}$$

and for the point $K'$ the coordinates are $(-\frac{1}{2}, -\frac{1}{2})$. Equation (E.12) shows that the intensity is given by a sum of squares, so that the two integrals represent the horizontal and vertical components of the resultant amplitude, and the intensity is proportional to the square of the line drawn from the origin to a point on the spiral. The spiral $OK$ represents the upper half and the spiral $OK'$ represents the lower half of the completely uncovered wave front.

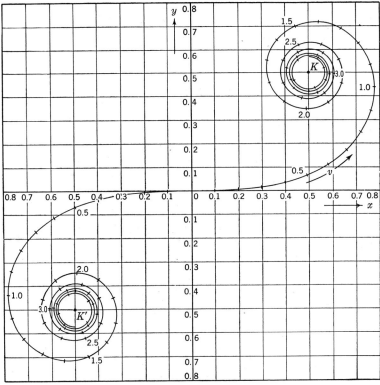

Fig. E.2. The Cornu spiral.

From Eqs. (E.13) and (E.14), $x = y = 0$ when $v = 0$, and the spiral passes through the origin about which it is symmetrical. The tangent to the curve makes the angle $\psi$ with the $x$ axis given by

$$\tan \psi = \frac{dy}{dx} = \tan \frac{\pi v^2}{2}$$

Therefore

$$\psi = \frac{\pi v^2}{2}$$

which shows that for $v = 0$ the curve is parallel to the $x$ axis at the origin. The element of length $ds$ along the spiral is $ds = \sqrt{dx^2 + dy^2} = dv$ so that $s = v$, and the value of $v$ is simply the distance from the origin measured along the spiral, as shown in Fig. E.2. The radius of curvature is given by $ds/d\psi = 1/\pi v$. Hence as $v$ increases, the radius decreases, forming the double spiral.

# APPENDIX II

Based on $V_\lambda = 1.000$ at 0.555 micron

| Wavelength, microns† | $V_\lambda$ | Wavelength, microns† | $V_\lambda$ | Wavelength, microns† | $V_\lambda$ |
|---|---|---|---|---|---|
| 0.400 | 0.00120 | 0.520 | 0.710 | 0.640 | 0.175 |
| 0.420 | 0.00400 | 0.530 | 0.862 | 0.650 | 0.107 |
| 0.430 | 0.0116 | 0.540 | 0.954 | 0.660 | 0.0610 |
| 0.440 | 0.0230 | 0.550 | 0.995 | 0.670 | 0.0320 |
| 0.450 | 0.0380 | 0.560 | 0.995 | 0.680 | 0.0170 |
| 0.460 | 0.0600 | 0.570 | 0.952 | 0.690 | 0.00820 |
| 0.470 | 0.0910 | 0.580 | 0.870 | 0.700 | 0.00410 |
| 0.480 | 0.139 | 0.590 | 0.757 | 0.710 | 0.00210 |
| 0.490 | 0.208 | 0.600 | 0.631 | 0.720 | 0.00105 |
| 0.500 | 0.323 | 0.610 | 0.503 | 0.730 | 0.000520 |
| 0.510 | 0.503 | 0.620 | 0.381 | 0.740 | 0.000250 |
|  |  | 0.630 | 0.265 | 0.750 | 0.000120 |

* From *Natl. Bur. Standards Sci. Papers*, 475, p. 174, 1923.
† 1 micron $= 10^{-4}$ cm $= 10^4$ A.

# ANSWERS TO ODD-NUMBERED PROBLEMS

## CHAPTER 1

**1.3.** $2'10.25''$.  **1.7.** $6.5 \times 10^{-3}$ mm.  **1.9.** (a) 0.6740.  (b) 42.36°.  **1.11.** 13.0 cm from top surface.  **1.15.** 1.00°, 1°; 2.50°, 2.5°; 5.02°, 5°; 7.58°, 7.5°; 10.20°, 10°; 12.89°, 12.5°; 15.69°, 15°; 18.62°, 17.5°; 21.73°, 20°.  **1.23.** (a) 21.1°.  (b) 4.52°.

## CHAPTER 2

**2.1.** 3.33 cm and 1.82 cm from circumference.  Both virtual, inside ball.  **2.3.** (a) 12.2 cm in front of the left vertex, virtual, (b) 1.34 cm in front of the left vertex, virtual.  **2.5.** Within the stopper 4.57 in. from its top, real, 0.358 mm in size.  **2.9.** At center.  **2.11.** 2.48 in. from center.  Virtual, magnified, erect.  **2.13.** 6.32 mm above vertex of meniscus.  Virtual.  **2.15.** $\frac{7}{6}$.

## CHAPTER 3

**3.1.** (a) $-30.0$ cm from mirror.  Real.  (b) 15.0 cm from mirror.  Virtual.  **3.3.** 40.0 cm, convex.  $\frac{1}{4}$.  **3.5.** 15.0 cm from mirror, 1.00 cm in size, virtual, erect.  **3.7.** 4.00 cm in size, $-15.0$ cm.  **3.11.** $\dfrac{49r^3 - 112rR^2 + 42r^2R(\sqrt{2} - 2)}{49r^2 - 112rR - 224R^2}$.

## CHAPTER 4

**4.1.** (a) 20.0 cm.  (b) 78.3 cm.  **4.3.** $-20.0$ cm.  **4.5.** $\infty$.  **4.7.** $-15.0$ cm from lens, 1.00 cm in size, virtual, erect.  **4.9.** $-15.0$ cm, 4.00 cm in size, real, erect.  **4.13.** $-78.0$ cm from third lens, 40.0 cm in size, virtual, erect.  **4.19.** (a) Greater than object distance, magnified, real, erect.  (b) Outside principal focus, virtual, inverted.  **4.23.** 20.0 cm from lens on the side away from mirror, magnified 8.00 times, real, erect.  **4.25.** 23.2 cm from concave lens on same side as object, diminished 0.893 times, virtual, erect.  **4.27.** 125 cm.  **4.29.** $-60.0$ cm.  **4.33.** 5.56 in. on side opposite from lenses, magnified 2.00 times, virtual, erect.

## CHAPTER 5

**5.1.** Corresponding to the values of $R_2$, reading from left to right, the values of $f'$, $h$, and $h'$ in centimeters are 8.00, 0, $-0.667$; 4.96, 0.276, $-0.413$; 4.17, 0.348, $-0.348$; 3.60, 0.400, $-0.300$; 2.82, 0.470, $-0.235$; $-36.0$, 4.00, 3.00; 20.6, $-1.14$, $-1.72$; 8.00, 0, $-3.33$; 5.76, 1.60, $-2.40$; 4.50, 2.50, $-1.88$; 36.0, $-20.0$, $-15.0$; 13.1, $-3.64$, $-5.46$.  **5.3.** $-5.81$ cm from face of larger radius, 4.22 cm in size, virtual, erect.  **5.5.** $-12.0$ cm.  $h = -24.0$ cm, $h' = 36.0$ cm.  Diverging.  **5.9.** 9.00 in. from first lens, 6.00 in. from second lens.  **5.11.** $6r$ from center of sphere.  **5.13.** 2.73 cm from second principal plane, 2.27 mm in size, real, erect.

## CHAPTER 6

**6.1.** (a) Aperture stop, circular opening.  Entrance pupil, circular opening.  Exit pupil, 0.667 cm to left of lens, 1.33 cm diameter.  (b) $f/2$.  (c) 1.00 cm from lens.  **6.3.** (a) Diaphragm.  (b) Entrance pupil, 3.33 cm from lens nearest object point, 3.33 cm diameter.  Exit pupil, 23.3 cm from lens nearest object point, 3.33 cm diameter.  **6.5.** Entrance pupil, larger focal-length lens.  Exit pupil, 2.20 cm to right of smaller focal-length lens, 0.300 cm diameter. 2.60°.  At exit pupil.  **6.7.** Entrance pupil, largest focal-length lens.  Exit pupil, 0.616 cm to right of last lens on right, 0.224 cm diameter. 2.78°.  At exit pupil.  **6.13.** (*a*) $G_2$.  (*b*) Entrance pupil, 12.4 cm to right of $L_1$, 3.14 cm diameter.  Exit pupil, 3.33 cm to left of $L_3$, 2.66 cm diameter. (*c*) $G_1$.  (*d*) Entrance window, 2.14 cm to right of $L_1$, 3.21 cm diameter.  Exit window, 14.1 cm to left of $L_3$, 3.97 cm diameter.

## CHAPTER 7

**7.3.** $-3.70 \times 10^{-5}$ cm $^{-1}$, $-92.6 \times 10^{-5}$ cm$^{-1}$.  **7.5.** (*a*) 11.6 cm.  (*c*) 0.725 cm. **7.13.** $8.04 \times 10^{-3}$ cm$^{-1}$, $-1.07$ cm.  **7.15.** 1:93.5.  **7.17.** $12.3 \times 10^{-4}$ cm$^{-1}$.  **7.19.** Linear function of $\sigma$.  **7.25.** Expressions apply to diverging lens.  **7.27.** (*b*)  $-21.3$ cm from mirror, $-27.9$ cm from mirror, $-6.6$ cm, 1.89 cm, 2.48 cm.  **7.31.** 10.5 cm and $-18.2$ cm.  **7.33.** (*a*) For the $C$ line, 0.761 cm from left vertex, $-0.571$ cm from right vertex.  For the $F$ line, 0.756 cm from left vertex, $-0.567$ cm from right vertex. (*b*) 0.626 cm.

## CHAPTER 8

**8.3.** (*a*) Concave, $-3.33$ diopters.  (*b*) $-29.0$ cm, $-3.45$ diopters.  **8.5.** 483 cm. **8.9.** (*a*) 24.0 cm.  (*b*) $-4.00$ cm.  **8.11.** 1.48 mm, 972.  **8.13.** (*a*) $1.11 \times 10^{-3}$ mm. (*b*) 62.5.  (*c*) $5.5\times$ or greater.  **8.15.** (*a*) 36 times, 49 times, 64 times.  (*b*) 0.735, 1, 1.  **8.19.** (*a*) 15.0 cm.  (*b*) 3.33.  **8.21.** 12.5-cm objective, $-2.50$-cm eyepiece.

## CHAPTER 9

**9.1.** (*a*)  $10.1 \times 10^3$ lumens, 671 lumens/watt.  (*b*) 25 watts, $14.4 \times 10^3$ lumens, 575 lumens/watt.  **9.3.** 0.135 lumen/cm².  **9.5.** $4.30 \times 10^{-2}$ lambert, $1.37 \times 10^{-2}$ candle/cm².  **9.7.** 1.77 lumens/ft².  **9.11.** $3.87 \times 10^3$ lumens/cm².

## CHAPTER 10

**10.5.** $y = 4 \sin [(\pi x/50) - 216°]$.  **10.7.** 290 cm.  **10.11.** (*b*) 9.14, 48.0°.

## CHAPTER 11

**11.1.** 0.347 cm.  **11.5.** 0.516°.  **11.7.** $5.56 \times 10^{-4}$ cm.  **11.11.** (*a*) 4%, (*b*) 100%. **11.13.** $2.70 \times 10^{-4}$ cm.  **11.15.** $1.11 \times 10^{-4}$ radian.  **11.17.** $6.28 \times 10^{-5}$ cm.  **11.21.** 18.  **11.23.** $4.87 \times 10^{-5}$ cm, 0.182 cm.

## CHAPTER 12

**12.1.** 1215.  **12.3.** 1.89°.  **12.5.** 1.00032.  **12.7.** 4000 A, 4210 A, 4444 A, 4705 A, 5000 A.  **12.11.** 1.62, 0.25%.  **12.13.** (*a*) $(8100/k)$ A.  (*b*) 2.

## CHAPTER 13

**13.3.** 0.486 mm.  **13.5.** $4/9\pi^2$, $4/25\pi^2$, $4/49\pi^2$, $4/81\pi^2$, $4/121\pi^2$.  **13.7.** Values of $\alpha$, $1.43\pi$, $2.46\pi$, $3.47\pi$, $4.48\pi$, $5.48\pi$.  Intensity ratios, 0.0472, 0.0165, 0.00834, 0.00503, 0.00336.  **13.9.** $4.80 \times 10^{-3}$ mm.  **13.17.** 375 cm.  **13.23.** (*a*) 1.39 mm, (*b*) 3.10 mm. **13.25.** Dark.  **13.37.** 0.0062%.

## CHAPTER 14

**14.1** (*a*)  $4.00 \times 10^{-3}$, (*b*) $8.39 \times 10^{-3}$ cm, (*c*) $6.31 \times 10^{-4}$ cm, (*d*) $3.36 \times 10^{-4}$ radian.  **14.3.** (*a*) 0.733 cm, (*b*) $6.71 \times 10^4$ m.  **14.5.** (*a*) 0.833.  (*b*) $1.60 \times 10^{-6}$ radian.  (*c*) 272.  **14.7.** 0.866.  **14.9.** $405 \times 10^3$.

## CHAPTER 15

**15.3.** 39.1/cm, $1.01 \times 10^{-17}$. **15.5.** $3.34/\text{gm}/\text{cm}^2$. **15.7.** (a) $2.90 \times 10^{23}$. (b) 0.192.
**15.9.** 0, $3.24 \times 10^{-3}$ A, $7.09 \times 10^{-3}$ A, $24.2 \times 10^{-3}$ A.

## CHAPTER 16

**16.3.** 59°16′. **16.5.** 3. **16.13.** $n_O = 1.658, n_E = 1.486$. **16.15.** Calcite, $7.85 \times 10^{-4}$ mm, $15.7 \times 10^{-4}$ mm. Quartz, $15.2 \times 10^{-3}$ mm, $30.4 \times 10^{-3}$ mm. **16.21.** (a) 33°15′. (b) $5.44 \times 10^{-7}$. (c) 0.15%. **16.23.** 16°12′.

## CHAPTER 17

**17.1.** Balmer, 6564.67 A, 4862.72 A, 4341.71 A; limit, 3647.04 A. Lyman, 1215.68 A, 1025.73 A, 972.54 A; limit, 911.76 A. Paschen, 18,756.2 A, 12,821.6 A, 10,941.1 A; limit, 8205.84 A. **17.3.** $125 \times 10^{13}$, $1.24 \times 10^4$ ergs/sec. **17.5.** 1.79 A. **17.11.** 1.373, 0.862, 0.011. **17.13.** 8.99 kilovolts. **17.15.** 1.40 cm$^{-1}$.

## CHAPTER 18

**18.1.** (a) 1.23 A, (b) $6.62 \times 10^{-19}$ A. **18.5.** $8.00 \times 10^{-5}$ cm, $8.28 \times 10^{-23}$ gm-cm/sec.

# INDEX